PROSE AND POETRY

(1856–1870)

BY

WILLIAM MORRIS

†

WILLIAM MORRIS

From a photograph by Emery Walker

PROSE AND POETRY

(1856–1870)

BY

WILLIAM MORRIS

INCLUDING 'THE DEFENCE OF GUENEVERE', 'THE LIFE
AND DEATH OF JASON', PROSE ROMANCES FROM
THE OXFORD AND CAMBRIDGE MAGAZINE
AND OTHER PROSE AND POETRY

HUMPHREY MILFORD
OXFORD UNIVERSITY PRESS
LONDON   EDINBURGH   GLASGOW
NEW YORK   TORONTO   MELBOURNE   BOMBAY
1913

OXFORD: HORACE HART
PRINTER TO THE UNIVERSITY

CONTENTS

THE demand for a second edition of this volume fortunately provides the publisher with an opportunity to include among the miscellaneous poems the two newly discovered sonnets ' Rhyme slayeth Shame ' and ' May grown a-cold ', not hitherto included in any collection of Morris's writings, except that just issued in the World's Classics, or mentioned in any book relating to the author. They will commend themselves as the only known companions of his sonnet on ' Grettir the Strong ', and will be valuable in connexion with his admirable review of Dante Gabriel Rossetti's Poems (see especially the remarks on sonnets, p. 650 of this book).

PROSE ROMANCES

FROM

THE OXFORD AND CAMBRIDGE MAGAZINE

1856

THE STORY OF THE UNKNOWN CHURCH

(*Oxford and Cambridge Magazine*, January 1856)

I was the master-mason of a church that was built more than six hundred years ago ; it is now two hundred years since that church vanished from the face of the earth ; it was destroyed utterly,—no fragment of it was left ; not even the great pillars that bore up the tower at the cross, where the choir used to join the nave. No one knows now even where it stood, only in this very autumn-tide, if you knew the place, you would see the heaps made by the earth-covered ruins heaving the yellow corn into glorious waves, so that the place where my church used to be is as beautiful now as when it stood in all its splendour. I do not remember very much about the land where my church was ; I have quite forgotten the name of it, but I know it was very beautiful, and even now, while I am thinking of it, comes a flood of old memories, and I almost seem to see it again,— that old beautiful land ! only dimly do I see it in spring and summer and winter, but I see it in autumn-tide clearly now ; yes, clearer, clearer, oh ! so bright and glorious ! yet it was beautiful too in spring, when the brown earth began to grow green : beautiful in summer, when the blue sky looked so much bluer, if you could hem a piece of it in between the new white carving ; beautiful in the solemn starry nights, so solemn that it almost reached agony—the awe and joy one had in their great beauty. But of all these beautiful times, I remember the whole only of autumn-tide ; the others come in bits to me ; I can think only of parts of them, but all of autumn ; and of all days and nights in autumn, I remember one more particularly. That autumn day the church was nearly finished, and the monks, for whom we were building the church, and the people, who lived in the town hard by, crowded round us oftentimes to watch us carving.

Now the great Church, and the buildings of the Abbey where the monks lived, were about three miles from the town, and the town stood on a hill overlooking the rich autumn country : it was girt about with great walls that had overhanging battlements, and towers at certain places all along the walls, and often we could see from the churchyard or the Abbey garden, the flash of helmets and spears, and the dim shadowy waving of banners, as the knights and lords and men-at-arms passed to and fro along the battlements ; and we could see too in the town the three spires of the three churches ; and the spire of the Cathedral, which was the tallest of the three, was gilt all over with gold, and always at night-time a great lamp shone from it that hung in the spire midway between the roof of the church and the cross at the top of the spire. The Abbey where we built the Church was not girt by stone walls, but by a circle of poplar trees, and whenever a wind passed over them, were it ever so little a breath, it set them all a-ripple ; and when the wind was high, they bowed and swayed very low, and the wind, as it lifted the leaves, and showed their silvery white sides, or as again in the lulls of it, it let them drop, kept on changing the trees from green to white, and white to green ; moreover, through the boughs and trunks of the poplars, we caught glimpses of the great golden corn sea, waving, waving, waving for leagues and leagues ; and among the corn grew burning scarlet poppies, and blue corn-flowers ; and the corn-flowers were so blue, that they gleamed, and seemed to burn with a steady light, as they grew beside the poppies among the gold of the wheat. Through the corn sea ran a blue river, and always green meadows and lines of tall poplars followed its windings. The old Church had been burned, and that was the reason why the monks caused me to build the new one ; the buildings of the Abbey were built at the same time as the burned-down Church, more than a hundred years before I was born, and they were on the north side of the Church, and joined to it by a cloister of round arches, and in the midst of the cloister was a lawn, and in the midst of that lawn, a fountain of marble, carved round about with flowers and strange beasts ; and at the edge of the lawn, near the round arches, were a great many sun-flowers that were all in blossom on that autumn day ; and up many of the pillars of the cloister crept passion-flowers and roses. Then farther from the Church, and past the cloister and its buildings, were many detached buildings, and a great garden round them, all within the circle of the poplar trees ; in the garden were trellises covered over with roses, and convolvolus, and the great-leaved fiery nasturtium ; and specially all along by the poplar trees were there trellises, but on these grew nothing but deep crimson roses ; the hollyhocks too were all out in blossom at that time, great spires of pink, and orange, and red, and white, with their soft, downy leaves. I said that nothing grew on the trellises by the poplars but crimson roses, but I was not quite right, for in many places the wild flowers had crept into the garden from without ; lush green briony, with green-white blossoms, that grows so fast, one could almost think that we see it grow, and deadly nightshade, La bella donna, O ! so beautiful ; red berry, and purple, yellow-spiked flower, and deadly, cruel-looking, dark green leaf, all growing together in the glorious days of early autumn. And in the midst of the great garden was a conduit, with its sides carved with histories from the Bible, and there was on it too, as on the fountain in the cloister, much carving of flowers and strange beasts. Now the Church itself was surrounded on every side but the north by the cemetery, and there were many graves there, both of monks and of laymen, and often the friends of those, whose bodies lay there, had planted flowers about the graves of those they loved. I remember one such particularly, for at the head of it was a cross of carved wood, and at the foot of it, facing the cross, three tall sun-flowers ; then in the midst of the cemetery was a cross of stone, carved on one side with the Crucifixion of our Lord Jesus Christ, and on the other with Our Lady holding the Divine Child. So that day, that I specially remember, in Autumn-tide, when the church was nearly finished, I was carving in the central porch of the west front ; (for I carved all those bas-reliefs in the west front with my own hand ;) beneath me my sister Margaret was carving at the flower-work, and the little quatrefoils that carry the signs of the zodiac and emblems of the months : now my sister Margaret was rather more than twenty years old at that time, and she was very beautiful, with dark brown hair and deep calm violet eyes. I had lived with her all my life, lived with her almost alone latterly, for our father and mother died when she was quite young, and I loved her very much, though I was not thinking of her just then, as she stood beneath me carving. Now the central porch was carved with a bas-relief of the Last Judgement, and it was divided into three parts by horizontal bands of deep flower-work. In the lowest division, just over the doors, was carved The Rising of the Dead ; above were angels blowing long trumpets, and Michael the Archangel weighing the souls, and the blessed led into heaven by angels, and the lost into hell by the devil ; and in the topmost division was the Judge of the world.

All the figures in the porch were finished except one, and I remember when I woke that morning my exulta-tion at the thought of my Church being so nearly finished ; I remember, too, how a kind of misgiving mingled with the exultation, which, try all I could, I was unable to shake off ; I thought then it was a rebuke for my pride, well, perhaps it was. The figure I had to carve was Abraham, sitting with a blossoming tree on each side of him, holding in his two hands the corners of his great robe, so that it made a mighty fold, wherein, with their hands crossed over their breasts, were the souls of the faithful, of whom he was called Father : I stood on the scaffolding for some time, while Margaret's chisel worked on bravely down below. I took mine in my hand, and stood so, listening to the noise of the masons inside, and two monks of the Abbey came and stood below me, and a knight, holding his little daughter by the hand, who every now and then looked up at him, and asked him strange questions. I did not think of these long, but began to think of Abraham, yet I could not think of him sitting there, quiet and solemn, while the Judgement-Trumpet was being blown ; I rather thought of him as he looked when he chased those kings so far ; riding far ahead of any of his company, with his mail-hood off his head, and lying in grim folds down his back, with the strong west wind blowing his wild black hair far out behind him, with the wind rippling the long scarlet pennon of his lance ; riding there amid the rocks and the sands alone ; with the last gleam of the armour of the beaten kings disappearing behind the winding of the pass ; with his company a long, long way behind, quite out of sight, though their trumpets sounded faintly among the clefts of the rocks ; and so I thought I saw him, till in his fierce chase he leapt, horse and man, into a deep river, quiet, swift, and smooth ; and there was something in the moving of the water-lilies as the breast of the horse swept them aside, that suddenly took away the thought of Abraham and brought a strange dream of lands I had never seen ; and the first was of a place where I was quite alone, standing by the side of a river, and there was the sound of singing a very long way off, but no living thing of any kind could be seen, and the land was quite flat, quite without hills, and quite without trees too, and the river wound very much, making all kinds of quaint curves, and on the side where I stood there grew nothing but long grass, but on the other side grew, quite on to the horizon, a great sea of red corn-poppies, only paths of white lilies wound all among them, with here and there a great golden sun-flower. So I looked down at the river by my feet, and saw how blue it was, and how, as the stream went swiftly by, it swayed to and fro the long green weeds, and I stood and looked at the river for long, till at last I felt some one touch me on the shoulder, and, looking round, I saw standing by me my friend Amyot, whom I love better than any one else in the world, but I thought in my dream that I was frightened when I saw him, for his face had changed so,

it was so bright and almost transparent, and his eyes
gleamed and shone as I had never seen them do before.
Oh ! he was so wondrously beautiful, so fearfully beautiful ! and as I looked at him the distant music swelled,
and seemed to come close up to me, and then swept by
us, and fainted away, at last died off entirely ; and then
I felt sick at heart, and faint, and parched, and I stooped
to drink of the water of the river, and as soon as the
water touched my lips, lo ! the river vanished, and the
flat country with its poppies and lilies, and I dreamed
that I was in a boat by myself again, floating in an
almost land-locked bay of the northern sea, under a cliff
of dark basalt. I was lying on my back in the boat,
looking up at the intensely blue sky, and a long low swell
from the outer sea lifted the boat up and let it fall again
and carried it gradually nearer and nearer towards the
dark cliff ; and as I moved on, I saw at last, on the top
of the cliff, a castle, with many towers, and on the highest
tower of the castle there was a great white banner
floating, with a red chevron on it, and three golden stars
on the chevron ; presently I saw too on one of the
towers, growing in a cranny of the worn stones, a great
bunch of golden and blood-red wall-flowers, and I
watched the wall-flowers and banner for long ; when
suddenly I heard a trumpet blow from the castle, and
saw a rush of armed men on to the battlements, and
there was a fierce fight, till at last it was ended, and one
went to the banner and pulled it down, and cast it over
the cliff into the sea, and it came down in long sweeps,
with the wind making little ripples in it ;—slowly, slowly
it came, till at last it fell over me and covered me from
my feet till over my breast, and I let it stay there and
looked again at the castle, and then I saw that there was
an amber-coloured banner floating over the castle in
place of the red chevron, and it was much larger than
the other : also now, a man stood on the battlements,
looking towards me ; he had a tilting helmet on, with
the visor down, and an amber-coloured surcoat over his
armour : his right hand was ungauntletted, and he held
it high above his head, and in his hand was the bunch

of wall-flowers that I had seen growing on the wall ; and his hand was white and small, like a woman's, for in my dream I could see even very far off things much clearer than we see real material things on the earth : presently he threw the wall-flowers over the cliff, and they fell in the boat just behind my head, and then I saw, looking down from the battlements of the castle, Amyot. He looked down towards me very sorrowfully, I thought, but, even as in the other dream, said nothing ; so I thought in my dream that I wept for very pity, and for love of him, for he looked as a man just risen from a long illness, and who will carry till he dies a dull pain about with him. He was very thin, and his long black hair drooped all about his face, as he leaned over the battlements looking at me : he was quite pale, and his cheeks were hollow, but his eyes large, and soft, and sad. So I reached out my arms to him, and suddenly I was walking with him in a lovely garden, and we said nothing, for the music which I had heard at first was sounding close to us now, and there were many birds in the boughs of the trees : oh, such birds ! gold and ruby, and emerald, but they sung not at all, but were quite silent, as though they too were listening to the music. Now all this time Amyot and I had been looking at each other, but just then I turned my head away from him, and as soon as I did so, the music ended with a long wail, and when I turned again Amyot was gone ; then I felt even more sad and sick at heart than I had before when I was by the river, and I leaned against a tree, and put my hands before my eyes. When I looked again the garden was gone, and I knew not where I was, and presently all my dreams were gone. The chips were flying bravely from the stone under my chisel at last, and all my thoughts now were in my carving, when I heard my name, ' Walter,' called, and when I looked down I saw one standing below me, whom I had seen in my dreams just before—Amyot. I had no hopes of seeing him for a long time, perhaps I might never see him again, I thought, for he was away (as I thought) fighting in the holy wars, and it made me almost beside myself to see

him standing close by me in the flesh. I got down from
my scaffolding as soon as I could, and all thoughts else
were soon drowned in the joy of having him by me;
Margaret, too, how glad she must have been, for she had
been betrothed to him for some time before he went to
the wars, and he had been five years away ; five years !
and how we had thought of him through those many
weary days ! how often his face had come before me !
his brave, honest face, the most beautiful among all the
faces of men and women I have ever seen.   Yes, I
remember how five years ago I held his hand as we came
together out of the cathedral of that great, far-off city,
whose name I forget now ; and then I remember the
stamping of the horses' feet ; I remember how his hand
left mine at last, and then, some one looking back at me
earnestly as they all rode on together—looking back,
with his hand on the saddle behind him, while the
trumpets sang in long solemn peals as they all rode on
together, with the glimmer of arms and the fluttering of
banners, and the clinking of the rings of the mail, that
sounded like the falling of many drops of water into the
deep, still waters of some pool that the rocks nearly
meet over ; and the gleam and flash of the swords, and
the glimmer of the lance-heads and the flutter of the
rippled banners, that streamed out from them, swept
past me, and were gone, and they seemed like a pageant
in a dream, whose meaning we know not ; and those
sounds too, the trumpets, and the clink of the mail, and
the thunder of the horse-hoofs, they seemed dream-like
too—and it was all like a dream that he should leave me,
for we had said that we should always be together ; but
he went away, and now he is come back again.

We were by his bed-side, Margaret and I ; I stood and
leaned over him, and my hair fell sideways over my face
and touched his face ; Margaret kneeled beside me,
quivering in every limb, not with pain, I think, but
rather shaken by a passion of earnest prayer.   After
some time (I know not how long), I looked up from his
face to the window underneath which he lay ; I do not
know what time of the day it was, but I know that it

was a glorious autumn day, a day soft with melting, golden haze : a vine and a rose grew together, and trailed half across the window, so that I could not see much of the beautiful blue sky, and nothing of town or country beyond ; the vine leaves were touched with red here and there, and three over-blown roses, light pink roses, hung amongst them. I remember dwelling on the strange lines the autumn had made in red on one of the gold-green vine leaves, and watching one leaf of one of the over-blown roses, expecting it to fall every minute ; but as I gazed, and felt disappointed that the rose leaf had not fallen yet, I felt my pain suddenly shoot through me, and I remembered what I had lost ; and then came bitter, bitter dreams,—dreams which had once made me happy,—dreams of the things I had hoped would be, of the things that would never be now ; they came between the fair vine leaves and rose blossoms, and that which lay before the window ; they came as before, perfect in colour and form, sweet sounds and shapes. But now in every one was something unutterably miserable ; they would not go away, they put out the steady glow of the golden haze, the sweet light of the sun through the vine leaves, the soft leaning of the full blown roses. I wandered in them for a long time ; at last I felt a hand put me aside gently, for I was standing at the head of—of the bed ; then some one kissed my forehead, and words were spoken—I know not what words. The bitter dreams left me for the bitterer reality at last ; for I had found him that morning lying dead, only the morning after I had seen him when he had come back from his long absence—I had found him lying dead, with his hands crossed downwards, with his eyes closed, as though the angels had done that for him ; and now when I looked at him he still lay there, and Margaret knelt by him with her face touching his : she was not quivering now, her lips moved not at all as they had done just before ; and so, suddenly those words came to my mind which she had spoken when she kissed me, and which at the time I had only heard with my outward hearing, for she had said, ' Walter, farewell, and Christ

keep you; but for me, I must be with him, for so
I promised him last night that I would never leave him
any more, and God will let me go.' And verily Margaret
and Amyot did go, and left me very lonely and sad.

It was just beneath the westernmost arch of the nave,
there I carved their tomb : I was a long time carving it ;
I did not think I should be so long at first, and I said,
' I shall die when I have finished carving it,' thinking
that would be a very short time. But so it happened
after I had carved those two whom I loved, lying with
clasped hands like husband and wife above their tomb,
that I could not yet leave carving it ; and so that
I might be near them I became a monk, and used to sit
in the choir and sing, thinking of the time when we should
all be together again. And as I had time I used to go
to the westernmost arch of the nave and work at the
tomb that was there under the great, sweeping arch ;
and in process of time I raised a marble canopy that
reached quite up to the top of the arch, and I painted
it too as fair as I could, and carved it all about with
many flowers and histories, and in them I carved the
faces of those I had known on earth (for I was not as
one on earth now, but seemed quite away out of the
world). And as I carved, sometimes the monks and other
people too would come and gaze, and watch how the
flowers grew ; and sometimes too as they gazed, they
would weep for pity, knowing how all had been. So my
life passed, and I lived in that abbey for twenty years
after he died, till one morning, quite early, when they
came into the church for matins, they found me lying
dead, with my chisel in my hand, underneath the last
lily of the tomb.

A DREAM

(*Oxford and Cambridge Magazine*, March 1856)

I DREAMED once, that four men sat by the winter fire talking and telling tales, in a house that the wind howled round.

And one of them, the eldest, said : ' When I was a boy, before you came to this land, that bar of red sand rock, which makes a fall in our river, had only just been formed ; for it used to stand above the river in a great cliff, tunnelled by a cave about midway between the green-growing grass and the green-flowing river ; and it fell one night, when you had not yet come to this land, no, nor your fathers.

' Now, concerning this cliff, or pike rather (for it was a tall slip of rock and not part of a range), many strange tales were told ; and my father used to say, that in his time many would have explored that cave, either from covetousness (expecting to find gold therein), or from that love of wonders which most young men have, but fear kept them back. Within the memory of man, however, some had entered, and, so men said, were never seen on earth again ; but my father said that the tales told concerning such, very far from deterring him (then quite a youth) from the quest of this cavern, made him all the more earnestly long to go ; so that one day in his fear, my grandfather, to prevent him, stabbed him in the shoulder, so that he was obliged to keep his bed for long ; and somehow he never went, and died at last without ever having seen the inside of the cavern.

' My father told me many wondrous tales about the place, whereof for a long time I have been able to remember nothing ; yet, by some means or another, a certain story has grown up in my heart, which I will tell you something of : a story which no living creature ever told me though I do not remember the time when

I knew it not. Yes, I will tell you some of it, not all
perhaps, but as much as I am allowed to tell.'

The man stopped and pondered awhile, leaning over
the fire where the flames slept under the caked coal : he
was an old man, and his hair was quite white. He spoke
again presently. ' And I have fancied sometimes, that
in some way, how I know not, I am mixed up with the
strange story I am going to tell you.' Again he ceased,
and gazed at the fire, bending his head down till his
beard touched his knees ; then, rousing himself, said in
a changed voice (for he had been speaking dreamily
hitherto) : ' That strange-looking old house that you all
know, with the limes and yew-trees before it, and the
double line of very old yew-trees leading up from the
gateway-tower to the porch—you know how no one will
live there now because it is so eerie, and how even that
bold bad lord that would come there, with his turbulent
followers, was driven out in shame and disgrace by
invisible agency. Well, in times past there dwelt in that
house an old grey man, who was lord of that estate, his
only daughter, and a young man, a kind of distant cousin
of the house, whom the lord had brought up from a boy,
as he was the orphan of a kinsman who had fallen in
combat in his quarrel. Now, as the young knight and
the young lady were both beautiful and brave, and loved
beauty and good things ardently, it was natural enough
that they should discover as they grew up that they
were in love with one another ; and afterwards, as they
went on loving one another, it was, alas ! not unnatural
that they should sometimes have half-quarrels, very few
and far between indeed, and slight to lookers-on, even
while they lasted, but nevertheless intensely bitter and
unhappy to the principal parties thereto. I suppose
their love then, whatever it has grown to since, was not
so all-absorbing as to merge all differences of opinion
and feeling, for again there were such differences then.
So, upon a time it happened, just when a great war had
arisen, and Lawrence (for that was the knight's name)
was sitting and thinking of war, and his departure from
home ; sitting there in a very grave, almost a stern

mood, that Ella, his betrothed, came in, gay and sprightly in a humour that Lawrence often enough could little understand, and this time liked less than ever, yet the bare sight of her made him yearn for her full heart, which he was not to have yet ; so he caught her by the hand, and tried to draw her down to him, but she let her hand lie loose in his, and did not answer the pressure in which his heart flowed to hers ; then he arose and stood before her, face to face, but she drew back a little, yet he kissed her on the mouth and said, though a rising in his throat almost choked his voice, " Ella, are you sorry I am going ? " " Yea," she said, " and nay, for you will shout my name among the sword-flashes, and you will fight for me." " Yes," he said, " for love and duty, dearest." " For duty ? ah ! I think, Lawrence, if it were not for me, you would stay at home and watch the clouds, or sit under the linden trees singing dismal love ditties of your own making, dear knight : truly, if you turn out a great warrior, I too shall live in fame, for I am certainly the making of your desire to fight." He let drop his hands from her shoulders, where he had laid them, and said, with a faint flush over his face, " You wrong me, Ella, for, though I have never wished to fight for the mere love of fighting, and though," (and here again he flushed a little) " and though I am not, I well know, so free of the fear of death as a good man would be, yet for this duty's sake, which is really a higher love, Ella, love of God, I trust I would risk life, nay honour, even if not willingly, yet cheerfully at least." " Still duty, duty," she said ; " you lay, Law- rence, as many people do, most tress on the point where you are weakest ; moreover, those knights who in time past have done wild, mad things merely at their ladies' word, scarcely did so for duty ; for they owed their lives to their country surely, to the cause of good, and should not have risked them for a whim, and yet you praised them the other day." " Did I ? " said Lawrence ; " well, and in a way they were much to be praised, for even blind love and obedience is well ; but reasonable love, reasonable obedience is so far better as to be almost a different thing ; yet, I think, if the knights did well partly, the ladies did altogether ill : for if they had faith in their lovers, and did this merely from a mad longing to see them do 'noble' deeds, then had they but little faith in God, Who can, and at His good pleasure does give time and opportunity to every man, if he will but watch for it, to serve Him with reasonable service, and gain love and all noble things in greater measure thereby : but if these ladies did as they did, that they might prove their knights, then surely did they lack faith both in God and man. I do not think that two friends even could live together on such terms but for lovers—ah ! Ella, Ella, why do you look so at me ? on this day, almost the last, we shall be together for long ; Ella, your face is changed, your eyes—O Christ ! help her and me, help her, good Lord." " Lawrence," she said, speaking quickly and in jerks, " dare you, for my sake, sleep this night in the cavern of the red pike ? for I say to you that, faithful or not, I doubt your courage." But she was startled when she saw him, and how the fiery blood rushed up to his forehead, then sank to his heart again, and his face became as pale as the face of a dead man : he looked at her and said, " Yes, Ella, I will go now ; for what matter where I go ? " He turned and moved toward the door ; he was almost gone, when that evil spirit left her, and she cried out aloud, passionately, eagerly : " Lawrence, Lawrence, come back once more, if only to strike me dead with your knightly sword." He hesitated, wavered, turned, and in another moment she was lying in his arms weeping into his hair.

‘ " And yet, Ella, the spoken word, the thought of our hearts cannot be recalled, I must go, and go this night too, only promise one thing." " Dearest what ? you are always right ! " " Love, you must promise that if I come not again by to-morrow at moonrise, you will go to the red pike, and, having entered the cavern, go where God leads you, and seek me, and never leave that quest, even if it end not but with death." " Lawrence, how your heart beats ! poor heart ! are you afraid that

I shall hesitate to promise to perform that which is
the only thing I could do ? I know I am not worthy to
be with you, yet I must be with you in body or soul,
or body and soul will die." They sat silent, and the
birds sang in the garden of lilies beyond ; then said Ella
again ; " Moreover, let us pray God to give us longer life,
so that if our natural lives are short for the accomplish-
ment of this quest, we may have more, yea, even many
more lives." " He will, my Ella," said Lawrence, " and
I think, nay, am sure that our wish will be granted ;
and I, too, will add a prayer, but will ask it very humbly,
namely, that he will give me another chance or more to
fight in his cause, another life to live instead of this
failure." " Let us pray too that we may meet, however
long the time be before our meeting," she said : so they
knelt down and prayed, hand fast locked in hand meantime ; and afterwards they sat in that chamber facing
the east, hard by the garden of lilies ; and the sun
fell from his noontide light gradually, lengthening the
shadows, and when he sank below the sky-line all the sky
was faint, tender, crimson on a ground of blue ; the
crimson faded too, and the moon began to rise, but when
her golden rim first showed over the wooded hills,
Lawrence arose ; they kissed one long trembling kiss,
and then he went and armed himself ; and their lips
did not meet again after that, for such a long, long time,
so many weary years ; for he had said : " Ella, watch
me from the porch, but touch me not again at this time ;
only, when the moon shows level with the lily-heads, go
into the porch and watch me from thence."

' And he was gone ;—you might have heard her heart
beating while the moon very slowly rose, till it shone
through the rose-covered trellises, level with the lily
heads ; then she went to the porch and stood there,—

' And she saw him walking down toward the gateway
tower, clad in his mail coat, with a bright, crestless
helmet on his head, and his trenchant sword newly
grinded, girt to his side ; and she watched him going
between the yew-trees, which began to throw shadows
from the shining of the harvest moon. She stood there

in the porch, and round by the corners of the eaves of it
looked down towards her and the inside of the porch two
serpent-dragons, carved in stone ; and on their scales,
and about their leering eyes, grew the yellow lichen ;
she shuddered as she saw them stare at her, and drew
closer toward the half-open door ; she, standing there,
clothed in white from her throat till over her feet,
altogether ungirdled ; and her long yellow hair, without
plait or band, fell down behind and lay along her shoulders,
quietly, because the night was without wind, and she too
was now standing scarcely moving a muscle.

'She gazed down the line of the yew-trees, and
watched how, as he went for the most part with a firm
step, he yet shrank somewhat from the shadows of the
yews ; his long brown hair flowing downward, swayed
with him as he walked ; and the golden threads interwoven with it, as the fashion was with the warriors in
those days, sparkled out from among it now and then ;
and the faint, far-off moonlight lit up the waves of his
mailcoat ; he walked fast, and was disappearing in the
shadows of the trees near the moat, but turned before
he was quite lost in them, and waved his ungauntletted
hand ; then she heard the challenge of the warder, the
falling of the drawbridge, the swing of the heavy wicket-
gate on its hinges ; and, into the brightening lights, and
deepening shadows of the moonlight he went from her
sight ; and she left the porch and went to the chapel, all
that night praying earnestly there.

'But he came not back again all the next day, and
Ella wandered about that house pale, and fretting her
heart away ; so when night came and the moon, she
arrayed herself in that same raiment that she had worn
on the night before, and went toward the river and the
red pike.

'The broad moon shone right over it by the time she
came to the river ; the pike rose up from the other side,
and she thought at first that she would have to go back
again, cross over the bridge, and so get to it ; but,
glancing down on the river just as she turned, she saw
a little boat fairly gilt and painted, and with a long

slender paddle in it, lying on the water, stretching out its silken painter as the stream drew it downwards, she entered it, and taking the paddle made for the other side ; the moon meanwhile turning the eddies to silver over the dark green water : she landed beneath the shadow of that great pile of sandstone, where the grass grew green, and the flowers sprung fair right up to the foot of the bare barren rock ; it was cut in many steps till it reached the cave, which was overhung by creepers and matted grass ; the stream swept the boat downwards, and Ella, her heart beating so as almost to stop her breath, mounted the steps slowly, slowly. She reached at last the platform below the cave, and turning, gave a long gaze at the moonlit country ; " her last," she said ; then she moved, and the cave hid her as the water of the warm seas close over the pearl-diver.

'Just so the night before had it hidden Lawrence. And they never came back, they two :—never, the people say. I wonder what their love has grown to now ; ah ! they love, I know, but cannot find each other yet : I wonder also if they ever will.'

So spoke Hugh the white-haired. But he who sat over against him, a soldier as it seemed, black-bearded, with wild grey eyes that his great brows hung over far ; he, while the others sat still, awed by some vague sense of spirits being very near them ; this man, Giles, cried out—' Never ? old Hugh, it is not so.—Speak ! I cannot tell you how it happened, but I know it was not so, not so :—speak quick, Hugh ! tell us all, all ! '

' Wait a little, my son, wait,' said Hugh ; ' the people indeed said they never came back again at all, but I, but I—Ah ! the time is long past over.' So he was silent, and sank his head on his breast, though his old thin lips moved, as if he talked softly to himself, and the light of past days flickered in his eyes.

Meanwhile Giles sat with his hands clasped finger over finger, tightly, ' till the knuckles whitened ; ' his lips were pressed firmly together ; his breast heaved as though it would burst, as though it must be rid of its secret. Suddenly he sprang up, and in a voice that

was a solemn chant, began : ' In full daylight, long ago,
on a slumberously-wrathful, thunderous afternoon of
summer ' ;—then across his chant ran the old man's
shrill voice : ' On an October day, packed close with
heavy-lying mist, which was more than mere autumn-
mist ' :—the solemn stately chanting dropped, the shrill
voice went on ; Giles sank down again, and Hugh
standing there, swaying to and fro to the measured
ringing of his own shrill voice, his long beard moving
with him, said :—

' On such a day, warm, and stifling so that one could
scarcely breathe even down by the sea-shore, I went
from bed to bed in the hospital of the pest-laden city
with my soothing draughts and medicines. And there
went with me a holy woman, her face pale with much
watching ; yet I think even without those same desolate
lonely watchings her face would still have been pale. She
was not beautiful, her face being somewhat peevish-
looking ; apt, she seemed, to be made angry by trifles,
and, even on her errand of mercy, she spoke roughly to
those she tended :—no, she was not beautiful, yet I could
not help gazing at her, for her eyes were very beautiful
and looked out from her ugly face as a fair maiden might
look from a grim prison between the window-bars of it.

' So, going through that hospital, I came to a bed at
last, whereon lay one who had not been struck down by
fever or plague, but had been smitten through the body
with a sword by certain robbers, so that he had narrowly
escaped death. Huge of frame, with stern suffering face
he lay there ; and I came to him, and asked him of his
hurt, and how he fared, while the day grew slowly toward
even, in that pest-chamber looking toward the west ;
the sister came to him soon and knelt down by his bedside to tend him.

' O Christ ! As the sun went down on that dim misty
day, the clouds and the thickly-packed mist cleared off,
to let him shine on us, on that chamber of woes and bitter
unpurifying tears ; and the sunlight wrapped those two,
the sick man and the ministering woman, shone on them
—changed, changed utterly. Good Lord ! How was I

struck dumb, nay, almost blinded by that change ; for there—yes there, while no man but I wondered ; there, instead of the unloving nurse, knelt a wonderfully beautiful maiden, clothed all in white, and with long golden hair down her back. Tenderly she gazed at the wounded man, as her hands were put about his head, lifting it up from the pillow but a very little ; and he no longer the grim, strong wounded man, but fair, and in the first bloom of youth ; a bright polished helmet crowned his head, a mail coat flowed over his breast, and his hair streamed down long from his head, while from among it here and there shone out threads of gold.

' So they spake thus in a quiet tone : '' Body and soul together again, Ella, love ; how long will it be now before the last time of all ? '' '' Long,'' she said, '' but the years pass ; talk no more, dearest, but let us think only, for the time is short, and our bodies call up memories, change love to better even than it was in the old time.''

' Silence so, while you might count a hundred, then with a great sigh : '' Farewell, Ella, for long,''—'' Farewell, Lawrence,'' and the sun sank, all was as before.

' But I stood at the foot of the bed pondering, till the sister coming to me, said : '' Master Physician, this is no time for dreaming ; act—the patients are waiting, the fell sickness grows worse in this hot close air ; feel ''— (and she swung open the casement), '' the outer air is no fresher than the air inside ; the wind blows dead toward the west, coming from the stagnant marshes ; the sea is like a stagnant pool too, you can scarce hear the sound of the long, low surge breaking.'' I turned from her and went up to the sick man, and said : '' Sir Knight, in spite of all the sickness about you, you yourself better strangely, and another month will see you with your sword girt to your side again.'' '' Thanks, kind master Hugh,'' he said, but impatiently, as if his mind were on other things, and he turned in his bed away from me restlessly.

' And till late that night I ministered to the sick in that hospital ; but when I went away, I walked down to

the sea, and paced there to and fro over the hard sand :
and the moon showed bloody with the hot mist, which
the sea would not take on its bosom, though the dull
east wind blew it onward continually. I walked there
pondering till a noise from over the sea made me turn
and look that way ; what was that coming over the sea ?
Laus Deo ! the WEST WIND : Hurrah ! I feel the joy
I felt then over again now, in all its intensity. How
came it over the sea ? first, far out to sea, so that it was
only just visible under the red-gleaming moonlight, far
out to sea, while the mists above grew troubled, and
wavered, a long level bar of white ; it grew nearer
quickly, it rushed on toward me fearfully fast, it
gathered form, strange, misty, intricate form—the
ravelled foam of the green sea ; then oh ! hurrah ! I was
wrapped in it,—the cold salt spray—drenched with it,
blinded by it, and when I could see again, I saw the great
green waves rising, nodding and breaking, all coming on
together ; and over them from wave to wave leaped the
joyous WEST WIND ; and the mist and the plague clouds
were sweeping back eastward in wild swirls ; and right
away were they swept at last, till they brooded over the
face of the dismal stagnant meres, many miles away
from our fair city, and there they pondered wrathfully
on their defeat.

'But somehow my life changed from the time when
I beheld the two lovers, and I grew old quickly.' He
ceased ; then after a short silence said again ; 'And
that was long ago, very long ago, I know not when it
happened.'

So he sank back again, and for a while no one spoke ;
till Giles said at last :

'Once in full daylight I saw a vision, while I was
waking, while the eyes of men were upon me : long ago
on the afternoon of a thunderous summer day, I sat
alone in my fair garden near the city ; for on that day
a mighty reward was to be given to the brave man who
had saved us all, leading us so mightily in that battle
a few days back ; now the very queen, the lady of the
land, whom all men reverenced almost as the Virgin

Mother, so kind and good and beautiful she was, was to crown him with flowers and gird a sword about him ; after the " Te Deum " had been sung for the victory, and almost all the city were at that time either in the Church, or hard by it, or else were by the hill that was near the river where the crowning was to be : but I sat alone in the garden of my house as I said ; sat grieving for the loss of my brave brother, who was slain by my side in that same fight.

'I sat beneath an elm tree ; and as I sat and pondered on that still, windless day, I heard suddenly a breath of air rustle through the boughs of the elm. I looked up, and my heart almost stopped beating, I knew not why, as I watched the path of that breeze over the bowing lilies and the rushes by the fountain ; but when I looked to the place whence the breeze had come, I became all at once aware of an appearance that told me why my heart stopped beating. Ah ! there they were, those two whom before I had but seen in dreams by night, now before my waking eyes in broad daylight. One, a knight (for so he seemed), with long hair mingled with golden threads, flowing over his mail-coat, and a bright crestless helmet on his head, his face sad-looking, but calm ; and by his side, but not touching him, walked a wondrously fair maiden, clad in white, her eyelids just shadowing her blue eyes : her arms and hands seeming to float along with her as she moved on quickly, yet very softly ; great rest on them both, though sorrow gleamed through it.

'When they came opposite to where I stood, these two stopped for a while, being in nowise shadowy, as I have heard men say ghosts are, but clear and distinct. They stopped close by me, as I stood motionless, unable to pray ; they turned to each other, face to face, and the maiden said, " Love, for this our last true meeting before the end of all, we need a witness ; let this man, softened by sorrow, even as we are, go with us."

'I never heard such music as her words were ; though I used to wonder when I was young whether the angels in heaven sung better than the choristers sang in our church, and though, even then the sound of the triumphant hymn came up to me in a breath of wind, and floated round me, making dreams, in that moment of awe and great dread, of the old long-past days in that old church, of her who lay under the pavement of it ; whose sweet voice once, once long ago, once only to me— yet I shall see her again.' He became silent as he said this, and no man cared to break in upon his thoughts, seeing the choking movement in his throat, the fierce clenching of hand and foot, the stiffening of the muscles all over him ; but soon, with an upward jerk of his head, he threw back the long elf locks that had fallen over his eyes while his head was bent down, and went on as before :

' The knight passed his hand across his brow, as if to clear away some mist that had gathered there, and said, in a deep murmurous voice, " Why the last time, dearest, why the last time ? Know you not how long a time remains yet ? the old man came last night to the ivory house and told me it would be a hundred years, ay, more, before the happy end." " So long," she said ; " so long ; ah ! love, what things words are ; yet this is the last time ; alas ! alas ! for the weary years ! my words, my sin ! " " O love, it is very terrible," he said ; " I could almost weep, old though I am, and grown cold with dwelling in the ivory house : O, Ella, if you only knew how cold it is there, in the starry nights when the north wind is stirring ; and there is no fair colour there, naught but the white ivory, with one narrow line of gleaming gold over every window, and a fathom's-breadth of burnished gold behind the throne. Ella, it was scarce well done of you to send me to the ivory house." " Is it so cold, love ? " she said, " I knew it not ; forgive me ! but as to the matter of a witness, some one we must have, and why not this man ? " " Rather old Hugh," he said, " or Cuthbert, his father ; they have both been witnesses before." " Cuthbert," said the maiden, solemnly, " has been dead twenty years ; Hugh died last night." ' (Now, as Giles said these words, carelessly, as though not heeding them particularly, a cold sickening shudder ran through the other two men, but he noted it not and went on.) ' " This man then be it," said the knight, and therewith they turned again, and moved on side by side as before ; nor said they any word to me, and yet I could not help following them, and we three moved on together, and soon I saw that my nature was changed, and that I was invisible for the time ; for, though the sun was high, I cast no shadow, neither did any man that we past notice us, as we made toward the hill by the riverside.

' And by the time we came there the queen was sitting at the top of it, under a throne of purple and gold, with a great band of knights gloriously armed on either side of her ; and their many banners floated over them. Then I felt that those two had left me, and that my own right visible nature was returned ; yet still did I feel strange, and as if I belonged not wholly to this earth. And I heard one say, in a low voice to his fellow, " See, sir Giles is here after all ; yet, how came he here, and why is he not in armour among the noble knights yonder, he who fought so well ? How wild he looks too ! " " Poor knight," said the other, " he is distraught with the loss of his brother ; let him be ; and see, here comes the noble stranger knight, our deliverer." As he spoke, we heard a great sound of trumpets, and therewithal a long line of knights on foot wound up the hill towards the throne, and the queen rose up, and the people shouted ; and, at the end of all the procession went slowly and majestically the stranger knight ; a man of noble presence he was, calm, and graceful to look on ; grandly he went amid the gleaming of their golden armour ; himself clad in the rent mail and tattered surcoat he had worn on the battle-day ; bareheaded, too ; for, in that fierce fight, in the thickest of it, just where he rallied our men, one smote off his helmet, and another, coming from behind, would have slain him, but that my lance bit into his breast.

' So, when they had come within some twenty paces of the throne, the rest halted, and he went up by himself toward the queen ; and she, taking the golden hilted

sword in her left hand, with her right hand caught him
by the wrist, when he would have knelt to her, and held
him so, tremblingly, and cried out, "No, no, thou
noblest of all knights, kneel not to me; have we not
heard of thee even before thou camest hither? how
many widows bless thee, how many orphans pray for
thee, how many happy ones that would be widows and
orphans but for thee, sing to their children, sing to their
sisters, of thy flashing sword, and the heart that guides
it! And now, O noble one! thou hast done the very
noblest deed of all, for thou hast kept grown men from
weeping shameful tears! Oh truly! the greatest I can
do for thee is very little; yet, see this sword, golden-
hilted, and the stones flash out from it," (then she hung
it round him) " and see this wreath of lilies and roses for
thy head; lilies no whiter than thy pure heart, roses no
tenderer than thy true love; and here, before all these
my subjects, I fold thee, noblest, in my arms, so, so."
Ay, truly it was strange enough! those two were together
again; not the queen and the stranger knight, but the
young-seeming knight and the maiden I had seen in the
garden. To my eyes they clung together there; though
they say, that to the eyes of all else, it was but for
a moment that the queen held both his hands in hers;
to me also, amid the shouting of the multitude, came an
under current of happy song: "Oh! truly, very truly,
my noblest, a hundred years will not be long after this."
"Hush! Ella, dearest, for talking makes the time
speed; think only."

'Pressed close to each other, as I saw it, their bosoms
heaved—but I looked away—alas! when I looked again,
I saw nought but the stately stranger knight, descending,
hand in hand, with the queen, flushed with joy and
triumph, and the people scattering flowers before them.

'And that was long ago, very long ago.' So he ceased;
then Osric, one of the two younger men, who had been
sitting in awe-struck silence all this time, said, with eyes
that dared not meet Giles's, in a terrified half whisper,
as though he meant not to speak, 'How long?' Giles
turned round and looked him full in the face, till he

dragged his eyes up to his own, then said, ' More than a hundred years ago.'

So they all sat silent, listening to the roar of the south-west wind ; and it blew the windows so, that they rocked in their frames.

Then suddenly, as they sat thus, came a knock at the door of the house ; so Hugh bowed his head to Osric, to signify that he should go and open the door ; so he arose, trembling, and went.

And as he opened the door the wind blew hard against him, and blew something white against his face, then blew it away again, and his face was blanched, even to his lips ; but he plucking up heart of grace, looked out, and there he saw, standing with her face upturned in speech to him, a wonderfully beautiful woman, clothed from her throat till over her feet in long white raiment, ungirt, unbroidered, and with a long veil, that was thrown off from her face, and hung from her head, streaming out in the blast of the wind ; which veil was what had struck against his face : beneath her veil her golden hair streamed out too, and with the veil, so that it touched his face now and then. She was very fair, but she did not look young either, because of her statue-like features. She spoke to him slowly and queenly ; ' I pray you give me shelter in your house for an hour, that I may rest, and so go on my journey again.' He was too much terrified to answer in words, and so only bowed his head ; and she swept past him in stately wise to the room where the others sat, and he followed her, trembling.

A cold shiver ran through the other men when she entered and bowed low to them, and they turned deadly pale, but dared not move ; and there she sat while they gazed at her, sitting there and wondering at her beauty, which seemed to grow every minute ; though she was plainly not young, oh no, but rather very, very old, who could say how old ? there she sat, and her long, long hair swept down in one curve from her head, and just touched the floor. Her face had the tokens of a deep sorrow on it, ah ! a mighty sorrow, yet not so mighty

as that it might mar her ineffable loveliness ; that
sorrow-mark seemed to gather too, and at last the
gloriously-slow music of her words flowed from her lips :
' Friends, has one with the appearance of a youth come
here lately ; one with long brown hair, interwoven with
threads of gold, flowing down from out of his polished
steel helmet ; with dark blue eyes and high white forehead, and mail-coat over his breast, where the light and
shadow lie in waves as he moves ; have you seen such
an one, very beautiful ? '

Then withal as they shook their heads fearfully in
answer, a great sigh rose up from her heart, and she said :
' Then must I go away again presently, and yet I thought
it was the last night of all.'

And so she sat awhile with her head resting on her
hand ; after, she arose as if about to go, and turned her
glorious head round to thank the master of the house ;
and they, strangely enough, though they were terrified
at her presence, were yet grieved when they saw that she
was going.

Just then the wind rose higher than ever before, yet
through the roar of it they could all hear plainly a knocking at the door again ; so the lady stopped when she
heard it, and, turning, looked full in the face of Herman
the youngest, who thereupon, being constrained by that
look, rose and went to the door ; and as before with
Osric, so now the wind blew strong against him ; and it
blew into his face, so as to blind him, tresses of soft
brown hair mingled with glittering threads of gold ; and
blinded so, he heard some one ask him musically,
solemnly, if a lady with golden hair and white raiment
was in that house ; so Herman, not answering in words,
because of his awe and fear, merely bowed his head ;
then he was 'ware of some one in bright armour passing
him, for the gleam of it was all about him, for as yet he
could not see clearly, being blinded by the hair that had
floated about him.

But presently he followed him into the room, and
there stood such an one as the lady had described ; the
wavering flame of the light gleamed from his polished

helmet, touched the golden threads that mingled with his hair, ran along the rings of his mail.

They stood opposite to each other for a little, he and the lady, as if they were somewhat shy of each other after their parting of a hundred years, in spite of the love which they had for each other : at last he made one step, and took off his gleaming helmet, laid it down softly, then spread abroad his arms, and she came to him, and they were clasped together, her head lying over his shoulder ; and the four men gazed, quite awe-struck.

And as they gazed, the bells of the church began to ring, for it was New-Year's-eve ; and still they clung together, and the bells rang on, and the old year died.

And there beneath the eyes of those four men the lovers slowly faded away into a heap of snow-white ashes. Then the four men kneeled down and prayed, and the next day they went to the priest, and told him all that had happened.

So the people took those ashes and buried them in their church, in a marble tomb, and above it they caused to be carved their figures lying with clasped hands ; and on the sides of it the history of the cave in the red pike.

And in my dream I saw the moon shining on the tomb, throwing fair colours on it from the painted glass ; till a sound of music rose, deepened, and fainted ; then I woke.

No memory labours longer from the deep
 Gold mines of thought to lift the hidden ore
That glimpses, moving up, than I from sleep
 To gather and tell o'er
Each little sound and sight.

FRANK'S SEALED LETTER

(*Oxford and Cambridge Magazine*, April 1856)

EVER since I can remember, even when I was quite
a child, people have always told me that I had no
perseverance, no strength of will; they have always
kept on saying to me, directly and indirectly, ' Unstable
as water thou shalt not excel '; and they have always
been quite wrong in this matter, for of all men I ever
heard of, I have the strongest will for good and evil.
I could soon find out whether a thing were possible or
not to me; then if it were not, I threw it away for ever,
never thought of it again, no regret, no longing for that,
it was past, and over to me; but if it were possible, and
I made up my mind to do it, then and there I began it,
and in due time finished it, turning neither to the right
hand nor the left, till it was done. So I did with all
things that I set my hand to.

Love only, and the wild restless passions that went
with it, were too strong for me, and they bent my strong
will, so that people think me now a weak man, with no
end to make for in the purposeless wanderings of my life.

Yes, my life is purposeless now. I have failed, I know,
but I know that I have fought too; I know the weary
struggle from day to day, in which, with my loins girded,
and my muscles all a-strain, I have fought, while years
and years have passed away. I know what they do not,
how that Passion trembled in my grasp, shook, staggered:
how I grew stronger and stronger; till when, as I stood
at last quivering with collected force, the light of victory
across my lips and brow, God's hand struck me, and I
fell at once, and without remedy; and am now a vanquished man; and really without any object in life, not
desiring death any more than life, or life any more than
death; a vanquished man, though no coward; forlorn,
hopeless, unloved, living now altogether in the past.

I will tell you how I fell, and then I pray you all to

pity me, and if you can, love me, and pray for me that
I may be forgiven.

I said, when I left her that day, that I would forget
her, look upon her as if she had never been ; coming and
going to and from that house, indeed, seeing her often,
talking to her, as to any other friendly and accomplished
lady ; but seeing Mabel, my Mabel, that had been, no
more. She was dead, and the twenty years that I had
lived with her, man and boy, and little child, were gone—
dead too, and forgotten. No shadow of them should rest
upon my path, I said. Meantime the world wanted help ;
I was strong and willing, and would help it. I saw all
about me men without a leader, looking and yearning
for one to come and help them. I would be that leader,
I said ; there was no reason for me to be bitter and
misanthropical, for I could forget the past utterly, could
be another man in short. Why ! I never loved that
woman there, with her heavy, sweeping, black hair, and
dreamily-passionate eyes ; that was some one past away
long ago. Who knows when he lived ? but I am the
man that knows, that feels all poetry and art, that can
create, that can sympathize with every man and woman
that ever lived—even with that cold, proud woman there,
without a heart, but with heavy, sweeping hair, and great
dreamily-passionate eyes, which might cause a weak man
to love her.

Yes, I said so when I left her—nay, even before I left
her, for in my agonized pleading I had said words that
made her cold, selfish blood run quick enough to speak
scornful things to me. ' Mabel ! ' I said, ' Mabel ! think
awhile before you turn from me for ever ! Am I not good
enough for you ? Yet tell me, I pray you, for God's sake,
what you would have me do ? what you would have me
make myself, and I will do that thing, make myself such,
whatever it is. Think how long I have worshipped you,
looked on all the world through your eyes. I loved you
as soon as I saw you, even when I was a child, before
I had reason almost ; and my love and my reason have
grown together, till now. Oh ! Mabel, think of the things
we have talked of together, thought of together ! Will

you ever find another man who thinks the same as you
do in everything ? Nay, but you must love me. Such
letters you have written me too ! Oh ! Mabel, Mabel,
I know God will never let love like mine go unrequited.
You love me, I know. I am sure of it ; you are trying me
only ; let it be enough now, my own Mabel, the only one
that loves me. See, do not I love you enough ? '

I fell there before her feet. I caught the hem of her
garment. I buried my face in its folds ; madly I strove
to convince myself that she was but trying me, that she
could not speak for her deep love, that it was a dream
only. Oh ! how I tried to wake, to find myself, with my
heart beating wildly, and the black night round me,
lying on my bed ; as often, when a child, I used to wake
from a dream of lions, and robbers, and ugly deaths, and
the devil, to find myself in the dear room, though it was
dark, my heart bounding with the fear of pursuit and
joy of escape.

But no dream breaks now, desperate, desperate,
earnest. The dreams have closed round me, and become
the dismallest reality, as I often used to fear those
other dreams might ; the walls of this fact are closed
round about me now like the sides of an iron chest,
hurrying on down some swift river, with the black water
above, to the measureless, rolling sea. I shall never any
more wake to anything but that.

For listen to what she said, you who are happy lovers.
Can you believe it ? I can scarce do so myself. I, not
looking up from where I lay, felt her lips curl into a cruel
smile, as she drew herself from my grasp, and said :

' Listen, Hugh. I call you "Hugh", by the way, not
because I am fond of you, but because surnames never
seemed to me to express anything ; they are quite meaningless. Hugh, I never loved you, never shall, nay,
something more. I am not quite sure that I do not hate
you, for coming to claim me as a right in this way, and
appealing to God against me. Who gave you any right
to be lord over me, and question my heart ? Why, for
this long time I have seen that you would claim me
at last, and your " love," which I now cast from me for

ever, and trample upon, so—so,—your "love", I say,
has been a bitterly heavy burden to me, dogging me up
and down, everywhere. You think my thoughts ? Yes,
verily, you who think yourself the teacher of such an one
as I am, have few thoughts of your own to think. What
do I want better than you ? Why, I want a man who is
brave and beautiful. You are a coward and a cripple.
Am I trying you ? No, Hugh ; there is no need for that.
I think I know you well enough, weak and irresolute,
you will never do anything great. I must marry a great
man—

> White honour shall be like a plaything to him,
> Borne lightly, a pet falcon on his wrist :
> One who can feel the very pulse o' the time,
> Instant to act, to plunge into the strife,
> And with a strong arm hold the rearing world.'

But before she had begun to quote, my life had changed.
While I lay there, in I know not what agony, that which
I have just said came suddenly across me. I became
calm all at once. I began to bend my passion beneath
my strong will ; the fight I fought so bravely had begun.

I rose up quietly before she began to quote, and when
she saw me standing there, so calmly, ay, and looking so
brave too, though I was a 'cripple and a coward', she
quailed before me, her voice fell, even in the midst of her
scornful speech ; then I thought, ' so cool, and can quote
pretty verses at such a time ! Oh ! but my revenge is
good, and sure too, it is almost as if I killed her, stabbed
her to the heart, here in this room.' Then my heart grew
quite obedient, and my purpose began to work, so that
I could speak with no shadow of passion in my words,
and with no forced unnatural calm either. I could seem,
and for years and years did seem, to be no hard cold man
of the world, no mere calculating machine for gauging
God's earth by modern science ; but a kindly genial
man ; though so full of knowledge, yet having room for
love too, and enthusiasm, and faith. Ah ! they who saw
me as such did not see the fight, did not see that bitter
passage in the room of the old house at Riston, where
the river widens.

I stood there silent for a very short time ; then, raising
my eyes to hers, said, ' Well, Mabel, I shall go up to
London, and see the publishers, and perhaps stay there
a day or two, so that I shall probably be back again at
Casley by Tuesday ; and I daresay I shall find time to
walk over to Riston on Wednesday or Thursday, to tell
you what we have determined on—good bye.' She
trembled, and turned pale, as I gave her my hand, and
said, ' good bye ', in a forced tone, that was in strong
contrast to my natural-seeming calmness. She was
frightened of me then, already. Good.

So I walked away from Riston to my own house at
Casley (which was about two miles from Riston), and got
ready to start for London ; then, about an hour after
I had parted from her, set out again across the fields to
the railway, that was five miles from my house. It was
on the afternoon of a lovely spring day ; I took a book
with me, a volume of poems just published, and my
dead friend's manuscript ; for my purpose in going to
London was to see to its publication.

Then, looking at that over which so many years of
toil and agony of striving had been spent, I thought of
him who wrote it ; thought how admirable he was, how
that glorious calm purpose of his shone through all his
restless energy. I thought, too, as I had never done
before, of the many, many ways he had helped me, and
my eyes filled with tears, as I remembered remorsefully
the slight return I had given him for his affection, my
forgetfulness of him in the years when I was happy.
I thought of his quiet, successful love, and that sweet
wife of his, the poor widow that was now, who lived at
Florence, watching the shadows come and go on her
husband's tomb, the rain that washed it, the sun and
moon that shone on it ; then how he had died at Florence,
and of the short letter he had written to me, or rather
that had been written, just before his death, by his wife,
from his dictation, and stained with the many tears of
the poor heart-broken lady. Those farewell words that
threw but a slight shadow over the happy days when
I loved Mabel, had more weight now, both for sorrow

and consolation ; for the thought that that dead man cared for me surely did me good, made me think more of the unseen world, less of the terrible earth-world that seemed all going wrong, and which the unseen was slowly righting.

I had the letter with me at that very time. I had taken it out with the manuscript, and together with that, another, a sealed letter that came with it, and which, according to the dying man's wish, I had never yet opened. I took out both the letters, and turning aside from the path sat down under a willow by the side of the river, a willow just growing grey-green with the spring. And there, to the music of the west wind through the slim boughs, to the very faint music of the river's flow, I read the two letters, and first the one I had read before.

' Dear friend, I am going the last journey, and I wish to say farewell before I go. My wife's tears fall fast, as she writes, and I am sorry to go, though, I think, not afraid to die. Two things I want to say to you : the first and least has to do with my writings ; I do not wish them to perish : you know I wrote, thinking I might do some one good ; will you see about this for me ? Do you know, Hugh, I never cared for any man so much as for you : there was something which drew me to you wonderfully ; it used to trouble me sometimes to think that you scarcely cared for me so much ; but only sometimes, for I saw that you knew this, and tried to love me more ; it was not your fault that you could not ; God bless you for the trying even ! When you see my wife, be kind to her ; we have had happy talk about you often, thinking what a great man you ought to be. Yet one thing more. I send you with this a sealed enclosure. On the day that you are married to Mabel, or on the day that she dies, still loving you, burn this unopened ; but, oh friend, if such a misfortune happen to you, as I scarce dare hint at even, then open it, and read it for the sake of, Frank.'

Then I remembered, sadly, how when I read this, I was angry at first, even with the dead man, for his suspicion ; only, when I thought of him dying, and how loving he was, my anger quickly sunk into regret for him ; not deep anguish, but quiet regret. Ah ! what a long time it was since I loved Mabel ! how I had conquered my raging passion ! Frank will surely applaud my resolution. Dear heart ! how wise he was in his loving simplicity.

I looked at the sealed letter ; it also was directed in his wife's handwriting ; I broke the seal, and saw Frank's writing there ; it was written, therefore, some time before his death.

How solemn the wind was through the willow boughs, how solemn the faint sound of the swirls of the lowland river ! I read—

' O Hugh, Hugh ! poor wounded heart ! I saw it all along, that she was not worthy of that heart stored up with so much love. I do not ask for that love, dear friend ; I know you cannot give it me ; I was never jealous of her ; and I know, moreover, that your love for her will not be wasted. I think, for my part, that there is One Who gathers up all such wandering love, and keeps it for Himself ; think, Hugh, of those many weary hours on the Cross ; in that way did they requite His Love then, and how do we requite it now ? Should He not then sympathize with all those whose love is not returned ?

' And, Hugh, sweet friend, I pray you, for Christ's love, never strive to forget the love you bore her in the days when you thought her noble, the noblest of all things, never cast away the gift of memory ; never cast it away for your ease, never even for the better serving of God ; He will help Himself, and does not want mere deeds ; you are weak, and love cannot live without memory. Oh ! Hugh ! if you do as I pray you, this remembered love will be a very bright crown to you up in Heaven ; meantime, may it not be that your love for others will grow, that you will love all men more, and me, perhaps, even much more ? And I, though I never see you again in the body till the Day of Doom, will nevertheless be near you in spirit, to comfort you some-

what through the days of your toiling on earth ; and
now, Frank prays God to bless poor wounded Hugh ! '

I ceased reading ; a dull pain came about my forehead
and eyes.   What ! must I be all alone in my struggle
with passion ? not even Frank to help me ? dear fellow !
to think how fond he was of me ! I am very very sorry
he cannot be with me in this fight ; for I must kill her
utterly in my memory, and I think, if he knew all, how
very noble I thought her, how altogether base she really
is, he would be with me after all.   Yet, Frank, though
I do not do this that you pray me to do, you shall still
be my friend, will you not ? you shall help me to become
more like you, if that is possible in any degree.

So, I determined to forget her ; and was I not successful, at first ; ah ! and for long too ? nevertheless, alas !
alas ! Frank's memory faded with her memory, and I did
not feel his spirit by me often, only sometimes, and
those were my weakest times, when I was least fit to
have him by me ; for then my purpose would give in
somewhat, and memory would come to me, not clear
and distinct, but only as a dull pain about my eyes and
forehead ; but my strong will could banish that, for I had
much work to do, trying to help my fellow-men, with
all my heart I thought.   I threw myself heart and soul
into that work, and joy grew up in my soul ; and I was
proud to think that she had not exhausted the world
for me.

Nor did I shrink once from the sight of her, but came
often, and saw her at her father's house at Riston, that
the broadening river flows by always ; nay, I sat at her
wedding, and saw her go up to the altar with firm step,
and heard her say her part in the unfaltering music of
her rich voice, wherein was neither doubt nor love ; and
there I prayed that the brave noble-hearted soldier, her
husband, might be happy with her, feeling no jealousy
of him, pitying him rather ; for I did not think that it
was in her nature to love any one but herself thoroughly.
Yet, what a Queen she looked on that marriage-day !
her black hair crowning her so, her great deep eyes
looking so full of all slumbering passion as of old, her

full lips underneath, whence the music came ; and, as she walked there between the grey walls of that Abbey where they were married, the light fell on her through the jewel-like windows, colouring strangely the white and gold of her gorgeous robes. She also seemed, or wished to seem, to have forgotten that spring-day at Riston ; at least, she spoke to me when she went away quite kindly, and very calmly : ' Good bye, Hugh, we hear of you already ; you will be a great man soon, and a good man you always were, and always will be ; and we shall think of you often, and always with pleasure.'

Yet I knew she hated me ; oh ! her hollow heart ! The dull pain came about my forehead and eyes ; somehow I could not keep up the farce just then. I spoke bitterly, a smile that I know now I should not have smiled, curling my lip. ' Well done, Mabel ! it is a nicely composed parting speech to an old friend ; but you were always good at that kind of thing. Forget you ? no— you are too handsome for that ; and, if I were a painter or sculptor, I would paint you or carve you from memory. As it is, I never forget beautiful faces—good bye : ' and I turned away from her a little without giving my hand. She grew pale at first, then flushed bright crimson, like a stormy sky, and turned from me with a scornful devil's glance.

She was gone, and a sharp pang of memory shot through me for a single instant, a warning of my fall which was to be. For a single instant I saw her sitting there, as of old, in the garden hard by the river, under the gold-dropping laburnums, heard her for a single instant singing wildly in her magnificent voice, as of old :

> ' Wearily, drearily,
> Half the day long,
> Flap the great banners
> High over the stone ;
> Strangely and eerily
> Sounds the wind's song,
> Bending the banner-poles.

> ' While, all alone,
> Watching the loophole's spark,
> Lie I, with life all dark,

> Feet tether'd, hands fetter'd
> Fast to the stone,
> The grim walls, square letter'd
> With prison'd men's groan.

> ' Still strain the banner-poles
> Through the wind's song,
> Westward the banner rolls
> Over my wrong.'

But it was gone directly, that pang ; everything, voice, face, and all : like the topmost twigs of some great tree-limb, that, as it rolls round and round, griding the gravel and mud at the bottom of a flooded river, shows doubtfully for a second, flashing wet in the February sunlight, then, sinking straightway, goes rolling on toward the sea, in the swift steady flow of the flooded river ; yet it appears again often, till it is washed ashore at last, who knows where or when ?

But for me, these pangs of memory did not come often ; nay, they came less and less frequently for long, till at last, in full triumph, as I thought it, I fell.

That marriage-day was more than two years after the day in April that I have told you of, when I read the sealed letter ; then, for three years after her marriage, I went on working, famous now, with many who almost worshipped me, for the words I had said, the many things I had taught them ; and I in return, verily loved these earnestly ; yet, round about me clung some shadow that was not the mere dulled memory of what had been, and it deepened sometimes in my drearier moods into fearful doubts that this last five years of my life had been, after all, a mistake, a miserable failure ; yet, still I had too much to do to go on doubting for long ; so these shadowy doubts had to hold back till, though I knew it not, a whole army of them was marching upon me in my fancied security.

Well, it was Spring-time, just about five years from that day ; I was living in London, and for the last few months had been working very hard indeed, writing and reading all day long and every day, often all night long also, and in those nights the hours would pass so quickly that the time between night-fall and dawn scarcely seemed ten minutes long. So I worked, worked so hard, that one day, one morning early, when I saw through my window, on waking about six o'clock, how blue the sky was, even above the London roofs, and remembered how, in the fields all about, it was the cowslip time of the year, I said to myself, ' No work to-day ; I will make holiday for once in the sweet spring-time. I will take a book with some tale in it, go into the country, and read it there, not striving particularly to remember it, but enjoying myself only.' And, as I said this, my heart beat with joy, like a boy's at thought of holiday. So I got up, and as I was dressing, I took up a volume of Shakespeare, and opened it at Troilus and Cressida, and read a line or two just at the place where the parting comes ; it almost brought the tears to my eyes. ' How soft-hearted I am this morning,' I said ; ' yet I will take this ; and read it ; it is quite a long time since I read any Shakespeare, and, I think, years and years since I have read Troilus and Cressida.' Yes, I was soft-hearted that morning, and when I looked in the glass and saw my puny deformed figure there, and my sallow thin face, eaten into many furrows by those five years, those furrows that gave a strange grotesque piteousness to the ugly features, I smiled at first, then almost wept for self-pity ; the tears were in my eyes again ; but I thought, ' I will not spoil my holiday,' and so forbore ; then I went out into the streets, with a certain kind of light-heartedness, which I knew might turn any moment into very deep sadness. The bells of a church, that I passed in my way Essex-ward, were ringing, and their music struck upon my heart so, that I walked the faster to get beyond their sound.

I was in the country soon : people called it an ugly country, I knew, that spreading of the broad marsh lands round the river Lea ; but I was so weary with my hard work that it seemed very lovely to me then ; indeed, I think I should not have despised it at any time. I was always a lover of the sad lowland country. I walked on, my mind keeping up a strange balance between joy and

sadness for some time, till gradually all the beauty of
things seemed to be stealing into my heart, and making
me very soft and womanish, so that, at last, when I was
now quite a long way off from the river Lea, and walking
close by the side of another little river, a mere brook,
all my heart was filled with sadness, and joy had no
place there at all ; all the songs of birds ringing through
the hedges, and about the willows ; all the sweet colours
of the sky, and the clouds that floated in the blue of
it ; of the tender fresh grass, and the sweet young shoots
of flowering things, were very pensive to me, pleasantly
so at first perhaps, but soon they were lying heavy on
me, with all the rest of things created ; for within my
heart rose memory, green and fresh as the young spring
leaves. Ah ! such thoughts of the old times came about
me thronging, that they almost made me faint. I tried
hard to shake them off ; I noticed every turn of the
banks of the little brook, every ripple of its waters over
the brown stones, every line of the broad-leaved water-
flowers ; I went down towards the brook, and, stooping
down, gathered a knot of lush marsh-marigolds ; then,
kneeling on both knees, bent over the water with my arm
stretched down to it, till both my hand and the yellow
flowers were making the swift-running little stream
bubble about them ; and, even as I did so, still stronger
and stronger came the memories, till they came quite
clear at last, those shapes and words of the past days.
I rose from the water in haste, and, getting on to the
road again, walked along tremblingly, my head bent
toward the earth, my wet hand and flowers marking
the dust of it as I went. Ah ! what was it all, that
picture of the old past days.

I see a little girl sitting on the grass, beneath the limes
in the hot summer-tide, with eyes fixed on the far away
blue hills, and seeing who knows what shapes there ;
for the boy by her side is reading to her wondrous stories
of knight and lady, and fairy thing, that lived in the
ancient days ; his voice trembles as he reads—

' And so Sir Isumbras, when he had slain the giant,
cut off his head, and came to the town where the lady

Alicia lived, bringing with him that grim thing, the
giant's head, and the people pressed all about him at the
gate, and brought him to the king, and all the court
was there, and the whole palace blazed with gold and
jewels. So there, among the ladies, was the Lady Alicia,
clothed in black, because she thought that through her
evil pride she had caused the death of the good knight
and true, who loved her : and when she saw Sir Isumbras
with the head of the giant, even before the king, and all,
she gave a great cry, and ran before all, and threw her
arms round about him.' ' Go on, Hugh,' says the little
girl, still looking into the blue distance, ' why do you
stop ? ' ' I was—I was looking at the picture, Mabel,'
says the boy. ' Oh ! is there a picture of that ? let's
see it ; ' and her eyes turn towards him at last. What
a very beautiful child she is ! ' Not exactly of that,'
says Hugh, blushing as their eyes meet, and, when she
looks away for a second, drawing his hand across his eyes,
for he is soft-hearted, ' not exactly of that, but afterwards,
where she crowns him at the tournament ; here it is.'
' Oh ! that is pretty though ; Hugh, I say Hugh ! '
' Yes,' says Hugh. ' Go and get me some of the forget-
me-not down by the brook there, and some of the pretty
white star-shaped flower ; I'll crown you too.' Off runs
Hugh, directly, carrying the book with him. ' Stop,
don't lose the place, Hugh ; here, give me the book.'
Back he goes, then starts again in a great hurry ; the
flowers are not easy to get, but they are got somehow ;
for, Hugh, though deformed, is yet tolerably active, and
for her. So, when the flowers come, she weaves them
into a crown, blue flowers golden-hearted, and white
ones star-shaped, with the green leaves between them.

Then she makes him kneel down, and, looking at the
picture in the fairy story-book, places him this way and
that, with her smooth brows knit into a puzzled frown ;
at last she says, ' It wont do somehow ; I can't make
it out. I say, Hugh,' she blurts out at last, ' I tell you
what, it wont do ; you are too ugly.' ' Never mind,
Mabel,' he says ; ' shall I go on reading again ? ' ' Yes,
you may go on.' Then she sits down ; and again her

eyes are fixed on the far-away blue hills, and Hugh is by her, reading again, only stumbling sometimes, seemingly not so much interested as he was before.

' Poor Hugh ! ' I said out aloud, for strangely, the thing was so strong, that it had almost wrought its own cure ; and I found myself looking at my old self, and at her, as at people in a story ; yet I was stunned as it were, and knew well that I was incapable of resistance against that memory now. Yes, I knew well what was coming.

I had by this time left the brook, and gone through a little village on the hill above, and on the other side of it ; then turned to my right into the forest, that was all about, the quaint hornbeam forest. There, sitting down, I took out the Troilus and Cressida I had brought with me, and began to read, saying to myself (though I did not believe it) that I would cast those memories quite away from me, be triumphantly victorious over them.

Yes, there under the hornbeams I read Troilus and Cressida, the play with the two disappointments in it, Hector dead, and Cressida unfaithful ; Troy and Troilus undone. And when I had finished, I thought no more of Troilus and Cressida, or of any one else in the wide world but Mabel.

' O Mabel ! ' I said, burying my face in the grass as I had before, long ago, in her long robes ; ' O Mabel ! could you not have loved me ? I would have loved you more than any woman was ever loved. Or if you could not love me, why did you speak as you did on that day ? I thought you so much above me, Mabel ; and yet I could not have spoken so to any one. O Mabel ! how will it be between us when we are dead ? O Lord ! help me, help me ! Is it coming over again ? '

For as I lay there, I saw again, as clearly as years ago, the room in the old house at Riston, at the noontide of the warm sunny spring weather. The black oak panelling, carved so quaintly, all round the room, whereon, in the space of sunlight that, pouring through the window, lit up the shadowed wall, danced the shadows of the young lime-leaves ; the great bay window, with its

shattered stone mullions, round which the creepers clung ;
the rustling of the hard magnolia leaves in the fresh
blast of the west wind ; the garden, with its clusters of
joyous golden daffodils under the acacia-trees, seen
through the open window ; and beyond that, rolling
and flashing in the sun, between its long lines of willows
and poplars, the mighty lowland river going to the sea.

And she sat there by the fire-place, where there was no
fire burning now. She sat by the cold hearth, with her
back to the window, her long hands laid on her knees,
bending forward a little, as if she were striving to look
through and through something that was far off—there
she sat, with her heavy, rolling, purple hair, like a queen's
crown above her white temples, with her great slum-
brously-passionate eyes, and her full lips underneath,
whence the music came. Except that the wind moved
a little some of the folds of her dress, she was as motionless and quiet as an old Egyptian statue, sitting out its
many thousand years of utter rest, that it may the
better ponder on its own greatness ; more lifeless by far
she looked than any one of the grey saints, that hang
through rain, and wind, and sunshine, in the porches
of the abbey which looks down on the low river waves.

And there was one watched her from near the door,
a man with long arms, crooked shoulders, and pale,
ugly-featured face, looking out from long, lank, black
hair. Yes, his face is pale always ; but now it is much
paler than usual, as pale almost as the face of a dead
man ; you can almost hear his heart beat as he stands
there ; the cold sweat gathers on his brow. Presently
he moves towards the lady ; he stands before her with
one hand raised, and resting on the mantel-shelf. You
can see his arm trembling as he does this ; he stands
so while you might count twenty, she never looking up
the while. Then, half choking, he says, ' Mabel, I want
to speak to you, if you please, for a moment ; ' and she
looks round with a calm, unconcerned look at first ; but
presently a scornful smile begins to flicker about the
corners of her mouth. Then that pale man says, ' Ah !
I have told you all the rest before ; ' for he knew the

meaning of the flickering smile—and that was five years ago.

And I shall never forget it while I live—never forget those words of hers—never forget a single line of her beautiful, cruel face, as she stood there five years ago. All the world may go by me now ; I care not. I cannot work any more. I think I must have had some purpose in coming here ; but I forget what it was. I will go back to London, and see if I can remember when I get there—so that day under the hornbeam trees I fell from my steady purpose of five years. I was vanquished then, once and for ever ; there was no more fighting for me any more.

And have I ever forgotten it—that day, and the words she spoke ? No, not for one moment. I have lived three years since then of bitter anguish. Every moment of that time has been utter pain and woe to me ; that is what my life has been these three years. And what death may be like I cannot tell ; I dare not even think for fear.

And I have fled from the world ; no one of all my worshippers knows what has become of me, and the people with whom I live now, call me a man without a purpose, without a will.

Yes, I wonder what death would be like. The Eure is deep at Louviers I know—deep, and runs very swiftly towards the Seine, past the cloth mills.

. . . .

Louviers ! Louviers ! What am I saying ? Where am I ? O Christ ! I hold the sealed letter—Frank's sealed letter, in my hand, the seal just broken. Five years ! Eight years ! It was but two hours ago that my head lay before her feet ; yet I seem to have lived those eight years. Then I have not been famous ; have not forgotten ; never sat under the hornbeams by Chigwell ; and she is sitting there, still perhaps in that same oak room.

How strange it is, fearfully strange, yet true ; for here is Frank's letter ; here is his manuscript, the ink on it, brown through the years of toil and longing. There close by my side the great river is going to the sea, and the wind goes softly through the willow-boughs this sunny spring afternoon.

And now what shall I do ? I know my will is strong, though I failed so in that dream I have awoke from. I know too, ' That a sorrow's crown of sorrow is remembering happier things.' Shall I wear this crown then while I live on earth, or forget, and be brave and strong ? Ah ! it must be a grand thing to be crowned ; and if it cannot be with gold and jewels, or better still, with the river flowers, then must it be with thorns. Shall I wear this or cast it from me ? I hear the wind going through the willow-boughs ; it seems to have a message for me.

' Good and true, faithful and brave, loving always, and crowned with all wisdom in the days gone by. He was all this and more. Trust your friend Hugh—your friend who loved you so, though you hardly knew it ; wear the crown of memory.' Yes, I will wear it ; and, O friend ! you who sent me this dream of good and evil, help me, I pray you, for I know how bitter it will be. Yes, I will wear it, and then, though never forgetting Mabel, and the things that have been, I may be happy at some time or another.

Yet I cannot see now how that can ever come to pass.

Oh, Mabel ! if you could only have loved me.

' Lord, keep my memory green.'

GERTHA'S LOVERS

IN FIVE CHAPTERS

(*Oxford and Cambridge Magazine*, July and August 1856)

CHAPTER I.—By the River

All thoughts, all passions, all delights,
Whatever stirs this mortal frame,
All are but ministers of love,
And feed his sacred flame.—*Coleridge.*

LONG ago there was a land, never mind where or when, a fair country and good to live in, rich with wealth of golden corn, beautiful with many woods, watered by great rivers, and pleasant trickling streams ; moreover, one extremity of it was bounded by the washing of the purple waves, and the other by the solemn watchfulness of the purple mountains.

In a fair lowland valley of this good land sat a maiden, one summer morning early, working with her needle, while she thought of other matters as women use. She was the daughter of a mere peasant, tiller of the kind soil, fisher in the silver waters of the river that flowed down past his cottage to the far-off city ; he lived from day to day seeing few people, the one or two neighbours who lived in the cottages hard by, the priest of the little hamlet, now and then an artizan travelling in search of work ; except, indeed, when he went to the wars ; for he was a fighting man, as were all the people of that country, when need was. His wife was dead these five years, and his daughter alone lived with him ; yet she, though of such lowly parentage, was very beautiful ; nor merely so, but grand and queen-like also ; such a woman as might inspire a whole people to any deed of wise daring for her love.

What thoughts were hers, as she sat working on that summer morning, the song of birds all about her, and the

lapping of the low, green river waves on the white sand
sounding fresh and pleasantly as the west wind blew
them toward her ? What thoughts ? Good thoughts,
surely. For the land wherein she dwelt—so fair a land,
so small a land, had never ceased to be desired by the
tyrant kings who bore rule round about. Always had
they made war against it ; never had they conquered,
though sometimes they were seemingly victorious in
a scattered fight here and there, through sheer force of
numbers ; for the dwellers in that good land were of
a different race to the lazy, slavish people who dwelt
about them. Many a song Gertha could sing you of how,
long, and long ago, they came from a land far over the
sea, where the snow-laden pine-forests, weird halls of
strange things, hang over the frozen waters for leagues,
and leagues, and leagues along the coasts that were the
cradles of mighty nations. Sailing over the sea then,
long ago, with their ships all a-blaze with the steel that
the heroes carried, they came to this land with their
wives and children, and here made desperate war with
the wild beasts, with savage swamps, dragon-inhabited,
daring famine, and death in all ugly shapes.

And they grew and grew, for God favoured them ;
and those who dwelt nearest to the ' Savage Land,' as it
used to be called, grew more and more like the strangers,
and their good rule spread ; and they had a mighty faith
withal that they should one day ring the world, going
westward ever till they reached their old home in the
east, left now so far behind.

Judge, therefore, whether the tyrant kings feared
these free, brave men ! Judge whether, growing more
and more cruel as they grew more and more fearful, they
strained the chain over the miserable millions of their
subjects so that with many it grew intolerable, and
was broken asunder ; so that, both in well-doing and in
wrong-doing, God's kingdom spread.

Think what armies went up against the good land ;
what plains and valleys were sown with swords and
spears and helmets, and the bones of valiant men ; and
from being nameless once, only thought of as the place

where such and such a tree grew very plenteous, where such a river ran, became now to be remembered to all time, nor to be forgotten in eternity.

Think of the desperate fights, in treacherous slippery fords, where the round stones rolled and shifted beneath the hurried trampling of men, fighting for life, and more than life, amid the plash of the reddened waters in the raw, gusty twilight of the February mornings ; or in close woods, little lighted up by the low sun just going to sink when the clouds looked thunderous in the summer evenings ; or with shouts from crag to crag of the great slate-cliffs, with wrathful thundering of rocks down into the thronged pass below, with unavailing arrow-flights, because arrows cannot pierce the mountains, or leap about among the clefts of the rocks where the mountaineers stand, fiercely joyous.

Think too of the many heads, old and young, beautiful and mean, wept over, not joyously indeed ; nay, who knows with what agony, yet at least with love unflecked by any wandering mote of the memory of shame or shrinking ; think of the many who, though they fought not at all with spear or sword, yet did, indeed, bear the brunt of many a battle, in patiently waiting through heart-sickening watchings, yet never losing hope, in patiently bearing unutterable misery of separation, yet never losing faith.

Had not Gertha then enough to think of, as she sat working hard by where the water lapped the white sand ? For this people were so drawn together, that through the love they bore to one another sprang terrible deeds of heroism, any one of which would be enough for a life-time's thought ; almost every man of that nation was a hero and a fit companion for the angels ; and the glory of their fathers, and how themselves might do deeds that would not shame them, were the things that the men thought of always ; and the women, for their part, looked to become wives to brave men, mothers to brave sons.

So now Gertha was singing rough spirit-stirring songs of the deeds of old, and thinking of them too with all her heart as she sang. Why she, weak woman as she was, had not she seen the enemies' ships hauled up on the island bank yonder, and burned there ? Were not the charred logs, which once, painted red and black, used to carry terror to the peaceful, slothful people of the islands, mouldering there yet, grown over by the long clinging briony ? Did not her eyes flash, her brow and cheeks flush with triumph, her heart swell and heave beneath her breast, when the war-music grew nearer and louder every moment ; and when she saw at last the little band of her dear countrymen hemming in the dejected prisoners, the white red-crossed banner floating over all, blessing all alike, knight, and sailor, and husband-man ; and when she saw, too, her own dear, dear father, brave among the bravest, marching there with bright eyes, and lips curled with joyous triumphant indignation, though the blood that he was marked withal did not come from his enemies' veins only ? Did she not then sing, joyously and loud-ringing, remembering these things and many others, while the west wind was joyous about her too, whispering to her softly many things concerning the land of promise ?

She sang about a king who lived long ago, a man wise and brave beyond all others, slain treacherously in a hunting party by emissaries of the enemy, and slain at the height of his wisdom and good rule ; and this was one of the songs that his people had embalmed his memory withal. So, as she sang, behold, the blowing of horns, and trampling as of horse, just as her voice rang clear with,

'The King rode out in the morning early,
   Went riding to hunting over the grass ;
   Ere the dew fell again that was then bright and pearly,
   O me !—what a sorrow had come to pass !'

And a great company rode past going to hunt indeed, riding slowly, between her and the river, so that she saw them all clearly enough, the two noble knights especially, who rode at the head of them ; one very grand and noble, young withal, yet looking as if he were made to burst asunder the thickest circles of the battle, to gather together from the most hopeless routs men enough to

face the foe, and go back fighting, to roll back the line
of fight when it wavered, to give strength to all warriors'
hearts : fancy such an one, so wise, yet so beautiful,
that he moved like the moving of music ; such tenderness
looked from his eyes, so lovingly the morning sun and
the sweet morning haze touched the waves of his golden
hair, as they rode on happily. He that rode beside him
was smaller and slenderer, smaller both in body and face,
and it seemed in mind and heart also ; there was
a troubled restless look about his eyes ; his thin lips
were drawn inward tightly, as if he were striving to keep
down words which he ought not to speak, or else sometimes very strangely, this look would change, the eyes
would glance about no more, yet look more eager and
strangely anxious than ever ; the thin lips would part
somewhat, as if he were striving to say something which
would not leave his heart ; but the great man's eyes
were large and serene, his lips full, his forehead clear,
broad, and white ; his companion was sallow, his forehead lower and rather narrow, his whole face drawn into
wrinkles that came not by age, for he was no older than
the other.

They past as they had come, and when the last note
of their horns had died away, Gertha went about her
household duties ; yet all that day, whatever she might
do, however much she tried to beat the phantom down,
that stately man with the golden hair floated always
before her eyes.

. . . .

Evening now, the sun was down, the hunt had swept
away past the cottage again, though not within sight of
it, and the two knights having lost their companions
were riding on slowly, their tired horses hanging down
their heads.

'Sire, where are we going to ? ' said the small dark
man ; ' I mean to say where past that beech-tree ? the
low swinging boughs of which will hit you about the end
of the nose, I should think : Ah ! his head goes down,
somewhat in good time ; he has escaped the beech-
bough.'

But the other answered no word, for he did not hear his friend speak, he was singing softly to himself :

> 'The King rode out in the morning early,
>   Went riding to hunting over the grass ;
> Ere the dew fell again which was then round and pearly,
>   O me !—what a sorrow had come to pass.'

He sang this twice or thrice with his head sunk down toward the saddle-bow, while the other knight gazed at him with a sad half smile, half sneer on his lips and eyes ; then with a sigh he turned him about and said, ' Pardon, Leuchnar, you said something I did not hear ; my mind was not in this wood, but somewhere else, I know not where. Leuchnar, we shall not find the hunt to-night ; let us, let us seek rest at that cottage that we passed this morning ; it seems to be the only house near.'

' Yea, my Lord Olaf,' said Leuchnar, smiling again in that bitter way, when he saw in spite of the twilight, both of the sunken sun and of the thick beech-wood, a great blush come over Olaf's face.

' Yea, for why should we not ? ' and as he said this, he fairly burst out into strange explosive laughter, that did not sound merry, yet was not repulsive, but sad only ; for Leuchnar was thinking of the ways of man, and found much to amuse him therein ; yet his laughter sounded sad in spite of himself, for he was not one who was made to laugh, somehow ; but what specially made him laugh now was this, that neither of them had forgotten that hour in the morning, and the maiden sitting alone near the river : each of them, as they burst through the greenest glades of the forest, with cry of hound and sound of horn, had, according to his faith, visions of a dark-haired maiden, sitting and singing, her eyes raised and fixed on one of them ; also both wished to go there again, and accordingly had been sad laggards in the hunt, and had lost themselves, not very unwillingly, perhaps ; yet now neither liked to confess his longing to the other ; Leuchnar would not even do so to himself, and for these reasons he laughed, and his laugh sounded strange and sad.

But Olaf knew that he was in love, and all day long he

had been nursing that love delightedly ; he blushed yet more at Leuchnar's laugh, for these two seldom needed to tell each other their thoughts in so many words, and certainly not this time. He bowed his head downwards in his confusion so low, that his gold curls, falling forward, mingled with the full black of his horse's mane, and growled out therefrom :

' You are a strange fellow, Leuchnar, though a good one ; but we will go.'

' Yea, to the peasant's cottage, my lord,' said Leuchnar, with his head raised, his eyes set straight forward, and his lips curled into something much more like a sneer than a smile ; thereat Olaf with a spring sat upright in his saddle, and glanced quickly on either side of him, as though something had stung him unawares ; afterwards they both turned their horses' heads aside, and rode slowly in the direction of the cottage, Leuchnar singing in a harsh voice, ' The King rode out in the morning early,'—' though the dew has fallen again,' he muttered ; whereat Olaf gave an uneasy side glance at him.

And soon they heard again the lapping of the river waves on the sand of the silver bay, only lower than before, because the wind had fallen. Then presently they drew rein before the cottage door, when the moon was already growing golden. Sigurd, Gertha's father, came to the door, and courteously held the stirrups of the knights while they dismounted, and they entered, and sat down to such fare as the peasant had, and Gertha served them. But they prayed her so to sit down, that at last it seemed discourteous to refuse them, and she sat down timidly.

Then said Sigurd, when they had eaten enough, ' I pray you tell me, fair knights, what news there is from the city, if you come from thence ; for there is a rumour of war hereabout, only uncertain as yet.'

' Nay, at the city,' Leuchnar said, ' there is certain news concerning one war, and even beside this, rumours of a great conspiracy between the surrounding rulers of slaves. The Emperor says that this valley always belonged to him ; though, indeed, he was not very anxious for it when poisonous swamps spread out on both sides of the river here ; or rather his ancestors laid no claim to it ; but now, at all events, he is coming to take his own, if he can get it ; coming by way (it is his only way, poor fellow !) of the mountain passes. Only, my lord Adolf is off to meet him with ten thousand men, and they are going to try the matter by arbitrement in this fashion ; marry, that if the valley belongs to the Emperor, he must know the way to it, and accordingly shall have it if he gets through the mountains in any other way than as a prisoner or dead corpse.'

Sigurd and Olaf laughed grimly at Leuchnar's conceit, and Gertha's eyes flashed ; while both the knights watched her without seeing how matters went with each other. 'Then,' said Sigurd again, 'Concerning the young king, fair knights, what is he ? ' Olaf's eyes twinkled at the question, and Leuchnar seeing that he wanted to answer, let him do so, watching him the while with a quaint amused look on his face. 'Why,' said Olaf, ' he is counted brave and wise, and being young, will, I hope, live long ; but he is very ugly.' Here he turned, and looked at his friend with a smile. Sigurd started and seemed disappointed, but Gertha turned very pale, and rose from her seat suddenly, nor would she sit down again all that evening.

Then Olaf saw that she knew he was the king, and somehow did not feel inclined to laugh any more, but grew stately and solemn, and rather silent too ; but Leuchnar talked much with Gertha, and he seemed to her to be very wise ; yet she remembered not what he said, scarcely heard it indeed, for was not the KING by her ; the king of all that dear people ; yet, above all, whether the other were so or not, *her* king ?

Poor maid ! she felt it was so hopeless ; nay, she said to herself, ' Even if he were to say he loved me, I should be obliged to deny my love ; for what would all the people say, that the king of so great a nation should marry a peasant girl, without learning or wealth, or wisdom, with nothing but a pretty face ? Ah ! we must be apart always in this world.'

And Olaf, the king, said, ' So Leuchnar loves her—
and I love her. Well, it will change his life, I think ; let
him have her ; poor fellow ! he has not got many to
love him. Besides, she is a peasant's daughter ; I am
a great king. Yet is she nobler than I am, for all my
kingship. Alas, I fear the people, not for myself, but
for her ; they will not understand her nobility ; they
will only see that which comes uppermost, her seeming
wisdom, her seeming goodness, which, perchance, will
not show to be so much greater than other women's, as
the queen's ought to do. Then withal to her, if, perchance,
at any time I am not quite sufficient to fill her heart,
will come a weariness of our palace life, a longing for old
places, old habits ; then sorrow, then death, through
years and years of tired pining, fought against, bravely
indeed, but always a terrible weight to such an one as
she is. Yet, if I knew she loved me, all this ought to
be put aside ; and yet, why should she love me ? And,
if she does not love me now, what hope is there ; for how
can we see each other any more, living such different far
apart lives ? But for Leuchnar this is otherwise ; he
may come and go often. Then he is wiser ; ah ! how
much wiser than I am ; can think and talk quite wonderfully, while I am but a mere fighting man ; how it
would change his life too, when he found any one to
love him infinitely, to think his thoughts, be one with
him, as people say. Yes, let Leuchnar have her.'

Those three so seeming-calm ! what stormy passions,
wild longings, passed through their hearts that evening !
Leuchnar seeming-genial with his good friendly talk, his
stories of brave deeds, told as if his heart were quite in
them ; speaking so much more like other men than his
wont was ; yet saying to himself, ' She .must see that
I love her ; when since I can remember have I talked
so ? ' Poor fellow ; how should she know that ? his
voice was to her as the voices of a dream, or perhaps
rather like grand music when it wakes a man ; for,
verily the glory of his tales got quite separated from him,
and in some dim way floated in a glory round about Olaf,
as far as Gertha was concerned. She heard his name,

the hero of every deed, which that far-distant knight,
Leuchnar, less present than his own tales, was telling of ;
whenever danger clung about the brave in those tales,
her heart beat for fear of her golden-haired, broad-
foreheaded hero ; she wondered often, as her heart
wandered even from those tales, why she did not fall
down before him and win his love or die. How then
could she think of Leuchnar ? Yet Olaf did think of
him, saw well through all his talking what he was thinking
of ; and, for his own part, though he did not talk aloud,
and though even what he said to himself had to do with
that subject dearest to him, yet none the less even to
himself choked down fiery longings, hardly, very hardly
to be restrained.

He tried hard to throw himself into Leuchnar's heart,
to think of the loneliness of the man, and his wonderful
power of concentrating every thought, every least spark
of passion, on some one thing ; he remembered how in
the years past he had clutched so eagerly at knowledge ;
how that knowledge had overmastered him, made him
more and more lonely year by year ; made him despise
others because they did not KNOW ; he remembered,
with a certain pang, how Leuchnar even despised him
for one time ; yes, he could bear just then to recall all
the bitter memories of that time ; how he saw it creeping
over his friend ; how he saw it struggled against, yet
still gaining, gaining so surely ; he called to mind that
day, when Leuchnar spoke his scorn out openly, bitterly
despising his own pride and himself the while ; he remembered how Leuchnar came back to him afterwards, when
knowledge failed him ; and yet how it was never the
same between them as it had been ; he remembered then
many a fight wherein they rode side by side together,
Leuchnar as brave as he, yet ever with that weight of
self-scorn upon him, that made him despise even his
bravery ; while Olaf rejoiced in his own, reverenced that
of others ; then he remembered how he was made king,
how the love of his countrymen became from that time
much more of a passion, true love, than it had been ; and
through all these things he tried to be Leuchnar, as it

were ; not such a hard thing for him ; for, through his unselfishness, he had gained that mighty power of sympathy for others, which no fiercest passion can altogether put aside, even for the time. So he, too, had his thoughts, not easily to be read by others, not to be expressed by himself.

So the night passed ; and they went to rest, or what seemed so, till they were wakened very early in the morning by the sound of a trumpet ringing all about the wooded river-shore ; the knights and Sigurd rose and went forth from the cottage, knowing the trumpet to be a friendly one ; and presently there met them a band of knights fully armed, who drew rein when they saw them.

'King Olaf,' said their leader, an old, white-haired knight, 'thank God we have found you ! When we reached the palace last night, after having lost you, there were waiting for us ambassadors, bringing with them declarations of war from the three Dukes and King Borrace ; so now, I pray you, quick back again ! I have sent all about for men, but the time presses, and there is a credible report that King Borrace has already begun his march toward the plain ; as for the three Dukes (whom may the Lord confound !), Lord Hugh's army will account for them, at any rate to hold them in check till we have beaten King Borrace ; but for him we must march presently, if we mean to catch him ; only come King Olaf, and all will be well.'

Then knelt Sigurd before the King, as he stood with eyes flashing, and cheek flushing, thinking how God's foes were hastening on to their destruction ; yet for all his joy he longed to see Gertha, perhaps for the last time ; for she was not there, neither did she come at Sigurd's call.

So the King smiled sorrowfully when Sigurd made excuse for her, saying that she feared so great a man as the King ; he could not help wishing she loved him, even though he meant to give her up : so he said ; he could not acknowledge to the full what a difference her love would make to him.

Then would he have given Sigurd presents of money

and jewels, but Sigurd would not take them ; only at the last, being constrained, he took the King's dagger, hilted with curiously wrought steel.

Then they all rode away together ; Barulf, the old man, by the King's side, and talking eagerly with him concerning the coming wars ; but Leuchnar fell into the rear, and said no word to any.

CHAPTER II

LEUCHNAR'S RIDE

THEN for some days each man wrought his best, that they might meet the invaders as they ought ; yet through all the work Leuchnar seemed very restless and uneasy, falling into staring fits, and starting from them suddenly ; but the king was calm and cheerful outwardly, whatever passion strove to fever him.

But one day when he was resting, leaning out of a window of the palace that was almost hidden by the heaped jasmine and clematis, he heard horse-hoofs, and presently saw Leuchnar, his sallow face drawn into one frown of eagerness, well mounted, lightly armed, just going to ride away, Olaf well knew whither.

A fierce pang shot through to Olaf's heart ; he felt dizzied and confused ; through the clematis stems and curled tendrils, through the mist rising from his own heart, he dimly saw Leuchnar gather himself together, raise his bridle-hand, and bend forward as his horse sprang up to the gallop ; he felt sick, his strong hands trembled ; and through the whirling of his brain, and the buzzing in his ears, he heard himself shout out : ' Good speed, Sir Leuchnar, with your wooing ! '

This was enough ; his heart sank, and his passion grew cool for the second, when he saw how fearfully Leuchnar's face changed at the well-understood words : troubled before as it had been, what was it now, when suddenly all the conscience of the man showed in that small spot of clay, his face ?

He turned his horse, and rode back swiftly ; Olaf waited for him there, scarce knowing what he did at first ; yet within a little, something, thoughts of approaching death perhaps, had steadied his brain, and kept his passion back : he heard soon the quick footsteps of some one striding far, and walked quietly towards the door, where he met Leuchnar, his teeth set, his lips a little open, that his hard-drawn breathings might not choke him, his black eyes fixed forward and shining grimly from under his heavy brows like pent-house roofs.

Olaf took him by the arm and gripped him hard ; but he tore it away fiercely ; he flung himself down before Olaf's feet.

' King Olaf,' he said passionately, ' I will not go, I will stay here then, if you look at me like that—with your broad white forehead and golden locks—you !— I will die here if I cannot live till I meet the enemy.'

Olaf stooped to raise him up, but he drew farther back from him ; then said, still kneeling :

' No word—no word yet, king, from you—was it not enough, Olaf, that you should take care of me, and love me in the days before you were king—me, a lonely discontented man, a black spot in the clear whiteness of the most loving people of the earth ? was it not enough that, on the day when all the people shouted for Olaf, calling him the wisest and the best, you, with the crown yet on your head, the holy oil not dry there, should take me by the hand, and say to all the knights and all the people, whom you loved so, whom I (God help me !) loved not ; " behold Leuchnar, my friend, who has given me all the wisdom I ever had ? " Ah, king ! had you looked on me at that moment and seen even then my curling lips saying to my false heart, " I am so much wiser than these simple ones ! "—but your clear eyes only looked straight forward, glancing over the heads of the people that was dear to you, despised by me. Was it not enough, King Olaf, that you, as the days passed, still keeping me the nearest to you, still asking me concerning everything, should be beginning to thaw my

hard heart and to shake my faith in the faithlessness of
Adam's sons ? were not these things enough, that you
also, first of all finding pretences to mar the nobleness
of your sacrifice even to your own heart, should give
your love up to me, not as I do now to you, noisily, but
quietly, without a word spoken ; then afterwards, when
you saw with what base eagerness I caught at that love
given up by you, and fearing terrible things for my
wretched soul if this went on, stopped me, like my
guardian angel, just now when I was sneaking off like
a thief in the night, and perhaps now—God help me !
God help me !—have perhaps even made me do one
thing in the whole course of my life which it is good to
have done in His eyes ? '

Then, as he knelt there, like a man before the presence
of God, the king spoke slowly, with humble face indeed,
and tearfully, but almost smiling, because all things
seemed so clear to him in a moment of prophetic vision.

' Dear Knight, your words seem like a bitter satire to
me ; for I did not call you back just now for your
salvation, but because my selfish passion (think of a
selfish king, Leuchnar ; what a misery !) my passion
carried me away : O, forgive me ! for indeed I wish you
to have her ; think now, how many cares, and joys too,
I have in tending this people that God has given me ;
I am sure that I shall not be quite unhappy for long,
whatever happens ; sometimes, perhaps, when I am
weary, sometimes in the dead night, sometimes in the
dying autumn, I shall have thoughts of her ; but they
will never be unbearable, because no power in earth or
heaven can keep me from loving her : it will be no shame
to you either, Leuchnar ; do you not remember, in past
days, how when we talked of this matter, you have often
said, (wherein even then I scarce agreed with you,) that
the love of man and woman should go before everything,
before all friendship, all duty, all honour even ? you
thought so then ; can you doubt now ? ' He ceased, and
said no word for a little ; then spoke doubtfully.

' And yet, and yet—are we not as men who reckon, as
they say, without their host ? What will Gertha say ?

ought we not to know before this great battle is fought,
from which, perchance, neither of us will come alive ?
and we march to-morrow, and I may not leave the council
and my work here : wherefore, dear Leuchnar, I pray
you on your allegiance mount again and ride quickly
away to that cottage, and ask her if she—loves you—
and if—if—Leuchnar, we may be near to death ; whatever happens we must be brothers—so God speed you
on your wooing.'

Leuchnar had risen while the king was speaking, and
stood before him till he ceased with head sunk down on
his breast ; then raised his face, radiant now with
a certain joy, to Olaf's ; he spoke no word, as though
that joy, or something else, confused and hurrying, that
went with it, was too great for him ; but, bending,
kissed the king's hand and departed.

Then Olaf again leaned from the window and watched
him go by again swiftly, till the sound of the horse-hoofs
had died away : then he turned toward the council
chamber, thinking :

' His face was not like the face of a man who is going
to do what he thinks wrong : I fear lest he go as my
ambassador—nay, do I *fear* ? Yet surely that will be
the best way to speed his own wooing—O, Gertha !
Gertha !—perhaps the sword will cut this knot so close
wound up together now ; yet I will not pray for that,
only that Leuchnar may live.'

Then presently he was in the midst of his lords. Oh
what a weary ride that was of Leuchnar's ! It was early
morning when he started, high noon by the time he drew
rein at the cottage door ; and that joy which at first he
had in his noble deed faded from off his face as the sun
rose higher, even as the dew did from off the face of the
meadows, and when he dismounted at that house of
Sigurd's, his face was woful and ghastly to look on.

He knocked at the door, then entered when no one
answered : he said out aloud, though he saw no one
there, as if he distrusted his power to repeat that lesson
got by heart with such pain : ' I bear a message to the
Lady Gertha.'

Only the cool duskiness of the heavy-shadowed oak beams met his eye, only the echo of his own hollow voice, and the chirp of the sparrows, the scream of the swifts,— met his ear.

For Gertha was not within ; but from the wood she had seen the glimmer of his arms in the hot noontide, and came down, stately and slow, unmoved to look on, but her heart of hearts wavering within her with hope and fear and ecstasy of love : perhaps (O poor heart, what wild hope !) it might be the king.

She met him just at the door from whence he had turned to seek her : he durst not meet her eyes, those grand fire-orbs that had pierced him through and through that other day ; if he had looked up at her face he would have seen the disappointment, the sickness of hope deferred, showing somewhat there in spite of her efforts to keep the appearance of it back.

He, with his face turned away, said, in a hard voice as before, ' I bear a message for the Lady Gertha.' No blush coloured her pale cheeks, no start or trembling went through her grand form ; she still held that flower in her hand, holding it with queenly sway, for it fitted in her hand like a sceptre : she said gently, ' If you want *Lady* Gertha, you must go elsewhere, my lord ; I am Sigurd the husbandman's daughter.'

' But you are Gertha that we heard sing that day,' he said fiercely, and turning his eager eyes suddenly on her.

' Yea,' she said, trembling a little now, and turning even paler ; for she saw how matters went with him, and feared, not any violence from him, for she soon read him through and through, but rather that he should fall down dead before her, his passion rent his heart so.

' Gertha, Olaf the king says, Will you be queen ? ' he said, still looking hungrily at her.

The crimson blood rushed up over her face, then went to her heart again, leaving her very lips grey. She paused a moment, with her arms stretched straight down, and her hands clenched : she said, without looking up :

' Tell him, " No " ; I am too lowly, not wise enough,

I should shame him; I will not be queen— But '

What wild passions rushed through poor Leuchnar's heart! how he fought with that Devil which had looked him steadily in the face so long, ever since he was born till now.

She stood there still before him, with arms stretched downward, hands clenched; he seized her by the wrist, and almost shrieked out; ' But what ?—Gertha ! Gertha ! before God, do you *love* him ? '

Her colour came again as she looked him in the face, put very close to hers now, so close that she felt his breath upon it; she said calmly, almost proudly, ' Yea, I love him; how could it be otherwise ? '

' Some token then, for Christ's sake; quick, Gertha ! and where will you be in the war time ? '

' My father goes with me to-morrow to the city. I shall dwell at St. Agnes' convent of nuns till Borrace is defeated.'

' Then some token !—here ! ' (and he tore down from the cottage eaves a bunch of golden stone-crop) ' if you love him (think of God, Gertha), kiss this.'

She bowed her head, and touched the yellow flowers with her lips; as she did so, he bent and kissed her forehead; then, with the flowers yet in his hand, he sprung impetuously to his saddle and galloped as if for his life. The Devil was conquered at last.

' Poor knight ! ' said Gertha, looking after him pityingly, ' then he loves me too; it seems wrong to feel happy when such a noble knight is so miserable.'

Yet she did feel very happy, and soon forgot poor Leuchnar and his sorrows, who was riding meanwhile wildly through the forest; yet, as he drew further from her, the madness of his passion abated a little; he gave his horse rest at last, and, dismounting, lay down on the ferns by the side of the forest-path, and there, utterly worn out in mind and body, fell asleep; a dreamless sleep it was at first, as deep as death almost, yet, as it grew lighter, he fell to dreaming, and at last woke from a dream wherein Gertha had come to him, shrieked out

that Olaf was slain, then thrown her arms about his neck ;
but, as he tried to kiss her, he awoke, and found himself
under the beech-boughs, his horse standing over him,
and the bridle, hanging loose from the bit, dangling
about his face ; for the horse doubted if he were dead.

He rose from that dream with a great wrench of his
heart, and, mounting, rode on soberly. The moon shone
down on him now, for he had slept far into the night.
The stone-crop was fading fast, and as he looked at it,
he doubted whether to curse it or bless it, but at last
raised it to his mouth and kissed it, knowing whose lips
had touched it before, looking half-fearfully over his
shoulder as he did so; perhaps he thought a little also how
Olaf's face would flush into perfect beauty for joy, when
he saw it; for joy mixed with a certain regret for himself.

So, when he reached the palace, quite late at night,
when the moon was already setting, he found Olaf standing in the great hall alone, looking pale and wearied.

Leuchnar came quite close to him, and said, taking his
hand and smiling a sick smile : ' Olaf, she sent you this,
kissing it.'

Olaf caught the faded flowers, kissed them a thousand
times, knelt, and held them against his heart, against his
forehead. He murmured—what words I know not, or,
knowing, shall not say ; while Leuchnar stood by with
that old bitter smile on his lips. Poor fellow ! he had
expected sudden clasping of Olaf's arms about him,
praise for his nobleness, consolation for his failure. Ah !
did he not know himself what a passion love was ? Then
why did he expect from so true a man as Olaf protestation
that he was the first when truly he was but the second ?
O ! you all know what it is to be second in such a race ;
it is to be nowhere. Why he, too, if he had been successful, would have forgotten Olaf, and the way his sword
flashed in the battle. It was only now in his disappointment that a certain natural instinct made him catch at
all the love that came across him of whatsoever kind.
That was why he thought so much of Olaf now. Yes,
and in a little time he did think of all this, and smiled no
more. ' Poor Leuchnar ! ' he said to himself, ' you must

be very far in the background now, know that for certain.
Then, did you not know all this when you knelt here
some twelve hours back ? O ! foolish Leuchnar ! yet,
poor Leuchnar, too ! '

And he was now so far from smiling that, but for his
manhood, he would have wept for self-pity. Moreover,
Olaf came to him and said, laying his hands on his
shoulders, and leaning forward towards his face :

' You are the noblest of all men, and will in nowise
lose your reward.'

And Leuchnar knew that, or he might have gone mad ;
yet he prayed that his reward might be death presently,
in the joyous battle.

So, on the morrow, they marched to meet King Borrace ;
and, on the evening of the third day, encamped but
a little distance from his pirates.

And when, on the next morning, they stood in battle
array, and the king rode up and down their line, Leuchnar
saw in his helm the bunch of stone-crop, now quite
withered.

Then that day, among the aspens, they joined battle.

CHAPTER III

THE LIGHT OF ISRAEL

THEN, in the midst of them, the old man rose up and
spoke, while all the rest sat silent, some gazing fixedly on
the ground, some on the fair dead king, that lay there
before them.

For he had been slain with one wound that had gone
right through his breast to the heart, and his body was
not hacked or disfigured. They had taken his rent
armour from off him, and washed his corpse, and spread
out his long yellow hair to right and left of his face, along
the samite cloth, purple, gold-starred, that he lay upon ;
and, behind him, at his head, they had laid his sword
and armour, the helm yet having that stone-crop in it,
the ends of the stalks at least ; for all the rest had been

MORRIS   F

shredded off in that fierce fight. Great waxen candles
burned all about him ; two priests sat at the head and
two at the foot of the bier, clad in gorgeous robes of
deep sorrowful purple, gold-embroidered ; for these men
reverenced man's body so, even when the soul was not
so near to it as it had been, that, in those hours of doubt
and danger, they thought the time well spent in making
the body of their king, of him the best and most beautiful
of all men, look as beautiful as God would ever have
dead bodies look.

So, while some gazed on the ground, some on the fair
dead king, none weeping, but all stern with thought ; for
they had to think of him as being present with them
in their council, not *dead*—while they gazed earnestly,
the old man, Barulf, arose and said,

' Sons of the men that go from east to west, and round
again to the east ! I advise you this day to do such
a deed of valour as you have never done yet. Death in
God's behalf, on the side of your friends, is not hard to
bear, brothers, even when it comes slow and lingering ;
but how glorious to die in a great battle, borne down by
over-many foes, to lie, never dead, but a living terror
for all time to God's enemies and ours, a living hope to
the sons of God. And to die altogether, beholding,
between the sword-strokes, the faces of dear friends all
a-light with intensest longing—is not that glorious ! '

Their stern faces lighted up with flushing of cheek and
flashing of eye as he spake ; for in their hearts was fear
of something far worse than dying on that field between
the aspens with friends' eyes upon them. But Barulf
went on.

' Yet, brothers, not this I bid you do. I give, as my
counsel, that we depart this night, taking with us nothing
but our arms, some small provision, and this dear dead
thing here : turn our backs upon the foe, and depart,
that we may reach the mother-city, where the women
and children are ; and I think I have good reasons for
this.'

' And how then shall we face the women and children ? '
said a young man moodily.

' Brother,' said Barulf, ' will you be a coward, indeed, from fear of being thought a coward ? your heart does not counsel this, I know ; and as for the women and children, are they mere beasts, so as not to understand this ? will they not say rather ? " These men are warriors, they cannot fear death ; then are they the braver to be so faithful, to be without fear of reproach for fear, so faithful to us above all things ; we will love them all the more." '

' But why should we not die here, fighting, Sir Barulf ? ' said another ; ' are there not men left when we are all dead ? '

' Yea, dear knight, men, but not men *enough*. Think awhile—Adolf with his ten thousand men, and God's snow and storm that are tens and tens of thousands, guard the passes against the emperor. Good—they are enough as it is ; but take away half for the defence of the cities, the mother-city above all, which is the weakest, the most beautiful, the fullest of women and children of all—and then would five thousand be enough to guard those passes ? Even as it is, were not this summer a cold one and the snows deep, the emperor might drive his serf-soldiers, with whip and sword-point over our dead soldiers' bodies : but suppose they were lessened, our heroes would indeed die in their places, and would doubtless slay many of the enemy ; but suppose they killed and wounded twice their own number, yet two days afterwards some 200,000 men would be marching over our land within fifty miles of the beautiful city.

' Again, Edwin and his 300 ships, diligently sailing into every nook and strait of the pirate island, and every day and night solemnly passing to and fro, with the white red-crossed banner at their mast-heads, guard the coast well ; but let him land half, nay a third only of his men for the defence of the city, and in a week the sea-port towns and villages, safe from all scath now, would be blazing very high toward the heavens, and King Borrace's red and black ship-sides would gleam with the reflection of the Greek fire, as the dragons of it leapt toward the harbour-mouth.

'Moreover, the Lord Hugh, in his fortified camp, holds his own well enough now against the three Dukes ; who prowl always like accursed cowardly wolves as they are, gnashing their teeth when they think that their provisions cannot last much longer, not more than another month ; and, stamping on the ground, invoke the devil, their cousin german, when they remember that not a blade of grass or ear of corn is left in the country behind them, laid waste as it was with fire, by the cruel fools as they marched : they, howling too for very rage when they see the wains in long lines entering Hugh's camp, and when they hear the merry sound of the trumpets, mingled often with the chaunting of the priests and the singing of men, singing about death that is no death. Ah ! they howl, the wolves disappointed enough now ; but suppose Hugh were to weaken his camp so as no longer to be able to send out his swarm of light-armed, who prevent the enemy from spoiling the yet unwasted country ; then, also, no longer fearing an attack, the Dukes march nearer to him, get themselves corn and wine, cut off his supplies, march past him at last with their 50,000 men, not easy to destroy *then*. For cowards as the Dukes are, and imbecile drivellers, knowing nothing of war, yet have they along with them crafty captains, who, when their highnesses' passions master them not, give good advice which is listened to, and the commoner sort, though robbers by nature and nurture, have yet a certain kind of courage, and much strength in body and skill of arms.'

In all the warriors' faces you might have seen a gloomy conviction that his counsel was good ; but they sat silent, it seemed such a shame to turn and flee before this enemy they had just beaten.

Yet never for a moment did they doubt but that their people would in the end prevail over the enemies that hemmed them in, whatever became of those 20,000 left alive there on the plain ; and Barulf spoke to the better part of all their hearts, when he said :

' Does it then seem so hard a thing to you, sons of the men that go westward, that we, having fought for three

days such a battle as this, should have at last to turn and
flee, carrying our dead king with us ? Oh ! it is hard,
very bitter and cruel, brothers ; yet is it God's will, and
in his sight, doubtless, is as glorious as if we all died
here in our places. And I am well assured that this and
all things else only hasten us westward ; it cannot be
in any of your hearts that this people should fail Nay,
rather our sons' sons in the after-time will speak of these
as glorious days in which the nations hedged us about,
but in which we prevailed mightily against them.—

' But for another matter '—and as he spoke, the
memory came across him bitterly that the king they had
chosen but two years since lay dead before them now :
then his face changed, and so it was with all of them,
now that they were free to think of that loss ; for, but
a little time back, he had been with them ; even just
now, as they talked in their old way of fresh battles,
and thought of the swinging of the swords, he had almost
seemed to be there alive ; but now—

One of the priests who sat by him had fallen asleep,
wearied out with tending the wounded and dying, and
his head had fallen on his breast ; another sat quite
upright with his hands laid on his knees, thinking
dreadful things of what was coming on the land ; the
third, a spare young man, black-haired and sallow-faced,
in his nervous anxiety twitched at the border of his cope
as he glanced about the tent, looking uneasily on the
face, first of one, then of another, of those that sat
there ; the fourth, as he sat, sad-faced and great-eyed,
thinking of his mother and sisters whom he had left in
a castle of the lowland country, had taken one long
yellow tress of the dead man's hair, and was absently
twining it about his fingers.

Then arose Leuchnar with about as miserable a look
on his face as a good man can ever have, and said :

' Sir Barulf, I know what you were about to say,
concerning the king ' (a shudder ran through them all),
' I have a message from the king to all of you. I was by
him when the spear pierced his true heart ; I drew him
a little out of the fight ; he said : " I am wounded to

death ; but, alive or dead, I must not leave this field, bury me just about where the enemy makes his last stand before he turns." For you see, knights, our dead lord was sure of this, that the fair city would be saved. Then the blood rising from his heart choked him somewhat, yet he said gaspingly : " Quick, Leuchnar, bend to my mouth." So I bent, and he said, faintly and hurriedly : " Undo my mail, and take the paper there, and give it to the lords and knights in council." So I took a paper from his breast over his heart ; the spear had pierced it through, and had carried some of it into the wound, and the trickling blood had stained it ; I took it from off the broken truncheon of the lance which was yet in the wound. I showed it to him, he bowed his head in token that all was well, when he had looked at it eagerly ; then he said : " I wish to go, draw out the truncheon, faithful and true ! poor Leuchnar ! " I drew it out ; there was a great rush of blood ; he smiled on me, and died.'

Thereon Leuchnar stepped from his place, and, going up to Barulf, gave him the paper, very much stained and torn. Barulf read it.

' Good saints, how strange ! do you know what is written in it, Sir Leuchnar ? '

' Nay, I but guess, Sir Barulf ; for I did not open it.'

' Listen, knights ! ' said Barulf, and he read : ' Knights and lords, if I die in this battle, as I think I shall, then (if so be it seem good to you) let Gertha, the daughter of Sigurd the husbandman, be queen in my stead ; she lodges in the mother-city, with the abbess of St. Agnes' Abbey of nuns.'

' Yes, I thought so,' said Leuchnar, scarcely however speaking to them, for he was thinking to himself of himself ; his sorrow seemed to have lessened much, even in the reading of that letter, for he thought : ' Now she is queen, and has this sorrow on her, I can serve her much better, and my love will not trouble her now as it would have done, for it will seem only like the love of a good subject to his mistress ; and I will lessen every grief of hers as it arises, loving her so, never vexing her

in the least ; O selfish Leuchnar, to be glad of her
sorrow ! yet I am glad, not of her sorrow, but of my
service that will be.'

These thoughts, and how many more, he thought in
a single instant of time ; how many pictures came up to
be gazed on as it were for a long time, in that instant !
pictures of his life before he saw her, and of the things
which in his mind belonged to her ; the white sandy shore
that the low waves broke on ; the feathering beech trees,
with their tender green leaves in the early summer ; king
Borrace's burnt ships, great logs clomb over by the
briony and clematis ; the high-roofed cottage, whereon
the loving golden-glowing stone-crop grew ; —they came
up before his eyes to be gazed at ; and the heavy waxen
candles burnt lower, the sleeping priest breathed heavily,
the others sat in painful silence, nursing their grief ;
which things Leuchnar saw not because of those sweet
pictures, even as they say that the drowning man, when
the first fierce pain and struggle is over, sees no more the
green, red-stained, swaying water-weeds, that lap his
eyes and mouth, sees rather his old home, and all the
things that have been, for memory is cruel-kind to men.

Still the candles flared and flickered in the gusts that
stirred the tent, for the wind was rising with the moon ;
and at last the one nearest the tent door was blown out
by a long blast, and the priest who had been sleeping
awoke, drew up his body with a start, trying to fix his
blinded blinking eyes on Sir Barulf's face, as waked men
use to do.

Thereat suddenly Barulf sprung to his feet, as if he
too was waking from sleep, and cried out aloud :

' Rouse ye, lords and knights, that we may march to
our queen ! for, for my part, our queen she shall be ;
all he said and did was right and true when he was alive ;
and he was, and is, the wisest of all men, and she too
is a right noble woman ; was it never told you, knights,
how she saved her father when king Borrace's men took
him prisoner ? What say you, shall she be our queen ? '

And they all said ' Yea.'

Then again said Barulf : ' Unless lords Edwin, Hugh,

and Adolf gainsay it (as I have no doubt they will not),
God save Queen Gertha ! '

Then they all stood up and said : ' God save Queen
Gertha ! '

And Barulf said : ' Send a herald round about the
army to proclaim Gertha queen, and to bid all to be
ready to march some two hours before the setting of the
moon. Cause also the knight who carries the great
banner to be present, that we may bury the king.'

So when all was ready, the noblest of the knights,
Barulf and Leuchnar among them, lifted up the bier
whereon the king lay, and they marched together towards
the burial-place ; and the standard-bearer bore the
great banner to flap above him, and the priests went
before and after, chaunting ; and a great body of knights
and soldiers went with them as they marched over the
plain ; and the great moon, risen now, struck on their
arms, threw the shadows of them weirdly on the dead
that lay so thick among the trees, looked down on by
the summer moon, rustled over by the full-leaved
aspens.

They went a full mile, till they came to a place ringed
about with aspen-trees, about which the enemy that past
day had been finally broken.

Here they buried him, standing about in a ring, in as
thick ranks as ever in the battle ; tearlessly and sternly
they watched the incense smoke rising white in the
moonlight, they listened to the chaunting, they lifted up
their voices, and very musically their sorrow of heart
was spoken.

' Listen ! ' said king Borrace's men, when they heard
the singing ; ' Hark to the psalm-singing dogs ! but by
about this time to-morrow they will be beginning to
leave off singing for good and all, for clearly the fools
will wait to be killed, and we shall kill them all, and then
hurrah for plunder ! '

But the next day about noontide, when they, (not
hurrying themselves, for they thought they were quite
safe,) when they reached the camp, behold it was empty,
for they all marched the night before, and were now

still marching along the dusty road leagues and leagues
from that battle-field.

Whereon king Borrace, instead of pursuing them,
returned to his camp, where he gnashed his teeth for
some half-hour or so, and held a great feast, he and his,
and stayed on that field for three days —' To give his
army rest,' he said.

CHAPTER IV

GERTHA THE QUEEN

AND meantime how did it fare with Gertha ?

The time passed slowly between hope and fear, and all
the time was weary with a sick longing that would have
been no less had he but gone out on a hunting expedition.
She had pity too for those who were sick with love and
dread, and all those who looked on her loved her.

Then one evening about sunset-time, as the nuns
were singing in their chapel and she with them, as the
low sun struck through the western window, and smote
upon the gold about the altar till it changed it to
a wonderful crimson, upon which the pale painted angels
that flecked the gold showed purer and paler than ever—
there came, on that sunset evening, far off and faint at
first, across, over the roofs of the houses up to the hill
whereon the Abbey stood, a sound of shouting mingled
with the wailing of women, and the still sadder and more
awful wailing of the great trumpets, which seemed to be
the gathered sorrow from the hearts of the men, who
themselves could not wail because of their manhood.

Tremblingly the nuns heard it, and their hymns
fainted and died, as that awful sound of the indignant
sorrow of a whole people going up to heaven rose and
deepened, and swept onward : and Gertha turned pale
even to the lips, and trembled too, at first, like an aspen-
leaf, her heart beating so the while that she could hear
the throbbings of it ; but with a mighty effort she put
back the trembling fever ; she said low to herself : ' He

is dead, and I must not die yet.' Then she left her seat and walked, pale in her face like a marble statue, up to the altar ; she turned round and faced the door and the sun, none hindering her, for they said, ' she waits for news about the battle.'

The sun was on her forehead at first as she stood still, but it sank lower till it touched her lips, and they seemed to quiver (though she held them still) in that flood of light.

So she stood, when lo ! the clash of arms in the vestibule, and there entered armed knights without bowing to the altar or crossing themselves, Leuchnar first, then Barulf and some twenty lords following him ; the others gazed about confusedly at first, but Leuchnar going before them all, walked swiftly up to the place where Gertha stood, and fell before her feet, spreading his arms out towards her as he did so, and his iron armour rattled with strange echo about the vaulted roof ; she did not look at him, her eyes beheld rather the far off battle-field, and Olaf lying there somewhere under the earth.

' Queen Gertha,' he began ; but his voice failed him for thronging memories ; Sir Barulf and the others drew reverently towards the two, and waited a little way off standing in a half circle : he heaved a great sigh, then bent lower yet, till his mail clinked against the step whereon she stood, then suddenly raised his passionate eyes to hers, and gazed till she was forced to look on him both with heart and eyes.

She beheld him pityingly : he said again : ' Queen Gertha ! ' (thereat she started) ' Queen Gertha, he is dead.'

' O Leuchnar, I heard the trumpets sing it so, therefore I stayed here for his message ; what is it ? '

' That you must be Queen over us yet awhile, Lady Gertha.'

' Ah ! and must I be ; may I not go to him at once ? for do you know, Leuchnar,' (and she stooped down low towards him, and laid her hand on his head as he knelt) ' do you know, I saw him just now lying pale and cold, waiting for me, his arms stretched out this way towards me, his changed eyes looking longingly.'

' O noblest,' he said, ' know you not with how many perils we are beset ? Whose spirit but his can help us through, and with whom does it dwell but with you ? '

She wept : ' Leuchnar, though He call for me so, yet perhaps that is because he is sick and weak and scarce knows what he says : and I know that in his heart he desires above all things the safety of this people that goes westward ; so I will be Queen till the last foe is vanquished—tell them so.'

Then he took her hand ; how strangely as he held it did the poor flesh of him quiver, how his heart melted in the midst of his body ! he held her hand—and said, ' I am Queen Gertha's liegeman.' Then sprung to his feet and called out aloud : ' Sir Barulf and Knights all, come and do homage to Gertha, our Queen ! '

Then each man knelt before her, and took her hand, and said, ' I am Queen Gertha's liegeman.'

Afterwards all standing about her together, but lower than she, clashed their swords and axes across her that rang out joyfully, wildly, half madly in that quiet place ; while the sun grew lower so that its light fell on her bosom, and her face above looked out sad and pale and calm from among the flashing steel.

So that day Gertha was made Queen. And then all throughout the city you might have heard the ringing of hammers on iron as the armourers did their work, and the clinking of the masons' trowels as they wrought at the walls, strengthening them ; for the walls had grown somewhat weak, as it was very many years since any enemy had threatened the city with a land army.

And on the sixth day came King Borrace, having wasted the land far and wide as he marched. Now when he had sent a herald to demand the surrender of that city, who had not even been suffered to enter it, but had been answered scornfully from the walls, he gnashed his teeth, and mounting a great black horse and armed with a mace rode about, ordering his battle.

Then also Gertha, leaving her hall of Council, went

round about the walls with a band of knights : over her robes of purple and crimson her glorious hair flowed loose, and a gold crown marked her, circling her head ; while in her hand she bore a slim white rod for a leader's staff.

Very faithful and true were all those in the town, both soldiers and women, but when she drew near to any, their faith grew so, that they seemed transported out of themselves ; the women wept for very love, and the men shouted 'Gertha! Gertha!' till all the air rang; and King Borrace muttered stupidly from between his teeth, ' They are praying to their gods, the fools.' Then, turning about, he said to one who was master of his artillery ; ' Gasgan, son of a dog, bring up the catapults and shoot me down that woman there—there she goes, poking her head over the battlements—quick, O wretch begotten by the Devil's ram.'

So Gasgan fixed his catapult and aimed the rugged stone at Gertha as she leaned over the wall, thinking, forgetting the fight and all, for him, just for a single instant.

He looked along the engine once, twice, thrice ; once, twice, thrice he started back without letting the catch slip. ' Dog,' said Borrace, riding up, ' why shootest not ? '

The man looked up with drops of cold sweat hanging to his brow, then stammered out,

' O my Lord, it is nothing,—that is, there is nothing there now, nor was there when I fitted the levers ; but when my hand went to the bolt, each time I saw standing before me that man, the King who was slain the other day, his sword drawn in his hand, and frowning on me terribly ; I cannot shoot, my Lord—O Lord, save me ! ' he shrieked at last, for Borrace, hitching up his great iron mace by its thong into his hand, began to swing it, putting back his lips from his teeth and setting his head forward.

' Son of a rotten sheep, can a ghost stop a stone from a petraria ? go and join King Olaf.' So he struck him on the uplifted face, between the eyes, and Gasgan fell dead without a groan, not to be known any more by his wife or mother even, for the mace had shattered his skull.

' Now then,' said Borrace, ' I will try the ghost of this fellow whom I slew once, and whom I will slay again, God being my help.'

He leapt down from his horse, and let his hand fall to the bolt, but just as he did so, before him, calm, but frowning, stood Olaf with bright-gleaming sword and yellow hair blown by the wind : ' Art thou not dead, then ? ' shouted Borrace furiously, and with a great curse he drew the bolt.

The stone flew fiercely enough, but not towards Gertha; it went sideways, and struck down two of Borrace's own lords, dashing the life out of the first and maiming the other for life. Borrace flung on to his horse, howling out like a mad dog, ' Witch ! Witch ! ' and like a man possessed galloped toward the city as though he would leap wall and ditch, screaming such mad blasphemy as cannot be written.

After him very swiftly galloped some fifty knights and men-at-arms for his protection, and but just in time ; for one of the city gates swung open, the drawbridge fell with a heavy thump, and out rode a single knight armed with a northern axe instead of a spear, slim in figure, but seeming to be good at war. He dashed through the first few of Borrace's horsemen, who came up in scattered fashion because they had been riding as in a race, unhorsing a man to right and left of him as he passed through them, then made right at the King ; as they met, Borrace struck out blind with rage at the knight, who putting aside the heavy mace smote him on the side of the helm, that he tumbled clean out of the saddle.

' Gertha ! Gertha ! ' shouted the knight, and he caught Borrace's horse by the bridle, and dashed off towards the gate again, where in the flanking towers the archers stood ready to cover his retreat ; for some twenty yards as they galloped furiously on, Borrace dragged in the stirrup, then the stirrup-leather broke, and his horse-men seeing him lie still there, gave up the pursuit of the victorious knight, which was the better advised, as

the first flight of arrows from the bowmen had already
slain three outright, and wounded five, and they were
again getting their strings to their ears.

' Gertha !   Leuchnar for Gertha ! '   rang from the
knight again, as he turned just before he crossed the
drawbridge ; but the last of the enemies stood up in his
stirrups and poised his lance in act to throw ; but before
it left his hand an arrow had leapt through his throat,
and he fell dead.   ' Gertha ! ' shouted the archer.   And
then again the drawbridge swayed up, letting little
stones fall into the moat from it, down rattled the
portcullis, and the heavy gate swung to.

Then presently arose mightily the cry of ' Gertha !
Gertha, the Queen ! '

But withal, when the pirates found that King Borrace
was not slain, but only very much bruised, they advanced
their engines, and the catapults and balistæ and rams
shook the wall, and made many sore cracks in the older
parts, and the arrows flew like hail, and the ' cats,' great
wooden towers covered with skins to protect them from
fire, began to rise against the town.

Nevertheless, through all that weary day, though the
defenders were so few for the great length of wall, they
fought cheerfully and with good faith, like the men they
were.

So that when they brought news to battered King
Borrace, who lay tossing on his bed, concerning how
little progress they had made, he gnashed his teeth, and
cursed and was right mad.

And all the while through the thunder of the balistæ
stones against the wall, through the howling of the
catapult stones as they came among them into the city,
through the gaunt uplifting of the misshapen rams,
through the noise of the sledge-hammers clamping the
iron bands of the cat-towers, through the whirr of arrows,
through wounds and weariness, and death of friends,
still rose the shout of ' Gertha ! Gertha the Queen !
Gertha ! '

Guess whether many people lay awake that night, or
rather whether any slept at all, save those who were

utterly wearied out by that day's fighting or by their own
restless excitement. Many did not even try to sleep,
but sat round about the cold hearth telling stories;
brave stories, mostly of the good old times that were
fathers to the good times now ; or else they would go
about the walls in an eager fever to see what was going
on ; and some there were who stood all that night by
the bed of some sorely wounded friend ; and some,
mother, lover, friend, stood also by bedsides holding the
cold hands with bitter thoughts that were hard to bear.

That night was dark, with much gusty wind and
a drizzle of rain, therefore, though it was August and
the days long, yet it was quite dark by nine o'clock,
and a little after twilight the enemies' petrariæ left off
playing, so that the besieged had rest : but before
daybreak the drizzle had changed to steady rain, the
wind having fallen.

Even before dawn the camp was a-stir, and two hours
afterwards the cat-towers were again building, and the
battering had begun again.

And so that day passed, through the rainy hours of it ;
and about two hours after noon the enemy tried to scale
the lowest part of the wall near the harbour. Thereupon
Gertha came to that part and looked on the fighters
from a tower with a circle of knights round about.
Therefore her people waxed so valiant, that though the
pirates, fighting like madmen, fixed the ladders to the
wall even through the storm of arrows and stones, (for
the tide was out and there was no water now round about
the wall,) they were nevertheless driven back with great
slaughter.

Also, on the other side of the town, one of the cat-
towers was fired, and many perished miserably therein.

That evening Gertha sat and took counsel with her
lords and knights ; whereon Leuchnar arose and said,
' Noble lady, we must make a sortie, and collect every
man, and every boy too, to guard the walls meanwhile,
for we are very few to guard so great a city, and the
enemy is very many ; half our men are utterly worn out
with these two days' fighting, coming so close upon their

long march ; the walls, either old and crumbling, or new and still damp, are cracked in twenty places : they are making a great raft for the crossing of the moat ; go to the open window, lady, and you will hear, though it is night, the sound of their hammers busy on it. When King Borrace can put on his armour again, (would that I had slain him outright !) we shall be attacked in twenty places at once, and then I fear it will go hard with the fair city ; we must make a night attack, and do all the burning and slaying that we may.'

' Dear knight,' said Barulf, ' you are young and wise, this thing must be done : let some one get together two thousand of our best men, and those that are least wearied ; let them be divided into two bands, and march out, the one by Gate St. George, the other by the East Gate ; you, Sir Leuchnar, shall lead the one out of Gate St. George, and I will lead the other.'

He said this last quite eagerly, and the colour sprang up to his face : Gertha looked at him half shyly, then spoke to him.

' Nay, Sir Barulf, are you not then too old for blushing ? Except for the last word your speech was very wise, but that spoilt it rather, for you must stay behind with us, some one else must go.'

She smiled serenely as she spoke ; indeed she seemed quite happy now, seeing prophetically perhaps that the end drew near.

' And I ? ' said Leuchnar, ' may I not go ? '

' Go, fair knight, and the Lord keep you from all harm.'

But Barulf said, smiling also ; ' As for me, Queen Gertha, you know best, so I will stay behind, and hope to get a good drive at the three Dukes ; they will keep, doubtless ; may the Lord make their hands light ! but who shall go in my stead ? '

She looked round the noble assembly, and her eyes fixed on a young knight who sat over against her ; their eyes met, and he seemed to Gertha to resemble somewhat her king, who was waiting for her near the poplar-trees. So she said :

' Sir knight, I know not your name ; you I mean, with

the blue surcoat and the golden Chevron on it ; but will
you take this service upon you ? '

He had been gazing at her all the time they had sat
there, and when he heard her speaking to him it must
have seemed to him as if they two were alone together,
for he looked this way and that, just as though he feared
that some one might hear what they said one to the
other ; he rose and fell before her feet, not knowing if
he were in Heaven or not, for his yearning was so strong
that it almost satisfied itself. He muttered something
almost inaudible about his unworthiness.

She gazed at him as he lay there with that inexpressible
pity and tenderness in her face, which made all men love
her so, trust in her.

'Wait, fair knight, and rise I pray you ; have you
Father or Mother alive yet ? '

'No, Lady,' he said, still kneeling, like a suppliant for
dear life.

'Any sisters or brothers ? '

'None, Lady Gertha, now.'

'Have you a Lover ? '

'Yea—one whom I love.'

Oh how the look of pity deepened in her eyes ! what
wonder that every nerve trembled in his body ?

'And would she give it to your charge to lead a
desperate sortie, young as you are, with "life all before
you," as men say ? '

'Will she bid me go ? ' he said.

'Poor boy !—yet go—in the after-time we shall
meet again, whatever happens, and you and Olaf will
be friends, and you will see all his glory. What is your
name ? '

'Richard.

'Farewell, Richard,' and she gave him her hand to
kiss ; then he departed, saying no word, and sat outside
for a minute or two, quite bewildered with his happiness.

Then came Leuchnar, and they went together to see
concerning the men they wanted, and as they went they
told each other that which was nearest their hearts :
then said Richard :

' This is about the happiest time of my life, since I was
a child ; shall we not fight well, Sir Leuchnar ? '

' Yes,' he said, ' we ought both to praise God, Sir
Richard, that, things being so, he has shown us so clearly
what to do ; I remember now how often in the past days
I used after my fashion to torment myself, with thinking
how ever I should pass the time if it chanced that my
love (when it came, for love of all kinds was long in
coming to my dull heart) should fail me ; and now God
calls us merely to spend a few hours in glorious fight,
and then doubtless he will give us forgetfulness till we
see her again : and all this I have not at all deserved,
for though men's lips formed themselves to speak my
name often, praising it for my many good deeds, yet the
heart knoweth its own bitterness, and I know wherefore
I did such things, not for God's glory, but for my glory.'

' Does not God then accept a man's deeds, even if he
stumble up to do them through mixed motives, part bad
and part good ? is it not written, " by their fruits ye
shall know them " ?—and your fruits—how often when
I have heard men talking of you have I longed to be like
you, so brave and wise and good ! '

' Ah ! the fruits, the fruits ! ' said Leuchnar, ' when
I think what the lawful fruits of my thoughts were,
I shudder to see how near the Devil's House I have
passed. Pray for me in the battle, Richard.'

' You are very good and humble, Leuchnar,' he said,
' and I know not what good the prayers of such an one
as I am could do you, but I will pray. Yet I myself have
been careless about deeds at all ; I have loved beauty so
much that I fear if any crime had at any time stood
between me and beauty I should have committed that
crime to reach it ; yet has God been so kind to me, and
kindest of all in this, that I who have done nothing all
my life long yet, should do this and then die.'

' And it is good to do one thing, and then die,' said
Leuchnar ; ' farewell.'

So they departed each to his own band ; and by this
time the rain had ceased, the wind had risen, and was
now blowing strong from the sea ; the clouds were

clearing off somewhat, but it was not quite bright ; moreover the moon, though it had risen, was pretty much behind the clouds.

The two thousand horsemen went, each thousand in its own direction, very quietly along the streets ; they opened Gate St. George quite quietly also, and Leuchnar passed out at the head of his men. Now on each side of that gate was a cat-tower ; so a hundred men were sent to each of these to burn them first ; they were then to follow the main body, doing such damage as they could to the petrariæ along their way : now this side of the camp happened to be very carelessly guarded, scarcely guarded at all in fact ; there was no one in the cats, and the guards about fifty in number, who ought to have been watching them, were asleep some twenty yards off ; so both parties succeeded in firing the cats, taking care to put such store of tow and flax mingled with pitch into them that it should be impossible to drown the flames ; moreover the guards awakened by the trampling of the horses and roar of the flames were put to the sword as they rose, sleepy, bewildered, unable to use their arms : then the two hundred men, burning as they went along the altogether unguarded petrariæ on their path, soon joined the main body, and they all rode on swiftly toward the camp, just beginning to stir because of the noise, and the flare of the burning cats. A few minutes' gallop brought Leuchnar to the foremost tents, which were fired, and then through the smoke and flame Leuchnar dashed into King Borrace's camp at the head of his thousand horsemen.

At first there was scarce any resistance, the men were cut down and speared as they ran half-armed from out of the burning tents, and the flames spread in the rising wind ; but the alarm too spreading, and many bands coming up in good order, Leuchnar was surrounded almost before he knew it ; so in a pause in the fight he looked about him to see how he and his could die most to the advantage of the People ; he listened and looked toward the East Gate, there were no flames to be seen in that quarter where Richard was to have fired the great balistæ and the rams and the raft for the crossing of the moat ; for, to leave Leuchnar about to do something desperate, some of King Borrace's men on that side had heard a stir in the town, and the bravest of them had gone to tell him : for at this time he was well nigh mad with his foil, and raged like the Devil himself, to whom indeed he must have been nearly related, and the service of telling him anything like bad news was indeed a desperate one. However as I said, some brave men plucked up heart of grace to go and tell him that the townsmen seemed to be about to make a sally on that side of the camp.

He answered them first of all by throwing four javelins at them, one after another ; for he had a sheaf of those weapons put by his bedside for that very purpose ; one of them was wounded by this javelin-flight, the others by careful dodging managed to avoid him : then at last he listened to them, and being rather sobered ordered 5,000 horsemen to fetch a compass and charge Richard's party in the rear when he was well drawn out towards the balistæ, which, as they were larger on this side, (for it was on this side that the enemy hoped most to make a breach,) were farther from the walls that they might be out of the range of the townsmen's engines.

So when Richard came out of the East Gate very softly, this band of 5,000 men was quite close to him, and the balistæ were guarded by a great body of archers and slingers ; and neither horsemen nor archers could be seen, because, the night being gusty, the moon was at that time behind the clouds : so then Rolf coming near to one of the great balistæ sent aside fifty men to fire it, who were straightway attacked in front and flank by arrow-flights, so that all those who were not armed in proof were either slain or too badly wounded to retreat ; the rest rode back in haste to the main body, which had halted as soon as Richard saw how matters went : then indeed would Sir Richard and all his men have died without helping Gertha, or the People that went westward, much, as men count help : but the Captain of those 5,000 thought he would not attack Richard from behind, lest he should ride down his own people in the darkness, who he saw had already had some contest with the townsmen ; but thinking that he would turn at once toward the town meant to fall on him as he retreated without order.

But Richard, seeing well how things had really gone, turned round to his men, and called out, ' Keep well together, and fight well for Gertha '—then, ' Sound trumpets, and Richard for Gertha ! ' So they dashed right at the camp at the gallop, and entered it close to Borrace's tent, where it was not deep but straggling.

Now Borrace, thinking that nothing else could happen but that the townsmen should all be slain close to the walls, was standing near his tent, talking to some of his Captains, and armed all save his helm ; for he was now well, or nearly well of his bruises, and intended to lead an attack the next day. So there he stood, and four Captains with him, he twirling his mace about in his nervous excitement, and sometimes looking uneasily at those that stood by, as if he thought they were getting something out of him. Judge of his astonishment when he heard Richard's shout of ' Gertha,' and then the thunder of the horse-hoofs.

' Curse that witch ! ' he ground out from between his teeth, ' shall I never hear the last of her ? only I think when I have seen her well burnt out of hand, after that '——

' For your life, my lord ! for your life ! they are coming this way, they will be over us in a minute ! ' and he turned and ran, and ran well too ; and Borrace also began to run, and got clear out of the way of the main body, and would have escaped but that a certain knight, espying him, and knowing well the villainous wolf's face of the man, as he looked over his shoulder, under the clearing moon, turned off a little and rode at him while he ran like ten men, crying out with a great laugh as he knocked him over, ' Twice, O King Borrace ! '

And indeed King Borrace was not knocked over thrice, for this time the brains were fairly knocked out of his smashed head by the great horsehoofs, the knight having disdained to use his sword on a runaway, and besides, being a genial sort of man, he had a kind of contemptuous pity for so stupid a brute, and thought to give him a chance.

However when the horsemen had ridden past, the Captains came back to see first of all what had become of their Lord and Master, for they had seen him go over, and with very mixed feelings. They found him as I said with his brains knocked out, and quite dead, whereat the first, Lord Robert, lifted his eyebrows and gave a long whistle in utter astonishment that so slight a matter as a horse should have slain him, for his head seemed to be solid and mostly of oak. But Sebald, the second of them, lifted his foot and dug his heel deep in the already fearfully lacerated face of the dead tyrant, saying as he did so,

‘ Beast and devil, remember my sister ! I told you then I would do this one time or other,’ (and again he stamped,) ‘ said so openly, yet you took me into your service instead of killing me as I hoped you would, madman that you were.’

For in his madness of half-satisfied vengeance it seemed to him that he had slain him with his own hands ; but suddenly it came across him how it was, and he said :

‘ Yet, O God ! to think that I am disappointed in my revenge : yet still it is pleasant to do this, though another man slew him ; ’ and again his heel came down on the dead King’s wretched face : then he stooped down and put his hands to the warm blood that flowed from the wounds, and raised them to his lips and drank, and the draught seemed to please him.

Meanwhile Gherard, the third Captain, who had at first stood still without saying a word and apparently in deep thought, suddenly started, and catching hold of Sebald by the shoulder said savagely : ‘ Fool ! can’t you stop that play-acting ? Keep it till you are by yourself, for it is thrown away upon us, I can tell you ; and don’t you see all of you that this must not be known ? quick ! quick ! help me to carry him into the tent ; here, Sebald, man, lift and quick—ah ! ’ he said, turning

round and glancing about uneasily, ' where is Erwelt ?
but you carry him while I '——

And he darted off after the fourth Captain (Erwelt),
who had somehow disappeared, a man of mincing
manners, very elaborately dressed.

So Sebald and Robert, as they lifted the body, saw
Gherard as he ran in great bounds towards Erwelt ;
they saw his hand slide down to his dagger, but there
was no weapon in the sheath ; he ground his teeth with
vexation, but still went on till he had overtaken his man ;
then he touched him on the shoulder and said : ' Erwelt,
I want to speak to you.' ' Well,' said the other, ' what
is it ? ' But his heart sank and he felt as if Death stood
before him, dart and all, as indeed he did, for Gherard
was a very strong man, and, as he saw Erwelt's hand go
down towards the dagger-hilt, he felled him with a quick
blow between the eyes, then before he could recover was
kneeling on him ; he dragged the broad double-edged
dagger from its jewelled sheath, and buried it thrice in
Erwelt's breast, then drew it across his throat from ear
to ear ; then, thrusting the dagger back again into its
sheath, after he had carefully wiped it on the white and
blue velvet of the dead man's dress, he sprang up and
ran back towards the King's tent, leaving the body to
lie piteously under the moon which was shining out
from dark purple hollows between the clouds.

The light of it flashed on the poor fop's jewels, shone
on his upturned face and gashed throat and feeble
nerveless hands. How much more dreadful was that
one corpse than all the many, lying now nearer to the
walls ; than those even who lay with ghastly breakings
of the whole frame torn by great stones ; or slain by
wounds that struck them hap-hazard in strange unlikely
places : or slain as they lay already wounded ; or who
lay with their bodies twisted into unimaginable writhings
brought about by pain and fear. All these and many
more, many, very many of each sort, they were altogether
less horrible than this one corpse of a *murdered man*.

The murderer found the others already in the tent, for
Robert had said : ' Sebald, don't let us see that ; you

and I know nothing about it for the present ; for we must hold together ; and for my part I vote that we let Gherard work for us, he is such a clever fellow.'

Sebald made no answer ; his eyes were dry, his throat was dry, his heart was dry with intense thinking if by any means he could extend his vengeance beyond the present world. He thought of all the curses he had ever heard ; how meaningless and uninventive they all seemed when set beside his hatred ! he thought so that I know not into what uttermost hell he had dragged his own heart ; he certainly did not feel as if he were on earth ; his head grew dizzy, he could scarcely walk under his burden, but somehow between them they managed to get the body into the tent unperceived.

Then he thought : ' I can bear this no longer, I must think of something else just now ; but I will make it the work of my whole life hereafter.'

So then Gherard burst in, muttering from between his teeth, ' so much for one marplot : ' and Sebald woke up and was in the world again.

So they began to talk, Robert sitting down and with his elbow on the table, stroking his cheek with his open hand ; Sebald standing still, with knit brows, and blood-stained hands crossed over his breast ; while Gherard walked up and down, twisting his fingers together behind his back, his cheek all a-flush and his eyes glistening—and Erwelt lay stiffening in the moonlight. So those three fell a-plotting.

Meanwhile such a hubbub and confusion had been going on before the walls as if the fiends were loose ; for the archers, when Richard had passed beyond hope of pursuit, having sent a few arrows into the darkness at nothing, turned and looked about them.

Now they knew nothing at all concerning those horse-men who had been sent to take Richard in the rear, so, seeing some helmets glittering in the somewhat doubtful moonlight, they advanced a little towards them, and, thinking as a matter of course that they were from the town, sent two or three flights of arrows among them as an experiment, getting ready to run away in case they

should be too many for them, doing all this before the
horsemen could shout out that they were from the camp ;
and when they did so, the townsmen, seeing clearly that
Richard and his men were away, opened a heavy fire on
everything that they saw, and Borrace's archers believed
that the horsemen lied, and still shot all they might.

Whereon the horsemen changed their minds, and
settled that these were another band of men from the
town whom they had not counted on, and so charged
with a good will, especially as the long-bows and crossbows and petrariæ were playing on them diligently from
the city-walls.

Now the archers were more numerous than the horsemen, and, though not so well armed, fought stoutly,
throwing away their bows and using their axes and
swords, nor did they find out their mistake till many
were slain both of horsemen and archers, and even then
they were quite ready to go on with that work from
sheer rage and vexation of heart ; but restraining
themselves, and being restrained by their leaders, they
got separated somehow, and marched back to their own
quarters, where one and all swore that they would stay,
nor move again that night for man or Devil, whatever
happened.

And so they fell to drinking all they might. But Sir
Richard and all his, having won through the camp with
but little opposition, (for the enemy were all drawn off
other-where,) crossed the river that lay beyond, by
a broad shallow ford that he knew well, (higher up it
passed by that cottage,) then took mere bridle-ways and
waggon-roads through the woods that lay beyond the
river, after he had told his men that he intended making
a circuit and falling from behind on that part of the
camp where Leuchnar was. 'For he is probably hard
pressed by this time,' said he, ' the sortie being from the
first somewhat desperate and wild, though necessary.'
And he made this circuit lest he should be cut off before
he could reach Leuchnar ; had he known that there
would be no pursuit, (there would have been but for
Borrace's death, and the happy clash between the horse-

men and archers)—had he known all this he would certainly not have gone so far about, or gone through such intricate ways where the men could not help straggling.

So the rain-drops fell in showers on their armour as they past, from the low tree-boughs brushed by their crests and lowered spears ; the moon flashed on the wet leaves that danced in the rushing sea-wind ; with whirr of swift wings the wood-pigeon left the wood.

How often had Richard wandered here in the past days ! what thoughts were his in those old times, of the glory of his coming manhood ! what wonder at the stories of lovers that he read, and their deeds ! what brave purposes never to be fulfilled ! yet he meant them then honestly enough, yet he was to do one deed at the last if only one, that was something ; and as he thought this he straightway drove thoughts of all other things from his mind, and thought of what he should do now.

He called a halt, and listened ; then perceiving clearly that there was no pursuit at all, he led his men out of the woods, by a way he knew well, round toward Gate St. George, but cautiously and quietly for fear of an attack from the camp.

Then after a while they halted again, and he heard the noise of the irregular *mêlée* I have told you about, and could scarce account for it ; he heard the noise of the fight about where Leuchnar was ; and he heard withal another sound that made his heart beat with hope : it was a far-off sound swelling and fainting in the rise and fall of the southwest wind that blew from over the sea, the sound of triumphant trumpets : he leaned forward from his saddle to listen better, and many a soldier's eyes sparkled as he cried out suddenly, ' Victory ! it is Edwin—quick to Leuchnar ! ' So away they went toward Gate St. George at a smart pace.

They drew rein when they came within a few minutes' gallop from the camp that their horses might not go blown into the battle, then advanced with as little noise as possible, till they drew near and saw the enormous masses of the enemy surging round something which they knew well to be Leuchnar in a desperate case.

Then shouted their leader, ' Richard ! Richard for Gertha ! ' and with one mighty charge, which scattered the enemy to right and left, they were buried in the enormous multitude that was in vain striving to break Leuchnar's array.

For he, trying to win his way back to the city that he might sally out at the East Gate to the aid of Sir Richard, beset as he thought he was, as he was doing this he was first cut off from the city and driven back towards the camp, and then surrounded.

Whereupon the horsemen having dismounted formed a great square with closely planted shields, and long spears set out like the teeth of a great beast, and on this square King Borrace's horsemen, that were King Borrace's no more now, had wasted their strength for long : for howsoever many men of it were slain by the arrows and slings or by the hurling of the long lances, yet the living filled up the places of the dead, and the square, though lessening every moment, was not broken when Richard made that charge, and joined Leuchnar : having hewn his way through with most of his men to that square of serried spears, ' Brother ! ' he shouted, ' hold out yet awhile, for Edwin is coming in triumph over the sea, and we must live till then.'

So they joined their two bands, and made a thicker and larger square than before, having cleared a space by one or two desperate charges, and soon the fight was fiercer than ever.

But the men fell fast before the arrow-flights and they grew utterly wearied with standing there on foot ; in pauses of the fight very anxiously did Richard and Leuchnar listen, and they heard a snatch now and then of the dear trumpet-music, and hoped, or tried to hope : yet it seemed that they must die before help came, the greater part at least.

Then an arrow whistled, and Leuchnar staggered and bowed forward ; he was wounded, not mortally indeed, but it dizzied and confused him. Almost at the same time the crowd opened, and there rose a shout of ' Gherard ! Gherard ! ' Forthwith a fresh band of

horsemen charged, all armed in proof and splendidly
mounted, with Gherard himself at the head of them.

How it all happened Richard scarce knew, but so it
was that they broke the terrible hedge of spears, and
presently each man found himself fighting separately or
with one or two friends about him ; tired men too
against fresh ones, men on foot against horsemen, and
all things seemed desperate.

Yet even then between all the clash of the battle
Richard heard the roar of the bells from all the belfries
and the shouting of the people. Edwin had landed.
Then as he thought of this he grew half mad to think
that they should die before the very eyes of their friends,
and shouted out ' Gertha ! fight on, brave lads, and
gather together all you may ! ' He with some half dozen
of his own men tried to gather others again, but, while
he struggled desperately, his great sword flashing this
way and that, but rising duller from every stroke because
of the blood on it, he was suddenly borne away, and
Leuchnar beheld him alone amidst a ring of foes, saw
his sword still flashing for a little, then saw him fall with
many wounds and lie dead, at peace at last.

He himself, though surrounded by a band of friends,
was sorely wounded ; and, sick with pain and loss of
blood, he had nearly fainted ; and the few around him
were falling, falling fast under axe and sword and spear,
when lo ! the gates open, and the cry of ' Edwin for
Gertha ! ' rings all about, thousands pour out of the
great gates, over the bridge, there is a sharp fight, and
the bodies at least of Leuchnar and Richard are rescued.

For the pirates are driven back to their camp, not to
stay quiet there for long ; for even as they stand at bay
about their tents the word goes that Borrace is slain ;
nor only so ; the moon sinks, the east begins to redden,
and within an hour after her setting many new spears
fleck the clear light ; the advanced guard of the Lord
Hugh's victorious army who have marched night-long
to come to the help of the fair city.

Close them all about, brave sons of the men that go
westward ! Borrace is dead, Gherard is dead, Erwelt is

dead, Sebald lies bleeding to death from four sore wounds, Robert fled soon, but was drowned in crossing the river.

The cats are on fire, the petrariæ are in ashes, all the camp is one blaze, everywhere the foe are throwing their arms away and crying for quarter, soon they are all slain, wounded, or prisoners.

Meanwhile a messenger, pale and worn out, is brought to Gertha, and kneels down before her feet ; he says, ' Lady, I have a message for you.' (O Gertha ! words spoken before.)

' Quick, good man,' she says, ' for these things draw to an end ; ' and a smile of quiet triumph passes across her pale face.

' Three days ago,' he says, ' the Emperor strove to force the passes ; he and three of his captains were slain, and my Lord Adolf will be here soon.'

' Thank God ! ' she says, ' but you, poor man, what reward for you ? ah ! sleep has overmastered him : ' for he has fallen forward before her so that his head rests on her feet ; she touches him, takes his hand to raise him up ; it is stone-cold, he is dead.

But for these men of King Borrace—let the wounded go to our hospitals that they may learn there something of love which they have not even dreamed about as yet ; let the slain be buried, and lie under the earth, under the grass among the roots of the land they came to conquer: let the prisoners depart unarmed, but with provisions for their journey, let them cross the frontier, and never trouble the good land more, lest a worse thing befall them.

CHAPTER V

WHAT EDITH THE HANDMAIDEN SAW FROM THE WAR-SADDLE

AND in the fresh morning sat Gertha the Queen in the body, while her spirit was a long way off, and round about her sat the Lords and Knights with flushed joyful faces, she alone pale though calm and serene, for she too was joyful.

Then into the midst of the great hall they bore
Leuchnar dying from his many wounds, not in great
pain, for his spirit was leaving his body gently, as if he
were worn out merely.

And Gertha rose from her throne and went to meet
them that bore him, and there was a flutter along the
tapestry that the hall was hung with, as the wind rushed
through the opened door, and therewithal Gertha woke,
her spirit came again as if Olaf had sent it.

So she gazed at him as he had hoped she might, as
a Queen on her faithful subject : before this, often
a certain uneasy feeling, not pity exactly, used to come
across her when she saw him ; it used to seem such
a hard thing to her that it should be thus ; it was just
such a feeling as might have turned to love with one less
constant than Gertha : but now even this was gone,
and Leuchnar felt that it was so, even by the look of
her eyes upon him.

And he, raising himself, hardly said to her, ' Queen
Gertha, I am come to say farewell for a little.'

' Poor Leuchnar, who loved me so ! '

' Nay,' he said, ' happy Leuchnar, who loves you still !
in the time to come it may be that lovers, when they
have not all they wish for, will say, " Oh ! that we
might be as Leuchnar, who died for Queen Gertha in
the old time ! " '

' True,' she said, ' farewell, Sir Leuchnar.'

Oh ! how eagerly he took her hand ! ' Happy
Leuchnar,' he said faintly, then, ' Domine, in manus
tuas,' and he fell asleep, his head falling back.

For a short time she stood, holding his dead hand ;
then gently disengaged it and laid it with the other one,
crossing them downwards.

Then they carried him out again silently ; and again
ran that tremour through the gold wrought hangings,
and her spirit had gone away again.

And within a while, as the great sun rose higher, came
the sound of trumpets, and the roar of the bells from
all the belfries : Adolf was come.

How near the end drew.

That noontide was windless, cloudless, and very bright, except that a soft haze had sprung up everywhere from the moist earth, into which all things far and fair melted.

She came from the midst of that knot of Lords that had clustered about her, and with her dark hair loose, stood in the balcony above the people, and through the hearts of all thrilled her clear speech.

'God has been very good to us, friends, and we have conquered, and now you must let me go as you promised. And you may grieve that I must go, and wish me back often, but still I must go : it is not only because I wish to go that I must leave you, but I cannot help it : I think, nay am sure, that this also is best both for you and me. If I were Queen much longer you would be disappointed with me, yet would not say so, because you love me.

'Think now ! I am but Gertha, the peasant's daughter, and I know it was only the spirit of your dead Lord working in me that made you love me so. But if I were Queen for long I should come to be only Gertha again ; so I must go. And if you will, let Barulf, who is old, but very wise, be King.'

There was sad silence for a little when she had finished, then a confused sound of weeping, and sobs, and earnest wishes went up towards the balcony, where she stood with her arms lying down her side : already she looked as if she were a different kind of being from them : she said,

'Will you have Barulf for your King ? if you will, say so to pleasure me ; then farewell.'

They shouted, ' Barulf ! God save King Barulf ! ' and lo ! even in that shout she had vanished, like an angel that comes from heaven when God lends him, and goes to heaven again when God calls him.

Gertha walked over the field of battle ; no meadow of sweet waving grass and lovely flowers, but something very horrible to gaze at, to pass over.

Yet she did not seem to take note of any of its horrors : her handmaiden was with her ; but when they came within fifty yards of the aspen circle where he lay, she charged her to stop, and watch all that came to pass there, that she might tell the people hereafter.

So the handmaiden sat down there on the mournful battle-field on some great war-saddle that had been thrown down there.

But Gertha, when she had kissed her, left her and walked toward those aspen-trees ; she was clad in her old peasants' raiment again, and was quite without ornament of gold or jewels ; only, her black hair hung braided on either side of her face and round about her head was a garland of yellow flowering stone-crop, such as he wore in his helmet that battle-day : but now when she entered the circle of aspens there seemed to be silence over all the earth, except that when she first stepped among the shadows of the trees, a faint breeze rose out of the south, and the lightly-hung leaves shivered, the golden haze trembled.

Now although all the rest of the battle-field was trodden into bloody mud, dry now again, but loaded with all dreadful things, this spot yet kept the summer flowers, neither was there any mark of his grave.

So there lay down Gertha, and the blue speedwell kissed her white cheek ; there her breath left her, and she lay very still, while the wind passed over her now and then, with hands laid across her breast.

Nevertheless this was what Edith, her handmaiden, said to Barulf the King, and his Lords and Knights :

' And so I sat on the war-saddle and watched, and as my Lady stepped forward to enter that circle of trees, I saw my Lord Olaf, the King, as clearly as before he died, step forward to meet her, and he caught her in his arms, and kissed her on the mouth and on both cheeks.

' And they two were together there for hours (talking it seemed), sometimes sitting on the flowers and grass ; (for that spot, my lords, is not trodden as the rest of the field is ;) sometimes walking from tree to tree with fingers interlaced.

But just about sunset time, I felt as if I must needs go and speak to my dear Lady once again, and hold her hand again : so I went up trembling ; and lo ! my Lord

Olaf was not there any more, and I saw my Lady Gertha only, lying dead upon the flowers, with her hands crossed over her breast, and a soft wind that came from the place where the sun had set shook the aspen leaves. So I came away.'

Thereat the King and his Knights wondered.

And the People raised a mighty Church above the place where they lay, in memory of Olaf's deeds and Gertha's love : and soon about the Church there gathered a fair City, that was very famous in the after-time.

Yet it was strange that this Church, though the people wrought at it with such zeal and love, was never finished : something told them to stop by then they had reached the transepts of it : and to this day the mighty fragment, still unfinished, towering so high above the city roofs toward the sky, seems like a mountain cliff that went a-wandering once, and by earnest longing of the low-landers was stayed among the poplar trees for ever.

SVEND AND HIS BRETHREN

(*Oxford and Cambridge Magazine*, August 1856)

A KING in the olden time ruled over a mighty nation : a proud man he must have been, any man who was king of that nation : hundreds of lords, each a prince over many people, sat about him in the council chamber, under the dim vault, that was blue like the vault of heaven, and shone with innumerable glistenings of golden stars.

North, south, east, and west, spread that land of his, the sea did not stop it ; his empire clomb the high mountains, and spread abroad its arms over the valleys of them ; all along the sea-line shone cities set with their crowns of towers in the midst of broad bays, each fit, it seemed, to be a harbour for the navies of all the world.

Inland the pastures and cornlands lay, chequered much with climbing, over-tumbling grape-vines, under the sun that crumbled their clods, and drew up the young wheat in the spring time, under the rain that made the long grass soft and fine, under all fair fertilizing influences : the streams leapt down from the mountain tops, or cleft their way through the ridged ravines : they grew great rivers, like seas each one.

The mountains were cloven, and gave forth from their scarred sides wealth of ore and splendour of marble ; all things this people that King Valdemar ruled over could do : they levelled mountains, that over the smooth roads the wains might go, laden with silk and spices from the sea : they drained lakes, that the land might yield more and more, as year by year the serfs, driven like cattle, but worse fed, worse housed, died slowly, scarce knowing that they had souls ; they builded them huge ships, and said that they were masters of the sea too ; only, I trow the sea was an unruly subject, and often sent them back their ships cut into more pieces

than the pines of them were, when the adze first fell
upon them ; they raised towers, and bridges, and marble
palaces with endless corridors rose-scented, and cooled
with welling fountains.

They sent great armies and fleets to all the points of
heaven that the wind blows from, who took and burned
many happy cities, wasted many fields and valleys,
blotted out from the memory of men the names of
nations, made their men's lives a hopeless shame and
misery to them, their women's lives disgrace, and then
—came home to have flowers thrown on them in showers,
to be feasted and called heroes.

Should not then their king be proud of them ? Moreover they could fashion stone and brass into the shapes
of men ; they could write books ; they knew the names
of the stars, and their number ; they knew what moved
the passions of men in the hearts of them, and could
draw you up cunningly, catalogues of virtues and vices ;
their wise men could prove to you that any lie was true,
that any truth was false, till your head grew dizzy, and
your heart sick, and you almost doubted if there were
a God.

Should not then their king be proud of them ? Their
men were strong in body, and moved about gracefully—
like dancers ; and the purple-black, scented hair of their
gold-clothed knights seemed to shoot out rays under the
blaze of light that shone like many suns in the king's
halls. Their women's faces were very fair in red and
white, their skins fair and half transparent like the
marble of their mountains, and their voices sounded
like the rising of soft music from step to step of their
own white palaces.

Should not then their king be proud of such a people,
who seemed to help so in carrying on the world to its
consummate perfection, which they even hoped their
grandchildren would see ?

Alas ! alas ! they were slaves—king and priest, noble
and burgher, just as much as the meanest tasked serf,
perhaps more even than he, for they were so willingly,
but he unwillingly enough.

They could do everything but justice, and truth, and mercy; therefore God's judgments hung over their heads, not fallen yet, but surely to fall one time or other.

For ages past they had warred against one people only, whom they could not utterly subdue : a feeble people in numbers, dwelling in the very midst of them, among the mountains ; yet now they were pressing them close ; acre after acre, with seas of blood to purchase each acre, had been wrested from the free people, and their end seemed drawing near ; and this time the king, Valdemar, had marched to their land with a great army, to make war on them, he boasted to himself, almost for the last time.

A walled town in the free land ; in that town, a house built of rough, splintery stones ; and in a great low-browed room of that house, a grey-haired man pacing to and fro impatiently : ' Will she never come ? ' he says, ' it is two hours since the sun set ; news, too, of the enemy's being in the land ; how dreadful if she is taken ! ' His great broad face is marked with many furrows made by the fierce restless energy of the man ; but there is a wearied look on it, the look of a man who, having done his best, is yet beaten ; he seemed to long to be gone and be at peace : he, the fighter in many battles, who often had seemed with his single arm to roll back the whole tide of fight, felt despairing enough now ; this last invasion, he thought, must surely quite settle the matter ; wave after wave, wave after wave, had broken on that dear land and been rolled back from it, and still the hungry sea pressed on ; they must be finally drowned in that sea ; how fearfully they had been tried for their sins. Back again to his anxiety concerning Cissela, his daughter, go his thoughts, and he still paces up and down wearily, stopping now and then to gaze intently on things which he had seen a hundred times ; and the night has altogether come on.

At last the blast of a horn from outside, challenge and counter-challenge, and the wicket to the court-yard is swung open ; for this house, being in a part of the city where the walls are somewhat weak, is a little fortress in itself, and is very carefully guarded. The old man's face brightened at the sound of the new comers, and he went toward the entrance of the house where he was met by two young knights fully armed, and a maiden. 'Thank God you are come,' he says; but stops when he sees her face, which is quite pale, almost wild with some sorrow. 'The saints! Cissela, what is it?' he says. 'Father, Eric will tell you.' Then suddenly a clang, for Eric has thrown on the ground a richly-jewelled sword, sheathed, and sets his foot on it, crunching the pearls on the sheath; then says, flinging up his head,— 'There, father, the enemy is in the land; may that happen to every one of them! but for my part I have accounted for two already.' 'Son Eric, son Eric, you talk for ever about yourself; quick, tell me about Cissela instead: if you go on boasting and talking always about yourself, you will come to no good end, son, after all.' But as he says this, he smiles nevertheless, and his eye glistens.

'Well, father, listen—such a strange thing she tells us, not to be believed, if she did not tell us herself; the enemy has suddenly got generous, one of them at least, which is something of a disappointment to me—ah! pardon, about myself again; and that is about myself too. Well, father, what am I to do?—But Cissela, she wandered some way from her maidens, when—ah! but I never could tell a story properly, let her tell it herself; here, Cissela!—well, well, I see she is better employed, talking namely, how should I know what! with Siur in the window-seat yonder—but she told us that, as she wandered almost by herself, she presently heard shouts and saw many of the enemy's knights riding quickly towards her; whereat she knelt only and prayed to God, who was very gracious to her; for when, as she thought, something dreadful was about to happen, the chief of the knights (a very noble-looking man, she said) rescued her, and, after he had gazed earnestly into her face, told her she might go back again to her own home, and her maids with her, if only she would tell him where she dwelt and her name; and withal he sent three

knights to escort her some way toward the city ; then
he turned and rode away with all his knights but those
three, who, when they knew that he had quite gone, she
says, began to talk horribly, saying things whereof in her
terror she understood the import only : then, before
worse came to pass came I and slew two, as I said, and
the other ran away " lustily with a good courage " ; and
that is the sword of one of the slain knights, or, as one
might rather call them, rascally caitiffs'.

The old man's thoughts seemed to have gone wandering after his son had finished ; for he said nothing for
some time, but at last spoke dejectedly.

'Eric, brave son, when I was your age I too hoped,
and my hopes are come to this at last ; you are blind in
your hopeful youth, Eric, and do not see that this king
(for the king it certainly was) will crush us, and not the
less surely because he is plainly not ungenerous, but
rather a good, courteous knight. Alas ! poor old Gunnar,
broken down now and ready to die, as your country is !
How often, in the olden time, thou used'st to say to
thyself, as thou didst ride at the head of our glorious
house, " this charge may finish this matter, this battle
must." They passed away, those gallant fights, and still
the foe pressed on, and hope, too, slowly ebbed away,
as the boundaries of our land grew less and less : behold
this is the last wave but one or two, and then for a sad
farewell to name and freedom. Yet, surely the end of
the world must come when we are swept from off the
face of the earth. God waits long, they say, before he
avenges his own.'

As he was speaking, Siur and Cissela came nearer to
him, and Cissela, all traces of her late terror gone from
her face now, raising her lips to his bended forehead,
kissed him fondly, and said, with glowing face,

'Father, how can I help our people ? Do they want
deaths ? I will die. Do they want happiness ? I will
live miserably through years and years, nor ever pray
for death.'

Some hope or other seemed growing up in his heart,
and showing through his face ; and he spoke again,

putting back the hair from off her face, and clasping it about with both his hands, while he stooped to kiss her.

' God remember your mother, Cissela ! Then it was no dream after all, but true perhaps, as indeed it seemed at the time ; but it must come quickly, that woman's deliverance, or not at all. When was it that I heard that old tale, that sounded even then true to my ears ? for we have not been punished for naught, my son ; that is not God's way. It comes across my memory somehow, mingled in a wonderful manner with the purple of the pines on the hill-side, with the fragrance of them borne from far towards me ; for know, my children, that in times past, long, long past now, we did an evil deed ; for our forefathers, who have been dead now, and forgiven so long ago, once mad with rage at some defeat from their enemies, fired a church, and burned therein many women who had fled thither for refuge ; and from that time a curse cleaves to us. Only they say, that at the last we may be saved from utter destruction by a woman ; I know not. God grant it may be so.'

Then she said, ' Father, brother, and you, Siur, come with me to the chapel ; I wish you to witness me make an oath.'

Her face was pale, her lips were pale, her golden hair was pale ; but not pale, it seemed, from any sinking of blood, but from gathering of intensest light from somewhere, her eyes perhaps, for they appeared to burn inwardly.

They followed the sweeping of her purple robe in silence through the low heavy-beamed passages : they entered the little chapel, dimly lighted by the moon that night, as it shone through one of the three arrow-slits of windows at the east end. There was little wealth of marble there, I trow ; little time had those fighting men for stone-smoothing. Albeit, one noted many semblances of flowers even in the dim half-light, and here and there the faces of BRAVE men, roughly cut enough, but grand, because the hand of the carver had followed his loving heart. Neither was there gold wanting to the altar and its canopy ; and above the low pillars of the nave hung banners, taken from the foe by the men of that house, gallant with gold and jewels.

She walked up to the altar and took the blessed book of the Gospels from the left side of it ; then knelt in prayer for a moment or two, while the three men stood behind her reverently. When she rose she made a sign to them, and from their scabbards gleamed three swords in the moonlight ; then, while they held them aloft, and pointed toward the altar, she opened the book at the page whereon was painted Christ the Lord dying on the cross, pale against the gleaming gold : she said, in a firm voice, ' Christ God, who diedst for all men, so help me, as I refuse not life, happiness, even honour, for this people whom I love.'

Then she kissed the face so pale against the gold, and knelt again.

But when she had risen, and before she could leave the space by the altar, Siur had stepped up to her, and seized her hurriedly, folding both his arms about her ; she let herself be held there, her bosom against his ; then he held her away from him a little space, holding her by the arms near the shoulder ; then he took her hands and led them across his shoulders, so that now she held him.

And they said nothing ; what could they say ? Do you know any word for what they meant ?

And the father and brother stood by, looking quite awestruck, more so they seemed than by her solemn oath. Till Siur, raising his head from where it lay, cried out aloud : ' May God forgive me as I am true to her ! hear you, father and brother ? '

Then said Cissela : ' May God help me in my need, as I am true to Siur.'

And the others went, and they two were left standing there alone, with no little awe over them, strange and shy as they had never yet been to each other. Cissela shuddered, and said in a quick whisper : ' Siur, on your knees ! and pray that these oaths may never clash.'

' Can they, Cissela ? ' he said.

' O love,' she cried, ' you have loosed my hand ; take it again, or I shall die Siur ! '

He took both her hands, he held them fast to his lips, to his forehead ; he said : ' No, God does not allow such things ; truth does not lie ; you are truth ; this need not be prayed for.'

She said : ' Oh, forgive me ! yet—yet this old chapel is damp and cold even in the burning summer weather. O knight Siur, something strikes through me ; I pray you kneel and pray.'

He looked steadily at her for a long time without answering, as if he were trying once for all to become indeed one with her ; then said : ' Yes, it is possible ; in no other way could you give up everything.'

Then he took from off his finger a thin golden ring, and broke it in two, and gave her the one half, saying : ' When will they come together ? '

Then within a while they left the chapel, and walked as in a dream between the dazzling lights of the hall, where the knights sat now, and between those lights sat down together, dreaming still the same dream each of them ; while all the knights shouted for Siur and Cissela. Even if a man had spent all his life looking for sorrowful things, even if he sought for them with all his heart and soul, and even though he had grown grey in that quest, yet would he have found nothing in all the world, or perhaps in all the stars either, so sorrowful as Cissela.

They had accepted her sacrifice after long deliberation, they had arrayed her in purple and scarlet, they had crowned her with gold wrought about with jewels, they had spread abroad the veil of her golden hair ; yet now, as they led her forth in the midst of the band of knights, her brother Eric holding fast her hand, each man felt like a murderer when he beheld her face, whereon was no tear, wherein was no writhing of muscle, twitching of nerve, wherein was no sorrow-mark of her own, but only the sorrow-mark which God sent her, and which she *must* perforce wear

Yet they had not caught eagerly at her offer, they had said at first almost to a man : ' Nay, this thing shall not be, let us die altogether rather than this.' Yet as they sat, and said this, to each man of the council came floating dim memories of that curse of the burned women, and its remedy ; to many it ran rhythmically, an old song better known by the music than the words, heard once and again, long ago, when the gusty wind overmastered the chestnut-boughs, and strewed the smooth sward with their star-leaves.

Withal came thoughts to each man, partly selfish, partly wise and just, concerning his own wife and children, concerning children yet unborn ; thoughts too of the glory of the old name ; all that had been suffered and done that the glorious free land might yet be a nation.

And the spirit of hope, never dead but sleeping only, woke up within their hearts : ' We may yet be a people,' they said to themselves, ' if we can but get breathing time.'

And as they thought these things, and doubted, Siur rose up in the midst of them and said : ' You are right in what you think, countrymen, and she is right ; she is altogether good and noble ; send her forth.'

Then, with one look of utter despair at her as she stood statue-like, he left the council, lest he should fall down and die in the midst of them, he said ; yet he died not then, but lived for many years afterwards.

But they rose from their seats, and when they were armed, and she royally arrayed, they went with her, leading her through the dear streets, whence you always saw the great pine-shadowed mountains ; she went away from all that was dear to her, to go and sit a crowned queen in the dreary marble palace, whose outer walls rose right up from the weary-hearted sea. She could not think, she durst not ; she feared, if she did, that she would curse her beauty, almost curse the name of love, curse Siur, though she knew he was right, for not slaying her ; she feared that she might curse God.

So she thought not at all, steeping her senses utterly in forgetfulness of the happy past, destroying all anticipation of the future : yet, as they left the city amid the tears of women, and fixed sorrowful gaze of men, she turned

round once, and stretched her arms out involuntarily,
like a dumb senseless thing, towards the place where she
was born, and where her life grew happier day by day,
and where his arms first crept round about her.

She turned away and thought, but in a cold speculative
manner, how it was possible that she was bearing this
sorrow ; as she often before had wondered, when slight
things vexed her overmuch, how people had such sorrows
and lived, and almost doubted if the pain was so much
greater in great sorrows than in small troubles, or
whether the nobleness only was greater, the pain not
sharper, but more lingering.

Halfway toward the camp the king's people met her ;
and over the trampled ground, where they had fought so
fiercely but a little time before, they spread breadth of
golden cloth, that her feet might not touch the arms
of her dead countrymen, or their brave bodies.

And so they came at last with many trumpet-blasts to
the king's tent, who stood at the door of it, to welcome
his bride that was to be : a noble man truly to look on,
kindly, and genial-eyed ; the red blood sprang up over
his face when she came near ; and she looked back no
more, but bowed before him almost to the ground, and
would have knelt, but that he caught her in his arms
and kissed her ; she was pale no more now ; and the
king, as he gazed delightedly at her, did not notice that
sorrow-mark, which was plain enough to her own people.

So the trumpets sounded again one long peal that
seemed to make all the air reel and quiver, and the
soldiers and lords shouted : 'Hurrah for the Peace-
Queen, Cissela ! '

.   .   .   .

' Come, Harald,' said a beautiful golden-haired boy to
one who was plainly his younger brother, ' Come, and let
us leave Robert here by the forge, and show our lady-
mother this beautiful thing. Sweet master armourer,
farewell.'

' Are you going to the queen then ? ' said the armourer.

' Yea,' said the boy, looking wonderingly at the strong
craftsman's eager face.

'But, nay; let me look at you awhile longer, you remind me so much of one I loved long ago in my own land. Stay awhile till your other brother goes with you.'

'Well, I will stay, and think of what you have been telling me ; I do not feel as if I should ever think of anything else for long together, as long as I live.'

So he sat down again on an old battered anvil, and seemed with his bright eyes to be beholding something in the land of dreams. A gallant dream it was he dreamed ; for he saw himself with his brothers and friends about him, seated on a throne, the justest king in all the earth, his people the lovingest of all people : he saw the ambassadors of the restored nations, that had been unjustly dealt with long ago ; everywhere love, and peace if possible, justice and truth at all events.

Alas ! he knew not that vengeance, so long delayed, must fall at last in his life-time ; he knew not that it takes longer to restore that whose growth has been through age and age, than the few years of a life-time ; yet was the reality good, if not as good as the dream.

Presently his twin-brother Robert woke him from that dream, calling out : ' Now, brother Svend, are we really ready ; see here ! but stop, kneel first ; there, now am I the Bishop.'

And he pulled his brother down on to his knees, and put on his head, where it fitted loosely enough now, hanging down from left to right, an iron crown fantastically wrought, which he himself, having just finished it, had taken out of the water, cool and dripping.

Robert and Harald laughed loud when they saw the crown hanging all askew, and the great drops rolling from it into Svend's eyes and down his cheeks, looking like tears : not so Svend ; he rose, holding the crown level on his head, holding it back, so that it pressed against his brow hard, and, first dashing the drops to right and left, caught his brother by the hand, and said : ' May I keep it, Robert ? I shall wear it some day.'

Yea,' said the other ; ' but it is a poor thing ; better let Siur put it in the furnace again and make it into sword hilts.'

Thereupon they began to go, Svend holding the crown in his hand : but as they were going, Siur called out : 'Yet will I sell my dagger at a price, Prince Svend, even as you wished at first, rather than give it you for nothing.'

'Well, for what ? ' said Svend, somewhat shortly, for he thought Siur was going back from his promise, which seemed ugly to him.

'Nay, be not angry, prince,' said the armourer, 'only I pray you to satisfy this whim of mine ; it is the first favour I have asked of you : will you ask the fair, noble lady, your mother, from Siur the smith, if she is happy now ? '

'Willingly, sweet master Siur, if it pleases you ; farewell.'

And with happy young faces they went away ; and when they were gone, Siur from a secret place drew out various weapons and armour, and began to work at them, having first drawn bolt and bar of his workshop carefully.

Svend, with Harald and Robert his two brethren, went their ways to the queen, and found her sitting alone in a fair court of the palace full of flowers, with a marble cloister round about it ; and when she saw them coming, she rose up to meet them, her three fair sons.

Truly as that right royal woman bent over them lovingly, there seemed little need of Siur's question.

So Svend showed her his dagger, but not the crown ; and she asked many questions concerning Siur the smith, about his way of talking and his face, the colour of his hair even, till the boys wondered, she questioned them so closely, with beaming eyes and glowing cheeks, so that Svend thought he had never before seen his mother look so beautiful.

Then Svend said : 'And, mother, don't be angry with Siur, will you ? because he sent a message to you by me.'

'Angry ! ' and straightway her soul was wandering where her body could not come, and for a moment or two she was living as before, with him close by her, in the old mountain land.

'Well, mother, he wanted me to ask you if you were happy now.'

'Did he, Svend, this man with brown hair, grizzled as you say it is now? Is his hair soft then, this Siur, going down on to his shoulders in waves? and his eyes, do they glow steadily, as if lighted up from his heart? and how does he speak? Did you not tell me that his words led you, whether you would or no, into dreamland? Ah well! tell him I am happy, but not so happy as we shall be, as we were. And so you, son Robert, are getting to be quite a cunning smith; but do you think you will ever beat Siur?'

'Ah, mother, no,' he said, 'there is something with him that makes him seem quite infinitely beyond all other workmen I have ever heard of.'

Some memory coming from that dreamland smote upon her heart more than the others; she blushed like a young girl, and said hesitatingly:

'Does he work with his left hand, son Robert; for I have heard that some men do so?' But in her heart she remembered how once, long ago in the old mountain country, in her father's house, some one had said that only men who were born so, could do cunningly with the left hand; and how Siur, then quite a boy, had said, 'Well, I will try:' and how, in a month or two, he had come to her with an armlet of silver, very curiously wrought, which he had done with his own left hand.

So Robert said: 'Yea, mother, he works with his left hand almost as much as with his right, and sometimes I have seen him change the hammer suddenly from his right hand to his left, with a kind of half smile, as one who would say, "Cannot I then?" and this more when he does smith's work in metal than when he works in marble; and once I heard him say when he did so, "I wonder where my first left hand work is; ah! I bide my time." I wonder also, mother, what he meant by that.'

She answered no word, but shook her arm free from its broad sleeve, and something glittered on it, near her wrist, something wrought out of silver set with quaint and uncouthly-cut stones of little value.

· · · · · · · · · ·

In the council chamber, among the lords, sat Svend

and his six brethren ; he chief of all in the wielding of sword or axe, in the government of people, in drawing the love of men and women to him ; perfect in face and body, in wisdom and strength was Svend : next to him sat Robert, cunning in working of marble, or wood, or brass ; all things could he make to look as if they lived, from the sweep of an angel's wings down to the slipping of a little field-mouse from under the sheaves in the harvest-time. Then there was Harald, who knew concerning all the stars of heaven and flowers of earth : Richard, who drew men's hearts from their bodies, with the words that swung to and fro in his glorious rhymes : William, to whom the air of heaven seemed a servant when the harp-strings quivered underneath his fingers : there were the two sailor-brothers, who the year before, young though they were, had come back from a long, perilous voyage, with news of an island they had found long and long away to the west, larger than any that this people knew of, but very fair and good, though uninhabited.

But now over all this noble brotherhood with its various gifts hung one cloud of sorrow ; their mother, the Peace-Queen Cissela was dead, she who had taught them truth and nobleness so well ; she was never to see the beginning of the end that they would work ; truly it seemed sad.

There sat the seven brothers in the council chamber, waiting for the king, speaking no word, only thinking drearily ; and under the pavement of the great church Cissela lay, and by the side of her tomb stood two men, old men both, Valdemar the king, and Siur.

So the king, after that he had gazed awhile on the carven face of her he had loved well, said at last :

' And now, Sir Carver, must you carve me also to lie there.' And he pointed to the vacant space by the side of the fair alabaster figure.

' O king,' said Siur, ' except for a very few strokes on steel, I have done work now, having carved the queen there ; I cannot do this thing for you.'

What was it sent a sharp pang of bitterest suspicion

through the very heart of the poor old man ? he looked steadfastly at him for a moment or two, as if he would know all secrets ; he could not, he had not strength of life enough to get to the bottom of things ; doubt vanished soon from his heart and his face under Siur's pitying gaze ; he said, ' Then perhaps I shall be my own statue,' and therewithal he sat down on the edge of the low marble tomb, and laid his right arm across her breast ; he fixed his eyes on the eastern belt of windows, and sat quite motionless and silent ; and he never knew that she loved him not.

But Siur, when he had gazed at him for awhile, stole away quietly, as we do when we fear to awaken a sleeper ; and the king never turned his head, but still sat there, never moving, scarce breathing, it seemed.

Siur stood in his own great hall (for his house was large), he stood before the daïs, and saw a fair sight, the work of his own hands

For, fronting him, against the wall were seven thrones, and behind them a cloth of samite of purple wrought with golden stars, and barred across from right to left with long bars of silver and crimson, and edged below with melancholy, fading green, like a September sunset ; and opposite each throne was a glittering suit of armour wrought wonderfully in bright steel, except that on the breast of each suit was a face worked marvellously in enamel, the face of Cissela in a glory of golden hair ; and the glory of that gold spread away from the breast on all sides, and ran cunningly along with the steel rings, in such a way as it is hard even to imagine : moreover, on the crest of each helm was wrought the phœnix, the never-dying bird, the only creature that knows the sun ; and by each suit lay a gleaming sword terrible to look at, steel from pommel to point, but wrought along the blade in burnished gold that outflashed the gleam of the steel, was written in fantastic letters the word ' Westward '.

So Siur gazed till he heard footsteps coming ; then he turned to meet them. And Svend and his brethren sat silent in the council chamber, till they heard a great noise and clamour of the people arise through all the streets ; then they rose to see what it might be. Meanwhile on the low marble tomb, under the dim sweeping vault sat, or rather lay, the king ; for, though his right arm still lay over her breast, his head had fallen forward, and rested now on the shoulder of the marble queen. There he lay, with strange confusion of his scarlet, gold-wrought robes ; silent, motionless, and dead. The seven brethren stood together on a marble terrace of the royal palace, that was dotted about on the balusters of it with white statues : they were helmetted, and armed to the teeth, only over their armour great black cloaks were thrown.

Now the whole great terrace was a-sway with the crowd of nobles and princes, and others that were neither nobles or princes, but true men only ; and these were helmetted and wrapped in black cloaks even as the princes were, only the crests of the princes' helms were wrought wonderfully with that bird, the phœnix, all flaming with new power, dying because its old body is not strong enough for its new-found power : and those on that terrace who were unarmed had anxious faces, some fearful, some stormy with Devil's rage at disappointment ; but among the faces of those helmed ones, though here and there you might see a pale face, there was no fear or rage, scarcely even any anxiety, but calm, brave joy seemed to be on all.

Above the heads of all men on that terrace shone out Svend's brave face, the golden hair flowing from out of his helmet : a smile of quiet confidence overflowing from his mighty heart, in the depths of which it was dwelling, just showed a very little on his eyes and lips.

While all the vast square, and all the windows and roofs even of the houses over against the palace, were alive with an innumerable sea of troubled raging faces, showing white, upturned from the undersea of their many-coloured raiment ; the murmur from them was like the sough of the first tempest-wind among the pines ; and the gleam of spears here and there like the last few gleams of the sun through the woods when the black thunder-clouds come up over all, soon to be shone through, those woods, by the gleam of the deep lightning.

Also sometimes the murmur would swell, and from the heart of it would come a fierce, hoarse, tearing, shattering roar, strangely discordant, of ' War ! War ! give us war, O king ! '

Then Svend stepping forward, his arms hidden under his long cloak as they hung down quietly, the smile on his face broadening somewhat, sent from his chest a mighty, effortless voice over all the raging :

' Hear, O ye people ! War with all that is ugly and base ; peace with all that is fair and good.—NO WAR with my brother's people.'

Just then one of those unhelmetted, creeping round about stealthily to the place where Svend stood, lifted his arm and smote at him with a dagger ; whereupon Svend, clearing his right arm from his cloak with his left, lifted up his glittering right hand, and the traitor fell to the earth groaning with a broken jaw, for Svend had smitten him on the mouth a backward blow with his open hand.

One shouted from the crowd, ' Aye, murderer Svend, slay our good nobles, as you poisoned the king your father, that you and your false brethren might oppress us with the memory of that Devil's witch, your mother ! '

The smile left Svend's face and heart now, he looked very stern as he said :

' Hear, O ye people ! In years past when I was a boy my dream of dreams was ever this, how I should make you good, and because good, happy, when I should become king over you ; but as year by year passed I saw my dream flitting ; the deep colours of it changed, faded, grew grey in the light of coming manhood ; nevertheless, God be my witness, that I have ever striven to make you just and true, hoping against hope continually ; and I had even determined to bear everything and stay with you, even though you should remain unjust and liars, for the sake of the few who really love me : but now, seeing that God has made you mad, and that his vengeance will speedily fall, take heed how you

cast out from you all that is good and true-hearted !
Once more—which choose you, Peace or War ? '

Between the good and the base, in the midst of the
passionate faces and changing colours stood the great
terrace, cold, and calm, and white, with its changeless
statues ; and for awhile there was silence.

Broken through at last by a yell, and the sharp whirr
of arrows, and the cling, clang, from the armour of the
terrace as Prince Harald staggered though unhurt,
struck by the broad point on the helmet.

' What ! War ? ' shouted Svend wrathfully, and his
voice sounded like a clap of thunder following the
lightning flash when a tower is struck. ' What ! war ?
swords for Svend ! round about the king, good men and
true ! Sons of the golden-haired, show these men WAR.'

As he spoke he let his black cloak fall, and up from
their sheaths sprang seven swords, steel from pommel to
point only ; on the blades of them in fantastic letters of
gold, shone the word WESTWARD.

Then all the terrace gleamed with steel, and amid the
hurtling of stones and whizz of arrows they began to go
westward.

. . . .

The streets ran with blood, the air was filled with
groans and curses, the low waves nearest the granite pier
were edged with blood, because they first caught the
drippings of the blood.

Then those of the people who durst stay on the pier
saw the ships of Svend's little fleet leaving one by one ;
for he had taken aboard those ten ships whosoever had
prayed to go, even at the last moment, wounded, or
dying even ; better so, for in their last moments came
thoughts of good things to many of them, and it was
good to be among the true.

But those haughty ones left behind, sullen and untamed,
but with a horrible indefinable dread on them that was
worse than death, or mere pain, howsoever fierce—these
saw all the ships go out of the harbour merrily with
swelling sail and dashing oar, and with joyous singing of
those aboard ; and Svend's was the last of all.

Whom they saw kneel down on the deck unhelmed,
then all sheathed their swords that were about him ;
and the Prince Robert took from Svend's hand an iron
crown fantastically wrought, and placed it on his head
as he knelt ; then he continued kneeling still, till, as the
ship drew further and further away from the harbour,
all things aboard of her became indistinct.

And they never saw Svend and his brethren again.

Here ends what William the Englishman wrote ; but
afterwards (in the night-time) he found the book of
a certain chronicler which saith :

' In the spring-time, in May, the 550th year from the
death of Svend the wonderful king, the good knights,
sailing due eastward, came to a harbour of a land they
knew not : wherein they saw many goodly ships, but of
a strange fashion like the ships of the ancients, and
destitute of any mariners : besides they saw no beacons
for the guidance of seamen, nor was there any sound of
bells or singing, though the city was vast, with many
goodly towers and palaces. So when they landed they
found that which is hardly to be believed, but which is
nevertheless true : for about the quays and about the
streets lay many people dead, or stood, but quite without
motion, and they were all white or about the colour of
new-hewn freestone, yet were they not statues but real
men, for they had, some of them, ghastly wounds which
showed their entrails, and the structure of their flesh,
and veins, and bones.

' Moreover the streets were red and wet with blood,
and the harbour waves were red with it, because it
dripped in great drops slowly from the quays.

' Then when the good knights saw this, they doubted
not but that it was a fearful punishment on this people
for sins of theirs ; thereupon they entered into a church
of that city and prayed God to pardon them ; afterwards,
going back to their ships, sailed away marvelling.

' And I John who wrote this history saw all this with
mine own eyes.'

LINDENBORG POOL [1]

(*Oxford and Cambridge Magazine*, September 1856)

I READ once in lazy humour Thorpe's 'Northern Mythology,' on a cold May night when the north wind was blowing ; in lazy humour, but when I came to the tale that is here amplified there was something in it that fixed my attention and made me think of it ; and whether I would or no, my thoughts ran in this way, as here follows.

So I felt obliged to write, and wrote accordingly, and by the time I had done the grey light filled all my room ; so I put out my candles, and went to bed, not without fear and trembling, for the morning twilight is so strange and lonely. This is what I wrote.

Yes, on that dark night, with that wild unsteady north wind howling, though it was Maytime, it was doubtless dismal enough in the forest, where the boughs clashed eerily, and where, as the wanderer in that place hurried along, strange forms half showed themselves to him, the more fearful because half seen in that way : dismal enough doubtless on wide moors where the great wind had it all its own way : dismal on the rivers creeping on and on between the marshlands, creeping through the willows, the water trickling through the locks, sounding faintly in the gusts of the wind.

Yet surely nowhere so dismal as by the side of that still pool.

I threw myself down on the ground there, utterly exhausted with my struggle against the wind, and with bearing the fathoms and fathoms of the heavily-leaded plumb-line that lay beside me.

Fierce as the wind was, it could not raise the leaden waters of that fearful pool, defended as they were by

[1] See Thorpe's 'Northern Mythology', vol. ii, p. 214.

the steep banks of dripping yellow clay, striped horribly here and there with ghastly uncertain green and blue.

They said no man could fathom it ; and yet all round the edges of it grew a rank crop of dreary reeds and segs, some round, some flat, but none ever flowering as other things flowered, never dying and being renewed, but always the same stiff array of unbroken reeds and segs, some round, some flat. Hard by me were two trees leafless and ugly, made, it seemed, only for the wind to go through with a wild sough on such nights as these ; and for a mile from that place were no other trees.

True, I could not see all this at that time, then, in the dark night, but I knew well that it was all there ; for much had I studied this pool in the day-time, trying to learn the secret of it ; many hours I had spent there, happy with a kind of happiness, because forgetful of the past. And even now, could I not hear the wind going through those trees, as it never went through any trees before or since ? could I not see gleams of the dismal moor ? could I not hear those reeds just taken by the wind, knocking against each other, the flat ones scraping all along the round ones ? Could I not hear, moreover, the slow trickling of the land-springs through the clay banks ?

The cold, chill horror of the place was too much for me ; I had never been there by night before, nobody had for quite a long time, and now to come on such a night ! If there had been any moon, the place would have looked more as it did by day ; besides, the moon shining on water is always so beautiful, on any water even : if it had been starlight, one could have looked at the stars and thought of the time when those fields were fertile and beautiful (for such a time was, I am sure), when the cowslips grew among the grass, and when there was promise of yellow-waving corn stained with poppies ; that time which the stars had seen, but which we had never seen, which even they would never see again—past time !

Ah ! what was that which touched my shoulder ?— Yes, I see, only a dead leaf.—Yes, to be here on this

eighth of May too of all nights in the year, the night of
that awful day when ten years ago I slew him, not
undeservedly, God knows, yet how dreadful it was !—
Another leaf ! and another !—Strange, those trees have
been dead this hundred years, I should think. How
sharp the wind is too, just as if I were moving along
and meeting it ;—why, I *am* moving ! what then, I am
not there after all ; where am I then ? there are the
trees ; no, they are freshly-planted oak saplings, the
very ones that those withered last-year's leaves were
blown on me from.

I have been dreaming then, and am on my road to the
lake : but what a young wood ! I must have lost my
way ; I never saw all this before. Well—I will walk on
stoutly.

May the Lord help my senses ! I am *riding* !—on
a mule ; a bell tinkles somewhere on him ; the wind
blows something about with a flapping sound : something ? in Heaven's name, what ? *My* long black robes.
—Why—when I left my house I was clad in serviceable
broadcloth of the nineteenth century.

I shall go mad—I am mad—I am gone to the Devil—
I have lost my identity ; who knows in what place, in
what age of the world I am living now ? Yet I will be
calm ; I have seen all these things before, in pictures
surely, or something like them. I am resigned, since it
is no worse than that. I am a priest then, in the dim,
far-off thirteenth century, riding, about midnight I
should say, to carry the blessed sacrament to some
dying man.

Soon I found that I was not alone ; a man was riding
close to me on a horse ; he was fantastically dressed,
more so than usual for that time, being striped all over
in vertical stripes of yellow and green, with quaint birds
like exaggerated storks in different attitudes counter-
changed on the stripes ; all this I saw by the lantern he
carried, in the light of which his debauched black eyes
quite flashed. On he went, unsteadily rolling, very
drunk, though it was the thirteenth century, but being
plainly used to that, he sat his horse fairly well.

I watched him in my proper nineteenth-century
character, with insatiable curiosity and intense amuse-
ment ; but as a quiet priest of a long-past age, with
contempt and disgust enough, not unmixed with fear
and anxiety.

He roared out snatches of doggrel verse as he went
along, drinking songs, hunting songs, robbing songs,
lust-songs, in a voice that sounded far and far above
the roaring of the wind, though that was high, and rolled
along the dark road that his lantern cast spikes of light
along ever so far, making the devils grin : and meanwhile
I, the priest, glanced from him wrathfully every now
and then to That which I carried very reverently in my
hand, and my blood curdled with shame and indignation ;
but being a shrewd priest, I knew well enough that
a sermon would be utterly thrown away on a man who
was drunk every day in the year, and, more especially,
very drunk then. So I held my peace, saying only under
my breath :

' Dixit insipiens in corde suo, Non est Deus. Corrupti sunt
et abominabiles facti sunt in studiis suis; non est qui faciat
bonum, non est usque ad unum : sepulchrum patens est guttur
eorum; linguis suis dolose agebant, venenum aspidum sub
labiis eorum. Dominum non invocaverunt; illic trepidaverunt
timore, ubi non erat timor. Quis dabit ex Sion salutare Israel ? '

and so I went on, thinking too at times about the man
who was dying and whom I was soon to see : he had
been a bold bad plundering baron, but was said lately
to have altered his way of life, having seen a miracle or
some such thing ; he had departed to keep a tournament
near his castle lately, but had been brought back sore
wounded, so this drunken servant, with some difficulty
and much unseasonable merriment, had made me understand, and now lay at the point of death, brought about
by unskilful tending and such like. Then I thought of
his face—a bad face, very bad, retreating forehead, small
twinkling eyes, projecting lower jaw ; and such a voice,
too, he had ! like the grunt of a boar mostly.

Now don't you think it strange that this face should be
the same, actually the same as the face of my enemy,

slain that very day ten years ago ? I did not hate him, either that man or the baron, but I wanted to see as little of him as possible, and I hoped that the ceremony would soon be over, and that I should be at liberty again.

And so with these thoughts and many others, but all thought strangely double, we went along, the varlet being too drunk to take much notice of me, only once, as he was singing some doggrel, like this, I think, making allowances for change of language and so forth :

'The Duke went to Treves
On the first of November;
His wife stay'd at Bonn—
Let me see, I remember;

'When the Duke came back
To look for his wife,
We came from Cologne,
And took the Duke's life;

'We hung him mid high
Between spire and pavement,
From their mouths dropp'd the cabbage
Of the carles in amazement.'

'Boo—hoo ! Church-rat ! Church-mouse ! Hilloa, Priest ! have you brought the pyx, eh ? '

From some cause or other he seemed to think this an excellent joke, for he almost shrieked with laughter as we went along ; but by this time we had reached the castle. Challenge, and counter-challenge, and we passed the outermost gate and began to go through some of the courts, in which stood lime trees here and there, growing green tenderly with that Maytime, though the north wind bit so keenly.

How strange again ! as I went farther, there seemed no doubt of it ; here in the aftertime came that pool, how I knew not ; but in the few moments that we were riding from the outer gate to the castle-porch I thought so intensely over the probable cause for the existence of that pool, that (how strange !) I could almost have thought I was back again listening to the oozing of the land-springs through the high clay banks there. I was wakened from that, before it grew too strong, by the

glare of many torches, and, dismounting, found myself
in the midst of some twenty attendants, with flushed
faces and wildly sparkling eyes, which they were vainly
trying to soften to due solemnity; mock solemnity
I had almost said, for they did not seem to think it
necessary to appear really solemn, and had difficulty
enough apparently in not prolonging indefinitely the
shout of laughter with which they had at first greeted
me. 'Take the holy Father to my Lord,' said one at
last, ' and we will go with him.'

So they led me up the stairs into the gorgeously-
furnished chamber; the light from the heavy waxen
candles was pleasant to my eyes after the glare and
twisted red smoke of the pine-torches; but all the
essences scattered about the chamber were not enough
to conquer the fiery breath of those about me.

I put on the alb and stole they brought me, and,
before I went up to the sick man, looked round on those
that were in the rooms; for the rooms opened one into
the other by many doors, across some of which hung
gorgeous tapestry; all the rooms seemed to have many
people, for some stood at these doors, and some passed
to and fro, swinging aside the heavy hangings; once
several people at once, seemingly quite by accident,
drew aside almost all the veils from the doors, and
showed an endless perspective of gorgeousness.

And at these things my heart fainted for horror. ' Had
not the Jews of late,' thought I, the priest, ' been very
much in the habit of crucifying children in mockery of
the Holiest, holding gorgeous feasts while they beheld
the poor innocents die? these men are Atheists, you are
in a trap, yet quit yourself like a man.'

' Ah, sharp one,' thought I, the author, ' where are you
at last? try to pray as a test.—Well, well, these things
are strangely like devils.—O man, you have talked about
bravery often, now is your time to practise it: once for
all trust in God, or I fear you are lost.'

Moreover it increased my horror that there was no
appearance of a woman in all these rooms; and yet was
there not? there, those things—I looked more intently;

yes, no doubt they were women, but all dressed like men ;—what a ghastly place !

' O man ! do your duty,' my angel said ; then in spite of the bloodshot eyes of man and woman there, in spite of their bold looks, they quailed before me.

I stepped up to the bedside, where under the velvet coverlid lay the dying man, his small sparkling eyes only (but dulled now by coming death) showing above the swathings. I was about to kneel down by the bedside to confess him, when one of those—things— called out (now they had just been whispering and sniggering together, but the priest in his righteous, brave scorn would not look at them ; the humbled author, half fearful, half trustful, dared not) : so one called out :

' Sir Priest, for three days our master has spoken no articulate word ; you must pass over all particulars ; ask for a sign only.'

Such a strange ghastly suspicion flashed across me just then ; but I choked it, and asked the dying man if he repented of his sins, and if he believed all that was necessary to salvation, and, if so, to make a sign, if he were able : the man moved a little and groaned ; so I took it for a sign, as he was clearly incapable either of speaking or moving, and accordingly began the service for the administration of the sacraments ; and as I began, those behind me and through all the rooms (I know it was through all of them) began to move about, in a bewildering dance-like motion, mazy and intricate ; yes, and presently music struck up through all those rooms, music and singing, lively and gay ; many of the tunes I had heard before (in the nineteenth century) ; I could have sworn to half a dozen of the polkas.

The rooms grew fuller and fuller of people ; they passed thick and fast between the rooms, and the hangings were continually rustling ; one fat old man with a big belly crept under the bed where I was, and wheezed and chuckled there, laughing and talking to one who stooped down and lifted up the hangings to look at him.

Still more and more people talking and singing and

laughing and twirling about, till my brain went round
and round, and I scarce knew what I did ; yet, somehow,
I could not leave off ; I dared not even look over my
shoulder, fearing lest I should see something so horrible
as to make me die.

So I got on with the service, and at last took the Pyx,
and took thereout the sacred wafer, whereupon was
a deep silence through all those rooms, which troubled
me, I think, more than all which had gone before, for
I knew well it did not mean reverence.

I held it up, that which I counted so holy, when lo !
great laughter, echoing like thunder-claps through all
the rooms, not dulled by the veiling hangings, for they
were all raised up together, and, with a slow upheaval of
the rich clothes among which he lay, with a sound that
was half snarl, half grunt, with helpless body swathed
in bedclothes, a huge *swine* that I had been shriving tore
from me the Holy Thing, deeply scoring my hand as
he did so with tusk and tooth, so that the red blood ran
quick on to the floor.

Therewithal he rolled down on to the floor, and lay
there helplessly, only able to roll to and fro, because of
the swathings.

Then right madly skirled the intolerable laughter,
rising to shrieks that were fearfuller than any scream of
agony I ever heard ; the hundreds of people through all
those grand rooms danced and wheeled about me,
shrieking, hemming me in with interlaced arms, the
women loosing their long hair and thrusting forward
their horribly-grinning unsexed faces toward me till I
felt their hot breath.

Oh ! how I hated them all ! almost hated all mankind
for their sakes ; how I longed to get right quit of all
men ; among whom, as it seemed, all sacredest things
even were made a mock of. I looked about me fiercely,
I sprang forward, and clutched a sword from the gilded
belt of one of those who stood near me ; with savage
blows that threw the blood about the gilded walls and
their hangings right over the heads of those—things—
I cleared myself from them, and tore down the great

stairs madly, yet could not, as in a dream, go fast enough, because of my passion.

I was out in the courtyard, among the lime trees soon, the north wind blowing freshly on my heated forehead in that dawn. The outer gate was locked and bolted ; I stooped and raised a great stone and sent it at the lock with all my strength, and I was stronger than ten men then ; iron and oak gave way before it, and through the ragged splinters I tore in reckless fury, like a wild horse through a hazel hedge.

And no one had pursued me. I knelt down on the dear green turf outside, and thanked God with streaming eyes for my deliverance, praying Him forgiveness for my unwilling share in that night's mockery.

Then I arose and turned to go, but even as I did so I heard a roar as if the world were coming in two, and looking toward the castle, saw, not a castle, but a great cloud of white lime-dust swaying this way and that in the gusts of the wind.

Then while the east grew bright there arose a hissing, gurgling noise, that swelled into the roar and wash of many waters, and by then the sun had risen a deep black lake lay before my feet.

And this is how I tried to fathom the Lindenborg Pool.

THE HOLLOW LAND. A TALE

(*Oxford and Cambridge Magazine*, September and October 1856)

CHAPTER I

Struggling in the World

We find in ancient story wonders many told,
Of heroes in great glory, with spirit free and bold ;
Of joyances and high-tides, of weeping and of woe,
Of noble recken striving, mote ye now wonders know.
Niebelungen Lied (see Carlyle's Miscellanies).

Do you know where it is—the Hollow Land ?

I have been looking for it now so long, trying to find it again—the Hollow Land—for there I saw my love first.

I wish to tell you how I found it first of all ; but I am old, my memory fails me : you must wait and let me think if I perchance can tell you how it happened.

Yea, in my ears is a confused noise of trumpet-blasts singing over desolate moors, in my ears and eyes a clashing and clanging of horse-hoofs, a ringing and glittering of steel ; drawn-back lips, set teeth, shouts, shrieks, and curses.

How was it that no one of us ever found it till that day? for it is near our country: but what time have we to look for it, or any good thing ; with such biting carking cares hemming us in on every side—cares about great things—mighty things : mighty things, O my brothers ! or rather little things enough, if we only knew it.

Lives past in turmoil, in making one another unhappy; in bitterest misunderstanding of our brothers' hearts, making those sad whom God has not made sad,—alas, alas ! what chance for any of us to find the Hollow Land ? what time even to look for it ?

Yet who has not dreamed of it ? Who, half miserable yet the while, for that he knows it is but a dream, has not felt the cool waves round his feet, the roses crowning him, and through the leaves of beech and lime the many whispering winds of the Hollow Land ?

Now, my name was Florian, and my house was the house of the Lilies ; and of that house was my father Lord, and after him my eldest brother Arnald ; and me they called Florian de Liliis.

Moreover, when my father was dead, there arose a feud between the Lilies' house and Red Harald ; and this that follows is the history of it.

Lady Swanhilda, Red Harald's mother, was a widow, with one son, Red Harald ; and when she had been in widowhood two years, being of princely blood, and besides comely and fierce, King Urrayne sent to demand her in marriage. And I remember seeing the procession leaving the town, when I was quite a child ; and many young knights and squires attended the Lady Swanhilda as pages, and amongst them Arnald, my eldest brother.

And as I gazed out of the window, I saw him walking by the side of her horse, dressed in white and gold very delicately ; but as he went it chanced that he stumbled. Now he was one of those that held a golden canopy over the lady's head, so that it now sunk into wrinkles, and the lady had to bow her head full low, and even then the gold brocade caught in one of the long slim gold flowers that were wrought round about the crown she wore. She flushed up in her rage, and her smooth face went suddenly into the carven wrinkles of a wooden water-spout, and she caught at the brocade with her left hand, and pulled it away furiously, so that the warp and woof were twisted out of their places, and many gold threads were left dangling about the crown ; but Swanhilda stared about when she rose, then smote my brother across the mouth with her gilded sceptre, and the red blood flowed all about his garments ; yet he only turned exceeding pale, and dared say no word, though he was heir to the house of the Lilies : but my small heart swelled with rage, and I vowed revenge, and, as it seems, he did too.

So when Swanhilda had been queen three years, she

suborned many of King Urrayne's knights and lords,
and slew her husband as he slept, and reigned in
his stead. And her son, Harald, grew up to manhood,
and was counted a strong knight, and well spoken of,
by then I first put on my armour.

Then, one night, as I lay dreaming, I felt a hand laid
on my face, and starting up saw Arnald before me fully
armed. He said, ' Florian, rise and arm.' I did so, all
but my helm, as he was.

He kissed me on the forehead ; his lips felt hot and
dry ; and when they brought torches, and I could see
his face plainly, I saw he was very pale. He said :

' Do you remember, Florian, this day sixteen years
ago ? It is a long time, but I shall never forget it unless
this night blots out its memory.'

I knew what he meant, and because my heart was
wicked, I rejoiced exceedingly at the thought of vengeance, so that I could not speak, but only laid my
palm across his lips.

' Good ; you have a good memory, Florian. See now,
I waited long and long : I said at first, I forgive her ;
but when the news came concerning the death of the
king, and how that she was shameless, I said I will take
it as a sign, if God does not punish her within certain
years, that He means me to do so ; and I have been
watching and watching now these two years for an
opportunity, and behold it is come at last ; and I think
God has certainly given her into our hands, for she rests
this night, this very Christmas Eve, at a small walled
town on the frontier, not two hours' gallop from this ;
they keep little ward there, and the night is wild :
moreover, the prior of a certain house of monks, just
without the walls, is my fast friend in this matter, for
she has done him some great injury. In the courtyard
below, a hundred and fifty knights and squires, all
faithful and true, are waiting for us : one moment and
we shall be gone.'

Then we both knelt down, and prayed God to give her
into our hands : we put on our helms, and went down
into the courtyard.

It was the first time I expected to use a sharp sword in anger, and I was full of joy as the muffled thunder of our horse-hoofs rolled through the bitter winter night.

In about an hour and a half we had crossed the frontier, and in half an hour more the greater part had halted in a wood near the Abbey, while I and a few others went up to the Abbey gates, and knocked loudly four times with my sword-hilt, stamping on the ground meantime. A long, low whistle answered me from within, which I in my turn answered : then the wicket opened, and a monk came out, holding a lantern. He seemed yet in the prime of life, and was a tall, powerful man. He held the lantern to my face, then smiled, and said, ' The banners hang low.' I gave the countersign, ' The crest is lopped off.' ' Good my son,' said he ; ' the ladders are within here. I dare not trust any of the brethren to carry them for you, though they love not the witch either, but are timorsome.'

' No matter,' I said, ' I have men here. So they entered and began to shoulder the tall ladders : the prior was very busy. ' You will find them just the right length, my son, trust me for that.' He seemed quite a jolly pleasant man, I could not understand his nursing furious revenge ; but his face darkened strangely whenever he happened to mention her name.

As we were starting he came and stood outside the gate, and putting his lantern down that the light of it might not confuse his sight, looked earnestly into the night, then said : ' The wind has fallen, the snow flakes get thinner and smaller every moment, in an hour it will be freezing hard, and will be quite clear ; everything depends upon the surprise being complete ; stop a few minutes yet, my son.' He went away chuckling, and returned presently with two more sturdy monks carrying something : they threw their burdens down before my feet, they consisted of all the white albs in the abbey : ' There, trust an old man, who has seen more than one stricken fight in his carnal days ; let the men who scale the walls put these over their arms, and they will not be seen in the least. God make your sword sharp, my son.'

So we departed, and when I met Arnald again, he said,
that what the prior had done was well thought of ; so
we agreed that I should take thirty men, an old squire
of our house, well skilled in war, along with them, scale
the walls as quietly as possible, and open the gates to
the rest.

I set off accordingly, after that with low laughing we
had put the albs all over us, wrapping the ladders also
in white. Then we crept very warily and slowly up the
wall ; the moat was frozen over, and on the ice the snow
lay quite thick ; we all thought that the guards must be
careless enough, when they did not even take the trouble
to break the ice in the moat. So we listened—there was
no sound at all, the Christmas midnight mass had long
ago been over, it was nearly three o'clock, and the moon
began to clear, there was scarce any snow falling now,
only a flake or two from some low hurrying cloud or
other : the wind sighed gently about the round towers
there, but it was bitter cold, for it had begun to freeze
again : we listened for some minutes, about a quarter of
an hour I think, then at a sign from me, they raised the
ladders carefully, muffled as they were at the top with
swathings of wool. I mounted first, old Squire Hugh
followed last ; noiselessly we ascended, and soon stood
all together on the walls ; then we carefully lowered the
ladders again with long ropes ; we got our swords and
axes from out of the folds of our priests' raiments, and
set forward, till we reached the first tower along the
wall ; the door was open, in the chamber at the top
there was a fire slowly smouldering, nothing else ; we
passed through it, and began to go down the spiral
staircase, I first, with my axe shortened in my hand.—
' What if we were surprised there,' I thought, and I
longed to be out in the air again ;—' What if the door
were fast at the bottom.'

As we passed the second chamber, we heard some one
within snoring loudly : I looked in quietly, and saw
a big man with long black hair, that fell off his pillow
and swept the ground, lying snoring, with his nose
turned up and his mouth open, but he seemed so sound

asleep that we did not stop to slay him.—Praise be !—
the door was open, without even a whispered word,
without a pause, we went on along the streets, on the
side that the drift had been on, because our garments
were white, for the wind being very strong all that day,
the houses on that side had caught in their cornices and
carvings, and on the rough stone and wood of them, so
much snow, that except here and there where the black
walls grinned out, they were quite white ; no man saw
us as we stole along, noiselessly because of the snow,
till we stood within 100 yards of the gates and their
house of guard.   And we stood because we heard the
voice of some one singing :

> ' Queen Mary's crown was gold,
>   King Joseph's crown was red,
> But Jesus' crown was diamond
>   That lit up all the bed
>   *Mariæ Virginis.*'

So they had some guards after all ; this was clearly the
sentinel that sung to keep the ghosts off.—Now for
a fight.—We drew nearer, a few yards nearer, then
stopped to free ourselves from our monks' clothes.

> ' Ships sail through the Heaven
>   With red banners dress'd,
> Carrying the planets seven
>   To see the white breast
>   *Mariæ Virginis.*'

Thereat he must have seen the waving of some alb or
other as it shivered down to the ground, for his spear fell
with a thud, and he seemed to be standing open-mouthed,
thinking something about ghosts ; then, plucking up
heart of grace, he roared out like ten bull-calves, and
dashed into the guard-house.

We followed smartly, but without hurry, and came up
to the door of it just as some dozen half-armed men
came tumbling out under our axes : thereupon, while
our men slew them, I blew a great blast upon my horn,
and Hugh with some others drew bolt and bar and
swung the gates wide open.

Then the men in the guard-house understood they

were taken in a trap, and began to stir with great confusion ; so lest they should get quite waked and armed,
I left Hugh at the gates with ten men, and myself led
the rest into that house. There while we slew all those
that yielded not, came Arnald with the others, bringing
our horses with them : then all the enemy threw their
arms down. And we counted our prisoners and found
them over fourscore ; therefore, not knowing what to
do with them (for they were too many to guard, and it
seemed unknightly to slay them all), we sent up some
bowmen to the walls, and turning our prisoners out of
gates, bid them run for their lives, which they did fast
enough, not knowing our numbers, and our men sent
a few flights of arrows among them that they might not
be undeceived.

Then the one or two prisoners that we had left, told us,
when we had crossed our axes over their heads, that the
people of the good town would not willingly fight us, in
that they hated the Queen ; that she was guarded at
the palace by some fifty knights, and that beside, there
were no others to oppose us in the town : so we set out
for the palace, spear in hand.

We had not gone far, before we heard some knights
coming, and soon, in a turn of the long street, we saw
them riding towards us ; when they caught sight of us
they seemed astonished, drew rein, and stood in some
confusion.

We did not slacken our pace for an instant, but rode
right at them with a yell, to which I lent myself with all
my heart.

After all they did not run away, but waited for us with
their spears held out ; I missed the man I had marked,
or hit him rather just on the top of the helm ; he bent
back, and the spear slipped over his head, but my horse
still kept on, and I felt presently such a crash that I
reeled in my saddle, and felt mad. He had lashed out
at me with his sword as I came on, hitting me in the ribs
(for my arm was raised), but only flatlings.

I was quite wild with rage, I turned, almost fell upon
him, caught him by the neck with both hands, and threw

him under the horse-hoofs, sighing with fury : I heard
Arnald's voice close to me, ' Well fought, Florian : ' and
I saw his great stern face bare among the iron, for he
had made a vow in remembrance of that blow always to
fight unhelmed ; I saw his great sword swinging, in wide
gyres, and hissing as it started up, just as if it were alive
and liked it.

So joy filled all my soul, and I fought with my heart, till
the big axe I swung felt like nothing but a little hammer
in my hand, except for its bitterness : and as for the
enemy, they went down like grass, so that we destroyed
them utterly, for those knights would neither yield nor
fly, but died as they stood, so that some fifteen of our
men also died there.

Then at last we came to the palace, where some
grooms and such like kept the gates armed, but some ran,
and some we took prisoners, one of whom died for sheer
terror in our hands, being stricken by no wound : for
he thought we would eat him.

These prisoners we questioned concerning the queen,
and so entered the great hall.

There Arnald sat down in the throne on the dais, and
laid his naked sword before him on the table : and on
each side of him sat such knights as there was room for,
and the others stood round about, while I took ten men,
and went to look for Swanhilda.

I found her soon, sitting by herself in a gorgeous
chamber. I almost pitied her when I saw her looking
so utterly desolate and despairing ; her beauty too had
faded, deep lines cut through her face. But when I
entered she knew who I was, and her look of intense
hatred was so fiend-like, that it changed my pity into
horror of her.

' Knight,' she said, ' who are you, and what do you
want, thus discourteously entering my chamber ? '

' I am Florian de Liliis, and I am to conduct you to
judgement.'

She sprung up, ' Curse you and your whole house,—
you I hate worse than any,—girl's face,—guards !
guards ! ' and she stamped on the ground, her veins

on the forehead swelled, her eyes grew round and flamed
out, as she kept crying for her guards, stamping the
while, for she seemed quite mad.

Then at last she remembered that she was in the
power of her enemies, she sat down, and lay with her
face between her hands, and wept passionately.

' Witch,'—I said between my closed teeth, ' will you
come, or must we carry you down to the great hall ? '

Neither would she come, but sat there, clutching at
her dress and tearing her hair.

Then I said, ' Bind her, and carry her down.' And
they did so.

I watched Arnald as we came in, there was no triumph
on his stern white face, but resolution enough, he had
made up his mind.

They placed her on a seat in the midst of the hall over
against the dais. He said, ' Unbind her, Florian.' They
did so, she raised her face, and glared defiance at us all,
as though she would die queenly after all.

Then rose up Arnald and said, ' Queen Swanhilda, we
judge you guilty of death, and because you are a queen
and of a noble house, you shall be slain by my knightly
sword, and I will even take the reproach of slaying
a woman, for no other hand than mine shall deal the
blow.'

Then she said, ' O false knight, show your warrant
from God, man, or devil.'

' This warrant from God, Swanhilda,' he said, holding
up his sword, ' listen !—fifteen years ago, when I was
just winning my spurs, you struck me, disgracing me
before all the people ; you cursed me, and meant that
curse well enough. Men of the house of the Lilies, what
sentence for that ? '

' Death ! ' they said.

' Listen !—afterwards you slew my cousin, your
husband, treacherously, in the most cursed way, stabbing
him in the throat, as the stars in the canopy above him
looked down on the shut eyes of him. Men of the house
of the Lily, what sentence for that ? '

' Death ! ' they said.

'Do you hear them, Queen ? there is warrant from man ; for the devil, I do not reverence him enough to take warrant from him, but, as I look at that face of yours, I think that even he has left you.'

And indeed just then all her pride seemed to leave her, she fell from the chair, and wallowed on the ground moaning, she wept like a child, so that the tears lay on the oak floor ; she prayed for another month of life ; she came to me and kneeled, and kissed my feet, and prayed piteously, so that water ran out of her mouth.

But I shuddered, and drew away ; it was like having an adder about one ; I could have pitied her had she died bravely, but for one like her to whine and whine !— pah !—

Then from the dais rang Arnald's voice terrible, much changed. ' Let there be an end of all this.' And he took his sword and strode through the hall towards her ; she rose from the ground and stood up, stooping a little, her head sunk between her shoulders, her black eyes turned up and gleaming, like a tigress about to spring. When he came within some six paces of her something in his eye daunted her, or perhaps the flashing of his terrible sword in the torch-light ; she threw her arms up with a great shriek, and dashed screaming about the hall. Arnald's lip never once curled with any scorn, no line in his face changed : he said, ' Bring her here and bind her.'

But when one came up to her to lay hold on her she first of all ran at him, hitting him with her head in the belly. Then while he stood doubled up for want of breath, and staring with his head up, she caught his sword from the girdle, and cut him across the shoulders, and many others she wounded sorely before they took her.

Then Arnald stood by the chair to which she was bound, and poised his sword, and there was a great silence.

Then he said, ' Men of the House of the Lilies, do you justify me in this, shall she die ? ' Straightway rang a great shout through the hall, but before it died away the sword had swept round, and therewithal was there no such thing as Swanhilda left upon the earth, for in no battle-field had Arnald struck truer blow. Then he turned to the few servants of the palace and said, ' Go now, bury this accursed woman, for she is a king's daughter.' Then to us all, ' Now knights, to horse and away, that we may reach the good town by about dawn.' So we mounted and rode off.

What a strange Christmas-day that was, for there, about nine o'clock in the morning, rode Red Harald into the good town to demand vengeance ; he went at once to the king, and the king promised that before nightfall that very day the matter should be judged ; albeit the king feared somewhat, because every third man you met in the streets had a blue cross on his shoulder, and some likeness of a lily, cut out or painted, stuck in his hat ; and this blue cross and lily were the bearings of our house, called ' De Liliis.' Now we had seen Red Harald pass through the streets, with a white banner borne before him, to show that he came peaceably as for this time ; but I trow he was thinking of other things than peace.

And he was called Red Harald first at this time, because over all his arms he wore a great scarlet cloth, that fell in heavy folds about his horse and all about him. Then, as he passed our house, some one pointed it out to him, rising there with its carving and its barred marble, but stronger than many a castle on the hill-tops, and its great overhanging battlement cast a mighty shadow down the wall and•across the street ; and above all rose the great tower, our banner floating proudly from the top, whereon was emblazoned on a white ground a blue cross, and on a blue ground four white lilies. And now faces were gazing from all the windows, and all the battlements were thronged ; so Harald turned, and rising in his stirrups, shook his clenched fist at our house ; natheless, as he did so, the east wind, coming down the street, caught up the corner of that scarlet cloth and drove it over his face, and therewithal disordering his long black hair, well nigh choked him, so that he bit both his hair and that cloth.

So from base to cope rose a mighty shout of triumph and defiance, and he passed on.

Then Arnald caused it to be cried, that all those who loved the good House of the Lilies should go to mass that morning in Saint Mary's Church, hard by our house. Now this church belonged to us, and the abbey that served it, and always we appointed the abbot of it on condition that our trumpets should sound all together when on high masses they sing the ' Gloria in Excelsis.' It was the largest and most beautiful of all the churches in the town, and had two exceeding high towers, which you could see from far off, even when you saw not the town or any of its other towers : and in one of these towers were twelve great bells, named after the twelve Apostles, one name being written on each one of them ; as Peter, Matthew, and so on ; and in the other tower was one great bell only, much larger than any of the others, and which was called Mary. Now this bell was never rung but when our house was in great danger, and it had this legend on it, ' When Mary rings the earth shakes ; ' and indeed from this we took our war cry, which was, ' Mary rings ; ' somewhat justifiably indeed, for the last time that Mary rung, on that day before nightfall there were four thousand bodies to be buried, which bodies wore neither cross nor lily.

So Arnald gave me in charge to tell the abbot to cause Mary to be tolled for an hour before mass that day.

The abbot leaned on my shoulder as I stood within the tower and looked at the twelve monks laying their hands to the ropes. Far up in the dimness I saw the wheel before it began to swing round about ; then it moved a little ; the twelve men bent down to the earth and a roar rose that shook the tower from base to spire-vane : backwards and forwards swept the wheel, as Mary now looked downwards towards earth, now looked up at the shadowy cone of the spire, shot across by bars of light from the dormers.

And the thunder of Mary was caught up by the wind and carried through all the country ; and when the good man heard it, he said goodbye to wife and child, slung his shield behind his back, and set forward with his spear sloped over his shoulder, and many a time, as he walked toward the good town, he tightened the belt that went about his waist, that he might stride the faster, so long and furiously did Mary toll.

And before the great bell, Mary, had ceased ringing, all the ways were full of armed men.

But at each door of the church of Saint Mary stood a row of men armed with axes, and when any came, meaning to go into the church, the two first of these would hold their axes (whose helves were about four feet long) over his head, and would ask him, ' Who went over the moon last night ? ' then if he answered nothing or at random they would bid him turn back, which he for the more part would be ready enough to do ; but some, striving to get through that row of men, were slain outright ; but if he were one of those that were friends to the House of the Lilies he would answer to that question, ' Mary and John.'

By the time the mass began the whole church was full, and in the nave and transept thereof were three thousand men, all of our house and all armed. But Arnald and myself, and Squire Hugh, and some others sat under a gold-fringed canopy near the choir ; and the abbot said mass, having his mitre on his head. Yet, as I watched him, it seemed to me that he must have something on beneath his priest's vestments, for he looked much fatter than usual, being really a tall lithe man.

Now, as they sung the ' Kyrie,' some one shouted from the other end of the church, ' My lord Arnald, they are slaying our people without ; ' for, indeed, all the square about the church was full of our people, who for the press had not been able to enter, and were standing there in no small dread of what might come to pass.

Then the abbot turned round from the altar, and began to fidget with the fastenings of his rich robes.

And they made a lane for us up to the west door then I put on my helm and we began to go up the nave, then suddenly the singing of the monks and all stopped.

I heard a clinking and a buzz of voices in the choir ;
I turned, and saw that the bright noon sun was shining
on the gold of the priest's vestments, as they lay on the
floor, and on the mail that the priests carried.

So we stopped, the choir gates swung open, and the
abbot marched out at the head of *his* men, all fully
armed, and began to strike up the psalm ' Exsurgat
Deus.'

When we got to the west door, there was indeed
a tumult, but as yet no slaying ; the square was all
a-flicker with steel, and we beheld a great body of
knights, at the head of them Red Harald and the king,
standing over against us ; but our people, pressed against
the houses, and into the corners of the square, were,
some striving to enter the doors, some beside themselves
with rage, shouting out to the others to charge ; withal,
some were pale and some were red with the blood that
had gathered to the wrathful faces of them.

Then said Arnald to those about him, ' Lift me up.'
So they laid a great shield on two lances, and these four
men carried, and thereon stood Arnald and gazed about
him.

Now the king was unhelmed, and his white hair (for
he was an old man) flowed down behind him on to his
saddle ; but Arnald's hair was cut short, and was red.

And all the bells rang.

Then the king said, ' O Arnald of the Lilies, will you
settle this quarrel by the judgement of God ? ' And
Arnald thrust up his chin, and said, ' Yea.' ' How then,'
said the king, ' and where ? ' ' Will it please you try
now ? ' said Arnald.

Then the king understood what he meant, and took in
his hand from behind tresses of his long white hair,
twisting them round his hand in his wrath, but yet said
no word, till I suppose his hair put him in mind of
something, and he raised it in both his hands above his
head, and shouted out aloud, ' O knights, hearken to
this traitor.' Whereat, indeed, the lances began to move
ominously. But Arnald spoke.

' O you king and lords, what have we to do with you ?

were we not free in the old time, up among the hills
there ? Wherefore give way, and we will go to the hills
again ; and if any man try to stop us, his blood be on
his own head ; wherefore now,' (and he turned) ' all you
House of the Lily, both soldiers and monks, let us go
forth together fearing nothing, for I think there is not
bone enough or muscle enough in these fellows here that
have a king that they should stop us withal, but only
skin and fat.'

And truly, no man dared to stop us, and we went.

CHAPTER II

FAILING IN THE WORLD

Now at that time we drove cattle in Red Harald's
land.

And we took no hoof but from the Lords and rich
men, but of these we had a mighty drove, both oxen
and sheep, and horses, and besides, even hawks and
hounds, and a huntsman or two to take care of them.

And, about noon, we drew away from the corn-lands
that lay beyond the pastures, and mingled with them,
and reached a wide moor, which was called ' Goliah's
Land.' I scarce know why, except that it belonged
neither to Red Harald or us, but was debatable.

And the cattle began to go slowly, and our horses were
tired, and the sun struck down very hot upon us, for
there was no shadow, and the day was cloudless.

All about the edge of the moor, except on the side
from which we had come was a rim of hills, not very
high, but very rocky and steep, otherwise the moor
itself was flat ; and through these hills was one pass,
guarded by our men, which pass led to the Hill castle
of the Lilies.

It was not wonderful, that of this moor many wild
stories were told, being such a strange lonely place, some
of them one knew, alas ! to be over true. In the old
time, before we went to the good town, this moor had

been the mustering place of our people, and our house had done deeds enough of blood and horror to turn our white lilies red, and our blue cross to a fiery one. But some of those wild tales I never believed ; they had to do mostly with men losing their way without any apparent cause, (for there were plenty of landmarks,) finding some well-known spot, and then, just beyond it, a place they had never even dreamed of.

'Florian ! Florian ! ' said Arnald, ' For God's sake stop ! as every one else is stopping to look at the hills yonder ; I always thought there was a curse upon us. What does God mean by shutting us up here ? Look at the cattle ; O Christ, they have found it out too ! See, some of them are turning to run back again towards Harald's land. Oh ! unhappy, unhappy, from that day forward ! '

He leaned forward, rested his head on his horse's neck, and wept like a child.

I felt so irritated with him, that I could almost have slain him then and there. Was he mad ? had these wild doings of ours turned his strong wise head ?

' Are you my brother Arnald, that I used to think such a grand man when I was a boy ? ' I said, ' or are you changed too, like everybody, and everything else ? What do *you* mean ? '

' Look ! look ! ' he said, grinding his teeth in agony.

I raised my eyes :. where was the one pass between the rim of stern rocks ? Nothing : the enemy behind us— that grim wall in front : what wonder that each man looked in his fellow's face for help, and found it not. Yet I refused to believe that there was any truth either in the wild stories that I had heard when I was a boy, or in this story told me so clearly by my eyes now.

I called out cheerily, ' Hugh, come here ! ' He came. ' What do you think of this ? Some mere dodge on Harald's part ? Are we cut off ? '

' Think ! Sir Florian ? God forgive me for ever thinking at all ; I have given up that long and long ago, because thirty years ago I thought this, that the House of Lilies would deserve anything in the way of bad fortune that God would send them : so I gave up thinking, and took to fighting. But if you think that Harald had anything to do with this, why—why—in God's name, I wish *I* could think so ! '

I felt a dull weight on my heart. Had our house been the devil's servants all along ? I thought we were God's servants.

The day was very still, but what little wind there was, was at our backs. I watched Hugh's face, not being able to answer him. He was the cleverest man at war that I have known, either before or since that day : sharper than any hound in ear and scent, clearer sighted than any eagle ; he was listening now intently. I saw a slight smile cross his face ; heard him mutter, ' Yes ! I think so : verily that is better, a great deal better.' Then he stood up in his stirrups, and shouted, ' Hurrah for the Lilies ! Mary rings ! ' ' Mary rings ! ' I shouted, though I did not know the reason for his exultation : my brother lifted his head, and smiled too, grimly. Then as I listened I heard clearly the sound of a trumpet, an enemy's trumpet too.

' After all, it was only mist, or some such thing,' I said, for the pass between the hills was clear enough now.

' Hurrah ! only mist,' said Arnald, quite elated ; ' Mary rings ! ' and we all began to think of fighting : for after all what joy is equal to that ?

There were five hundred of us ; two hundred spears, the rest archers ; and both archers and men at arms were picked men.

' How many of them are we to expect ? ' said I.

' Not under a thousand, certainly, probably more, Sir Florian.' (My brother Arnald, by the way, had knighted me before we left the good town, and Hugh liked to give me the handle to my name. How was it, by the way, that no one had ever made *him* a knight ?)

' Let every one look to his arms and horse, and come away from these silly cows' sons ! ' shouted Arnald.

Hugh said, ' They will be here in an hour, fair Sir.'

So we got clear of the cattle, and dismounted, and both

ourselves took food and drink, and our horses ; afterwards we tightened our saddle-girths, shook our great pots of helmets on, except Arnald, whose rusty-red hair had been his only head-piece in battle for years and years, and stood with our spears close by our horses, leaving room for the archers to retreat between our ranks ; and they got their arrows ready, and planted their stakes before a little peat moss : and there we waited, and saw their pennons at last floating high above the corn of the fertile land, then heard their many horse-hoofs ring upon the hard-parched moor, and the archers began to shoot.

. . . .

It had been a strange battle ; we had never fought better, and yet withal it had ended in a retreat ; indeed all along every man but Arnald and myself, even Hugh, had been trying at least to get the enemy between him and the way toward the pass ; and now we were all drifting that way, the enemy trying to cut us off, but never able to stop us, because he could only throw small bodies of men in our way, whom we scattered and put to flight in their turn.

I never cared less for my life than then ; indeed, in spite of all my boasting and hardness of belief, I should have been happy to have died, such a strange weight of apprehension was on me ; and yet I got no scratch even. I had soon put off my great helm, and was fighting in my mail-coif only : and here I swear that three knights together charged me, aiming at my bare face, yet never touched me ; for, as for one, I put his lance aside with my sword, and the other two in some most wonderful manner got their spears locked in each other's armour, and so had to submit to be knocked off their horses.

And we still neared the pass, and began to see distinctly the ferns that grew on the rocks, and the fair country between the rift in them, spreading out there, blue-shadowed.

Whereupon came a great rush of men of both sides, striking side blows at each other, spitting, cursing, and shrieking, as they tore away like a herd of wild hogs. So, being careless of life, as I said, I drew rein, and turning my horse, waited quietly for them; and I knotted the reins, and laid them on the horse's neck, and stroked him, that he whinnied; then got both my hands to my sword.

Then, as they came on, I noted hurriedly that the first man was one of Arnald's men, and one of our men behind him leaned forward to prod him with his spear, but could not reach so far, till he himself was run through the eye with a spear, and throwing his arms up fell dead with a shriek. Also I noted concerning this first man that the laces of his helmet were loose, and when he saw me he lifted his *left* hand to his head, took off his helm and cast it at me, and still tore on; the helmet flew over my head, and I sitting still there, swung out, hitting him on the neck; his head flew right off, for the mail no more held than a piece of silk.

'Mary rings,' and my horse whinnied again, and we both of us went at it, and fairly stopped that rout, so that there was a knot of quite close and desperate fighting, wherein we had the best of that fight and slew most of them, albeit my horse was slain and my mail-coif cut through. Then I bade a squire fetch me another horse, and began meanwhile to upbraid those knights for running in such a strange disorderly race, instead of standing and fighting cleverly.

Moreover we had drifted even in this successful fight still nearer to the pass, so that the conies who dwelt there were beginning to consider whether they should not run into their holes.

But one of those knights said : 'Be not angry with me, Sir Florian, but do you think you will go to Heaven ?'

'The saints ! I hope so,' I said, but one who stood near him whispered to him to hold his peace, so I cried out :

'O friend ! I hold this world and all therein so cheap now, that I see not anything in it but shame which can any longer anger me ; wherefore speak out.'

'Then, Sir Florian, men say that at your christening some fiend took on him the likeness of a priest and strove to baptize you in the Devil's name, but God had

mercy on you so that the fiend could not choose but
baptize you in the name of the most holy Trinity : and
yet men say that you hardly believe any doctrine such
as other men do, and will at the end only go to Heaven
round about as it were, not at all by the intercession of
our Lady ; they say too that you can see no ghosts or
other wonders, whatever happens to other Christian men.'

I smiled.—' Well, friend, I scarcely call this a disadvan-
tage, moreover what has it to do with the matter in hand ? '

How was this in Heaven's name ? we had been quite
still, resting, while this talk was going on, but we could
hear the hawks chattering from the rocks, we were so
close now.

And my heart sunk within me, there was no reason why
this should not be true ; there was no reason why anything should not be true.

' This, Sir Florian,' said the knight again, ' how would
you feel inclined to fight if you thought that everything
about you was mere glamour ; this earth here the rocks,
the sun, the sky ? I do not know where I am for certain,
I do not know that it is not midnight instead of undern :
I do not know if I have been fighting men or only
simulacra—but I think, we all think, that we have been
led into some devil's trap or other, and—and—may God
forgive me my sins !—I wish I had never been born.'

There now ! he was weeping—they all wept—how
strange it was to see those rough, bearded men blubbering
there, and snivelling till the tears ran over their armour
and mingled with the blood, so that it dropped down to
the earth in a dim, dull, red rain.

My eyes indeed were dry, but then so was my heart ;
I felt far worse than weeping came to, but nevertheless
I spoke cheerily.

' Dear friends, where are your old men's hearts gone
to now ? See now ! this is a punishment for our sins,
is it ? well, for our forefathers' sins or our own ? if the
first, O brothers, be very sure that if we bear it manfully
God will have something very good in store for us
hereafter ; but if for our sins, is it not certain that He
cares for us yet, for note that He suffers the wicked to

go their own ways pretty much ; moreover brave men,
brothers, ought to be the masters of *simulacra*—come,
is it so hard to die once for all ? '

Still no answer came from them, they sighed heavily
only. I heard the sound of more than one or two swords
as they rattled back to their scabbards : nay, one knight,
stripping himself of surcoat and hauberk, and drawing
his dagger, looked at me with a grim smile, and said,
' Sir Florian, do so ! ' then he drew the dagger across
his throat and he fell back dead.

They shuddered, those brave men, and crossed themselves. And I had no heart to say a word more, but
mounted the horse which had been brought to me and
rode away slowly for a few yards ; then I became aware
that there was a great silence over the whole field.

So I lifted my eyes and looked, and behold no man
struck at another.

Then from out of a band of horsemen came Harald,
and he was covered all over with a great scarlet cloth as
before, put on over the head, and flowing all about his
horse, but rent with the fight. He put off his helm and
drew back his mail-coif, then took a trumpet from the
hand of a herald and blew strongly.

And in the midst of his blast I heard a voice call out :
' O Florian ! come and speak to me for the last time ! '

So when I turned I beheld Arnald standing by himself,
but near him stood Hugh and ten others with drawn
swords.

Then I wept, and so went to him, weeping ; and he
said, ' Thou seest, brother, that we must die, and I think
by some horrible and unheard-of death, and the House
of the Lilies is just dying too ; and now I repent me of
Swanhilda's death ; now I know that it was a poor
cowardly piece of revenge, instead of a brave act of
justice ; thus has God shown us the right.

' O Florian ! curse me ! So will it be straighter ; truly
thy mother when she bore thee did not think of this ;
rather saw thee in the tourney at this time, in her fond
hopes, glittering with gold and doing knightly ; or else
mingling thy brown locks with the golden hair of some

maiden weeping for the love of thee. God forgive me !
God forgive me ! '

' What harm, brother ? ' I said, ' this is only failing in
the world ; what if we had not failed, in a little while it
would have made no difference ; truly just now I felt
very miserable, but now it has passed away, and I am
happy.'

' O brave heart ! ' he said, ' yet we shall part just now,
Florian, farewell.'

' The road is long,' I said, ' farewell.'

Then we kissed each other, and Hugh and the others
wept.

Now all this time the trumpets had been ringing,
ringing, great doleful peals, then they ceased, and above
all sounded Red Harald's voice.

(So I looked round towards that pass, and when I
looked I no longer doubted any of those wild tales of
glamour concerning Goliah's Land ; for though the rocks
were the same, and though the conies still stood gazing
at the doors of their dwellings, though the hawks still
cried out shrilly, though the fern still shook in the wind,
yet beyond, oh such a land ! not to be described by any
because of its great beauty, lying, a great *hollow* land,
the rocks going down on this side in precipices, then
reaches and reaches of loveliest country, trees and
flowers, and corn, then the hills, green and blue, and
purple, till their ledges reached the white snowy mountains at last. Then with all manner of strange feelings,
' my heart in the midst of my body was even like
melting wax.')

' O you House of the Lily ! you are conquered—yet
I will take vengeance only on a few, therefore let all
those who wish to live come and pile their swords, and
shields, and helms behind me in three great heaps, and
swear fealty afterwards to me ; yes, all but the false
knights Arnald and Florian.'

We were holding each other's hands and gazing, and
we saw all our knights, yea, all but Squire Hugh and his
ten heroes, pass over the field singly, or in groups of
three or four, with their heads hanging down in shame,

and they cast down their notched swords and dinted,
lilied shields, and brave-crested helms into three great
heaps, behind Red Harald, then stood behind, no man
speaking to his fellow, or touching him.

Then dolefully the great trumpets sang over the dying
House of the Lily, and Red Harald led his men forward,
but slowly : on they came, spear and mail glittering in
the sunlight ; and I turned and looked at that good
land, and a shuddering delight seized my soul.

But I felt my brother's hand leave mine, and saw him
turn his horse's head and ride swiftly toward the pass ;
that was a strange pass now.

And at the edge he stopped, turned round and called
out aloud, ' I pray thee, Harald, forgive me ! now
farewell all ! '

Then the horse gave one bound forward, and we heard
the poor creature's scream when he felt that he must die,
and we heard afterwards (for we were near enough for
that even) a clang and a crash.

So I turned me about to Hugh, and he understood me
though I could not speak.

We shouted all together, ' Mary rings,' then laid our
bridles on the necks of our horses, spurred forward, and—
in five minutes they were all slain, and I was down
among the horse-hoofs.

Not slain though, not wounded. Red Harald smiled
grimly when he saw me rise and lash out again ; he and
some ten others dismounted, and holding their long
spears out, I went back—back, back,—I saw what it
meant, and sheathed my sword, and their laughter rolled
all about, and I too smiled.

Presently they all stopped, and I felt the last foot of
turf giving under my feet ; I looked down and saw the
crack there widening ; then in a moment I fell, and
a cloud of dust and earth rolled after me ; then again
their mirth rose into thunder-peals of laughter. But
through it all I heard Red Harald shout, ' Silence !
evil dogs ! '

For as I fell I stretched out my arms, and caught
a tuft of yellow broom some three feet from the brow,

and hung there by the hands, my feet being loose in the air.

Then Red Harald came and stood on the precipice above me, his great axe over his shoulder ; and he looked down on me not ferociously, almost kindly, while the wind from the Hollow Land blew about his red raiment, tattered and dusty now.

And I felt happy, though it pained me to hold straining by the broom, yet I said, ' I will hold out to the last.'

It was not long, the plant itself gave way and I fell, and as I fell I fainted.

CHAPTER III

Leaving the World.—Fytte the First

I had thought when I fell that I should never wake again ; but I woke at last : for a long time I was quite dizzied and could see nothing at all : horrible doubts came creeping over me ; I half expected to see presently great half-formed shapes come rolling up to me to crush me ; some thing fiery, not strange, too utterly horrible to be strange, but utterly vile and ugly, the sight of which would have killed me when I was upon the earth, come rolling up to torment me. In fact I doubted if I were in hell.

I knew I deserved to be, but I prayed, and then it came into my mind that I could not pray if I were in hell.

Also there seemed to be a cool green light all about me, which was sweet.

Then presently I heard a glorious voice ring out clear, close to me—

> ' Christ keep the Hollow Land
> Through the sweet spring-tide,
> When the apple-blossoms bless
> The lowly bent hill side.'

Thereat my eyes were slowly unsealed, and I saw the blessedest sight I have ever seen before or since : for I saw my Love.

She sat about five yards from me on a great grey stone that had much moss on it, one of the many scattered along the side of the stream by which I lay ; she was clad in loose white raiment close to her hands and throat ; her feet were bare, her hair hung loose a long way down, but some of it lay on her knees : I said ' white ' raiment, but long spikes of light scarlet went down from the throat, lost here and there in the shadows of the folds, and growing smaller and smaller, died before they reached her feet.

I was lying with my head resting on soft moss that some one had gathered and placed under me. She, when she saw me moving and awake, came and stood over me with a gracious smile.—She was so lovely and tender to look at, and so kind, yet withal no one, man or woman, had ever frightened me half so much.

She was not fair in white and red, like many beautiful women are, being rather pale, but like ivory for smoothness, and her hair was quite golden, not light yellow, but dusky golden.

I tried to get up on my feet, but was too weak, and sunk back again. She said :

' No, not just yet, do not trouble yourself or try to remember anything just at present.'

There withal she kneeled down, and hung over me closer.

' To-morrow you may, perhaps, have something hard to do or bear, I know, but now you must be as happy as you can be, quietly happy. Why did you start and turn pale when I came to you ? Do you not know who I am ? Nay, but you do, I see ; and I have been waiting here so long for you ; so you must have expected to see me.—You cannot be frightened of me, are you ? '

But I could not answer a word, but all the time strange knowledge, strange feelings were filling my brain and my heart, she said :

' You are tired ; rest, and dream happily.'

So she sat by me, and sung to lull me to sleep, while I turned on my elbow, and watched the waving of her throat : and the singing of all the poets I had ever heard, and of many others too, not born till years long after I was dead, floated all about me as she sung, and I did indeed dream happily.

When I awoke it was the time of the cold dawn, and the colours were gathering themselves together, whereat in fatherly approving fashion the sun sent all across the east long bars of scarlet and orange that after faded through yellow to green and blue.

And she sat by me still ; I think she had been sitting there and singing all the time ; all through hot yesterday, for I had been sleeping day-long and night-long, all through the falling evening under moonlight and star-light the night through.

And now it was dawn, and I think too that neither of us had moved at all ; for the last thing I remembered before I went to sleep was the tips of her fingers brushing my cheek, as she knelt over me with down-drooping arm, and still now I felt them there. Moreover she was just finishing some fainting measure that died before it had time to get painful in its passion.

Dear Lord ! how I loved her ! yet did I not dare to touch her, or even speak to her. She smiled with delight when she saw I was awake again, and slid down her hand on to mine, but some shuddering dread made me draw it away again hurriedly ; then I saw the smile leave her face : what would I not have given for courage to hold her body quite tight to mine ? but I was so weak. She said :

' Have you been very happy ? '

' Yea,' I said.

It was the first word I had spoken there, and my voice sounded strange.

' Ah ! ' she said, ' you will talk more when you get used to the air of the Hollow Land. Have you been thinking of your past life at all ? If not, try to think of it. What thing in Heaven or Earth do you wish for most ? '

Still I said no word ; but she said in a wearied way :

' Well now, I think you will be strong enough to get to your feet and walk ; take my hand and try.'

Therewith she held it out : I strove hard to be brave enough to take it, but could not ; I only turned away shuddering, sick, and grieved to the heart's core of me ; then struggling hard with hand and knee and elbow, I scarce rose, and stood up totteringly; while she watched me sadly, still holding out her hand.

But as I rose, in my swinging to and fro the steel sheath of my sword struck her on the hand so that the blood flowed from it, which she stood looking at for a while, then dropped it downwards, and turned to look at me, for I was going.

Then as I walked she followed me, so I stopped and turned and said almost fiercely :

' I am going alone to look for my brother.'

The vehemence with which I spoke, or something else, burst some blood-vessel within my throat, and we both stood there with the blood running from us on to the grass and summer flowers.

She said : ' If you find him, wait with him till I come.'

' Yea,' and I turned and left her, following the course of the stream upwards, and as I went I heard her low singing that almost broke my heart for its sadness.

And I went painfully because of my weakness, and because also of the great stones ; and sometimes I went along a spot of earth where the river had been used to flow in flood-time, and which was now bare of everything but stones ; and the sun, now risen high, poured down on everything a great flood of fierce light and scorching heat, and burnt me sorely, so that I almost fainted.

But about noontide I entered a wood close by the stream, a beech-wood, intending to rest myself ; the herbage was thin and scattered there, sprouting up from amid the leaf-sheaths and nuts of the beeches, which had fallen year after year on that same spot ; the outside boughs swept low down, the air itself seemed green when you entered within the shadow of the branches, they over-roofed the place so with tender green, only here and there showing spots of blue.

But what lay at the foot of a great beech tree but some dead knight in armour, only the helmet off ?

A wolf was prowling round about it, who ran away
snarling when he saw me coming.

So I went up to that dead knight, and fell on my knees
before him, laying my head on his breast, for it was
Arnald.

He was quite cold, but had not been dead for very
long; I would not believe him dead, but went down to the
stream and brought him water, tried to make him drink
—what would you ? he was as dead as Swanhilda :
neither came there any answer to my cries that afternoon
but the moaning of the wood-doves in the beeches.

So then I sat down and took his head on my knees,
and closed the eyes, and wept quietly while the sun sunk
lower.

But a little after sunset I heard a rustle through the
leaves, that was not the wind, and looking up my eyes
met the pitying eyes of that maiden.

Something stirred rebelliously within me ; I ceased
weeping, and said :

' It is unjust, unfair : What right had Swanhilda to
live ? did not God give her up to us ? How much better
was he than ten Swanhildas ? and look you—See !—he
is DEAD.'

Now this I shrieked out, being mad ; and though
I trembled when I saw some stormy wrath that vexed
her very heart and loving lips, gathering on her face,
I yet sat there looking at her and screaming, screaming,
till all the place rang.

But when growing hoarse and breathless I ceased ; she
said, with straightened brow and scornful mouth :

' So ! bravely done ! must I then, though I am a
woman, call you a liar, for saying God is unjust ? You
to punish her, had not God then punished her already ?
How many times when she woke in the dead night do
you suppose she missed seeing King Urrayne's pale face
and hacked head lying on the pillow by her side ?
Whether by night or day, what things but screams did
she hear when the wind blew loud round about the
Palace corners ? And did not that face too, often come
before her, pale and bleeding as it was long ago, and

gaze at her from unhappy eyes? poor eyes! with changed purpose in them—no more hope of converting the world when that blow was once struck, truly it was very wicked—no more dreams, but only fierce struggles with the Devil for very life, no more dreams but failure at last, and death, happier so in the Hollow Land.'

She grew so pitying as she gazed at his dead face that I began to weep again unreasonably, while she saw not that I was weeping, but looked only on Arnald's face, but after turned on me frowning.

'Unjust! yes truly unjust enough to take away life and all hope from her; you have done a base cowardly act, you and your brother here, disguise it as you may; you deserve all God's judgements—you——'

But I turned my eyes and wet face to her, and said:

'Do not curse me—there—do not look like Swanhilda: for see now, you said at first that you had been waiting long for me, give me your hand now, for I love you so.'

Then she came and knelt by where I sat, and I caught her in my arms, and she prayed to be forgiven.

'O, Florian! I have indeed waited long for you, and when I saw you my heart was filled with joy, but you would neither touch me nor speak to me, so that I became almost mad,—forgive me, we will be so happy now. O! do you know this is what I have been waiting for all these years; it made me glad I know, when I was a little baby in my mother's arms to think I was born for this; and afterwards, as I grew up, I used to watch every breath of wind through the beech-boughs, every turn of the silver poplar leaves, thinking it might be you or some news of you.'

Then I rose and drew her up with me; but she knelt again by my brother's side, and kissed him, and said:

'O brother! the Hollow Land is only second best of the places God has made, for Heaven also is the work of His hand.'

Afterwards we dug a deep grave among the beech-roots and there we buried Arnald de Liliis.

And I have never seen him since, scarcely even in dreams; surely God has had mercy on him, for he was very leal and true and brave ; he loved many men, and was kind and gentle to his friends, neither did he hate any but Swanhilda.

But as for us two, Margaret and me, I cannot tell you concerning our happiness, such things cannot be told ; only this I know, that we abode continually in the Hollow Land until I lost it.

Moreover this I can tell you. Margaret was walking with me, as she often walked near the place where I had first seen her ; presently we came upon a woman sitting, dressed in scarlet and gold raiment, with her head laid down on her knees ; likewise we heard her sobbing.

' Margaret, who is she ? ' I said : ' I knew not that any dwelt in the Hollow Land but us two only.'

She said, ' I know not who she is, only sometimes, these many years, I have seen her scarlet robe flaming from far away, amid the quiet green grass : but I was never so near her as this. Florian, I am afraid : let us come away.'

FYTTE THE SECOND

SUCH a horrible grey November day it was, the fog-smell all about, the fog creeping into our very bones.

And I sat there, trying to recollect, at any rate something, under those fir-trees that I ought to have known so well.

Just think now ; I had lost my best years somewhere ; for I was past the prime of life, my hair and beard were scattered with white, my body was growing weaker, my memory of all things was very faint.

My raiment, purple and scarlet and blue once, was so stained that you could scarce call it any colour, was so tattered that it scarce covered my body, though it seemed once to have fallen in heavy folds to my feet, and still, when I rose to walk, though the miserable November mist lay in great drops upon my bare breast, yet was I obliged to wind my raiment over my arm, it draggled so (wretched, slimy, textureless thing !) in the brown mud.

On my head was a light morion, which pressed on my brow and pained me ; so I put my hand up to take it off ; but when I touched it I stood still in my walk shuddering ; I nearly fell to the earth with shame and sick horror ; for I laid my hand on a lump of slimy earth with worms coiled up in it. I could scarce forbear from shrieking, but breathing such a prayer as I could think of, I raised my hand again and seized it firmly. Worse horror still ! the rust had eaten it into holes, and I gripped my own hair as well as the rotting steel, the sharp edge of which cut into my fingers ; but setting my teeth, gave a great wrench, for I knew that if I let go of it then, no power on the earth or under it could make me touch it again. God be praised ! I tore it off and cast it far from me ; I saw the earth, and the worms and green weeds and sun-begotten slime, whirling out from it radiatingly, as it spun round about.

I was girt with a sword too, the leathern belt of which had shrunk and squeezed my waist : dead leaves had gathered in knots about the buckles of it, the gilded handle was encrusted with clay in many parts, the velvet sheath miserably worn.

But, verily, when I took hold of the hilt, and dreaded lest instead of a sword I should find a serpent in my hand ; lo ! then, I drew out my own true blade and shook it flawless from hilt to point, gleaming white in that mist.

Therefore it sent a thrill of joy to my heart, to know that there was one friend left me yet : I sheathed it again carefully, and undoing it from my waist, hung it about my neck.

Then catching up my rags in my arms, I drew them up till my legs and feet were altogether clear from them, afterwards folded my arms over my breast, gave a long leap and ran, looking downward, but not giving heed to my way.

Once or twice I fell over stumps of trees, and such-like, for it was a cut-down wood that I was in, but I rose always, though bleeding and confused, and went on still ; sometimes tearing madly through briars and gorse bushes, so that my blood dropped on the dead leaves as I went.

I ran in this way for about an hour ; then I heard a gurgling and splashing of waters ; I gave a great shout and leapt strongly, with shut eyes, and the black water closed over me.

When I rose again, I saw near me a boat with a man in it ; but the shore was far off ; I struck out toward the boat, but my clothes which I had knotted and folded about me, weighed me down terribly.

The man looked at me, and began to paddle toward me with the oar he held in his left hand, having in his right a long, slender spear, barbed like a fish-hook ; perhaps, I thought, it is some fishing spear ; moreover his raiment was of scarlet, with upright stripes of yellow and black all over it.

When my eye caught his, a smile widened his mouth as if some one had made a joke ; but I was beginning to sink, and indeed my head was almost under water just as he came and stood above me, but before it went quite under, I saw his spear gleam, then *felt* it in my shoulder, and for the present, felt nothing else.

When I woke I was on the bank of that river ; the flooded waters went hurrying past me ; no boat on them now ; from the river the ground went up in gentle slopes till it grew a great hill, and there, on that hill-top,— Yes, I might forget many things, almost everything, but not that, not the old castle of my fathers up among the hills, its towers blackened now and shattered, yet still no enemy's banner waved from it.

So I said I would go and die there ; and at this thought I drew my sword, which yet hung about my neck, and shook it in the air till the true steel quivered ; then began to pace toward the castle. I was quite naked, no rag about me ; I took no heed of that, only thanking God that my sword was left, and so toiled up the hill. I entered the castle soon by the outer court ; I knew the way so well, that I did not lift my eyes from the ground, but walked on over the lowered drawbridge through the unguarded gates, and stood in the great hall at last—

my father's hall—as bare of everything but my sword as
when I came into the world fifty years before : I had
as little clothes, as little wealth, less memory and thought,
I verily believe, than then.

So I lifted up my eyes and gazed ; no glass in the
windows, no hangings on the walls ; the vaulting yet
held good throughout, but seemed to be going ; the
mortar had fallen out from between the stones, and grass
and fern grew in the joints ; the marble pavement was
in some places gone, and water stood about in puddles,
though one scarce knew how it had got there.

No hangings on the walls—no ; yet, strange to say,
instead of them, the walls blazed from end to end with
scarlet paintings, only striped across with green damp-
marks in many places, some falling bodily from the wall,
the plaster hanging down with the fading colour on it.

In all of them, except for the shadows and the faces
of the figures, there was scarce any colour but scarlet
and yellow ; here and there it seemed the painter,
whoever it was, had tried to make his trees or his grass
green, but it would not do ; some ghastly thoughts must
have filled his head, for all the green went presently
into yellow, out-sweeping through the picture dismally.
But the faces were painted to the very life, or it seemed
so ;—there were only five of them, however, that were
very marked or came much in the foreground ; and four
of these I knew well, though I did not then remember
the names of those that had borne them. They were Red
Harald, Swanhilda, Arnald, and myself. The fifth I did
not know ; it was a woman's, and very beautiful.

Then I saw that in some parts a small penthouse roof
had been built over the paintings, to keep them from the
weather. Near one of these stood a man painting,
clothed in red, with stripes of yellow and black : then
I knew that it was the same man who had saved me from
drowning by spearing me through the shoulder ; so
I went up to him, and saw furthermore that he was
girt with a heavy sword.

He turned round when he saw me coming, and asked
me fiercely what I did there.

I asked why he was painting in my castle.

Thereupon, with that same grim smile widening his mouth as heretofore, he said, ' I paint God's judgements.'

And as he spoke, he rattled the sword in his scabbard ; but I said,

' Well, then, you paint them very badly. Listen ; I know God's judgements much better than you do. See now ; I will teach you God's judgements, and you shall teach me painting.'

While I spoke he still rattled his sword, and when I had done, shut his right eye tight, screwing his nose on one side ; then said :

' You have got no clothes on, and may go to the devil ! What do *you* know about God's judgements ? '

' Well, they are not all yellow and red, at all events ; you ought to know better.'

He screamed out, ' O you fool ! yellow and red ! Gold and blood, what do they make ? '

' Well,' I said ; ' what ? '

' HELL ! ' And, coming close up to me, he struck me with his open hand in the face, so that the colour with which his hand was smeared was dabbed about my face. The blow almost threw me down ; and, while I staggered, he rushed at me furiously with his sword. Perhaps it was good for me that I had got no clothes on ; for, being utterly unencumbered, I leapt this way and that, and avoided his fierce, eager strokes till I could collect myself somewhat ; while he had a heavy scarlet cloak on that trailed on the ground, and which he often trod on, so that he stumbled.

He very nearly slew me during the first few minutes, for it was not strange that, together with other matters, I should have forgotten the art of fence : but yet, as I went on, and sometimes bounded about the hall under the whizzing of his sword, as he rested sometimes, leaning on it, as the point sometimes touched my bare flesh, nay, once as the whole sword fell flatlings on my head and made my eyes start out, I remembered the old joy that I used to have, and the *swy*, *swy*, of the sharp edge, as one gazed between one's horse's ears ; moreover, at last, one fierce swift stroke, just touching me below the throat, tore up the skin all down my body, and fell heavy on my thigh, so that I drew my breath in and turned white ; then first, as I swung my sword round my head, our blades met, oh ! to hear that *tchink* again ! and I felt the notch my sword made in his, and swung out at him ; but he guarded it and returned on me ; I guarded right and left, and grew warm, and opened my mouth to shout, but knew not what to say ; and our sword points fell on the floor together : then, when we had panted awhile, I wiped from my face the blood that had been dashed over it, shook my sword and cut at him, then we spun round and round in a mad waltz to the measured music of our meeting swords, and sometimes either wounded the other somewhat, but not much, till I beat down his sword on to his head, that he fell grovelling, but not cut through. Verily, thereupon my lips opened mightily with ' Mary rings.'

Then, when he had gotten to his feet, I went at him again, he staggering back, guarding wildly ; I cut at his head ; he put his sword up confusedly, so I fitted both hands to my hilt, and smote him mightily under the arm : then his shriek mingled with my shout, made a strange sound together ; he rolled over and over, dead, as I thought.

I walked about the hall in great exultation at first, striking my sword point on the floor every now and then, till I grew faint with loss of blood ; then I went to my enemy and stripped off some of his clothes to bind up my wounds withal ; afterwards I found in a corner bread and wine, and I eat and drank thereof.

Then I went back to him, and looked, and a thought struck me, and I took some of his paints and brushes, and, kneeling down, painted his face thus, with stripes of yellow and red, crossing each other at right angles ; and in each of the squares so made I put a spot of black, after the manner of the painted letters in the prayer-books and romances when they are ornamented.

So I stood back as painters use, folded my arms, and admired my own handiwork. Yet there struck me as being something so utterly doleful in the man's white face, and the blood running all about him, and washing off the stains of paint from his face and hands, and splashed clothes, that my heart misgave me, and I hoped that he was not dead ; I took some water from a vessel he had been using for his painting, and, kneeling, washed his face.

Was it some resemblance to my father's dead face, which I had seen when I was young, that made me pity him ? I laid my hand upon his heart, and felt it beating feebly ; so I lifted him up gently, and carried him towards a heap of straw that he seemed used to lie upon ; there I stripped him and looked to his wounds, and used leech-craft, the memory of which God gave me for this purpose, I suppose, and within seven days I found that he would not die.

Afterwards, as I wandered about the castle, I came to a room in one of the upper stories, that had still the roof on, and windows in it with painted glass, and there I found green raiment and swords and armour, and I clothed myself.

So when he got well I asked him what his name was, and he me, and we both of us said, ' truly I know not.' Then said I, ' but we must call each other some name, even as men call days.'

' Call me Swerker,' he said, ' some priest I knew once had that name.'

' And me Wulf,' said I, ' though wherefore I know not.'

Then he said :

' Wulf, I will teach you painting now, come and learn.'

Then I tried to learn painting till I thought I should die, but at last learned it through very much pain and grief.

And, as the years went on and we grew old and grey, we painted purple pictures and green ones instead of the scarlet and yellow, so that the walls looked altered, and always we painted God's judgements.

And we would sit in the sunset and watch them with the golden light changing them, as we yet hoped God would change both us and our works.

Often too we would sit outside the walls and look at the trees and sky, and the ways of the few men and women we saw ; therefrom sometimes befell adventures.

Once there went past a great funeral of some king going to his own country, not as he had hoped to go, but stiff and colourless, spices filling up the place of his heart.

And first went by very many knights, with long bright hauberks on, that fell down before their knees as they rode, and they all had tilting-helms on with the same crest, so that their faces were quite hidden : and this crest was two hands clasped together tightly as though they were the hands of one praying forgiveness from the one he loves best ; and the crest was wrought in gold.

Moreover, they had on over their hauberks surcoats which were half scarlet and half purple, strewn about with golden stars.

Also long lances, that had forked knights'-pennons, half purple and half scarlet, strewn with golden stars.

And these went by with no sound but the fall of their horse-hoofs.

And they went slowly, so slowly that we counted them all, five thousand five hundred and fifty-five.

Then went by many fair maidens whose hair was loose and yellow, and who were all clad in green raiment ungirded, and shod with golden shoes.

These also we counted, being five hundred ; moreover some of the outermost of them, viz., one maiden to every twenty, had long silver trumpets, which they swung out to right and left, blowing them, and their sound was very sad.

Then many priests, and bishops, and abbots, who wore white albs and golden copes over them ; and they all sang together mournfully, ' *Propter amnem Babylonis ;* ' and these were three hundred.

After that came a great knot of the Lords, who wore tilting helmets and surcoats emblazoned with each one his own device ; only each had in his hand a small staff two feet long whereon was a pennon of scarlet and purple. These also were three hundred.

And in the midst of these was a great car hung down to the ground with purple, drawn by grey horses whose trappings were half scarlet, half purple.

And on this car lay the King, whose head and hands were bare ; and he had on him a surcoat, half purple and half scarlet, strewn with golden stars.

And his head rested on a tilting helmet, whose crest was the hands of one praying passionately for forgiveness.

But his own hands lay by his side as if he had just fallen asleep.

And all about the car were little banners, half purple and half scarlet, strewn with golden stars.

Then the King, who counted but as one, went by also.

And after him came again many maidens clad in ungirt white raiment strewn with scarlet flowers, and their hair was loose and yellow and their feet bare : and, except for the falling of their feet and the rustle of the wind through their raiment, they went past quite silently. These also were five hundred.

Then lastly came many young knights with long bright hauberks falling over their knees as they rode, and surcoats, half scarlet and half purple, strewn with golden stars ; they bore long lances with forked pennons which were half purple, half scarlet, strewn with golden stars ; their heads and their hands were bare, but they bore shields, each one of them, which were of bright steel wrought cunningly in the midst with that bearing of the two hands of one who prays for forgiveness ; which was done in gold. These were but five hundred.

Then they all went by winding up and up the hill roads, and, when the last of them had departed out of our sight, we put down our heads and wept, and I said, ' Sing us one of the songs of the Hollow Land.'

Then he whom I had called Swerker put his hand into his bosom, and slowly drew out a long, long tress of black hair, and laid it on his knee and smoothed it, weeping on it : So then I left him there and went and armed myself, and brought armour for him.

And then came back to him and threw the armour down so that it clanged, and said :

' O ! Harald, let us go ! '

He did not seem surprised that I called him by the right name, but rose and armed himself, and then he looked a good knight ; so we set forth.

And in a turn of the long road we came suddenly upon a most fair woman, clothed in scarlet, who sat and sobbed, holding her face between her hands, and her hair was very black.

And when Harald saw her, he stood and gazed at her for long through the bars of his helmet, then suddenly turned, and said :

' Florian, I must stop here ; do you go on to the Hollow Land. Farewell.'

' Farewell.' And then I went on, never turning back, and him I never saw more.

And so I went on, quite lonely, but happy, till I had reached the Hollow Land.

Into which I let myself down most carefully, by the jutting rocks and bushes and strange trailing flowers, and there lay down and fell asleep.

FYTTE THE THIRD

And I was waked by some one singing ; I felt very happy ; I felt young again ; I had fair delicate raiment on, my sword was gone, and my armour ; I tried to think where I was, and could not for my happiness ; I tried to listen to the words of the song. Nothing, only an old echo in my ears, only all manner of strange scenes from my wretched past life before my eyes in a dim, far-off manner : then at last, slowly, without effort, I heard what she sang.

'Christ keep the Hollow Land
　　All the summer-tide ;
Still we cannot understand
　　Where the waters glide ;

'Only dimly seeing them
　　Coldly slipping through
Many green-lipp'd cavern mouths,
　　Where the hills are blue.'

'Then,' she said, 'come now and look for it, love, a hollow city in the Hollow Land.'

I kissed Margaret, and we went.

.   .   .   .

Through the golden streets under the purple shadows of the houses we went, and the slow fanning backward and forward of the many-coloured banners cooled us : we two alone ; there was no one with us, no soul will ever be able to tell what we said, how we looked.

At last we came to a fair palace, cloistered off in the old time, before the city grew golden from the din and hubbub of traffic ; those who dwelt there in the old ungolden times had had their own joys, their own sorrows, apart from the joys and sorrows of the multitude: so, in like manner, was it now cloistered off from the eager leaning and brotherhood of the golden dwellings : so now it had its own gaiety, its own solemnity, apart from theirs ; unchanged, unchangeable, were its marble walls, whatever else changed about it.

We stopped before the gates and trembled, and clasped each other closer ; for there among the marble leafage and tendrils that were round and under and over the archway that held the golden valves, were wrought two figures of a man and woman, winged and garlanded, whose raiment flashed with stars ; and their faces were like faces we had seen or half seen in some dream long and long and long ago, so that we trembled with awe and delight ; and I turned, and seeing Margaret, saw that her face was that face seen or half seen long and long and long ago ; and in the shining of her eyes I saw that other face, seen in that way and no other long and long and long ago—my face.

And then we walked together toward the golden gates, and opened them, and no man gainsaid us.

And before us lay a great space of flowers.

GOLDEN WINGS

(*Oxford and Cambridge Magazine*, December 1856)

> Lyf lythes to meo
> Twa wordes or three,
> Of one who was fair and free,
> And fell in his fight.
> *Sir Percival.*

I SUPPOSE my birth was somewhat after the birth of Sir Percival of Galles, for I never saw my father, and my mother brought me up quaintly ; not like a poor man's son, though, indeed, we had little money, and lived in a lone place : it was on a bit of waste land near a river ; moist, and without trees ; on the drier parts of it folks had built cottages—see, I can count them on my fingers— six cottages, of which ours was one.

Likewise, there was a little chapel, with a yew tree and graves in the church-yard—graves—yes, a great many graves, more than in the yards of many Minsters I have seen, because people fought a battle once near us, and buried many bodies in deep pits, to the east of the chapel ; but this was before I was born.

I have talked to old knights since who fought in that battle, and who told me that it was all about an old lady that they fought ; indeed, this lady, who was a queen, was afterwards, by her own wish, buried in the aforesaid chapel in a most fair tomb ; her image was of latoun gilt, and with a colour on it ; her hands and face were of silver, and her hair, gilded and most curiously wrought, flowed down from her head over the marble.

It was a strange thing to see that gold and brass and marble inside that rough chapel which stood on the marshy common, near the river.

Now, every St. Peter's day, when the sun was at its hottest, in the midsummer noontide, my mother (though

at other times she only wore such clothes as the folk
about us) would dress herself most richly, and shut the
shutters against all the windows, and light great candles,
and sit as though she were a queen, till the evening :
sitting and working at a frame, and singing as she
worked.

And what she worked at was two wings, wrought in
gold, on a blue ground.

And as for what she sung, I could never understand it,
though I know now it was not in Latin.

And she used to charge me straightly never to let any
man into the house on St. Peter's day ; therefore, I and
our dog, which was a great old bloodhound, always kept
the door together.

But one St. Peter's day, when I was nearly twenty,
I sat in the house watching the door with the bloodhound, and I was sleepy, because of the shut-up heat
and my mother's singing, so I began to nod, and at last,
though the dog often shook me by the hair to keep me
awake, went fast asleep, and began to dream a foolish
dream without hearing, as men sometimes do : for I
thought that my mother and I were walking to mass
through the snow on a Christmas day, but my mother
carried a live goose in her hand, holding it by the neck,
instead of her rosary, and that I went along by her side,
not walking, but turning somersaults like a mountebank,
my head never touching the ground ; when we got to
the chapel-door, the old priest met us, and said to my
mother, ' Why dame alive, your head is turned green !
Ah ! never mind, I will go and say mass, but don't let
little Mary there go ' and he pointed to the goose, and
went.

Then mass begun, but in the midst of it, the priest
said out loud, ' Oh I forgot,' and turning round to us
began to wag his grey head and white beard, throwing
his head right back, and sinking his chin on his breast
alternately ; and when we saw him do this, we presently
began also to knock our heads against the wall, keeping
time with him and with each other, till the priest said,
' Peter ! it's dragon-time now,' whereat the roof flew

off, and a great yellow dragon came down on the chapel-floor with a flop, and danced about clumsily, wriggling his fat tail, and saying to a sort of tune, ' O the Devil, the Devil, the Devil, O the Devil,' so I went up to him, and put my hand on his breast, meaning to slay him, and so awoke, and found myself standing up with my hand on the breast of an armed knight ; the door lay flat on the ground, and under it lay Hector, our dog, whining and dying.

For eight hours I had been asleep ; on awaking, the blood rushed up into my face, I heard my mother's low mysterious song behind me, and knew not what harm might happen to her and me, if that knight's coming made her cease in it ; so I struck him with my left hand, where his face was bare under his mail coif, and getting my sword in my right, drove its point under his hawberk, so that it came out behind, and he fell, turned over on his face, and died.

Then, because my mother still went on working and singing, I said no word, but let him lie there and put the door up again, and found Hector dead.

I then sat down again and polished my sword with a piece of leather after I had wiped the blood from it ; and in an hour my mother arose from her work, and raising me from where I was sitting, kissed my brow, saying, ' Well done, Lionel, you have slain your greatest foe, and now the people will know you for what you are before you die—Ah God ! though not before *I* die.'

So I said, ' Who is he, mother ? he seems to be some Lord ; am I a Lord then ? '

' A King, if the people will but know it,' she said.

Then she knelt down by the dead body, turned it round again, so that it lay face uppermost as before, then said :

' And so it has all come to this, has it ? To think that you should run on my son's sword-point at last, after all the wrong you have done me and mine ; now must I work carefully, lest when you are dead you should still do me harm, for that you are a King—Lionel ! '

' Yea, Mother.'

'Come here and see ; this is what I have wrought these many Peter's days by day, and often other times by night.'

'It is a surcoat, Mother ; for me ? '

'Yea, but take a spade, and come into the wood.'

So we went, and my mother gazed about her for a while as if she were looking for something, but then suddenly went forward with her eyes on the ground, and she said to me :

'Is it not strange, that I who know the very place I am going to take you to, as well as our own garden, should have a sudden fear come over me that I should not find it after all ; though for these nineteen years I have watched the trees change and change all about it—ah ! here, stop now.'

We stopped before a great oak ; a beech tree was behind us—she said, 'Dig, Lionel, hereabouts.'

So I dug and for an hour found nothing but beech roots, while my mother seemed as if she were going mad, sometimes running about muttering to herself, sometimes stooping into the hole and howling, sometimes throwing herself on the grass and twisting her hands together above her head ; she went once down the hill to a pool that had filled an old gravel pit, and came back dripping and with wild eyes ; 'I am too hot,' she said, 'far too hot this St. Peter's day.'

Clink just then from my spade against iron ; my mother screamed, and I dug with all my might for another hour, and then beheld a chest of heavy wood bound with iron ready to be heaved out of the hole ; 'Now, Lionel, weigh it out—hard for your life ! '

And with some trouble I got the chest out ; she gave me a key, I unlocked the chest, and took out another wrapped in lead, which also I unlocked with a silver key that my mother gave me, and behold therein lay armour —mail for the whole body, made of very small rings wrought most wonderfully, for every ring was fashioned like a serpent, and though they were so small yet could you see their scales and their eyes, and of some even the forked tongue was on it, and lay on the rivet, and the rings were gilded here and there into patterns and flowers so that the gleam of it was most glorious.— And the mail coif was all gilded and had red and blue stones at the rivets ; and the tilting helm (inside which the mail lay when I saw it first) was gilded also, and had flowers pricked out on it ; and the chain of it was silver, and the crest was two gold wings. And there was a shield of blue set with red stones, which had two gold wings for a cognizance ; and the hilt of the sword was gold, with angels wrought in green and blue all up it, and the eyes in their wings were of pearls and red stones, and the sheath was of silver with green flowers on it.

Now when I saw this armour and understood that my mother would have me put it on, and ride out without fear, leaving her alone, I cast myself down on the grass so that I might not see its beauty (for it made me mad), and strove to think ; but what thoughts soever came to me were only of the things that would be, glory in the midst of ladies, battle-joy among knights, honour from all kings and princes and people—these things.

But my mother wept softly above me, till I arose with a great shudder of delight and drew the edges of the hawberk over my cheek, I liked so to feel the rings slipping, slipping, till they fell off altogether ; then I said :

' O Lord God that made the world, if I might only die in this armour ! '

Then my mother helped me to put it on, and I felt strange and new in it, and yet I had neither lance nor horse.

So when we reached the cottage again she said : ' See now, Lionel, you must take this knight's horse and his lance, and ride away, or else the people will come here to kill another king ; and when you are gone, you will never see me any more in life.'

I wept thereat, but she said :

' Nay, but see here.'

And taking the dead knight's lance from among the garden lilies, she rent from it the pennon (which had a sword on a red ground for bearing), and cast it carelessly on the ground, then she bound about it a pennon with my bearing, gold wings on a blue ground ; she bid me bear the Knight's body, all armed as he was, to put on him his helm and lay him on the floor at her bed's foot, also to break his sword and cast it on our hearthstone ; all which things I did.

Afterwards she put the surcoat on me, and then lying down in her gorgeous raiment on her bed, she spread her arms out in the form of a cross, shut her eyes, and said :

' Kiss me, Lionel, for I am tired.'

And after I had kissed her she died.

And I mounted my dead foe's horse and rode away ; neither did I ever know what wrong that was which he had done me, not while I was in the body at least.

And do not blame me for not burying my mother ; I left her there because, though she did not say so to me, yet I knew the thoughts of her heart, and that the thing she had wished so earnestly for these years, and years, and years, had been but to lie dead with him lying dead close to her.

So I rode all that night, for I could not stop because of the thoughts that were in me, and, stopping at this place and that, in three days came to the city.

And there the King held his court with great pomp.

And so I went to the palace, and asked to see the King ; whereupon they brought me into the great hall where he was with all his knights, and my heart swelled within me to think that I too was a King.

So I prayed him to make me a knight, and he spake graciously, and asked me my name ; so when I had told it him, and said that I was a king's son, he pondered, not knowing what to do, for I could not tell him whose son I was.

Whereupon one of the knights came near me and shaded his eyes with his hand as one does in a bright sun, meaning to mock at me for my shining armour, and he drew nearer and nearer till his long stiff beard just touched me, and then I smote him on the face, and he fell on the floor.

So the King being in a rage, roared out from the door,
' Slay him ! ' but I put my shield before me and drew
my sword, and the women drew together aside and
whispered fearfully, and while some of the knights took
spears and stood about me, others got their armour on.

And as we stood thus we heard a horn blow, and then
an armed knight came into the hall and drew near to
the King ; and one of the maidens behind me, came
and laid her hand on my shoulder ; so I turned and saw
that she was very fair, and then I was glad, but she
whispered to me :

' Sir Squire, for a love I have for your face and gold
armour, I will give you good counsel ; go presently to
the King and say to him : " In the name of Alys des
Roses and Sir Guy le Bon Amant I pray you three boons,"
—do this, and you will be alive, and a knight by to-
morrow, otherwise I think hardly the one or the other.'

' The Lord reward you, damoyzel,' I said. Then I saw
that the King had left talking with that knight and was
just going to stand up and say something out loud, so
I went quickly and called out with a loud voice :

' O King Gilbert of the rose-land, I, Lionel of the
Golden Wings, pray of you three boons in the name of
Alys des Roses and Sir Guy le Bon Amant.'

Then the King gnashed his teeth, because he had
promised if ever his daughter Alys des Roses came back
safe again, he would on that day grant any three boons
to the first man who asked them, even if he were his
greatest foe. He said, ' Well, then, take them, what are
they ? '

' First, my life ; then, that you should make me
a knight ; and thirdly, that you should take me into
your service.'

He said, ' I will do this, and moreover, I forgive you
freely if you will be my true man.'

Then we heard shouting arise through all the city
because they were bringing the Lady Alys from the ship
up to the palace, and the people came to the windows,
and the houses were hung with cloths and banners of
silk and gold, that swung down right from the eaves to

the ground ; likewise the bells all rang : and within a while they entered the palace, and the trumpets rang and men shouted, so that my head whirled ; and they entered the hall, and the King went down from the daïs to meet them.

Now a band of knights and of damoyzels went before and behind, and in the midst Sir Guy led the Lady Alys by the hand, and he was a most stately knight, strong and fair.

And I indeed noted the first band of knights and damoyzels well, and wondered at the noble presence of the knights, and was filled with joy when I beheld the maids, because of their great beauty ; the second band I did not see, for when they passed I was leaning back against the wall, wishing to die with my hands before my face.

But when I could see, she was hanging about her father's neck, weeping, and she never left him all that night, but held his hand in feast and dance, and even when I was made knight, while the King with his right hand laid his sword over my shoulder, she held his left hand and was close to me.

And the next day they held a grand tourney, that I might be proven ; and I had never fought with knights before, yet I did not doubt. And Alys sat under a green canopy, that she might give the degree to the best knight, and by her sat the good knight Sir Guy, in a long robe, for he did not mean to joust that day ; and indeed at first none but young knights jousted, for they thought that I should not do much.

But I, looking up to the green canopy, overthrew so many of them, that the elder knights began to arm, and I grew most joyful as I met them, and no man unhorsed me ; and always I broke my spear fairly, or else overthrew my adversary.

Now that maiden who counselled me in the hall, told me afterwards that as I fought, the Lady Alys held fast to the rail before her, and leaned forward and was most pale, never answering any word that any one might say to her, till the Knight Guy said to her in anger : ' Alys !

what ails you ? you would have been glad enough to speak to me when King Wadrayns carried you off shrieking, or that other time when the chain went round about you, and the faggots began to smoke in the Brown City : do you not love me any longer ? O Alys, Alys ! just think a little, and do not break your faith with me ; God hates nothing so much as this. Sweet, try to love me, even for your own sake ! See, am I not kind to you ?'

That maiden said that she turned round to him wonderingly, as if she had not caught his meaning, and that just for one second, then stretched out over the lists again.

Now till about this time I had made no cry as I jousted. But there came against me a very tall knight, on a great horse, and when we met our spears both shivered, and he howled with vexation, for he wished to slay me, being the brother of that knight I had struck down in the hall the day before.

And they say that when Alys heard his howl sounding faintly through the bars of his great helm, she trembled ; but I know not, for I was stronger than that knight, and when we fought with swords, I struck him right out of his saddle, and near slew him with that stroke.

Whereupon I shouted ' Alys,' out aloud, and she blushed red for pleasure, and Sir Guy took note of it, and rose up in a rage and ran down and armed.

Then presently I saw a great knight come riding in with three black chevrons on a gold shield : and so he began to ride at me, and at first we only broke both our spears, but then he drew his sword, and fought quite in another way to what the other knights had, so that I saw at once that I had no chance against him : nevertheless, for a long time he availed nothing, though he wounded me here and there, but at last drove his sword right through mine, through my shield and my helm, and I fell, and lay like one dead.

And thereat the King cried out to cease, and the degree was given to Sir Guy, because I had overthrown forty knights and he had overthrown me.

Then they told me, I was carried out of the lists and

laid in a hostelry near the palace, and Guy went up to the pavilion where Alys was and she crowned him, both of them being very pale, for she doubted if I were slain, and he knew that she did not love him, thinking before that she did ; for he was good and true, and had saved her life and honour, and she (poor maid !) wished to please her father, and strove to think that all was right.

But I was by no means slain, for the sword had only cleft my helm, and when I came to myself again I felt despair of all things, because I knew not that she loved me, for how should she, knowing nothing of me ? likewise dust had been cast on my gold wings, and she saw it done.

Then I heard a great crying in the street, that sounded strangely in the quiet night, so I sent to ask what it might be : and there came presently into my chamber a man in gilded armour ; he was an old man, and his hair and beard were gray, and behind him came six men armed, who carried a dead body of a young man between them, and I said, ' What is it ? who is he ? ' Then the old man, whose head was heavy for grief, said : ' Oh, sir ! this is my son ; for as we went yesterday with our merchandize some twenty miles from this fair town, we passed by a certain hold, and therefrom came a knight and men-at-arms, who when my son would have fought with them, overthrew him and bound him, and me and all our men they said they would slay if we did ought ; so then they cut out my son's eyes, and cut off his hands, and then said, " The Knight of High Gard takes these for tribute." Therewithal they departed, taking with them my son's eyes and his hands on a platter ; and when they were gone I would have followed them, and slain some of them at least, but my own people would not suffer me, and for grief and pain my son's heart burst, and he died, and behold I am here.'

Then I thought I could win glory, and I was much rejoiced thereat, and said to the old man,

Would you love to be revenged ? '

But he set his teeth, and pulled at the skirt of his surcoat, as hardly for his passion he said, ' Yes.'

'Then,' I said, 'I will go and try to slay this knight, if you will show me the way to La Haute Garde.'

And he, taking my hand, said, 'O glorious knight, let us go now!' And he did not ask who I was, or whether I was a good knight, but began to go down the stairs at once, so I put on my armour and followed him.

And we two set forth alone to La Haute Garde, for no man else dared follow us, and I rejoiced in thinking that while Guy was sitting at the King's table feasting, I was riding out to slay the King's enemies, for it never once seemed possible to me that I should be worsted.

It was getting light again by then we came in sight of High Gard; we wound up the hill on foot, for it was very steep; I blew at the gates a great blast which was even as though the stag should blow his own mort, or like the blast that Balen heard.

For in a very short while the gates opened and a great band of armed men, more than thirty I think, and a knight on horseback among them, who was armed in red, stood before us, and on one side of him was a serving-man with a silver dish, on the other, one with a butcher's cleaver, a knife, and pincers.

So when the knight saw us he said, 'What, are you come to pay tribute in person, old man, and is this another fair son? Good sir, how is your lady?'

So I said grimly, being in a rage, 'I have a will to slay you.'

But I could scarce say so before the old merchant rushed at the red knight with a yell, who without moving slew his horse with an axe, and then the men-at-arms speared the old man, slaying him as one would an otter or a rat.

Afterwards they were going to set on me, but the red knight held them back, saying: 'Nay, I am enough,' and we spurred our horses.

As we met, I felt just as if some one had thrown a dull brown cloth over my eyes, and I felt the wretched spear-point slip off his helm; then I felt a great pain somewhere, that did not seem to be in my body, but in the world, or the sky, or something of that sort.

And I know not how long that pain seemed to last now, but I think years, though really I grew well and sane again in a few weeks.

And when I woke, scarce knowing whether I was in the world or heaven or hell, I heard some one singing.

I tried to listen but could not, because I did not know where I was, and was thinking of that ; I missed verse after verse of the song, this song, till at last I saw I must be in the King's palace.

There was a window by my bed, I looked out at it, and saw that I was high up ; down in the street the people were going to and fro, and there was a knot of folks gathered about a minstrel, who sat on the edge of a fountain, with his head laid sideways on his shoulder, and nursing one leg on the other ; he was singing only, having no instrument, and he sang the song I had tried to listen to, I heard some of it now :

> ' He was fair and free,
>   At every tourney
>   He wan the degree,
>   Sir Guy the good knight.
>
> ' He wan Alys the fair,
>   The king's own daughtere,
>   With all her gold hair,
>   That shone well bright.
>
> ' He saved a good knight,
>   Who also was wight,
>   And had wingès bright
>   On a blue shield.
>
> ' And he slew the Knight,
>   Of the High Gard in fight,
>   In red weed that was dight
>   In the open field.'

I fell back in my bed and wept, for I was weak with my illness ; to think of this ! truly this man was a perfect knight, and deserved to win Alys. Ah ! well ! but was this the glory I was to have, and no one believed that I was a King's son.

And so I passed days and nights, thinking of my dishonour and misery, and my utter loneliness ; no one cared for me ; verily, I think, if any one had spoken to me lovingly, I should have fallen on his neck and died, while I was so weak.

But I grew strong at last, and began to walk about, and in the Palace Pleasaunce, one day, I met Sir Guy walking by himself.

So I told him how that I thanked him with all my heart for my life, but he said it was only what a good knight ought to do ; for that hearing the mad enterprise I had ridden on, he had followed me swiftly with a few knights, and so saved me.

He looked stately and grand as he spoke, yet I did not love him, nay, rather hated him, though I tried hard not to do so, for there was some air of pitiless triumph and coldness of heart in him that froze me ; so scornfully, too, he said that about ' my mad enterprise,' as though I *must* be wrong in everything I did. Yet afterwards, as I came to know more, I pitied him instead of hating ; but at that time I thought his life was without a shadow, for I did not know that the Lady Alys loved him not.

And now I turned from him, and walked slowly up and down the garden-paths, not exactly thinking, but with some ghosts of former thoughts passing through my mind. The day, too, was most lovely, as it grew towards evening, and I had all the joy of a man lately sick in the flowers and all things ; if any bells at that time had begun to chime, I think I should have lain down on the grass and wept ; but now there was but the noise of the bees in the yellow musk, and that had not music enough to bring me sorrow.

And as I walked I stooped and picked a great orange lily, and held it in my hand, and lo ! down the garden-walk, the same fair damozel that had before this given me good counsel in the hall.

Thereat I was very glad, and walked to meet her smiling, but she was very grave, and said :

' Fair sir, the Lady Alys des Roses wishes to see you in her chamber.'

I could not answer a word, but turned, and went with her while she walked slowly beside me, thinking deeply, and picking a rose to pieces as she went ; and I, too, thought much, what could she want me for ? surely, but for one thing ; and yet—and yet.

But when we came to the lady's chamber, behold ! before the door stood a tall knight, fair and strong, and in armour, save his head, who seemed to be guarding the door, though not so as to seem so to all men.

He kissed the damozel eagerly, and then she said to me, ' This is Sir William de la Fosse, my true knight ; ' so the knight took my hand and seemed to have such joy of me, that all the blood came up to my face for pure delight.

But then the damozel Blanche opened the door and bade me go in while she abode still without ; so I entered, when I had put aside the heavy silken hanging that filled the doorway.

And there sat Alys ; she arose when she saw me, and stood pale, and with her lips apart, and her hands hanging loose by her side.

And then all doubt and sorrow went quite away from me ; I did not even feel drunk with joy, but rather felt that I could take it all in, lose no least fragment of it ; then at once I felt that I was beautiful, and brave and true ; I had no doubt as to what I should do now.

I went up to her, and first kissed her on the forehead, and then on the feet, and then drew her to me, and with my arms round about her, and her arms hanging loose, and her lips dropped, we held our lips together so long that my eyes failed me, and I could not see her, till I looked at her green raiment.

And she had never spoken to me yet ; she seemed just then as if she were going to, for she lifted her eyes to mine, and opened her mouth ; but she only said, ' Dear Lionel,' and fell forward as though she were faint ; and again I held her, and kissed her all over ; and then she loosed her hair that it fell to her feet, and when I clipped her next, she threw it over me, that it fell all over my scarlet robes like trickling of some golden well in Paradise.

Then within a while, we called in the Lady Blanche and Sir William de la Fosse, and while they talked about what we should do, we sat together and kissed ; and what they said, I know not.

But I remember, that that night, quite late, Alys and I rode out side by side from the good city in the midst of a great band of knights and men-at-arms, and other bands drew to us as we went, and in three days we reached Sir William's castle, which was called 'La Garde des Chevaliers.'

And straightway he caused toll the great bell, and to hang out from the highest tower a great banner of red and gold, cut into so many points that it seemed as if it were tattered ; for this was the custom of his house when they wanted their vassals together.

And Alys and I stood up in the tower by the great bell as they tolled it ; I remember now that I had passed my hand underneath her hair, so that the fingers of it folded over and just lay on her cheek ; she gazed down on the bell, and at every deafening stroke she drew in her breath and opened her eyes to a wide stare downwards.

But on the very day that we came, they arrayed her in gold and flowers (and there were angels and knights and ladies wrought on her gold raiment), and I waited for an hour in the chapel till she came, listening to the swallows outside, and gazing with parted lips at the pictures on the golden walls ; but when she came, I knelt down before the altar, and she knelt down and kissed my lips ; and then the priest came in, and the singers and the censer-boys ; and that chapel was soon confusedly full of golden raiment, and incense, and ladies and singing ; in the midst of which I wedded Alys.

And men came into knights' gard till we had two thousand men in it, and great store of munitions of war and provisions.

But Alys and I lived happily together in the painted hall and in the fair water-meadows, and as yet no one came against us.

And still her talk was of deeds of arms, and she was never tired of letting the serpent rings of my mail slip off her wrist and long hand, and she would kiss my

shield and helm and the gold wings on my surcoat, my
mother's work, and would talk of the ineffable joy that
would be when we had fought through all the evil that
was coming on us.

Also she would take my sword and lay it on her knees
and talk to it, telling it how much she loved me.

Yea in all things, O Lord God, Thou knowest that my
love was a very child, like thy angels. Oh ! my wise
soft-handed love ! endless passion ! endless longing
always satisfied !

Think you that the shouting curses of the trumpet
broke off our love, or in any ways lessened it ? no, most
certainly, but from the time the siege began, her cheeks
grew thinner, and her passionate face seemed more and
more a part of me ; now too, whenever I happened to
see her between the grim fighting she would do nothing
but kiss me all the time, or wring my hands, or take
my head on her breast, being so eagerly passionate that
sometimes a pang shot through me that she might die.

Till one day they made a breach in the wall, and when
I heard of it for the first time, I sickened, and could not
call on God ; but Alys cut me a tress of her yellow hair
and tied it in my helm, and armed me, and saying no
word, led me down to the breach by the hand, and then
went back most ghastly pale.

So there on the one side of the breach were the spears
of William de la Fosse and Lionel of the Gold Wings, and
on the other the spears of King Gilbert and Sir Guy le
Bon Amant, but the King himself was not there ; Sir Guy
was.

Well,—what would you have ? in this world never yet
could two thousand men stand against twenty thousand ;
we were almost pushed back with their spear-points,
they were so close together :—slay six of them and the
spears were as thick as ever ; but if two of our men fell
there was straightway a hole.

Yet just at the end of this we drove them back in one
charge two yards beyond the breach, and behold in the
front rank, Sir Guy, utterly fearless, cool, and collected ;
nevertheless, with one stroke I broke his helm, and he

fell to the ground before the two armies, even as I fell
that day in the lists ; and we drove them twenty feet
farther, yet they saved Sir Guy.

Well, again,—what would you have ? They drove us
back again, and they drove us into our inner castle-walls.
And I was the last to go in, and just as I was entering,
the boldest and nearest of the enemy clutched at my
love's hair in my helm, shouting out quite loud, ' Whore's
hair for John the goldsmith ! '

At the hearing of which blasphemy, the Lord gave me
such strength, that I turned and caught him by the ribs
with my left hand, and with my right, by sheer strength,
I tore off his helm and part of his nose with it, and then
swinging him round about, dashed his brains out against
the castle-walls.

Yet thereby was I nearly slain, for they surrounded me,
only Sir William and the others charged out and rescued
me, but hardly.

May the Lord help all true men ! In an hour we were
all fighting pell mell on the walls of the castle itself, and
some were slain outright, and some were wounded, and
some yielded themselves and received mercy ; but I had
scarce the heart to fight any more, because I thought of
Alys lying with her face upon the floor and her agonized
hands outspread, trying to clutch something, trying to
hold to the cracks of the boarding. So when I had seen
William de la Fosse slain by many men, I cast my shield
and helm over the battlements, and gazed about for
a second, and lo ! on one of the flanking towers, my
gold wings still floated by the side of William's white
lion, and in the other one I knew my poor Love, whom
they had left quite alone, was lying.

So then I turned into a dark passage and ran till I
reached the tower stairs, up that too I sprang as though
a ghost were after me, I did so long to kiss her again
before I died, to soothe her too, so that she should not
feel this day, when in the aftertimes she thought of it
as wholly miserable to her. For I knew they would
neither slay her nor treat her cruelly, for in sooth all
loved her, only they would make her marry Sir Guy le
Bon Amant.

In the topmost room I found her, alas ! alas ! lying on
the floor, as I said ; I came to her and kissed her head
as she lay, then raised her up ; and I took all my armour
off and broke my sword over my knee.

And then I led her to the window away from the
fighting, from whence we only saw the quiet country, and
kissed her lips till she wept and looked no longer sad
and wretched ; then I said to her :—

' Now, O Love, we must part for a little, it is time for
me to go and die.'

' Why should you go away ? ' she said, ' they will
come here quick enough, no doubt, and I shall have you
longer with me if you stay ; I do not turn sick at the
sight of blood.'

' O my poor Love ! ' And I could not go because of
the praying face ; surely God would grant anything to
such a face as that.

' Oh ! ' she said, ' you will let me have you yet a little
longer, I see ; also let me kiss your feet.'

She threw herself down and kissed them, and then did
not get up again at once, but lay there holding my feet.

And while she lay there, behold a sudden tramping
that she did not hear, and over the green hangings the
gleam of helmets that she did not see, and then one
pushed aside the hangings with his spear, and there
stood the armed men.

' Will not somebody weep for my darling ? '

She sprung up from my feet with a low, bitter moan,
most terrible to hear, she kissed me once on the lips, and
then stood aside, with her dear head thrown back, and
holding her lovely loose hair strained over her outspread
arms, as though she were wearied of all things that had
been or that might be.

Then one thrust me through the breast with a spear,
and another with his sword,which was three inches broad,
gave me a stroke across the thighs that hit to the bone ;
and as I fell forward one cleft me to the teeth with his
axe.

And then I heard my darling shriek.

THE DEFENCE OF GUENEVERE,
AND OTHER POEMS

1858

THE DEFENCE OF GUENEVERE

BUT, knowing now that they would have her speak,
She threw her wet hair backward from her brow,
Her hand close to her mouth touching her cheek,

As though she had had there a shameful blow,
And feeling it shameful to feel ought but shame
All through her heart, yet felt her cheek burned so,

She must a little touch it ; like one lame
She walked away from Gauwaine, with her head
Still lifted up ; and on her cheek of flame

The tears dried quick ; she stopped at last and said :
' O knights and lords, it seems but little skill   11
To talk of well-known things past now and dead.

' God wot I ought to say, I have done ill,
And pray you all forgiveness heartily !
Because you must be right such great lords—still

' Listen, suppose your time were come to die,
And you were quite alone and very weak ;
Yea, laid a dying while very mightily

' The wind was ruffling up the narrow streak
Of river through your broad lands running well :   20
Suppose a hush should come, then some one speak :

' " One of these cloths is heaven, and one is hell,
Now choose one cloth for ever, which they be,
I will not tell you, you must somehow tell

' " Of your own strength and mightiness ; here, see ! "
Yea, yea, my lord, and you to ope your eyes,
At foot of your familiar bed to see

' A great God's angel standing, with such dyes,
Not known on earth, on his great wings, and hands,
Held out two ways, light from the inner skies   30

' Showing him well, and making his commands
Seem to be God's commands, moreover, too,
Holding within his hands the cloths on wands ;

' And one of these strange choosing cloths was blue,
Wavy and long and one cut short and red ;
No man could tell the better of the two.

' After a shivering half-hour you said,
" God help ! heaven's colour, the blue ; " and he said,
    " hell."
Perhaps you then would roll upon your bed,

' And cry to all good men that loved you well,   40
" Ah Christ ! if only I had known, known, known ; "
Launcelot went away, then I could tell,

' Like wisest man how all things would be, moan,
And roll and hurt myself, and long to die,
And yet fear much to die for what was sown.

' Nevertheless you, O Sir Gauwaine, lie,
Whatever may have happened through these years,
God knows I speak truth, saying that you lie.'

Her voice was low at first, being full of tears,
But as it cleared, it grew full loud and shrill,   50
Growing a windy shriek in all men's ears,

A ringing in their startled brains, until
She said that Gauwaine lied, then her voice sunk,
And her great eyes began again to fill,

Though still she stood right up, and never shrunk,
But spoke on bravely, glorious lady fair !
Whatever tears her full lips may have drunk,

She stood, and seemed to think, and wrung her hair,
Spoke out at last with no more trace of shame,
With passionate twisting of her body there :   60

' It chanced upon a day that Launcelot came
To dwell at Arthur's court : at Christmas-time
This happened ; when the heralds sung his name,

' " Son of King Ban of Benwick," seemed to chime
Along with all the bells that rang that day,
O'er the white roofs, with little change of rhyme.

' Christmas and whitened winter passed away,
And over me the April sunshine came,
Made very awful with black hail-clouds, yea

' And in the Summer I grew white with flame,   70
And bowed my head down—Autumn, and the sick
Sure knowledge things would never be the same,

' However often Spring might be most thick
Of blossoms and buds, smote on me, and I grew
Careless of most things, let the clock tick, tick,

' To my unhappy pulse, that beat right through
My eager body ; while I laughed out loud,
And let my lips curl up at false or true,

' Seemed cold and shallow without any cloud.
Behold my judges, then the cloths were brought :   80
While I was dizzied thus, old thoughts would crowd,

' Belonging to the time ere I was bought
By Arthur's great name and his little love,
Must I give up for ever then, I thought,

' That which I deemed would ever round me move
Glorifying all things ; for a little word,
Scarce ever meant at all, must I now prove

' Stone-cold for ever ? Pray you, does the Lord
Will that all folks should be quite happy and good ?
I love God now a little, if this cord   90

' Were broken, once for all what striving could
Make me love anything in earth or heaven.
So day by day it grew, as if one should

' Slip slowly down some path worn smooth and even,
Down to a cool sea on a summer day ;
Yet still in slipping was there some small leaven

' Of stretched hands catching small stones by the way,
Until one surely reached the sea at last,
And felt strange new joy as the worn head lay

' Back, with the hair like sea-weed ; yea all past   100
Sweat of the forehead, dryness of the lips,
Washed utterly out by the dear waves o'ercast

' In the lone sea, far off from any ships !
Do I not know now of a day in Spring ?
No minute of that wild day ever slips

' From out my memory ; I hear thrushes sing,
And wheresoever I may be, straightway
Thoughts of it all come up with most fresh sting ;

' I was half mad with beauty on that day,
And went without my ladies all alone,   110
In a quiet garden walled round every way ;

' I was right joyful of that wall of stone,
That shut the flowers and trees up with the sky,
And trebled all the beauty : to the bone,

' Yea right through to my heart, grown very shy
With weary thoughts, it pierced, and made me glad ;
Exceedingly glad, and I knew verily,

' A little thing just then had made me mad ;
I dared not think, as I was wont to do,
Sometimes, upon my beauty ; if I had   120

' Held out my long hand up against the blue,
And, looking on the tenderly darken'd fingers,
Thought that by rights one ought to see quite through,

' There, see you, where the soft still light yet lingers,
Round by the edges ; what should I have done,
If this had joined with yellow spotted singers,

' And startling green drawn upward by the sun ?
But shouting, loosed out, see now ! all my hair,
And trancedly stood watching the west wind run

' With faintest half-heard breathing sound—why there
I lose my head e'en now in doing this ;   131
But shortly listen—In that garden fair

' Came Launcelot walking ; this is true, the kiss
Wherewith we kissed in meeting that spring day,
I scarce dare talk of the remember'd bliss,

' When both our mouths went wandering in one way,
And aching sorely, met among the leaves ;
Our hands being left behind strained far away.

' Never within a yard of my bright sleeves
Had Launcelot come before—and now, so nigh !   140
After that day why is it Guenevere grieves ?

' Nevertheless you, O Sir Gauwaine, lie,
Whatever happened on through all those years,
God knows I speak truth, saying that you lie.

' Being such a lady could I weep these tears
If this were true ?   A great queen such as I
Having sinn'd this way, straight her conscience sears ;

' And afterwards she liveth hatefully,
Slaying and poisoning, certes never weeps,—
Gauwaine be friends now, speak me lovingly.   150

' Do I not see how God's dear pity creeps
All through your frame, and trembles in your mouth ?
Remember in what grave your mother sleeps,

' Buried in some place far down in the south,
Men are forgetting as I speak to you ;
By her head sever'd in that awful drouth

' Of pity that drew Agravaine's fell blow,
I pray your pity ! let me not scream out
For ever after, when the shrill winds blow

' Through half your castle-locks ! let me not shout   160
For ever after in the winter night
When you ride out alone ! in battle-rout

' Let not my rusting tears make your sword light !
Ah ! God of mercy how he turns away !
So, ever must I dress me to the fight,

' So—let God's justice work ! Gauwaine, I say,
See me hew down your proofs : yea all men know
Even as you said how Mellyagraunce one day,

' One bitter day in *la Fausse Garde*, for so
All good knights held it after, saw—   170
Yea, sirs, by cursed unknightly outrage ; though

' You, Gauwaine, held his word without a flaw,
This Mellyagraunce saw blood upon my bed—
Whose blood then pray you ? is there any law

' To make a queen say why some spots of red
Lie on her coverlet ? or will you say,
" Your hands are white, lady, as when you wed,

' " Where did you bleed ? " and must I stammer out—
      " Nay,
I blush indeed, fair lord, only to rend
My sleeve up to my shoulder, where there lay   180

' " A knife-point last night : " so must I defend
The honour of the lady Guenevere ?
Not so, fair lords, even if the world should end

' This very day, and you were judges here
Instead of God. Did you see Mellyagraunce
When Launcelot stood by him ? what white fear

' Curdled his blood, and how his teeth did dance,
His side sink in ? as my knight cried and said,
" Slayer of unarm'd men, here is a chance !

' " Setter of traps, I pray you guard your head,   190
By God I am so glad to fight with you,
Stripper of ladies, that my hand feels lead

' " For driving weight ; hurrah now ! draw and do,
For all my wounds are moving in my breast,
And I am getting mad with waiting so."

' He struck his hands together o'er the beast,
Who fell down flat, and grovell'd at his feet,
And groan'd at being slain so young—" at least."

' My knight said, " Rise you, sir, who are so fleet
At catching ladies, half-arm'd will I fight,   200
My left side all uncovered ! " then I weet,

' Up sprang Sir Mellyagraunce with great delight
Upon his knave's face ; not until just then
Did I quite hate him, as I saw my knight

' Along the lists look to my stake and pen
With such a joyous smile, it made me sigh
From agony beneath my waist-chain, when

' The fight began, and to me they drew nigh ;
Ever Sir Launcelot kept him on the right,
And traversed warily, and ever high   210

' And fast leapt caitiff's sword, until my knight
Sudden threw up his sword to his left hand,
Caught it, and swung it ; that was all the fight.

' Except a spout of blood on the hot land ;
For it was hottest summer ; and I know
I wonder'd how the fire, while I should stand,

' And burn, against the heat, would quiver so,
Yards above my head ; thus these matters went ;
Which things were only warnings of the woe

' That fell on me. Yet Mellyagraunce was shent,   220
For Mellyagraunce had fought against the Lord ;
Therefore, my lords, take heed lest you be blent

' With all this wickedness ; say no rash word
Against me, being so beautiful ; my eyes,
Wept all away to grey, may bring some sword

' To drown you in your blood ; see my breast rise,
Like waves of purple sea, as here I stand ;
And how my arms are moved in wonderful wise,

' Yea also at my full heart's strong command,
See through my long throat how the words go up   230
In ripples to my mouth ; how in my hand

' The shadow lies like wine within a cup
Of marvellously colour'd gold ; yea now
This little wind is rising, look you up,

' And wonder how the light is falling so
Within my moving tresses : will you dare,
When you have looked a little on my brow,

' To say this thing is vile ? or will you care
For any plausible lies of cunning woof,
When you can see my face with no lie there   240

' For ever ? am I not a gracious proof—
" But in your chamber Launcelot was found "—
Is there a good knight then would stand aloof,

' When a queen says with gentle queenly sound :
" O true as steel come now and talk with me,
I love to see your step upon the ground

' " Unwavering, also well I love to see
That gracious smile light up your face, and hear
Your wonderful words, that all mean verily

' " The thing they seem to mean : good friend, so dear
To me in everything, come here to-night,   251
Or else the hours will pass most dull and drear ;

' " If you come not, I fear this time I might
Get thinking over much of times gone by,
When I was young, and green hope was in sight ;

' " For no man cares now to know why I sigh ;
And no man comes to sing me pleasant songs,
Nor any brings me the sweet flowers that lie

' " So thick in the gardens ; therefore one so longs
To see you, Launcelot ; that we may be   260
Like children once again, free from all wrongs

' " Just for one night." Did he not come to me ?
What thing could keep true Launcelot away
If I said " come " ? there was one less than three

' In my quiet room that night, and we were gay ;
Till sudden I rose up, weak, pale, and sick,
Because a bawling broke our dream up, yea

' I looked at Launcelot's face and could not speak,
For he looked helpless too, for a little while ;
Then I remember how I tried to shriek,   270

' And could not, but fell down ; from tile to tile
The stones they threw up rattled o'er my head,
And made me dizzier ; till within a while

' My maids were all about me, and my head
On Launcelot's breast was being soothed away
From its white chattering, until Launcelot said—

' By God ! I will not tell you more to-day,
Judge any way you will—what matters it ?
You know quite well the story of that fray,

' How Launcelot still'd their bawling, the mad fit   280
That caught up Gauwaine—all, all, verily,
But just that which would save me ; these things flit.

' Nevertheless you, O Sir Gauwaine, lie,
Whatever may have happen'd these long years,
God knows I speak truth, saying that you lie !

' All I have said is truth, by Christ's dear tears.'
She would not speak another word, but stood
Turn'd sideways ; listening, like a man who hears

His brother's trumpet sounding through the wood
Of his foes' lances. She lean'd eagerly,   290
And gave a slight spring sometimes, as she could

At last hear something really ; joyfully
Her cheek grew crimson, as the headlong speed
Of the roan charger drew all men to see,
The knight who came was Launcelot at good need.

KING ARTHUR'S TOMB

HOT August noon—already on that day
  Since sunrise through the Wiltshire downs, most sad
Of mouth and eye, he had gone leagues of way ;
  Ay and by night, till whether good or bad

He was, he knew not, though he knew perchance
  That he was Launcelot, the bravest knight
Of all who since the world was, have borne lance,
  Or swung their swords in wrong cause or in right.

Nay, he knew nothing now, except that where
  The Glastonbury gilded towers shine,   10
A lady dwelt, whose name was Guenevere ;
  This he knew also ; that some fingers twine,

Not only in a man's hair, even his heart,
  (Making him good or bad I mean,) but in his life,
Skies, earth, men's looks and deeds, all that has part,
  Not being ourselves, in that half-sleep, half-strife,

(Strange sleep, strange strife,) that men call living ; so
  Was Launcelot most glad when the moon rose,
Because it brought new memories of her—' Lo,
  Between the trees a large moon, the wind lows   20

' Not loud, but as a cow begins to low,
  Wishing for strength to make the herdsman hear :
The ripe corn gathereth dew ; yea, long ago,
  In the old garden life, my Guenevere

' Loved to sit still among the flowers, till night
  Had quite come on, hair loosen'd, for she said,
Smiling like heaven, that its fairness might
  Draw up the wind sooner to cool her head.

' Now while I ride how quick the moon gets small,
  As it did then—I tell myself a tale   30
That will not last beyond the whitewashed wall,
  Thoughts of some joust must help me through the vale,

' Keep this till after—How Sir Gareth ran
  A good course that day under my Queen's eyes,
And how she sway'd laughing at Dinadan—
  No—back again, the other thoughts will rise,

' And yet I think so fast 'twill end right soon—
  Verily then I think, that Guenevere,
Made sad by dew and wind, and tree-barred moon,
  Did love me more than ever, was more dear   40

' To me than ever, she would let me lie
  And kiss her feet, or, if I sat behind,
Would drop her hand and arm most tenderly,
  And touch my mouth. And she would let me wind

' Her hair around my neck, so that it fell
  Upon my red robe, strange in the twilight
With many unnamed colours, till the bell
  Of her mouth on my cheek sent a delight   .

' Through all my ways of being ; like the stroke
  Wherewith God threw all men upon the face   50
When he took Enoch, and when Enoch woke
  With a changed body in the happy place.

' Once, I remember, as I sat beside,
  She turn'd a little, and laid back her head
And slept upon my breast : I almost died
  In those night-watches with my love and dread,

' There lily-like she bow'd her head and slept,
  And I breathed low, and did not dare to move,
But sat and quiver'd inwardly, thoughts crept,
  And frighten'd me with pulses of my Love.   60

' The stars shone out above the doubtful green
  Of her boddice, in the green sky overhead ;
Pale in the green sky were the stars I ween,
  Because the moon shone like a star she shed

' When she dwelt up in heaven a while ago,
  And ruled all things but God : the night went on,
The wind grew cold, and the white moon grew low
  One hand had fallen down, and now lay on

' My cold stiff palm ; there were no colours then
   For near an hour, and I fell asleep   70
In spite of all my striving, even when
   I held her whose name-letters make me leap.

' I did not sleep long, feeling that in sleep
   I did some loved one wrong, so that the sun
Had only just arisen from the deep
   Still land of colours, when before me one

' Stood whom I knew, but scarcely dared to touch,
   She seemed to have changed so in the night ;
Moreover she held scarlet lilies, such
   As Maiden Margaret bears upon the light   80

' Of the great church walls, natheless did I walk
   Through the fresh wet woods, and the wheat that morn,
Touching her hair and hand and mouth, and talk
   Of love we held, nigh hid among the corn.

' Back to the palace, ere the sun grew high,
   We went, and in a cool green room all day
I gazed upon the arras giddily,
   Where the wind set the silken kings a-sway.

' I could not hold her hand, or see her face ;
   For which may God forgive me ! but I think,   90
Howsoever, that she was not in that place.'
   These memories Launcelot was quick to drink ;

And when these fell, some paces past the wall,
   There rose yet others, but they wearied more,
And tasted not so sweet ; they did not fall
   So soon, but vaguely wrenched his strained heart sore

In shadowy slipping from his grasp ; these gone,
   A longing followed ; if he might but touch
That Guenevere at once ! Still night, the lone
   Grey horse's head before him vex'd him much,   100

In steady nodding over the grey road—
   Still night, and night, and night, and emptied heart
Of any stories ; what a dismal load
   Time grew at last, yea, when the night did part,

And let the sun flame over all, still there
　　The horse's grey ears turn'd this way and that,
And still he watch'd them twitching in the glare
　　Of the morning sun, behind them still he sat,

Quite wearied out with all the wretched night,
　　Until about the dustiest of the day,   110
On the last down's brow he drew his rein in sight
　　Of the Glastonbury roofs that choke the way.

And he was now quite giddy as before,
　　When she slept by him, tired out and her hair
Was mingled with the rushes on the floor,
　　And he, being tired too, was scarce aware

Of her presence ; yet as he sat and gazed,
　　A shiver ran throughout him, and his breath
Came slower, he seem'd suddenly amazed,
　　As though he had not heard of Arthur's death.   120

This for a moment only, presently
　　He rode on giddy still, until he reach'd
A place of apple-trees, by the thorn-tree
　　Wherefrom St. Joseph in the days past preached.

Dazed there he laid his head upon a tomb,
　　Not knowing it was Arthur's, at which sight
One of her maidens told her, ' he is come,'
　　And she went forth to meet him ; yet a blight

Had settled on her, all her robes were black,
　　With a long white veil only ; she went slow,   130
As one walks to be slain, her eyes did lack
　　Half her old glory, yea, alas ! the glow

Had left her face and hands ; this was because
　　As she lay last night on her purple bed,
Wishing for morning, grudging every pause
　　Of the palace clocks, until that Launcelot's head

Should lie on her breast, with all her golden hair
　　Each side—when suddenly the thing grew drear,
In morning twilight, when the grey downs bare
　　Grew into lumps of sin to Guenevere.   140

At first she sàid no word, but lay quite still,
 Only her mouth was open, and her eyes
Gazed wretchedly about from hill to hill ;
 As though she asked, not with so much surprise

As tired disgust, what made them stand up there
 So cold and grey. After, a spasm took
Her face, and all her frame, she caught her hair,
 All her hair, in both hands, terribly she shook,

And rose till she was sitting in the bed, 149
 Set her teeth hard, and shut her eyes and seem'd
As though she would have torn it from her head,
 Natheless she dropp'd it, lay down, as she deem'd

It matter'd not whatever she might do—
 O Lord Christ ! pity on her ghastly face !
Those dismal hours while the cloudless blue
 Drew the sun higher—He did give her grace ;

Because at last she rose up from her bed,
 And put her raiment on, and knelt before
The blessed rood, and with her dry lips said,
 Muttering the words against the marble floor . 160

' Unless you pardon, what shall I do, Lord,
 But go to hell ? and there see day by day
Foul deed on deed, hear foulest word on word,
 For ever and ever, such as on the way

' To Camelot I heard once from a churl,
 That curled me up upon my jennet's neck
With bitter shame ; how then, Lord, should I curl
 For ages and for ages ? dost thou reck

' That I am beautiful, Lord, even as you
 And your dear Mother ? why did I forget 170
You were so beautiful, and good, and true,
 That you loved me so, Guenevere ?   O yet

' If even I go hell, I cannot choose
 But love you, Christ, yea, though I cannot keep
From loving Launcelot ; O Christ ! must I lose
 My own heart's love ? see though I cannot weep,

' Yet am I very sorry for my sin ;
   Moreover, Christ, I cannot bear that hell,
I am most fain to love you, and to win
   A place in heaven some time—I cannot tell—   180

'Speak to me, Christ ! I kiss, kiss, kiss your feet ;
   Ah ! now I weep ! '—The maid said, ' By the tomb
He waiteth for you, lady,' coming fleet,
   Not knowing what woe filled up all the room.

So Guenevere rose and went to meet him there,
   He did not hear her coming, as he lay
On Arthur's head, till some of her long hair
   Brush'd on the new-cut stone—' Well done ! to pray

' For Arthur, my dear lord, the greatest king
   That ever lived.' ' Guenevere ! Guenevere !   190
Do you not know me, are you gone mad ? fling
   Your arms and hair about me, lest I fear

' You are not Guenevere, but some other thing.'
   ' Pray you forgive me, fair lord Launcelot !
I am not mad, but I am sick ; they cling,
   God's curses, unto such as I am ; not

' Ever again shall we twine arms and lips.'
   ' Yea, she is mad : thy heavy law, O Lord,
Is very tight about her now, and grips
   Her poor heart, so that no right word   200

' Can reach her mouth ; so, Lord, forgive her now,
   That she not knowing what she does, being mad,
Kills me in this way—Guenevere, bend low
   And kiss me once ! for God's love kiss me ! sad

' Though your face is, you look much kinder now ;
   Yea once, once for the last time kiss me, lest I die.'
' Christ ! my hot lips are very near his brow,
   Help me to save his soul !—Yea, verily,

' Across my husband's head, fair Launcelot !
   Fair serpent mark'd with V upon the head !   210
This thing we did while yet he was alive,
   Why not, O twisting knight, now he is dead ?

' Yea, shake ! shake now and shiver ! if you can
    Remember anything for agony,
Pray you remember how when the wind ran
    One cool spring evening through fair aspen-tree,

' And elm and oak about the palace there,
    The king came back from battle, and I stood
To meet him, with my ladies, on the stair,
    My face made beautiful with my young blood.'   220

' Will she lie now, Lord God ? ' ' Remember too,
    Wrung heart, how first before the knights there came
A royal bier, hung round with green and blue,
    About it shone great tapers with sick flame.

' And thereupon Lucius, the Emperor,
    Lay royal-robed, but stone-cold now and dead,
Not able to hold sword or sceptre more,
    But not quite grim ; because his cloven head

' Bore no marks now of Launcelot's bitter sword,
    Being by embalmers deftly solder'd up ;   230
So still it seem'd the face of a great lord,
    Being mended as a craftsman mends a cup.

' Also the heralds sung rejoicingly
    To their long trumpets ; " Fallen under shield,
Here lieth Lucius, King of Italy,
    Slain by Lord Launcelot in open field."

' Thereat the people shouted " Launcelot ! "
    And through the spears I saw you drawing nigh,
You and Lord Arthur—nay, I saw you not,
    But rather Arthur, God would not let die,   240

' I hoped, these many years, he should grow great,
    And in his great arms still encircle me,
Kissing my face, half-blinded with the heat
    Of king's love for the queen I used to be.

' Launcelot, Launcelot, why did he take your hand,
    When he had kissed me in his kingly way ?
Saying, " This is the knight whom all the land
    Calls Arthur's banner, sword, and shield to-day ;

' " Cherish him, love." Why did your long lips cleave
   In such strange way unto my fingers then ?   250
So eagerly glad to kiss, so loath to leave
   When you rose up ? Why among helmed men

' Could I always tell you by your long strong arms,
   And sway like an angel's in your saddle there ?
Why sicken'd I so often with alarms
   Over the tilt-yard ? Why were you more fair

' Than aspens in the autumn at their best ?
   Why did you fill all lands with your great fame,
So that Breuse even, as he rode, fear'd lest
   At turning of the way your shield should flame ?   260

' Was it nought then, my agony and strife ?
   When as day passed by day, year after year,
I found I could not live a righteous life ?
   Didst ever think queens held their truth dear ?

' O, but your lips say, " Yea, but she was cold
   Sometimes, always uncertain as the spring ;
When I was sad she would be overbold,
   Longing for kisses ; " when war-bells did ring,

' The back-toll'd bells of noisy Camelot '—
   ' Now, Lord God, listen ! listen, Guenevere,   270
Though I am weak just now, I think there's not
   A man who dares to say, " You hated her,

' " And left her moaning while you fought your fill
   In the daisied meadows ; " lo you her thin hand,
That on the carven stone can not keep still,
   Because she loves me against God's command,

' Has often been quite wet with tear on tear,
   Tears Launcelot keeps somewhere, surely not
In his own heart, perhaps in Heaven, where
   He will not be these ages.'—' Launcelot !   280

Loud lips, wrung heart ! I say, when the bells rang,
   The noisy back-toll'd bells of Camelot,
There were two spots on earth, the thrushes sang
   In the lonely gardens where my love was not,

' Where I was almost weeping ; I dared not
    Weep quite in those days, lest one maid should say,
In tittering whispers ; "Where is Launcelot
    To wipe with some kerchief those tears away ? "

' Another answer sharply with brows knit,
    And warning hand up, scarcely lower though,   290
" You speak too loud, see you, she heareth it,
    This tigress fair has claws, as I well know,

' " As Launcelot knows too, the poor knight ! well-a-
        day !
    Why met he not with Iseult from the West,
Or, better still, Iseult of Brittany,
    Perchance indeed quite ladyless were best."

' Alas, my maids, you loved not overmuch
    Queen Guenevere, uncertain as sunshine
In March ; forgive me ! for my sin being such,
    About my whole life, all my deeds did twine,   300

' Made me quite wicked ; as I found out then,
    I think ; in the lonely palace, where each morn
We went, my maids and I, to say prayers when
    They sang mass in the chapel on the lawn.

' And every morn I scarce could pray at all,
    For Launcelot's red-golden hair would play,
Instead of sunlight, on the painted wall,
    Mingled with dreams of what the priest did say ;

' Grim curses out of Peter and of Paul ;
    Judging of strange sins in Leviticus ;   310
Another sort of writing on the wall,
    Scored deep across the painted heads of us.

' Christ sitting with the woman at the well,
    And Mary Magdalen repenting there,
Her dimmed eyes scorch'd and red at sight of hell
    So hardly 'scaped, no gold light on her hair.

' And if the priest said anything that seem'd
    To touch upon the sin they said we did,—
(This in their teeth) they look'd as if they deem'd
    That I was spying what thoughts might be hid   320

' Under green-cover'd bosoms, heaving quick
    Beneath quick thoughts ; while they grew red with
        shame,
And gazed down at their feet—while I felt sick,
    And almost shriek'd if one should call my name.

' The thrushes sang in the lone garden there—
    But where you were the birds were scared I trow—
Clanging of arms about pavilions fair,
    Mixed with the knights' laughs ; there, as I well know,

' Rode Launcelot, the king of all the band,
    And scowling Gauwaine, like the night in day,   330
And handsome Gareth, with his great white hand
    Curl'd round the helm-crest, ere he join'd the fray ;

' And merry Dinadan with sharp dark face,
    All true knights loved to see ; and in the fight
Great Tristram, and though helmed you could trace
    In all his bearing the frank noble knight ;

' And by him Palomydes, helmet off,
    He fought, his face brush'd by his hair,
Red heavy swinging hair ; he fear'd a scoff   339
    So overmuch, though what true knight would dare

' To mock that face, fretted with useless care,
    And bitter useless striving after love ?
O Palomydes, with much honour bear
    Beast Glatysaunt upon your shield, above

' Your helm that hides the swinging of your hair,
    And think of Iseult, as your sword drives through
Much mail and plate—O God, let me be there
    A little time, as I was long ago !

' Because stout Gareth lets his spear fall low,
    Gauwaine, and Launcelot, and Dinadan   350
Are helm'd and waiting ; let the trumpets go !
    Bend over, ladies, to see all you can !

' Clench teeth, dames, yea, clasp hands, for Gareth's spear
    Throws Kay from out his saddle, like a stone
From a castle-window when the foe draws near—
    " Iseult ! "—Sir Dinadan rolleth overthrown.

' " Iseult "—again—the pieces of each spear
    Fly fathoms up, and both the great steeds reel ;
" Tristram for Iseult ! "   " Iseult ! " and " Guenevere,"
    The ladies' names bite verily like steel.   360

' They bite—bite me, Lord God !—I shall go mad,
    Or else die kissing him, he is so pale,
He thinks me mad already, O bad ! bad !
    Let me lie down a little while and wail.'

' No longer so, rise up, I pray you, love,
    And slay me really, then we shall be heal'd,
Perchance, in the aftertime by God above.'
    ' Banner of Arthur—with black-blended shield

' Sinister-wise across the fair gold ground !
    Here let me tell you what a knight you are,   370
O sword and shield of Arthur ! you are found
    A crooked sword, I think, that leaves a scar

' On the bearer's arm, so be he thinks it straight,
    Twisted Malay's crease beautiful blue-grey,
Poison'd with sweet fruit ; as he found too late,
    My husband Arthur, on some bitter day !

' O sickle cutting hemlock the day long !
    That the husbandman across his shoulder hangs,
And, going homeward about evensong,   379
    Dies the next morning, struck through by the fangs !

' Banner, and sword, and shield, you dare not pray to die,
    Lest you meet Arthur in the other world,
And knowing who you are, he pass you by,
    Taking short turns that he may watch you curl'd

' Body and face and limbs in agony,
    Lest he weep presently and go away,
Saying, " I loved him once," with a sad sigh—
    Now I have slain him, Lord, let me go too, I pray.
                        [LAUNCELOT *falls.*

' Alas, alas ! I know not what to do,
  If I run fast it is perchance that I   390
May fall and stun myself, much better so,
  Never, never again ! not even when I die.'

LAUNCELOT, *on awaking*.

' I stretch'd my hands towards her and fell down,
  How long I lay in swoon I cannot tell :
My head and hands were bleeding from the stone,
  When I rose up, also I heard a bell.'

SIR GALAHAD, A CHRISTMAS MYSTERY

IT is the longest night in all the year,
  Near on the day when the Lord Christ was born ;
Six hours ago I came and sat down here,
  And ponder'd sadly, wearied and forlorn.

The winter wind that pass'd the chapel-door,
  Sang out a moody tune, that went right well
With mine own thoughts : I look'd down on the floor,
  Between my feet, until I heard a bell

Sound a long way off through the forest deep,
  And toll on steadily ; a drowsiness   10
Came on me, so that I fell half asleep,
  As I sat there not moving : less and less

I saw the melted snow that hung in beads
  Upon my steel-shoes ; less and less I saw
Between the tiles the bunches of small weeds :
  Heartless and stupid, with no touch of awe

Upon me, half-shut eyes upon the ground,
  I thought ; O ! Galahad, the days go by,
Stop and cast up now that which you have found,
  So sorely you have wrought and painfully.   20

Night after night your horse treads down alone
  The sere damp fern, night after night you sit
Holding the bridle like a man of stone,
  Dismal, unfriended, what thing comes of it.

And what if Palomydes also ride,
  And over many a mountain and bare heath
Follow the questing beast with none beside ?
  Is he not able still to hold his breath

With thoughts of Iseult ? doth he not grow pale
  With weary striving, to seem best of all   30
To her, ' as she is best,' he saith ? to fail
  Is nothing to him, he can never fall.

For unto such a man love-sorrow is
  So dear a thing unto his constant heart,
That even if he never win one kiss,
  Or touch from Iseult, it will never part.

And he will never know her to be worse
  Than in his happiest dreams he thinks she is :
Good knight, and faithful, you have 'scaped the curse
  In wonderful-wise ; you have great store of bliss.   40

Yea, what if Father Launcelot ride out,
  Can he not think of Guenevere's arms, round,
Warm and lithe, about his neck, and shout
  Till all the place grows joyful with the sound ?

And when he lists can often see her face,
  And think, ' Next month I kiss you, or next week,
And still you think of me : ' therefore the place
  Grows very pleasant, whatsoever he seek.

But me, who ride alone, some carle shall find
  Dead in my arms in the half-melted snow,   50
When all unkindly with the shifting wind,
  The thaw comes on at Candlemas : I know

Indeed that they will say : ' This Galahad
  If he had lived had been a right good knight ;
Ah ! poor chaste body ! ' but they will be glad,
  Not most alone, but all, when in their sight

That very evening in their scarlet sleeves
  The gay-dress'd minstrels sing ; no maid will talk
Of sitting on my tomb, until the leaves,
  Grown big upon the bushes of the walk,   60

East of the Palace-pleasaunce, make it hard
  To see the minster therefrom : well-a-day !
Before the trees by autumn were well bared,
  I saw a damozel with gentle play,

Within that very walk say last farewell
  To her dear knight, just riding out to find
(Why should I choke to say it ?) the Sangreal,
  And their last kisses sunk into my mind,

Yea, for she stood lean'd forward on his breast,
  Rather, scarce stood ; the back of one dear hand,   70
That it might well be kiss'd, she held and press'd
  Against his lips ; long time they stood there, fann'd

By gentle gusts of quiet frosty wind,
  Till Mador de la porte a-going by,
And my own horsehoofs roused them ; they untwined,
  And parted like a dream. In this way I,

With sleepy face bent to the chapel floor,
  Kept musing half asleep, till suddenly
A sharp bell rang from close beside the door,
  And I leapt up when something pass'd me by,   80

Shrill ringing going with it, still half blind
  I stagger'd after, a great sense of awe
At every step kept gathering on my mind,
  Thereat I have no marvel, for I saw

One sitting on the altar as a throne,
  Whose face no man could say he did not know,
And though the bell still rang, he sat alone,
  With raiment half blood-red, half white as snow.

Right so I fell upon the floor and knelt,
  Not as one kneels in church when mass is said,   90
But in a heap, quite nerveless, for I felt
  The first time what a thing was perfect dread.
MORRIS   P

But mightily the gentle voice came down :
   ' Rise up, and look and listen, Galahad,
Good knight of God, for you will see no frown
   Upon my face ; I come to make you glad.

' For that you say that you are all alone,
   I will be with you always, and fear not
You are uncared for, though no maiden moan
   Above your empty tomb ; for Launcelot,   100

' He in good time shall be my servant too,
   Meantime, take note whose sword first made him
     knight,
And who has loved him alway, yea, and who
   Still trusts him alway, though in all men's sight,

' He is just what you know, O Galahad,
   This love is happy even as you say,
But would you for a little time be glad,
   To make ME sorry long day after day ?

' Her warm arms round his neck half-throttle Me,
   The hot love-tears burn deep like spots of lead,   110
Yea, and the years pass quick : right dismally
   Will Launcelot at one time hang his head ;

' Yea, old and shrivell'd he shall win my love.
   Poor Palomydes fretting out his soul !
Not always is he able, son, to move
   His love, and do it honour : needs must roll

' The proudest destrier sometimes in the dust,
   And then 'tis weary work ; he strives beside
Seem better than he is, so that his trust
   Is always on what chances may betide ;   120

' And so he wears away, my servant, too,
   When all these things are gone, and wretchedly
He sits and longs to moan for Iseult, who
   Is no care now to Palomydes : see,

' O good son Galahad, upon this day,
   Now even, all these things are on your side,
But these you fight not for ; look up, I say,
   And see how I can love you, for no pride

'Closes your eyes, no vain lust keeps them down.
   See now you have ME always ; following   130
That holy vision, Galahad, go on,
   Until at last you come to Me to sing

' In Heaven always, and to walk around
   The garden where I am : ' he ceased, my face
And wretched body fell upon the ground ;
   And when I look'd again, the holy place

Was empty ; but right so the bell again
   Came to the chapel-door, there entered
Two angels first, in white, without a stain,
   And scarlet wings, then after them a bed,   140

Four ladies bore, and set it down beneath
   The very altar-step, and while for fear
I scarcely dared to move or draw my breath,
   These holy ladies gently came a-near,

And quite unarm'd me, saying : ' Galahad,
   Rest here awhile and sleep, and take no thought
Of any other thing than being glad ;
   Hither the Sangreal will be shortly brought,

' Yet must you sleep the while it stayeth here.'
   Right so they went away, and I, being weary,   150
Slept long and dream'd of Heaven : the bell comes near,
   I doubt it grows to morning. Miserere !

*Enter Two Angels in white, with scarlet wings ; also
    Four Ladies in gowns of red and green ; also an
    Angel, bearing in his hands a surcoat of white, with
    a red cross.*

AN ANGEL.

O servant of the high God, Galahad !
   Rise and be arm'd, the Sangreal is gone forth
Through the great forest, and you must be had
   Unto the sea that lieth on the north :

There shall you find the wondrous ship wherein
 The spindles of King Solomon are laid,
And the sword that no man draweth without sin,
 But if he be most pure : and there is stay'd,   160

Hard by, Sir Launcelot, whom you will meet
 In some short space upon that ship : first, though,
Will come here presently that lady sweet,
 Sister of Percival, whom you well know,

And with her Bors and Percival : stand now,
 These ladies will to arm you.

     FIRST LADY, *putting on the hauberke.*
       Galahad,
That I may stand so close beneath your brow,
 I, Margaret of Antioch, am glad.

     SECOND LADY, *girding him with the sword.*
That I may stand and touch you with my hand.
 O Galahad, I, Cecily, am glad.   170

     THIRD LADY, *buckling on the spurs.*
That I may kneel while up above you stand,
 And gaze at me, O holy Galahad,

I, Lucy, am most glad.

     FOURTH LADY, *putting on the basnet.*
      O gentle knight,
That you bow down to us in reverence,
We are most glad, I, Katherine, with delight
 Must needs fall trembling.

     ANGEL, *putting on the crossed surcoat.*
      Galahad, we go hence,

For here, amid the straying of the snow,
 Come Percival's sister, Bors, and Percival.
     [*The Four Ladies carry out the bed,*
      and all go but Galahad.

GALAHAD.

How still and quiet everything seems now :
  They come, too, for I hear the horsehoofs fall.   180

Enter Sir Bors, Sir Percival, *and* his Sister.

Fair friends and gentle lady, God you save !
  A many marvels have been here to-night ;
Tell me what news of Launcelot you have,
  And has God's body ever been in sight ?

SIR BORS.

Why, as for seeing that same holy thing,
  As we were riding slowly side by side,
An hour ago, we heard a sweet voice sing,
  And through the bare twigs saw a great light glide,

With many-colour'd raiment, but far off,   189
  And so pass'd quickly—from the court nought good ;
Poor merry Dinadan, that with jape and scoff
  Kept us all merry, in a little wood

Was found all hack'd and dead : Sir Lionel
  And Gauwaine have come back from the great quest,
Just merely shamed ; and Lauvaine, who loved well
  Your father Launcelot, at the king's behest

Went out to seek him, but was almost slain,
  Perhaps is dead now ; everywhere
The knights come foil'd from the great quest, in vain ;
  In vain they struggle for the vision fair   200

THE CHAPEL IN LYONESS [1]

SIR OZANA LE CURE HARDY.   SIR GALAHAD.
SIR BORS DE GANYS.

SIR OZANA.

ALL day long and every day,
From Christmas-Eve to Whit-Sunday,
Within that Chapel-aisle I lay,
    And no man came a-near.

Naked to the waist was I,
And deep within my breast did lie,
Though no man any blood could spy,
    The truncheon of a spear.

No meat did ever pass my lips.
Those days—(Alas ! the sunlight slips   10
From off the gilded parclose, dips,
    And night comes on apace.)

My arms lay back behind my head ;
Over my raised-up knees was spread
A samite cloth of white and red ;
    A rose lay on my face.

Many a time I tried to shout ;
But as in dream of battle-rout,
My frozen speech would not well out ;
    I could not even weep.   20

With inward sigh I see the sun
Fade off the pillars one by one,
My heart faints when the day is done,
    Because I cannot sleep.

[1] This poem had previously appeared in *The Oxford and Cambridge Magazine,* September 1856.

Sometimes strange thoughts pass through my head ;
Not like a tomb is this my bed,
Yet oft I think that I am dead ;
    That round my tomb is writ,

' Ozana of the hardy heart,
    Knight of the Table Round,   30
Pray for his soul, lords, of your part ;
    A true knight he was found.'

Ah ! me, I cannot fathom it.   [*He sleeps.*

Sir Galahad.

All day long and every day,
Till his madness pass'd away,
I watch'd Ozana as he lay
    Within the gilded screen.

All my singing moved him not :
As I sung my heart grew hot,
With the thought of Launcelot   40
    Far away, I ween.

So I went a little space
From out the chapel, bathed my face
In the stream that runs apace
    By the churchyard wall.

There I pluck'd a faint wild rose,
Hard by where the linden grows
Sighing over silver rows
    Of the lilies tall.

I laid the flower across his mouth ;   50
The sparkling drops seem'd good for drouth ;
He smiled, turn'd round toward the south,
    Held up a golden tress.

The light smote on it from the west :
He drew the covering from his breast,
Against his heart that hair he prest ;
    Death him soon will bless.

Sir Bors.

I enter'd by the western door ;
　　I saw a knight's helm lying there :
I raised my eyes from off the floor,   60
　　And caught the gleaming of his hair.

I stept full softly up to him ;
　　I laid my chin upon his head ;
I felt him smile ; my eyes did swim,
　　I was so glad he was not dead.

I heard Ozana murmur low,
　　' There comes no sleep nor any love.'
But Galahad stoop'd and kiss'd his brow :
　　He shiver'd ; I saw his pale lips move.

Sir Ozana.

There comes no sleep nor any love ;   70
　　Ah me ! I shiver with delight.
I am so weak I cannot move ;
　　God move me to thee, dear, to-night !
Christ help ! I have but little wit :
My life went wrong ; I see it writ,

' Ozana of the hardy heart,
　　Knight of the Table Round,
Pray for his soul, lords, on your part ;
　　A good knight he was found.'   79
Now I begin to fathom it.   [He dies.

Sir Bors.

Galahad sits dreamily :
What strange things may his eyes see,
Great blue eyes fix'd full on me ?
On his soul, Lord, have mercy.

Sir Galahad.

Ozana, shall I pray for thee ?
　　Her cheek is laid to thine ;
No long time hence, also I see
　　Thy wasted fingers twine

Within the tresses of her hair
   That shineth gloriously,   90
Thinly outspread in the clear air
   Against the jasper sea.[1]

SIR PETER HARPDON'S END

In an English castle in Poictou.

Sir PETER HARPDON, *a Gascon knight in the English
service, and* JOHN CURZON, *his lieutenant.*

JOHN CURZON.

OF those three prisoners, that before you came
We took down at St. John's hard by the mill,
Two are good masons ; we have tools enough,
And you have skill to set them working.

SIR PETER.

                    So—

What are their names ?

JOHN CURZON.
              Why, Jacques Aquadent,
And Peter Plombiere, but—

SIR PETER.
                What colour'd hair
Has Peter now ? has Jacques got bow legs ?

JOHN CURZON.
Why, sir, you jest—what matters Jacques' hair,
Or Peter's legs to us ?

SIR PETER.
          O ! John, John, John !
Throw all your mason's tools down the deep well,   10
Hang Peter up and Jacques ; they're no good,
We shall not build, man.

---

[1] In place of the last six lines *The Oxford and Cambridge Magazine*,
September 1856, has these two:
       Her hair against the jasper sea
       Wondrously doth shine.

JOHN CURZON [*going*].

              Shall I call the guard
To hang them, sir ? and yet, sir, for the tools,
We'd better keep them still ; sir, fare you well.
               [*Muttering as he goes.*
What have I done that he should jape at me ?
And why not build ? the walls are weak enough,
And we've two masons and a heap of tools.
              [*Goes, still muttering.*

SIR PETER.

To think a man should have a lump like that
For his lieutenant ! I must call him back,
Or else, as surely as St. George is dead,   20
He'll hang our friends the masons—here, John ! John !

JOHN CURZON.

At your good service, sir.

SIR PETER.

            Come now, and talk
This weighty matter out ; there—we've no stone
To mend our walls with,—neither brick nor stone.

JOHN CURZON.

There is a quarry, sir, some ten miles off.

SIR PETER.

We are not strong enough to send ten men
Ten miles to fetch us stone enough to build,
In three hours' time they would be taken or slain,
The cursed Frenchmen ride abroad so thick.

JOHN CURZON.

But we can send some villaynes to get stone.   30

SIR PETER.

Alas ! John, that we cannot bring them back,
They would go off to Clisson or Sanxere,

And tell them we were weak in walls and men,
Then down go we ; for, look you, times are changed,
And now no longer does the country shake
At sound of English names ; our captains fade
From off our muster-rolls. At Lusac bridge
I dare say you may even yet see the hole
That Chandos beat in dying ; far in Spain
Pembroke is prisoner ; Phelton prisoner here ;   40
Manny lies buried in the Charterhouse ;
Oliver Clisson turn'd these years agone ;
The Captal died in prison ; and, over all,
Edward the prince lies underneath the ground,
Edward the king is dead, at Westminster
The carvers smooth the curls of his long beard,
Everything goes to rack—eh ! and we too.
Now, Curzon, listen ; if they come, these French,
Whom have I got to lean on here, but you ?
A man can die but once, will you die then,   50
Your brave sword in your hand, thoughts in your heart
Of all the deeds we have done here in France—
And yet may do ? So God will have your soul,
Whoever has your body.

JOHN CURZON.

                              Why, sir, I
Will fight till the last moment, until then
Will do whate'er you tell me. Now I see
We must e'en leave the walls ; well, well, perhaps
They're stronger than I think for ; pity, though !
For some few tons of stone, if Guesclin comes.

SIR PETER.

Farewell, John, pray you watch the Gascons well,   60
I doubt them.

JOHN CURZON.
                    Truly, sir, I will watch well. [Goes.

SIR PETER.
Farewell, good lump ! and yet, when all is said,
'Tis a good lump. Why then, if Guesclin comes ;

Some dozen stones from his petrariae,
And, under shelter of his crossbows, just
An hour's steady work with pickaxes,
Then a great noise—some dozen swords and glaives
A-playing on my basnet all at once,
And little more cross purposes on earth
For me.
       Now this is hard : a month ago,
And a few minutes' talk had set things right
'Twixt me and Alice ;—if she had a doubt,
As (may Heaven bless her !) I scarce think she had,
'Twas but their hammer, hammer in her ears,
Of ' how Sir Peter fail'd at Lusac bridge : '
And ' how he was grown moody of late days ;
And ' how Sir Lambert ' (think now !) ' his dear friend,
His sweet, dear cousin, could not but confess
That Peter's talk tended towards the French,
Which he ' (for instance Lambert) ' was glad of,   80
Being ' (Lambert, you see) ' on the French side.'
                          Well,
If I could but have seen her on that day,
Then, when they sent me off !
                  I like to think,
Although it hurts me, makes my head twist, what,
If I had seen her, what I should have said,
What she, my darling, would have said and done.
As thus perchance—
            To find her sitting there,
In the window-seat, not looking well at all,
Crying perhaps, and I say quietly ;
' Alice ! ' she looks up, chokes a sob, looks grave,   90
Changes from pale to red, but, ere she speaks,
Straightway I kneel down there on both my knees,
And say : ' O lady, have I sinn'd, your knight ?
That still you ever let me walk alone
In the rose garden, that you sing no songs
When I am by, that ever in the dance
You quietly walk away when I come near ?
Now that I have you, will you go, think you ? '

Ere she could answer I would speak again,
Still kneeling there.
     ' What ! they have frighted you,
By hanging burs, and clumsily carven puppets, 101
Round my good name ; but afterwards, my love,
I will say what this means ; this moment, see !
Do I kneel here, and can you doubt me ? Yea,'
(For she would put her hands upon my face,)
' Yea, that is best, yea feel, love, am I changed ? '
And she would say : ' Good knight, come, kiss my lips ! '
And afterwards as I sat there would say :

' Please a poor silly girl by telling me
What all those things they talk of really were, 110
For it is true you did not help Chandos,
And true, poor love ! you could not come to me
When I was in such peril.'
      I should say :
' I am like Balen, all things turn to blame—
I did not come to you ? At Bergerath
The constable had held us close shut up,
If from the barriers I had made three steps,
I should have been but slain ; at Lusac, too,
We struggled in a marish half the day,
And came too late at last : you know, my love, 120
How heavy men and horses are all arm'd.
All that Sir Lambert said was pure, unmix'd,
Quite groundless lies ; as you can think, sweet love.'

She, holding tight my hand as we sat there,
Started a little at Sir Lambert's name,
But otherwise she listen'd scarce at all
To what I said. Then with moist, weeping eyes
And quivering lips, that scarcely let her speak,
She said, ' I love you.'

     Other words were few,
The remnant of that hour ; her hand smooth'd down
My foolish head ; she kiss'd me all about 131
My face, and through the tangles of my beard
Her little fingers crept.

O ! God, my Alice,
Not this good way : my lord but sent and said
That Lambert's sayings were taken at their worth,
Therefore that day I was to start, and keep
This hold against the French ; and I am here,—
                              [*Looks out of the window.*
A sprawling lonely gard with rotten walls,
And no one to bring aid if Guesclin comes,
Or any other.
                There's a pennon now !   140
At last.
            But not the constable's, whose arms,
I wonder, does it bear ?   Three golden rings
On a red ground ; my cousin's by the rood !
Well, I should like to kill him, certainly,
But to be kill'd by him—
                              [*A trumpet sounds.*
                That's for a herald ;
I doubt this does not mean assaulting yet.

Enter JOHN CURZON.
What says the herald of our cousin, sir ?

JOHN CURZON.
So please you, sir, concerning your estate,
He has good will to talk with you.

SIR PETER.
                              Outside,
I'll talk with him, close by the gate St. Ives.   150
Is he unarm'd ?

JOHN CURZON.
Yea, sir, in a long gown.

SIR PETER.
Then bid them bring me hither my furr'd gown
With the long sleeves, and under it I'll wear,
By Lambert's leave, a secret coat of mail ;
And will you lend me, John, your little axe ?

I mean the one with Paul wrought on the blade ?
And I will carry it inside my sleeve,
Good to be ready always—you, John, go
And bid them set up many suits of arms,
Bows, archgays, lances, in the base-court, and   160
Yourself, from the south postern setting out,
With twenty men, be ready to break through
Their unguarded rear when I cry out ' St. George ! '

JOHN CURZON.
How, sir ! will you attack him unawares,
And slay him unarm'd ?

SIR PETER.
                    Trust me, John, I know
The reason why he comes here with sleeved gown,
Fit to hide axes up. So, let us go.

                                        [*They go.*

Outside the castle by the great gate ; Sir Lambert *and*
        Sir Peter *seated ; guards attending each, the rest of*
        Sir Lambert's *men drawn up about a furlong off.*

SIR PETER.
And if I choose to take the losing side
Still, does it hurt you ?

SIR LAMBERT.
                    O ! no hurt to me ;
I see you sneering, ' Why take trouble then,   170
Seeing you love me not ? ' look you, our house
(Which, taken altogether, I love much)
Had better be upon the right side now,
If, once for all, it wishes to bear rule
As such a house should : cousin, you're too wise
To feed your hope up fat, that this fair France
Will ever draw two ways again ; this side
The French, wrong-headed, all a-jar
With envious longings ; and the other side
The order'd English, orderly led on   180

By those two Edwards through all wrong and right,
And muddling right and wrong to a thick broth
With that long stick, their strength.   This is all changed,
The true French win, on either side you have
Cool-headed men, good at a tilting match,
And good at setting battles in array,
And good at squeezing taxes at due time ;
Therefore by nature we French being here
Upon our own big land—

[SIR PETER *laughs aloud*.
Well Peter ! well !

What makes you laugh ?

SIR PETER.
Hearing you sweat to prove
All this I know so well ; but you have read   191
The siege of Troy ?

SIR LAMBERT.
O ! yea, I know it well.

SIR PETER.
There ! they were wrong, as wrong as men could be ;
For, as I think, they found it such delight
To see fair Helen going through their town :
Yea, any little common thing she did
(As stooping to pick a flower) seem'd so strange,
So new in its great beauty, that they said :
' Here we will keep her living in this town,
Till all burns up together.'   And so, fought,   200
In a mad whirl of knowing they were wrong ;
Yea, they fought well, and ever, like a man
That hangs legs off the ground by both his hands,
Over some great height, did they struggle sore,
Quite sure to slip at last ; wherefore, take note
How almost all men, reading that sad siege,
Hold for the Trojans ; as I did at least,
Thought Hector the best knight a long way :
Now
Why should I not do this thing that I think,

For even when I come to count the gains,   210
I have them my side : men will talk, you know,
(We talk of Hector, dead so long agone,)
When I am dead, of how this Peter clung
To what he thought the right ; of how he died,
Perchance, at last, doing some desperate deed
Few men would care do now, and this is gain
To me, as ease and money is to you,
Moreover, too, I like the straining game
Of striving well to hold up things that fall ;
So one becomes great ; see you ! in good times   220
All men live well together, and you, too,
Live dull and happy—happy ? not so quick,
Suppose sharp thoughts begin to burn you up.
Why then, but just to fight as I do now,
A halter round my neck, would be great bliss.
O ! I am well off.   [*Aside.*
          Talk, and talk, and talk,
I know this man has come to murder me,
And yet I talk still.

SIR LAMBERT.

          If your side were right,
You might be, though you lost ; but if I said,
' You are a traitor, being, as you are,   230
Born Frenchman.' What are Edwards unto you,
Or Richards ?

SIR PETER.

          Nay, hold there, my Lambert, hold !
For fear your zeal should bring you to some harm,
Don't call me traitor.

SIR LAMBERT.

          Furthermore, my knight,
Men call you slippery on your losing side,
When at Bordeaux I was ambassador,
I heard them say so, and could scarce say ' Nay.'
          [*He takes hold of something in his
                    sleeve, and rises.*

SIR PETER (*rising*).
They lied—and you lie, not for the first time.
What have you got there, fumbling up your sleeve,
A stolen purse ?

SIR LAMBERT.
                    Nay, liar in your teeth !   240
Dead liar too ; St Dennis and St. Lambert !
                    [*Strikes at* Sir Peter *with a dagger.*

SIR PETER (*striking him flatlings with his axe*).
How thief ! thief ! thief ! so there, fair thief, so there,
St. George Guienne ! glaives for the castellan !
You French, you are but dead, unless you lay
Your spears upon the earth. St. George Guienne !

Well done, John Curzon, how he has them now.

In the Castle.

JOHN CURZON.
What shall we do with all these prisoners, sir ?

SIR PETER
Why put them all to ransom, those that can
Pay anything, but not too light though, John,
Seeing we have them on the hip : for those   250
That have no money, that being certified,
Why turn them out of doors before they spy ;
But bring Sir Lambert guarded unto me.

JOHN CURZON.
I will, fair sir.   [*He goes,*

SIR PETER.
            I do not wish to kill him,
Although I think I ought ; he shall go mark'd,
By all the saints, though !

Enter Lambert (*guarded*).

                 Now, Sir Lambert, now !
What sort of death do you expect to get,
Being taken this way ?

              Sɪʀ Lᴀᴍʙᴇʀᴛ.

                 Cousin ! cousin ! think !
I am your own blood ; may God pardon me !
I am not fit to die ; if you knew all,   260
All I have done since I was young and good.
O ! you would give me yet another chance,
As God would, that I might wash all clear out,
By serving you and Him. Let me go now !
And I will pay you down more golden crowns
Of ransom than the king would !

              Sɪʀ Pᴇᴛᴇʀ.

                   Well, stand back,
And do not touch me ! No, you shall not die,
Nor yet pay ransom. You, John Curzon, cause
Some carpenters to build a scaffold, high,
Outside the gate ; when it is built, sound out   270
To all good folks, ' Come, see a traitor punish'd ! '
Take me my knight, and set him up thereon,
And let the hangman shave his head quite clean,
And cut his ears off close up to the head ;
And cause the minstrels all the while to play
Soft music, and good singing ; for this day
Is my high day of triumph ; is it not,
Sir Lambert ?

              Sɪʀ Lᴀᴍʙᴇʀᴛ.

             Ah ! on your own blood,
Own name, you heap this foul disgrace ? you dare,
With hands and fame thus sullied, to go back   280
And take the Lady Alice—

              Sɪʀ Pᴇᴛᴇʀ.

                Say her name
Again, and you are dead, slain here by me.

Why should I talk with you, I'm master here,
And do not want your schooling ; is it not
My mercy that you are not dangling dead
There in the gateway with a broken neck ?

SIR LAMBERT.

Such mercy ! why not kill me then outright ?
To die is nothing ; but to live that all
May point their fingers ! yea, I'd rather die.

JOHN CURZON.

Why, will it make you any uglier man   290
To lose your ears ? they're much too big for you,
You ugly Judas !

SIR PETER.

Hold, John !   [*To* Lambert.
            That's your choice,
To die, mind ! Then you shall die—Lambert mine,
I thank you now for choosing this so well,
It saves me much perplexity and doubt ;
Perchance an ill deed too, for half I count
This sparing traitors is an ill deed.
                            Well,
Lambert, die bravely, and we're almost friends.

SIR LAMBERT, *grovelling.*

O God ! this is a fiend and not a man ;
Will some one save me from him ? help, help, help !
I will not die.

SIR PETER.

            Why, what is this I see ?   301
A man who is a knight, and bandied words
So well just now with me, is lying down,
Gone mad for fear like this ! So, so, you thought
You knew the worst, and might say what you pleased.
I should have guess'd this from a man like you.
Eh ! righteous Job would give up skin for skin,
Yea, all a man can have for simple life,

And we talk fine, yea, even a hound like this,
Who needs must know that when he dies, deep hell
Will hold him fast for ever—so fine we talk,   311
' Would rather die '—all that. Now sir, get up !
And choose again : shall it be head sans ears,
Or trunk sans head ?
             John Curzon, pull him up !
What, life then ? go and build the scaffold, John.

Lambert, I hope that never on this earth
We meet again ; that you'll turn out a monk,
And mend the life I give you, so, farewell,
I'm sorry you're a rascal. John, despatch.

In the French camp before the Castle.

Sir Peter *prisoner,* Guesclin, Clisson, Sir Lambert.

SIR PETER.

So now is come the ending of my life ;   320
If I could clear this sickening lump away
That sticks in my dry throat, and say a word,
Guesclin might listen.

GUESCLIN.

             Tell me, fair sir knight,
If you have been clean liver before God,
And then you need not fear much ; as for me,
I cannot say I hate you, yet my oath,
And cousin Lambert's ears here clench the thing.

SIR PETER.

I knew you could not hate me, therefore I
Am bold to pray for life ; 'twill harm your cause
To hang knights of good name, harm here in France
I have small doubt, at any rate hereafter   331
Men will remember you another way
Than I should care to be remember'd, ah !
Although hot lead runs through me for my blood,
All this falls cold as though I said, ' Sweet lords,
Give back my falcon ! '

See how young I am,
Do you care altogether more for France,
Say rather one French faction, than for all
The state of Christendom ? a gallant knight,
As (yea, by God !) I have been, is more worth   340
Than many castles ; will you bring this death,
For a mere act of justice, on my head ?

   Think how it ends all, death ! all other things
Can somehow be retrieved, yea, send me forth
Naked and maimed, rather than slay me here ;
Then somehow will I get me other clothes,
And somehow will I get me some poor horse,
And, somehow clad in poor old rusty arms,
Will ride and smite among the serried glaives,
Fear not death so ; for I can tilt right well,   350
Let me not say ' I could ' ; I know all tricks,
That sway the sharp sword cunningly ; ah you,
You, my Lord Clisson, in the other days
Have seen me learning these, yea, call to mind,
How in the trodden corn by Chartrés town,
When you were nearly swooning from the back
Of your black horse, those three blades slid at once
From off my sword's edge ; pray for me, my lord !

                    CLISSON.

Nay, this is pitiful, to see him die.
My Lord the Constable, I pray you note   360
That you are losing some few thousand crowns
By slaying this man ; also think ; his lands
Along the Garonne river lie for leagues,
And are right rich, a many mills he has,
Three abbeys of grey monks do hold of him,
Though wishing well for Clement, as we do ;
I know the next heir, his old uncle, well,
Who does not care two deniers for the knight
As things go now, but slay him, and then see,
How he will bristle up like any perch,   370
With curves of spears. What ! do not doubt, my lord,
You'll get the money, this man saved my life,

And I will buy him for two thousand crowns ;
Well, five then—eh ! what ! ' No ' again ? well then,
Ten thousand crowns ?

GUESCLIN.

         My sweet lord, much I grieve
I cannot please you, yea, good sooth, I grieve
This knight must die, as verily he must ;
For I have sworn it, so men take him out,
Use him not roughly.

SIR LAMBERT, *coming forward.*
            Music, do you know,
Music will suit you well, I think, because   380
You look so mild, like Laurence being grill'd ;
Or perhaps music soft and slow, because
This is high day of triumph unto me,
Is it not, Peter ?
         You are frighten'd, though,
Eh ! you are pale, because this hurts you much,
Whose life was pleasant to you, not like mine,
You ruin'd wretch ! Men mock me in the streets,
Only in whispers loud, because I am
Friend of the Constable ; will this please you,
Unhappy Peter ? once a-going home,   390
Without my servants, and a little drunk,
At midnight through the lone dim lamp-lit streets,
A whore came up and spat into my eyes,
(Rather to blind me than to make me see),
But she was very drunk, and tottering back,
Even in the middle of her laughter, fell
And cut her head against the pointed stones,
While I lean'd on my staff, and look'd at her,
And cried, being drunk.
         Girls would not spit at you,
You are so handsome, I think verily   400
Most ladies would be glad to kiss your eyes,
And yet you will be hung like a cur dog
Five minutes hence, and grow black in the face,
And curl your toes up. Therefore I am glad.

Guess why I stand and talk this nonsense now,
With Guesclin getting ready to play chess,
And Clisson doing something with his sword,
I can't see what, talking to Guesclin though,
I don't know what about, perhaps of you.
But, cousin Peter, while I stroke your beard,   410
Let me say this, I'd like to tell you now
That your life hung upon a game of chess,
That if, say, my squire Robert here should beat,
Why you should live, but hang if I beat him ;
Then guess, clever Peter, what I should do then ,
Well, give it up ? why, Peter, I should let
My squire Robert beat me, then you would think
That you were safe, you know ; Eh ? not at all,
But I should keep you three days in some hold,
Giving you salt to eat, which would be kind,   420
Considering the tax there is on salt ;
And afterwards should let you go, perhaps ?
No I should not, but I should hang you, sir,
With a red rope in lieu of mere grey rope.

But I forgot, you have not told me yet
If you can guess why I talk nonsense thus,
Instead of drinking wine while you are hang'd ?
You are not quick at guessing, give it up.
This is the reason ; here I hold your hand,
And watch you growing paler, see you writhe,   430
And this, my Peter, is a joy so dear,
I cannot by all striving tell you how
I love it, nor I think, good man, would you
Quite understand my great delight therein ;
You, when you had me underneath you once,
Spat as it were, and said, ' Go take him out,'
(That they might do that thing to me whereat,
E'en now this long time off I could well shriek,)
And then you tried forget I ever lived,
And sunk your hating into other things ;   440
While I—St. Dennis ! though, I think you'll faint,
Your lips are grey so ; yes, you will, unless
You let it out and weep like a hurt child ;

Hurrah ! you do now. Do not go just yet,
For I am Alice, am right like her now ;
Will you not kiss me on the lips, my love ?—

CLISSON.

You filthy beast, stand back and let him go,
Or by God's eyes I'll choke you.
                    [*Kneeling to* Sir Peter.
                         Fair sir knight,
I kneel upon my knees and pray to you
That you would pardon me for this your death ;   450
God knows how much I wish you still alive,
Also how heartily I strove to save
Your life at this time ; yea, he knows quite well,
(I swear it, so forgive me !) how I would,
If it were possible, give up my life
Upon this grass for yours ; fair knight, although,
He knowing all things knows this thing too, well,
Yet when you see his face some short time hence
Tell him I tried to save you.

SIR PETER.

                         O ! my lord,
I cannot say this is as good as life,   460
But yet it makes me feel far happier now,
And if at all, after a thousand years,
I see God's face, I will speak loud and bold,
And tell Him you were kind, and like Himself ;
Sir, may God bless you !
                    Did you note how I
Fell weeping just now ? pray you, do not think
That Lambert's taunts did this, I hardly heard
The base things that he said, being deep in thought
Of all things that have happen'd since I was
A little child ; and so at last I thought   470
Of my true lady : truly, sir, it seem'd
No longer gone than yesterday, that this
Was the sole reason God let me be born
Twenty five years ago, that I might love
Her, my sweet lady, and be loved by her ;

This seem'd so yesterday, to-day death comes,
And is so bitter strong, I cannot see
Why I was born.
        But as a last request,
I pray you, O kind Clisson, send some man,
Some good man, mind you, to say how I died,   480
And take my last love to her : fare-you-well,
And may God keep you ; I must go now, lest
I grow too sick with thinking on these things ;
Likewise my feet are wearied of the earth,
From whence I shall be lifted up right soon.
                        [As he goes.
Ah me ! shamed too, I wept at fear of death ;
And yet not so, I only wept because
There was no beautiful lady to kiss me
Before I died, and sweetly wish good speed
From her dear lips. O for some lady, though   490
I saw her ne'er before ; Alice, my love,
I do not ask for ; Clisson was right kind,
If he had been a woman, I should die
Without this sickness : but I am all wrong,
So wrong and hopelessly afraid to die.
There, I will go.
        My God ! how sick I am,
If only she could come and kiss me now.

    The Hotel de la Barde, Bordeaux.
The LADY ALICE DE LA BARDE *looking out of a window*
           into the street.
No news yet ! surely, still he holds his own ;
That garde stands well ; I mind me passing it
Some months ago ; God grant the walls are strong !
I heard some knights say something yestereve,   501
I tried hard to forget : words far apart
Struck on my heart ; something like this ; one said,
' What eh ! a Gascon with an English name,
Harpdon ? ' then nought, but afterwards, ' Poictou.'
As one who answers to a question ask'd ;
Then carelessly regretful came, ' No, no.'
Whereto in answer loud and eagerly,

One said, ' Impossible !   Christ, what foul play ! '
And went off angrily ; and while thenceforth   510
I hurried gaspingly afraid, I heard,
' Guesclin ; ' ' Five thousand men-at-arms ; ' ' Clisson.'
My heart misgives me it is all in vain
I send these succours ; and in good time there !
Their trumpet sounds, ah ! here they are ; good knights,
God up in Heaven keep you.
      If they come
And find him prisoner—for I can't believe
Guesclin will slay him, even though they storm—
(The last horse turns the corner.)
       God in Heaven !
What have I got to thinking of at last !   520
That thief I will not name is with Guesclin,
Who loves him for his lands.   My love ! my love !
O, if I lose you after all the past,
What shall I do ?
     I cannot bear the noise
And light street out there, with this thought alive,
Like any curling snake within my brain ;
Let me just hide my head within these soft
Deep cushions, there to try and think it out.
      [*Lying in the window-seat.*
I cannot hear much noise now, and I think
That I shall go to sleep : it all sounds dim   530
And faint, and I shall soon forget most things ;
Yea, almost that I am alive and here ;
It goes slow, comes slow, like a big mill-wheel
On some broad stream, with long green weeds a-sway,
And soft and slow it rises and it falls,
Still going onward.
    Lying so, one kiss,
And I should be in Avalon asleep,
Among the poppies, and the yellow flowers ;
And they should brush my cheek, my hair being spread
Far out among the stems ; soft mice and small   540
Eating and creeping all about my feet,
Red shod and tired ; and the flies should come
Creeping o'er my broad eyelids unafraid ;

And there should be a noise of water going,
Clear blue, fresh water breaking on the slates,
Likewise the flies should creep—God's eyes! God help,
A trumpet?   I will run fast, leap adown
The slippery sea-stairs, where the crabs fight.

                                        Ah!

I was half dreaming, but the trumpet's true,
He stops here at our house.   The Clisson arms?   550
Ah, now for news.   But I must hold my heart,
And be quite gentle till he is gone out ;
And afterwards,—but he is still alive,
He must be still alive.

                Enter a Squire *of* Clisson's.
                        Good day, fair sir,
I give you welcome, knowing whence you come.

                        SQUIRE.

My Lady Alice de la Barde, I come
From Oliver Clisson, knight and mighty lord,
Bringing you tidings :   I make bold to hope
You will not count me villain, even if
They wring your heart ;   nor hold me still in hate.   560
For I am but a mouthpiece after all,
A mouthpiece, too, of one who wishes well
To you and your's.

                        ALICE.

                Can you talk faster, sir,
Get over all this quicker ?   fix your eyes
On mine, I pray you, and whate'er you see,
Still go on talking fast, unless I fall,
Or bid you stop.

                        SQUIRE.

                I pray your pardon then,
And, looking in your eyes, fair lady, say
I am unhappy that your knight is dead.
Take heart, and listen !   let me tell you all.   570
We were five thousand goodly men-at-arms,

And scant five hundred had he in that hold ;
His rotten sand-stone walls were wet with rain,
And fell in lumps wherever a stone hit ;
Yet for three days about the barrier there
The deadly glaives were gather'd, laid across,
And push'd and pull'd ; the fourth our engines came ;
But still amid the crash of falling walls,
And roar of lombards, rattle of hard bolts,
The steady bow-strings flash'd, and still stream'd out
St. George's banner, and the seven swords,   581
And still they cried, ' St. George Guienne,' until
Their walls were flat as Jericho's of old,
And our rush came, and cut them from the keep.

ALICE.

Stop, sir, and tell me if you slew him then,
And where he died, if you can really mean
That Peter Harpdon, the good knight, is dead ?

SQUIRE.

Fair lady, in the base-court——

ALICE.

                              What base-court ?
What do you talk of ?   Nay, go on, go on ;
'Twas only something gone within my head :   590
Do you not know, one turns one's head round quick,
And something cracks there with sore pain ? go on,
And still look at my eyes.

SQUIRE.

                    Almost alone,
There in the base-court fought he with his sword,
Using his left hand much, more than the wont
Of most knights now-a-days ; our men gave back,
For wheresoever he hit a downright blow,
Some one fell bleeding, for no plate could hold
Against the sway of body and great arm ;
Till he grew tired, and some man (no ! not I,   600
I swear not I, fair lady, as I live !)

Thrust at him with a glaive between the knees,
And threw him ; down he fell, sword undermost ;
Many fell on him, crying out their cries,
Tore his sword from him, tore his helm off, and——

ALICE.

Yea, slew him ; I am much too young to live,
Fair God, so let me die.
                                    You have done well,
Done all your message gently, pray you go,
Our knights will make you cheer ; moreover, take
This bag of franks for your expenses.
                                    [*The* Squire *kneels.*
                                    But   610
You do not go ; still looking at my face,
You kneel ! what, squire, do you mock me then ?
You need not tell me who has set you on,
But tell me only, 'tis a made-up tale.
You are some lover may-be, or his friend ;
Sir, if you loved me once, or your friend loved,
Think, is it not enough that I kneel down
And kiss your feet ? your jest will be right good
If you give in now, carry it too far,
And 'twill be cruel ; not yet ? but you weep   620
Almost, as though you loved me ; love me then,
And go to Heaven by telling all your sport,
And I will kiss you, then with all my heart,
Upon the mouth ; O ! what can I do then
To move you ?

SQUIRE.

                        Lady fair, forgive me still !
You know I am so sorry, but my tale
Is not yet finish'd :
                        So they bound his hands,
And brought him tall and pale to Guesclin's tent,
Who, seeing him, leant his head upon his hand,
And ponder'd somewhile, afterwards, looking up—   630
Fair dame, what shall I say ?

ALICE.
                    Yea, I know now,
Good squire, you may go now with my thanks.

SQUIRE.

Yet, lady, for your own sake I say this,
Yea, for my own sake, too, and Clisson's sake.
When Guesclin told him he must be hanged soon,
Within a while he lifted up his head
And spoke for his own life ; not crouching, though,
As abjectly afraid to die, nor yet
Sullenly brave as many a thief will die ;
Nor yet as one that plays at japes with God :   640
Few words he spoke ; not so much what he said
Moved us, I think, as, saying it, there played
Strange tenderness from that big soldier there
About his pleading ; eagerness to live
Because folk loved him, and he loved them back,
And many gallant plans unfinish'd now
For ever. Clisson's heart, which may God bless !
Was moved to pray for him, but all in vain ;
Wherefore I bring this message :
                              That he waits,
Still loving you, within the little church   650
Whose windows, with the one eye of the light
Over the altar, every night behold
The great dim broken walls he strove to keep !

There my Lord Clisson did his burial well.
Now, lady, I will go ; God give you rest !

ALICE.

Thank Clisson from me, squire, and farewell !
And now to keep myself from going mad.
Christ ! I have been a many times to church,
And, ever since my mother taught me prayers,
Have used them daily, but to-day I wish   660
To pray another way ; come face to face,
O Christ, that I may clasp your knees and pray,

I know not what, at any rate come now
From one of many places where you are ;
Either in Heaven amid thick angel wings,
Or sitting on the altar strange with gems,
Or high up in the dustiness of the apse ;
Let us go, You and I, a long way off,
To the little damp, dark, Poitevin church ;
While you sit on the coffin in the dark,   670
Will I lie down, my face on the bare stone
Between your feet, and chatter anything
I have heard long ago, what matters it
So I may keep you there, your solemn face
And long hair even-flowing on each side,
Until you love me well enough to speak,
And give me comfort ; yea, till o'er your chin,
And cloven red beard the great tears roll down
In pity for my misery, and I die,
Kissed over by you.

             Eh Guesclin ! if I were   680
Like Countess Mountfort now, that kiss'd the knight,
Across the salt sea come to fight for her ;
Ah ! just to go about with many knights,
Wherever you went, and somehow on one day,
In a thick wood to catch you off your guard,
Let you find, you and your some fifty friends,
Nothing but arrows wheresoe'er you turn'd,
Yea, and red crosses, great spears over them ;
And so, between a lane of my true men,
To walk up pale and stern and tall, and with   690
My arms on my surcoat, and his therewith,
And then to make you kneel, O knight Guesclin ;
And then—alas ! alas ! when all is said,
What could I do but let you go again,
Being pitiful woman ?   I get no revenge,
Whatever happens ; and I get no comfort,
I am but weak, and cannot move my feet,
But as men bid me.

             Strange I do not die.
Suppose this had not happen'd after all ;
I will lean out again and watch for news.   700

I wonder how long I can still feel thus,
As though I watch'd for news, feel as I did
Just half-an-hour ago, before this news.
How all the street is humming, some men sing,
And some men talk ; some look up at the house,
Then lay their heads together and look grave ;
Their laughter pains me sorely in the heart,
Their thoughtful talking makes my head turn round,
Yea, some men sing, what is it then they sing ?
Eh Launcelot, and love and fate and death ; 710
They ought to sing of him who was as wight
As Launcelot or Wade, and yet avail'd
Just nothing, but to fail and fail and fail,
And so at last to die and leave me here,
Alone and wretched ; yea, perhaps they will,
When many years are past, make songs of us ;
God help me, though, truly I never thought
That I should make a story in this way,
A story that his eyes can never see.

[*One sings from outside.*]

Therefore be it believed 720
Whatsoever he grieved,
Whan his horse was relieved,
    This Launcelot,

Beat down on his knee,
Right valiant was he
God's body to see,
    Though he saw it not.

Right valiant to move,
But for his sad love
The high God above 730
    Stinted his praise.

Yet so he was glad
That his son Lord Galahad
That high joyaunce had
    All his life-days.

> *Sing we therefore then*
> *Launcelot's praise again,*
> *For he wan crownés ten,*
>   *If he wan not twelve.*

> *To his death from his birth*   740
> *He was muckle of worth,*
> *Lay him in the cold earth,*
>   *A long grave ye may delve.*

> *Omnes homines benedicite!*
> *This last fitte ye may see,*
> *All men pray for me,*
> *Who made this history*
> *Cunning and fairly.*

RAPUNZEL

THE PRINCE, *being in the wood near the tower*
in the evening.

I COULD not even think
  What made me weep that day
When out of the council-hall
  The courtiers pass'd away,—

THE WITCH.

Rapunzel, Rapunzel,
  Let down your hair!

RAPUNZEL.

Is it not true that every day
She climbeth up the same strange way,
Her scarlet cloak spread broad and gay,
    Over my golden hair ?   10

THE PRINCE.

And left me there alone,
  To think on what they said ;
'Thou art a king's own son,
  'Tis fit that thou should'st wed.'

THE WITCH.
Rapunzel, Rapunzel,
Let down your hair !

RAPUNZEL.
When I undo the knotted mass,
Fathoms below the shadows pass
Over my hair along the grass.
    O my golden hair !   20

THE PRINCE.
I put my armour on,
  Thinking on what they said ;
' Thou art a king's own son,
  'Tis fit that thou should'st wed.'

THE WITCH.
Rapunzel, Rapunzel,
Let down your hair !

RAPUNZEL.
See on the marble parapet
I lean my brow, strive to forget
That fathoms below my hair grows wet
    With the dew, my golden hair.   30

THE PRINCE.
I rode throughout the town,
  Men did not bow the head,
Though I was the king's own son ;
  ' He rides to dream,' they said.

THE WITCH.
Rapunzel, Rapunzel,
Wind up your hair !

RAPUNZEL.
See, on the marble parapet
The faint red stains with tears are wet ;
The long years pass, no help comes yet
    To free my golden hair.   40

The Prince.

For leagues and leagues I rode,
  Till hot my armour grew,
Till underneath the leaves
  I felt the evening dew.

The Witch.

Rapunzel, Rapunzel,
  Weep through your hair !

Rapunzel.

And yet—but I am growing old,
For want of love my heart is cold,
Years pass, the while I loose and fold
    The fathoms of my hair.   50

The Prince, *in the morning*.

I have heard tales of men, who in the night
  Saw paths of stars let down to earth from heaven,
Who follow'd them until they reach'd the light
  Wherein they dwell, whose sins are all forgiven ;

But who went backward when they saw the gate
  Of diamond, nor dared to enter in ;
All their life long they were content to wait,
  Purging them patiently of every sin.

I must have had a dream of some such thing,
  And now am just awaking from that dream ;   60
For even in grey dawn those strange words ring
  Through heart and brain, and still I see that gleam.

For in my dream at sunset-time I lay
  Beneath these beeches, mail and helmet off,
Right full of joy that I had come away
  From court ; for I was patient of the scoff

That met me always there from day to day,
  From any knave or coward of them all ;
I was content to live that wretched way ;
  For truly till I left the council-hall,   70

And rode forth arm'd beneath the burning sun,
   My gleams of happiness were faint and few,
But then I saw my real life had begun,
   And that I should be strong quite well I knew.

For I was riding out to look for love,
   Therefore the birds within the thickets sung,
Even in hot noontide, as I pass'd, above
   The elms o'ersway'd with longing towards me hung.

Now some few fathoms from the place where I
   Lay in the beech-wood, was a tower fair,   80
The marble corners faint against the sky ;
   And dreamily I wonder'd what lived there :

Because it seem'd a dwelling for a queen,
   No belfry for the swinging of great bells ;
No bolt or stone had ever crush'd the green
   Shafts, amber and rose walls, no soot that tells

Of the Norse torches burning up the roofs,
   On the flower-carven marble could I see ;
But rather on all sides I saw the proofs
   Of a great loneliness that sicken'd me ;   90

Making me feel a doubt that was not fear,
   Whether my whole life long had been a dream,
And I should wake up soon in some place, where
   The piled-up arms of the fighting angels gleam ;

Not born as yet, but going to be born,
   No naked baby as I was at first,
But an armèd knight, whom fire, hate and scorn
   Could turn from nothing : my heart almost burst

Beneath the beeches, as I lay a-dreaming,
   I tried so hard to read this riddle through,   100
To catch some golden cord that I saw gleaming
   Like gossamer against the autumn blue.

But while I ponder'd these things, from the wood
   There came a black-hair'd woman, tall and bold,
Who strode straight up to where the tower stood,
   And cried out shrilly words, whereon behold—

THE WITCH, *from the tower*.
Rapunzel, Rapunzel,
Let down your hair !

THE PRINCE.

Ah Christ ! it was no dream then, but there stood
  (She comes again) a maiden passing fair,   110
Against the roof, with face turn'd to the wood,
  Bearing within her arms waves of her yellow hair.

I read my riddle when I saw her stand,
  Poor love ! her face quite pale against her hair,
Praying to all the leagues of empty land
  To save her from the woe she suffer'd there.

To think ! they trod upon her golden hair
  In the witches' sabbaths ; it was a delight
For these foul things, while she, with thin feet bare,
  Stood on the roof upon the winter night,   120

To plait her dear hair into many plaits,
  And then, while God's eye look'd upon the thing,
In the very likenesses of Devil's bats,
  Upon the ends of her long hair to swing.

And now she stood above the parapet,
  And, spreading out her arms, let her hair flow,
Beneath that veil her smooth white forehead set
  Upon the marble, more I do not know ;

Because before my eyes a film of gold
  Floated, as now it floats.   O unknown love,   130
Would that I could thy yellow stair behold,
  If still thou standest with lead roof above !

THE WITCH, *as she passes*.
Is there any who will dare
To climb up the yellow stair,
Glorious Rapunzel's golden hair ?

The Prince.

If it would please God make you sing again,
  I think that I might very sweetly die,
My soul somehow reach heaven in joyous pain,
  My heavy body on the beech-nuts lie.

Now I remember ; what a most strange year,   140
  Most strange and awful, in the beechen wood
I have pass'd now ; I still have a faint fear
  It is a kind of dream not understood.

I have seen no one in this wood except
  The witch and her ; have heard no human tones,
But when the witches' revelry has crept
  Between the very jointing of my bones.

Ah ! I know now ; I could not go away,
  But needs must stop to hear her sing that song
She always sings at dawning of the day.   150
  I am not happy here, for I am strong,

And every morning do I whet my sword,
  Yet Rapunzel still weeps within the tower,
And still God ties me down to the green sward,
  Because I cannot see the gold stair floating lower.

Rapunzel *sings from the tower.*

My mother taught me prayers
To say when I had need !
I have so many cares,
That I can take no heed
Of many words in them ;   160
But I remember this :
Christ, bring me to thy bliss.
Mary, maid withouten wem,
Keep me ! I am lone, I wis,
Yet besides I have made this
By myself : *Give me a kiss,*
Dear God, dwelling up in heaven!
Also : *Send me a true knight,*
Lord Christ, with a steel sword, bright,

Broad, and trenchant ; yea, and seven   170
Spans from hilt to point, O Lord !
And let the handle of his sword
Be gold on silver, Lord in heaven !
Such a sword as I see gleam
Sometimes, when they let me dream.

Yea, besides, I have made this :
Lord, give Mary a dear kiss,
And let gold Michael, who look'd down,
When I was there, on Rouen town
From the spire, bring me that kiss   180
On a lily ! Lord, do this !

These prayers on the dreadful nights,
When the witches plait my hair,
And the fearfullest of sights
On the earth and in the air,
Will not let me close my eyes,
I murmur often, mix'd with sighs,
That my weak heart will not hold
At some things that I behold.
Nay, not sighs, but quiet groans,   190
That swell out the little bones
Of my bosom ; till a trance
God sends in middle of that dance,
And I behold the countenance
Of Michael, and can feel no more
The bitter east wind biting sore
My naked feet ; can see no more
The crayfish on the leaden floor,
That mock with feeler and grim claw.

Yea, often in that happy trance,   200
Beside the blessed countenance
Of golden Michael, on the spire
Glowing all crimson in the fire
Of sunset, I behold a face,
Which sometime, if God give me grace,
May kiss me in this very place.

Evening in the tower.

RAPUNZEL

It grows half way between the dark and light ;
   Love, we have been six hours here alone,
I fear that she will come before the night,
   And if she finds us thus we are undone.   210

THE PRINCE.

Nay, draw a little nearer, that your breath
   May touch my lips, let my cheek feel your arm ;
Now tell me, did you ever see a death,
   Or ever see a man take mortal harm ?

RAPUNZEL.

Once came two knights and fought with swords below,
   And while they fought I scarce could look at all,
My head swam so, after a moaning low
   Drew my eyes down ; I saw against the wall

One knight lean dead, bleeding from head and breast,
   Yet seem'd it like a line of poppies red   220
In the golden twilight, as he took his rest,
   In the dusky time he scarcely seemed dead.

But the other, on his face six paces off,
   Lay moaning, and the old familiar name
He mutter'd through the grass, seem'd like a scoff
   Of some lost soul remembering his past fame.

His helm all dinted lay beside him there,
   The visor-bars were twisted towards the face,
The crest, which was a lady very fair,
   Wrought wonderfully, was shifted from its place.

The shower'd mail-rings on the speed-walk lay,   231
   Perhaps my eyes were dazzled with the light
That blazed in the west, yet surely on that day
   Some crimson thing had changed the grass from bright

Pure green I love so.   But the knight who died
   Lay there for days after the other went ;
Until one day I heard a voice that cried,
   ' Fair knight, I see Sir Robert we were sent

' To carry dead or living to the king.'
 So the knights came and bore him straight away
On their lance truncheons, such a batter'd thing, 241
 His mother had not known him on that day,

But for his helm-crest, a gold lady fair
 Wrought wonderfully.

The Prince.

     Ah, they were brothers then,
And often rode together, doubtless where
 The swords were thickest, and were loyal men,

Until they fell in these same evil dreams.

Rapunzel.

 Yea, love ; but shall we not depart from hence ?
The white moon groweth golden fast, and gleams
 Between the aspen stems ; I fear—and yet a sense

Of fluttering victory comes over me, 251
 That will not let me fear aright ; my heart—
Feel how it beats, love, strives to get to thee,
 I breathe so fast that my lips needs must part ;

Your breath swims round my mouth, but let us go.

The Prince.

I, Sebald, also, pluck from off the staff
The crimson banner, let it lie below,
 Above it in the wind let grasses laugh.

Now let us go, love, down the winding stair,
 With fingers intertwined : ay, feel my sword ! 260
I wrought it long ago, with golden hair
 Flowing about the hilts, because a word,

Sung by a minstrel old, had set me dreaming
 Of a sweet bow'd-down face with yellow hair,
Betwixt green leaves I used to see it gleaming,
 A half smile on the lips, though lines of care

Had sunk the cheeks, and made the great eyes hollow ;
  What other work in all the world had I,
But through all turns of fate that face to follow ?
  But wars and business kept me there to die.   270

O child, I should have slain my brother, too,
  My brother, Love, lain moaning in the grass,
Had I not ridden out to look for you,
  When I had watch'd the gilded courtiers pass

From the golden hall.   But it is strange your name
  Is not the same the minstrel sung of yore ;
You call'd it Rapunzel, 'tis not the name.
  See, love, the stems shine through the open door.

Morning in the woods.

RAPUNZEL.

O Love ! me and my unknown name you have well won ;
  The witch's name was Rapunzel ; eh ! not so sweet ?
No !—but is this real grass, love, that I tread upon ?
  What call they these blue flowers that lean across my
    feet ?

THE PRINCE.

Dip down your dear face in the dewy grass, O love !
  And ever let the sweet slim harebells tenderly hung,
Kiss both your parted lips ; and I will hang above,
  And try to sing that song the dreamy harper sung.

He sings.[1]

  'Twixt the sunlight and the shade
  Float up memories of my maid,
    God, remember Guendolen !

  Gold or gems she did not wear,   290
  But her yellow rippled hair,
    Like a veil, hid Guendolen !

[1] This song appeared in *The Oxford and Cambridge Magazine*, July,
1856, under the title ' Hands '.   In the magazine, the eighth line
preceded the seventh.

'Twixt the sunlight and the shade,
My rough hands so strangely made,
   Folded Golden Guendolen ;

Hands used to grip the sword-hilt hard,
Framed her face, while on the sward
   Tears fell down from Guendolen.

Guendolen now speaks no word,
Hands fold round about the sword.   300
   Now no more of Guendolen.

Only 'twixt the light and shade
Floating memories of my maid
   Make me pray for Guendolen.

GUENDOLEN.

I kiss thee, new-found name ; but I will never go :
   Your hands need never grip the hammer'd sword again,
But all my golden hair shall ever round you flow,
   Between the light and shade from Golden Guendolen.

Afterwards, in the Palace.

KING SEBALD

I took my armour off,
   Put on king's robes of gold,   310
Over her kirtle green
   The gold fell fold on fold.

THE WITCH, *out of hell.*
Guendolen ! Guendolen !
One lock of hair !

GUENDOLEN.

I am so glad, for every day
He kisses me much the same way
As in the tower ; under the sway
   Of all my golden hair.

King Sebald.

We rode throughout the town,
  A gold crown on my head,   320
Through all the gold-hung streets,
  ' Praise God ! ' the people said.

The Witch.

Guendolen ! Guendolen !
Lend me your hair !

Guendolen.

Verily, I seem like one
Who, when day is almost done,
Through a thick wood meets the sun
  That blazes in her hair.

King Sebald.

Yea, at the palace gates,
  ' Praise God ! ' the great knights said,   330
For Sebald the high king,
  And the lady's golden head.'

The Witch.

Woe is me ! Guendolen
Sweeps back her hair.

Guendolen.

Nothing wretched now, no screams ;
I was unhappy once in dreams,
And even now a harsh voice seems
  To hang about my hair.

The Witch.

Woe ! that any man could dare
To climb up the yellow stair,   340
Glorious Guendolen's golden hair.

CONCERNING GEFFRAY TESTE NOIRE

AND if you meet the Canon of Chimay,
    As going to Ortaise you well may do,
Greet him from John of Castel Neuf, and say,
    All that I tell you, for all this is true.

This Geffray Teste Noire was a Gascon thief,
    Who, under shadow of the English name,
Pilled all such towns and countries as were lief
    To King Charles and St. Dennis ; thought it blame

If anything escaped him ; so my lord,
    The Duke of Berry, sent Sir John Bonne Lance,   10
And other knights, good players with the sword,
    To check this thief, and give the land a chance.

Therefore we set our bastides round the tower
    That Geffray held, the strong thief ! like a king,
High perch'd upon the rock of Ventadour,
    Hopelessly strong by Christ ! it was mid spring,

When first I joined the little army there
    With ten good spears ; Auvergne is hot, each day
We sweated armed before the barrier,
    Good feats of arms were done there often—eh ?   20

Your brother was slain there ?   I mind me now,
    A right good man-at-arms, God pardon him !
I think 'twas Geffray smote him on the brow
    With some spiked axe, and while he totter'd, dim

About the eyes, the spear of Alleyne Roux
    Slipped through his camaille and his throat ; well, well !
Alleyne is paid now ; your name Alleyne too ?
    Mary ! how strange—but this tale I would tell—

For spite of all our bastides, damned Blackhead
    Would ride abroad whene'er he chose to ride,   30
We could not stop him ; many a burgher bled
    Dear gold all round his girdle ; far and wide

The villaynes dwelt in utter misery
  'Twixt us and thief Sir Geffray ; hauled this way
By Sir Bonne Lance at one time, he gone by,
  Down comes this Teste Noire on another day.

And therefore they dig up the stone, grind corn,
  Hew wood, draw water, yea, they lived, in short,
As I said just now, utterly forlorn,   39
  Till this our knave and blackhead was out-fought.

So Bonne Lance fretted, thinking of some trap
  Day after day, till on a time he said ;
' John of Newcastle, if we have good hap,
  We catch our thief in two days.' ' How ? ' I said.

' Why, Sir, to-day he rideth out again,
  Hoping to take well certain sumpter mules
From Carcassonne, going with little train,
  Because, forsooth, he thinketh us mere fools ;

' But if we set an ambush in some wood,
  He is but dead ; so, Sir, take thirty spears   50
To Verville forest, if it seem you good.'
  Then felt I like the horse in Job, who hears

The dancing trumpet sound, and we went forth ;
  And my red lion on the spear-head flapped,
As faster than the cool wind we rode North,
  Towards the wood of Verville ; thus it happed.

We rode a soft space on that day while spies
  Got news about Sir Geffray ; the red wine
Under the road-side bush was clear ; the flies,
  The dragon-flies I mind me most, did shine   60

In brighter arms than ever I put on ;
  So—' Geffray,' said our spies, ' would pass that way
Next day at sundown ; ' then he must be won ;
  And so we enter'd Verville wood next day,

In the afternoon ; through it the highway runs,
  'Twixt copses of green hazel, very thick,
And underneath, with glimmering of suns,
  The primroses are happy ; the dews lick

The soft green moss.   ' Put cloths about your arms
   Lest they should glitter ; surely they will go   70
In a long thin line, watchful for alarms,
   With all their carriages of booty, so—

' Lay down my pennon in the grass—Lord God !
   What have we lying here ? will they be cold,
I wonder, being so bare, above the sod,
   Instead of under ?   This was a knight too, fold

' Lying on fold of ancient rusted mail ;
   No plate at all, gold rowels to the spurs,
And see the quiet gleam of turquoise pale
   Along the ceinture ; but the long time blurs   80

' Even the tinder of his coat to nought,
   Except these scraps of leather ; see how white
The skull is, loose within the coif !   He fought
   A good fight, maybe, ere he was slain quite.

' No armour on the legs too ; strange in faith—
   A little skeleton for a knight though—ah !
This one is bigger, truly without scathe
   His enemies escaped not—ribs driven out far,—

' That must have reach'd the heart, I doubt—how now,
   What say you, Aldovrand—a woman ? why ? '   90
' Under the coif a gold wreath on the brow,
   Yea, see the hair not gone to powder, lie,

' Golden, no doubt, once—yea, and very small—
   This for a knight ; but for a dame, my lord,
These loose-hung bones seem shapely still, and tall,—
   Didst ever see a woman's bones, my lord ? '

Often, God help me ! I remember when
   I was a simple boy, fifteen years old,
The Jacquerie froze up the blood of men
   With their fell deeds, not fit now to be told :   100

God help again ! we enter'd Beauvais town,
   Slaying them fast, whereto I help'd, mere boy
As I was then ; we gentles cut them down,
   These burners and defilers, with great joy.

Reason for that, too, in the great church there
  These fiends had lit a fire, that soon went out,
The church at Beauvais being so great and fair—
  My father, who was by me, gave a shout

Between a beast's howl and a woman's scream,   109
  Then, panting, chuckled to me : ' John, look ! look !
Count the dames' skeletons ! ' From some bad dream
  Like a man just awaked, my father shook ;

And I, being faint with smelling the burnt bones,
  And very hot with fighting down the street,
And sick of such a life, fell down, with groans
  My head went weakly nodding to my feet.—

—An arrow had gone through her tender throat,
  And her right wrist was broken ; then I saw
The reason why she had on that war-coat,
  Their story came out clear without a flaw ;   120

For when he knew that they were being waylaid,
  He threw it over her, yea, hood and all ;
Whereby he was much hack'd, while they were stay'd
  By those their murderers ; many an one did fall

Beneath his arm, no doubt, so that he clear'd
  Their circle, bore his death-wound out of it ;
But as they rode, some archer least afear'd
  Drew a strong bow, and thereby she was hit.

Still as he rode he knew not she was dead,
  Thought her but fainted from her broken wrist,   130
He bound with his great leathern belt—she bled ?
  Who knows ! he bled too, neither was there miss'd

The beating of her heart, his heart beat well
  For both of them, till here, within this wood,
He died scarce sorry ; easy this to tell ;
  After these years the flowers forget their blood.—

How could it be ? never before that day,
  However much a soldier I might be,
Could I look on a skeleton and say
  I care not for it, shudder not—now see,   140

Over those bones I sat and pored for hours,
    And thought, and dream'd, and still I scarce could see
The small white bones that lay upon the flowers,
    But evermore I saw the lady ; she

With her dear gentle walking leading in,
    By a chain of silver twined about her wrists,
Her loving knight, mounted and arm'd to win
    Great honour for her, fighting in the lists.

O most pale face, that brings such joy and sorrow
    Into men's hearts—yea, too, so piercing sharp   150
That joy is, that it marcheth nigh to sorrow
    For ever—like an overwinded harp.

Your face must hurt me always ; pray you now,
    Doth it not hurt you too ? seemeth some pain
To hold you always, pain to hold your brow
    So smooth, unwrinkled ever ; yea again,

Your long eyes where the lids seem like to drop,
    Would you not, lady, were they shut fast, feel
Far merrier ? there so high they will not stop,
    They are most sly to glide forth and to steal   160

Into my heart ; *I kiss their soft lids there,*
    And in green garden scarce can stop my lips
From wandering on your face, but that your hair
    Falls down and tangles me, back my face slips.

Or say your mouth—I saw you drink red wine
    Once at a feast ; how slowly it sank in,
As though you fear'd that some wild fate might twine
    Within that cup, and slay you for a sin.

And when you talk your lips do arch and move
    In such wise that a language new I know   170
Besides their sound ; they quiver, too, with love
    When you are standing silent ; know this, too,

I saw you kissing once, like a curved sword
    That bites with all its edge, did your lips lie,
Curled gently, slowly, long time could afford
    For caught-up breathings ; like a dying sigh

They gather'd up their lines and went away,
    And still kept twitching with a sort of smile,
As likely to be weeping presently,—   179
    Your hands too—how I watch'd them all the while!

' Cry out St. Peter now,' quoth Aldovrand ;
    I cried, ' St. Peter,' broke out from the wood
With all my spears ; we met them hand to hand,
    And shortly slew them ; natheless, by the rood,

We caught not Blackhead then, or any day ;
    Months after that he died at last in bed,
From a wound pick'd up at a barrier-fray ;
    That same year's end a steel bolt in the head,

And much bad living kill'd Teste Noire at last ;
    John Froissart knoweth he is dead by now,   190
No doubt, but knoweth not this tale just past ;
    Perchance then you can tell him what I show.

In my new castle, down beside the Eure,
    There is a little chapel of squared stone,
Painted inside and out ; in green nook pure
    There did I lay them, every wearied bone ;

And over it they lay, with stone-white hands
    Clasped fast together, hair made bright with gold
This Jaques Picard, known through many lands,
    Wrought cunningly ; he's dead now—I am old.   200

A GOOD KNIGHT IN PRISON

SIR GUY, *being in the court of a Pagan castle.*

THIS castle where I dwell, it stands
A long way off from Christian lands,
A long way off my lady's hands,
A long way off the aspen trees,
And murmur of the lime-tree bees.

But down the Valley of the Rose
My lady often hawking goes,
Heavy of cheer ; oft turns behind,
Leaning towards the western wind,
Because it bringeth to her mind   10
Sad whisperings of happy times,
The face of him who sings these rhymes.

King Guilbert rides beside her there,
Bends low and calls her very fair,
And strives, by pulling down his hair,
To hide from my dear lady's ken
The grisly gash I gave him, when
I cut him down at Camelot ;
However he strives, he hides it not,
That tourney will not be forgot,   20
Besides, it is King Guilbert's lot,
Whatever he says she answers not.

Now tell me, you that are in love,
From the king's son to the wood-dove,
Which is the better, he or I ?

For this king means that I should die
In this lone Pagan castle, where
The flowers droop in the bad air
On the September evening.

Look, now I take mine ease and sing,   30
Counting as but a little thing
The foolish spite of a bad king.

For these vile things that hem me in,
These Pagan beasts who live in sin,
The sickly flowers pale and wan,
The grim blue-bearded castellan,
The stanchions half worn-out with rust,
Whereto their banner vile they trust—
Why, all these things I hold them just
Like dragons in a missal-book,   40
Wherein, whenever we may look,
We see no horror, yea, delight
We have, the colours are so bright ;
Likewise we note the specks of white,
And the great plates of burnish'd gold.

Just so this Pagan castle old,
And everything I can see there,
Sick-pining in the marshland air,
I note ; I will go over now,
Like one who paints with knitted brow,   50
The flowers and all things one by one,
From the snail on the wall to the setting sun.

Four great walls, and a little one
That leads down to the barbican,
Which walls with many spears they man,
When news comes to the castellan
Of Launcelot being in the land.

And as I sit here, close at hand
Four spikes of sad sick sunflowers stand,
The castellan with a long wand   60
Cuts down their leaves as he goes by,
Ponderingly, with screw'd-up eye,
And fingers twisted in his beard—
Nay, was it a knight's shout I heard ?
I have a hope makes me afeard :
It cannot be, but if some dream
Just for a minute made me deem
I saw among the flowers there
My lady's face with long red hair,

Pale, ivory-colour'd dear face come,   70
As I was wont to see her some
Fading September afternoon,
And kiss me, saying nothing, soon
To leave me by myself again ;
    Could I get this by longing : vain !

    The castellan is gone : I see
On one broad yellow flower a bee
Drunk with much honey—
                        Christ ! again,
Some distant knight's voice brings me pain
I thought I had forgot to feel,   80
I never heard the blissful steel
These ten years past ; year after year,
Through all my hopeless sojourn here,
No Christian pennon has been near ;
Laus Deo ! the dragging wind draws on
Over the marshes, battle won,
Knights' shouts, and axes hammering,
Yea, quicker now the dint and ring
Of flying hoofs ; ah ! castellan,
When they come back count man for man,   90
Say whom you miss.

        THE PAGANS, *from the battlements.*
                    Mahound to aid !
Why flee ye so like men dismay'd ?

        THE PAGANS, *from without.*
Nay, haste ! for here is Launcelot,
Who follows quick upon us, hot
And shouting with his men-at-arms.

            SIR GUY.
Also the Pagans raise alarms,
And ring the bells for fear ; at last
My prison walls will be well past.

Sir Launcelot, *from outside.*

Ho ! in the name of the Trinity,
Let down the drawbridge quick to me,   100
And open doors, that I may see
Guy the good knight.

The Pagans, *from the battlements.*

              Nay, Launcelot,
With mere big words ye win us not.

Sir Launcelot.

Bid Miles bring up la perriere,
And archers clear the vile walls there,
Bring back the notches to the ear,
Shoot well together ! God to aid !
These miscreants will be well paid.

Hurrah ! all goes together ; Miles
Is good to win my lady's smiles   110
For his good shooting—Launcelot !
On knights a-pace ! this game is hot !

Sir Guy *sayeth afterwards*

I said, I go to meet her now,
And saying so, I felt a blow
From some clench'd hand across my brow,
And fell down on the sunflowers
Just as a hammering smote my ears,
After which this I felt in sooth ;
My bare hands throttling without ruth
The hairy-throated castellan ;   120
Then a grim fight with those that ran
To slay me, while I shouted, ' God
For the Lady Mary ! ' deep I trod
That evening in my own red blood ;
Nevertheless so stiff I stood,
That when the knights burst the old wood
Of the castle-doors, I was not dead.

I kiss the Lady Mary's head,
Her lips, and her hair golden red,
Because to-day we have been wed.   130

OLD LOVE

' You must be very old, Sir Giles, '
   I said ; he said : ' Yea, very old : '
Whereat the mournfullest of smiles
   Creased his dry skin with many a fold.

' They hammer'd out my basnet point
   Into a round salade, ' he said,
' The basnet being quite out of joint,
   Natheless the salade rasps my head. '

He gazed at the great fire awhile :
   ' And you are getting old, Sir John ; '   10
(He said this with that cunning smile
   That was most sad ;) ' we both wear on,

' Knights come to court and look at me,
   With eyebrows up, except my lord,
And my dear lady, none I see
   That know the ways of my old sword. '

(My lady ! at that word no pang
   Stopp'd all my blood.) ' But tell me, John,
Is it quite true that pagans hang
   So thick about the east, that on   20

' The eastern sea no Venice flag
   Can fly unpaid for ? ' ' True, ' I said,
' And in such way the miscreants drag
   Christ's cross upon the ground, I dread

' That Constantine must fall this year. '
   Within my heart ; ' These things are small ;
This is not small, that things outwear
   I thought were made for ever, yea, all,

' All things go soon or late ; ' I said—
   I saw the duke in court next day ;   30
Just as before, his grand great head
   Above his gold robes dreaming lay,

Only his face was paler ; there
  I saw his duchess sit by him ;
And she—she was changed more ; her hair
  Before my eyes that used to swim,

And make me dizzy with great bliss
  Once, when I used to watch her sit—
Her hair is bright still, yet it is
  As though some dust were thrown on it.   40

Her eyes are shallower, as though
  Some grey glass were behind ; her brow
And cheeks the straining bones show through,
  Are not so good for kissing now.

Her lips are drier now she is
  A great duke's wife these many years,
They will not shudder with a kiss
  As once they did, being moist with tears.

Also her hands have lost that way
  Of clinging that they used to have ;   50
They look'd quite easy, as they lay
  Upon the silken cushions brave

With broidery of the apples green
  My Lord Duke bears upon his shield.
Her face, alas ! that I have seen
  Look fresher than an April field,

This is all gone now ; gone also
  Her tender walking ; when she walks
She is most queenly I well know,
  And she is fair still :—as the stalks   60

Of faded summer-lilies are,
  So is she grown now unto me
This spring-time, when the flowers star
  The meadows, birds sing wonderfully.

I warrant once she used to cling
  About his neck, and kiss'd him so,
And then his coming step would ring
  Joy-bells for her,—some time ago.

Ah ! sometimes like an idle dream
  That hinders true life overmuch,   70
Sometimes like a lost heaven, these seem.—
  This love is not so hard to smutch.

THE GILLIFLOWER OF GOLD

A GOLDEN gilliflower to-day
I wore upon my helm alway,
And won the prize of this tourney.
    Hah ! hah ! la belle jaune giroflée.

However well Sir Giles might sit,
His sun was weak to wither it,
Lord Miles's blood was dew on it :
    Hah ! hah ! la belle jaune giroflée.

Although my spear in splinters flew,
From John's steel-coat my eye was true ;   10
I wheel'd about, and cried for you,
    Hah ! hah ! la belle jaune giroflée.

Yea, do not doubt my heart was good,
Though my sword flew like rotten wood,
To shout, although I scarcely stood,
    Hah ! hah ! la belle jaune giroflée.

My hand was steady too, to take
My axe from round my neck, and break
John's steel-coat up for my love's sake.
    Hah ! hah ! la belle jaune giroflée.   20

When I stood in my tent again,
Arming afresh, I felt a pain
Take hold of me, I was so fain—
    Hah ! hah ! la belle jaune giroflée.

To hear : ' *Honneur aux fils des preux !* '
Right in my ears again, and shew
The gilliflower blossom'd new.
    Hah ! hah ! la belle jaune giroflée.

The Sieur Guillaume against me came,
His tabard bore three points of flame   30
From a red heart : with little blame—
  Hah ! hah ! la belle jaune giroflée.

Our tough spears crackled up like straw ;
He was the first to turn and draw
His sword, that had nor speck nor flaw,—
  Hah ! hah ! la belle jaune giroflée.

But I felt weaker than a maid,
And my brain, dizzied and afraid,
Within my helm a fierce tune play'd,—
  Hah ! hah ! la belle jaune giroflée.   40

Until I thought of your dear head,
Bow'd to the gilliflower bed,
The yellow flowers stain'd with red ;—
  Hah ! hah ! la belle jaune giroflée.

Crash ! how the swords met, ' *giroflée !* '
The fierce tune in my helm would play,
' *La belle ! la belle ! jaune giroflée !* '
  Hah ! hah ! la belle jaune giroflée.

Once more the great swords met again,
' *La belle ! la belle !* ' but who fell then ?   50
Le Sieur Guillaume, who struck down ten ;—
  Hah ! hah ! la belle jaune giroflée.

And as with mazed and unarm'd face,
Toward my own crown and the Queen's place,
They led me at a gentle pace—
  Hah ! hah ! la belle jaune giroflée.

I almost saw your quiet head
Bow'd o'er the gilliflower bed,
The yellow flowers stain'd with red—
  Hah ! hah ! la belle jaune giroflée.   60

SHAMEFUL DEATH

THERE were four of us about that bed ;
  The mass-priest knelt at the side,
I and his mother stood at the head,
  Over his feet lay the bride ;
We were quite sure that he was dead,
  Though his eyes were open wide.

He did not die in the night,
  He did not die in the day,
But in the morning twilight
  His spirit pass'd away,   10
When neither sun nor moon was bright,
  And the trees were merely grey.

He was not slain with the sword,
  Knight's axe, or the knightly spear,
Yet spoke he never a word
  After he came in here ;
I cut away the cord
  From the neck of my brother dear.

He did not strike one blow,
  For the recreants came behind,   20
In a place where the hornbeams grow,
  A path right hard to find,
For the hornbeam boughs swing so,
  That the twilight makes it blind.

They lighted a great torch then,
  When his arms were pinion'd fast,
Sir John the knight of the Fen,
  Sir Guy of the Dolorous Blast,
With knights threescore and ten,
  Hung brave Lord Hugh at last.   30

I am threescore and ten,
  And my hair is all turn'd grey,
But I met Sir John of the Fen
  Long ago on a summer day,

And am glad to think of the moment when
   I took his life away.

I am threescore and ten,
   And my strength is mostly pass'd,
But long ago I and my men,
   When the sky was overcast,   40
And the smoke roll'd over the reeds of the fen,
   Slew Guy of the Dolorous Blast.

And now, knights all of you,
   I pray you pray for Sir Hugh,
A good knight and a true,
   And for Alice, his wife, pray too.

THE EVE OF CRECY

GOLD on her head, and gold on her feet,
And gold where the hems of her kirtle meet,
And a golden girdle round my sweet ;—
   Ah ! qu'elle est belle La Marguerite.

Margaret's maids are fair to see,
Freshly dress'd and pleasantly ;
Margaret's hair falls down to her knee ;—
   Ah ! qu'elle est belle La Marguerite.

If I were rich I would kiss her feet,
I would kiss the place where the gold hems meet,   10
And the golden girdle round my sweet—
   Ah ! qu'elle est belle La Marguerite.

Ah me ! I have never touch'd her hand ;
When the arriere-ban goes through the land,
Six basnets under my pennon stand ;—
   Ah ! qu'elle est belle La Marguerite.

And many an one grins under his hood :
' Sir Lambert de Bois, with all his men good,
Has neither food nor firewood ; '—
    Ah ! qu'elle est belle La Marguerite.   20

If I were rich I would kiss her feet,
And the golden girdle of my sweet,
And thereabouts where the gold hems meet ;—
    Ah ! qu'elle est belle La Marguerite.

Yet even now it is good to think,
While my few poor varlets grumble and drink
In my desolate hall, where the fires sink,—
    Ah ! qu'elle est belle La Marguerite.

Of Margaret sitting glorious there,
In glory of gold and glory of hair,   30
And glory of glorious face most fair ;—
    Ah ! qu'elle est belle La Marguerite.

Likewise to-night I make good cheer,
Because this battle draweth near :
For what have I to lose or fear ?—
    Ah ! qu'elle est belle La Marguerite.

For, look you, my horse is good to prance
A right fair measure in this war-dance,
Before the eyes of Philip of France ;—
    Ah ! qu'elle est belle La Marguerite.   40

And sometime it may hap, perdie,
While my new towers stand up three and three,
And my hall gets painted fair to see—
    Ah ! qu'elle est belle La Marguerite—

That folks may say : ' Times change, by the rood,
For Lambert, banneret of the wood,
Has heaps of food and firewood ;—
    Ah ! qu'elle est belle La Marguerite.

' And wonderful eyes, too, under the hood
Of a damsel of right noble blood : '   50
St. Ives, for Lambert of the wood !—
    Ah ! qu'elle est belle La Marguerite.

THE JUDGEMENT OF GOD

' SWERVE to the left, son Roger,' he said,
  ' When you catch his eyes through the helmet-slit,
Swerve to the left, then out at his head,
  And the Lord God give you joy of it ! '

The blue owls on my father's hood
  Were a little dimm'd as I turn'd away ;
This giving up of blood for blood
  Will finish here somehow to day.

So—when I walk'd out from the tent,
  Their howling almost blinded me ;   10
Yet for all that I was not bent
  By any shame.   Hard by, the sea

Made a noise like the aspens where
  We did that wrong, but now the place
Is very pleasant, and the air
  Blows. cool on any passer's face.

And all the wrong is gather'd now
  Into the circle of these lists—
Yea, howl out, butchers ! tell me how
  His hands were cut off at the wrists ;   20

And how Lord Roger bore his face
  A league above his spear-point, high
Above the owls, to that strong place
  Among the waters—yea, yea, cry :

' What a brave champion we have got !
  Sir Oliver, the flower of all
The Hainault knights.'   The day being hot,
  He sat beneath a broad white pall,

White linen over all his steel ;
  What a good knight he look'd ! his sword   30
Laid thwart his knees ; he liked to feel
  Its steadfast edge clear as his word.

And he look'd solemn ; how his love
  Smiled whitely on him, sick with fear !
How all the ladies up above
  Twisted their pretty hands ! so near

The fighting was—Ellayne ! Ellayne !
  They cannot love like you can, who
Would burn your hands off, if that pain
  Could win a kiss—am I not true   40

To you for ever ? therefore I
  Do not fear death or anything ;
If I should limp home wounded, why,
  While I lay sick you would but sing,

And soothe me into quiet sleep.
  If they spat on the recreaunt knight,
Threw stones at him, and cursed him deep,
  Why then—what then ; your hand would light

So gently on his drawn-up face,
  And you would kiss him, and in soft   50
Cool scented clothes would lap him, pace
  The quiet room and weep oft,—oft

Would turn and smile, and brush his cheek
  With your sweet chin and mouth ; and in
The order'd garden you would seek
  The biggest roses—any sin,

And these say : ' No more now my knight,
  Or God's knight any longer '—you,
Being than they so much more white,
  So much more pure and good and true,   60

Will cling to me for ever—there,
  Is not that wrong turn'd right at last
Through all these years, and I wash'd clean ?
  Say, yea, Ellayne ; the time is past,

Since on that Christmas-day last year
  Up to your feet the fire crept,
And the smoke through the brown leaves sere
  Blinded your dear eyes that you wept ;

Was it not I that caught you then,
    And kiss'd you on the saddle bow ?   70
Did not the blue owl mark the men
    Whose spears stood like the corn a-row ?

This Oliver is a right good knight,
    And must needs beat me, as I fear,
Unless I catch him in the fight,
    My father's crafty way—John, here !

Bring up the men from the south gate,
    To help me if I fall or win,
For even if I beat, their hate
    Will grow to more than this mere grin.   80

THE LITTLE TOWER

Up and away through the drifting rain !
Let us ride to the Little Tower again,

Up and away from the council-board !
Do on the hauberk, gird on the sword.

The king is blind with gnashing his teeth,
Change gilded scabbard to leather sheath :

Though our arms are wet with the slanting rain,
This is joy to ride to my love again :

I laugh in his face when he bids me yield ;
Who knows one field from the other field,   10

For the grey rain driveth all astray ?—
Which way through the floods, good carle, I pray ?

' The left side yet ! the left side yet !
Till your hand strikes on the bridge parapet.'

' Yea so : the causeway holdeth good
Under the water ? '   ' Hard as wood ;

Right away to the uplands ; speed, good knight.'
Seven hours yet before the light.

Shake the wet off on the upland road ;
My taberd has grown a heavy load.   20

What matter ? up and down hill after hill ;
Dead grey night for five hours still.

The hill-road droppeth lower again,
Lower, down to the poplar plain.

No furlong farther for us to-night,
The Little Tower draweth in sight ;

They are ringing the bells, and the torches glare,
Therefore the roofs of wet slate stare.

There she stands, and her yellow hair slantingly
Drifts the same way that the rain goes by.   30

Who will be faithful to us to-day,
With little but hard glaive-strokes for pay ?

The grim king fumes at the council-board :
' Three more days, and then the sword ;

Three more days, and my sword through his head ;
And above his white brows, pale and dead,

A paper crown on the top of the spire ;
And for her the stake and the witches' fire.'

Therefore though it be long ere day,
Take axe and pick and spade, I pray.   40

Break the dams down all over the plain :
God send us three more days such rain :

Block all the upland roads with trees ;
The Little Tower with no great ease

Is won, I warrant ; bid them bring
Much sheep and oxen, everything

The spits are wont to turn with ; wine
And wheaten bread, that we may dine

In plenty each day of the siege ;
Good friends, ye know me no hard liege ;   50

My lady is right fair, see ye !
Pray God to keep you frank and free.

Love Isabeau, keep goodly cheer ;
The Little Tower will stand well here

Many a year when we are dead,
And over it our green and red,
Barred with the Lady's golden head ;
From mere old age when we are dead.

THE SAILING OF THE SWORD

ACROSS the empty garden-beds,
　When the Sword went out to sea,
I scarcely saw my sisters' heads
　Bowed each beside a tree.
I could not see the castle leads,
　When the Sword went out to sea.

Alicia wore a scarlet gown,
　When the Sword went out to sea,
But Ursula's was russet brown :
　For the mist we could not see
The scarlet roofs of the good town,
　When the Sword went out to sea.

Green holly in Alicia's hand,
　When the Sword went out to sea ;
With sere oak-leaves did Ursula stand ;
　O ! yet alas for me !
I did but bear a peel'd white wand,
　When the Sword went out to sea.

O, russet brown and scarlet bright,
　When the Sword went out to sea,
My sisters wore ; I wore but white :
　Red, brown, and white, are three ;
Three damozels ; each had a knight,
　When the Sword went out to sea.

Sir Robert shouted loud, and said,
  When the Sword went out to sea,
' Alicia, while I see thy head,
    What shall I bring for thee ? '
' O, my sweet lord, a ruby red : '
  The Sword went out to sea.   30

Sir Miles said, while the sails hung down,
  When the Sword went out to sea,
' Oh, Ursula ! while I see the town,
    What shall I bring for thee ? '
' Dear knight, bring back a falcon brown : '
  The Sword went out to sea.

But my Roland, no word he said
  When the Sword went out to sea :
But only turn'd away his head,—
    A quick shriek came from me :   40
' Come back, dear lord, to your white maid ; '—
  The Sword went out to sea.

The hot sun bit the garden-beds,
  When the Sword came back from sea ;
Beneath an apple-tree our heads
    Stretched out toward the sea ;
Grey gleam'd the thirsty castle-leads,
  When the Sword came back from sea.

Lord Robert brought a ruby red,
  When the Sword came back from sea ;   50
He kissed Alicia on the head :
    ' I am come back to thee ;
'Tis time, sweet love, that we were wed,
  Now the Sword is back from sea ! '

Sir Miles he bore a falcon brown,
  When the Sword came back from sea ;
His arms went round tall Ursula's gown,—
    ' What joy, O love, but thee ?
Let us be wed in the good town,
  Now the Sword is back from sea ! '   60

My heart grew sick, no more afraid,
　When the Sword came back from sea;
Upon the deck a tall white maid
　Sat on Lord Roland's knee;
His chin was press'd upon her head,
　When the Sword came back from sea!

SPELL-BOUND

How weary is it none can tell,
　How dismally the days go by!
I hear the tinkling of the bell,
　I see the cross against the sky.

The year wears round to autumn-tide,
　Yet comes no reaper to the corn;
The golden land is like a bride
　When first she knows herself forlorn—

She sits and weeps with all her hair
　Laid downward over tender hands;　　10
For stained silk she hath no care,
　No care for broken ivory wands;

The silver cups beside her stand;
　The golden stars on the blue roof
Yet glitter, though against her hand
　His cold sword presses for a proof

He is not dead, but gone away.
　How many hours did she wait
For me, I wonder?　Till the day
　Had faded wholly, and the gate　　20

Clanged to behind returning knights?
　I wonder did she raise her head
And go away, fleeing the lights;
　And lay the samite on her bed,

The wedding samite strewn with pearls :
  Then sit with hands laid on her knees,
Shuddering at half-heard sound of girls
  That chatter outside in the breeze ?

I wonder did her poor heart throb
  At distant tramp of coming knight ?   30
How often did the choking sob
  Raise up her head and lips ?   The light,

Did it come on her unawares,
  And drag her sternly down before
People who loved her not ? in prayers
  Did she say one name and no more ?

And once—all songs they ever sung,
  All tales they ever told to me,
This only burden through them rung :
  O ! golden love that waitest me,   40

The days pass on, pass on a pace,
  Sometimes I have a little rest
In fairest dreams, when on thy face
  My lips lie, or thy hands are prest

About my forehead, and thy lips
  Draw near and nearer to mine own ;
But when the vision from me slips,
  In colourless dawn I lie and moan,

And wander forth with fever'd blood,
  That makes me start at little things,   50
The blackbird screaming from the wood,
  The sudden whirr of pheasants' wings.

O ! dearest, scarcely seen by me—
  But when that wild time had gone by,
And in these arms I folded thee,
  Who ever thought those days could die ?

Yet now I wait, and you wait too,
    For what perchance may never come ;
You think I have forgotten you,
    That I grew tired and went home.   60

But what if some day as I stood
    Against the wall with strained hands,
And turn'd my face toward the wood,
    Away from all the golden lands ;

And saw you come with tired feet,
    And pale face thin and wan with care,
And stained raiment no more neat,
    The white dust lying on your hair :—

Then I should say, I could not come ;
    This land was my wide prison, dear ;   70
I could not choose but go ; at home
    There is a wizard whom I fear :

He bound me round with silken chains
    I could not break ; he set me here
Above the golden-waving plains,
    Where never reaper cometh near.

And you have brought me my good sword,
    Wherewith in happy days of old
I won you well from knight and lord ;
    My heart upswells and I grow bold.   80

But I shall die unless you stand,
    —Half lying now, you are so weak,—
Within my arms, unless your hand
    Pass to and fro across my cheek.

THE WIND

Ah ! no, no, it is nothing, surely nothing at all,
Only the wild-going wind round by the garden-wall,
For the dawn just now is breaking, the wind beginning
to fall.
 Wind, wind ! thou art sad, art thou kind ?
 Wind, wind, unhappy ! thou art blind,
 Yet still thou wanderest the lily-seed to find.

So I will sit, and think and think of the days gone by,
Never moving my chair for fear the dogs should cry,
Making no noise at all while the flambeau burns awry.
For my chair is heavy and carved, and with sweeping
green behind   10
It is hung, and the dragons thereon grin out in the gusts
of the wind ;
On its folds an orange lies, with a deep gash cut in the
rind.
 Wind, wind ! thou art sad, art thou kind ?
 Wind, wind, unhappy ! thou art blind,
 Yet still thou wanderest the lily-seed to find.

If I move my chair it will scream, and the orange will
roll out far,
And the faint yellow juice ooze out like blood from
a wizard's jar ;
And the dogs will howl for those who went last month
to the war.
 Wind, wind ! thou art sad, art thou kind ?
 Wind, wind, unhappy ! thou art blind,   20
 Yet still thou wanderest the lily-seed to find.

So I will sit and think of love that is over and past,
O ! so long ago—yes, I will be quiet at last ;
Whether I like it or not, a grim half-slumber is cast
Over my worn old brains, that touches the roots of my
heart,
And above my half-shut eyes the blue roof 'gins to part,
And show the blue spring sky, till I am ready to start

From out of the green-hung chair ; but something keeps
me still,
And I fall in a dream that I walk'd with her on the side
of a hill,
Dotted—for was it not spring ?—with tufts of the
daffodil.   30
  Wind, wind ! thou art sad, art thou kind ?
  Wind, wind, unhappy ! thou art blind,
  Yet still thou wanderest the lily-seed to find.

And Margaret as she walk'd held a painted book in her
hand ;
Her finger kept the place; I caught her, we both did stand
Face to face, on the top of the highest hill in the land.
  Wind, wind ! thou art sad, art thou kind ?
  Wind, wind, unhappy ! thou art blind,
  Yet still thou wanderest the lily-seed to find.

I held to her long bare arms, but she shudder'd away
from me,   40
While the flush went out of her face as her head fell back
on a tree,
And a spasm caught her mouth, fearful for me to see ;

And still I held to her arms till her shoulder touch'd my
mail,
Weeping she totter'd forward, so glad that I should
prevail,
And her hair went over my robe, like a gold flag over
a sail.
  Wind, wind ! thou art sad, art thou kind ?
  Wind, wind, unhappy ! thou art blind,
  Yet still thou wanderest the lily-seed to find.

I kiss'd her hard by the ear, and she kiss'd me on the
brow,
And then lay down on the grass, where the mark on the
moss is now,   50
And spread her arms out wide while I went down below.
  Wind, wind ! thou art sad, art thou kind ?
  Wind, wind, unhappy ! thou art blind,
  Yet still thou wanderest the lily-seed to find.

And then I walk'd for a space to and fro on the side of
    the hill,
Till I gather'd and held in my arms great sheaves of the
    daffodil,
And when I came again my Margaret lay there still.

I piled them high and high above her heaving breast,
How they were caught and held in her loose ungirded
    vest !   59
But one beneath her arm died, happy so to be prest !
          Wind, wind ! thou art sad, art thou kind ?
          Wind, wind, unhappy ! thou art blind,
          Yet still thou wanderest the lily-seed to find.

Again I turn'd my back and went away for an hour ;
She said no word when I came again, so, flower by flower,
I counted the daffodils over, and cast them languidly
    lower.
          Wind, wind ! thou art sad, art thou kind ?
          Wind, wind, unhappy ! thou art blind,
          Yet still thou wanderest the lily-seed to find.

My dry hands shook and shook as the green gown
    show'd again,   70
Clear'd from the yellow flowers, and I grew hollow with
    pain,
And on to us both there fell from the sun-shower drops
    of rain.
          Wind, wind ! thou art sad, art thou kind ?
          Wind, wind, unhappy ! thou art blind,
          Yet still thou wanderest the lily-seed to find.

Alas ! alas ! there was blood on the very quiet breast,
Blood lay in the many folds of the loose ungirded vest,
Blood lay upon her arm where the flower had been prest.

I shriek'd and leapt from my chair, and the orange
    roll'd out far,
The faint yellow juice oozed out like blood from a
    wizard's jar ;   80
And then in march'd the ghosts of those that had gone
    to the war.

I knew them by the arms that I was used to paint
Upon their long thin shields ; but the colours were all
    grown faint,
And faint upon their banner was Olaf, king and saint.

Wind, wind ! thou art sad, art thou kind ?
Wind, wind, unhappy ! thou art blind,
Yet still thou wanderest the lily-seed to find.

THE BLUE CLOSET

THE DAMOZELS.

LADY ALICE, Lady Louise,
Between the wash of the tumbling seas
We are ready to sing, if so ye please ;
So lay your long hands on the keys ;
    Sing, ' *Laudate pueri.*'

And ever the great bell overhead
Boom'd in the wind a knell for the dead,
Though no one toll'd it, a knell for the dead.

LADY LOUISE.

Sister, let the measure swell
Not too loud ; for you sing not well   10
If you drown the faint boom of the bell ;
    He is weary, so am I.

And ever the chevron overhead
Flapp'd on the banner of the dead ;
(Was he asleep, or was he dead ?)

LADY ALICE.

Alice the Queen, and Louise the Queen,
Two damozels wearing purple and green,
Four lone ladies dwelling here
From day to day and year to year ;
And there is none to let us go ;   20
To break the locks of the doors below,
Or shovel away the heaped-up snow ;
And when we die no man will know
That we are dead ; but they give us leave,

Once every year on Christmas-eve,
To sing in the Closet Blue one song ;
And we should be so long, so long,
If we dared, in singing ; for dream on dream,
They float on in a happy stream ;
Float from the gold strings, float from the keys,   30
Float from the open'd lips of Louise ;
But, alas ! the sea-salt oozes through
The chinks of the tiles of the Closet Blue ;
And ever the great bell overhead
Booms in the wind a knell for the dead,
The wind plays on it a knell for the dead.

[*They sing all together.*]

How long ago was it, how long ago,
He came to this tower with hands full of snow ?

' Kneel down, O love Louise, kneel down,' he said,
And sprinkled the dusty snow over my head.   40

He watch'd the snow melting, it ran through my hair,
Ran over my shoulders, white shoulders and bare.

' I cannot weep for thee, poor love Louise,
For my tears are all hidden deep under the seas ;

' In a gold and blue casket she keeps all my tears,
But my eyes are no longer blue, as in old years ;

' Yea, they grow grey with time, grow small and dry,
I am so feeble now, would I might die.'

And in truth the great bell overhead
Left off his pealing for the dead,   50
Perchance, because the wind was dead.

Will he come back again, or is he dead ?
O ! is he sleeping, my scarf round his head ?

Or did they strangle him as he lay there,
With the long scarlet scarf I used to wear ?

Only I pray thee, Lord, let him come here !
Both his soul and his body to me are most dear.

Dear Lord, that loves me, I wait to receive
Either body or spirit this wild Christmas-eve.

Through the floor shot up a lily red,   60
With a patch of earth from the land of the dead,
For he was strong in the land of the dead.

What matter that his cheeks were pale,
  His kind kiss'd lips all grey ?
' O, love Louise, have you waited long ? '
  ' O, my lord Arthur, yea.'

What if his hair that brush'd her cheek
  Was stiff with frozen rime ?
His eyes were grown quite blue again,
  As in the happy time.   70

' O, love Louise, this is the key
  Of the happy golden land !
O, sisters, cross the bridge with me,
  My eyes are full of sand.
What matter that I cannot see,
  If ye take me by the hand ? '

And ever the great bell overhead,
And the tumbling seas mourn'd for the dead ;
For their song ceased, and they were dead.   79

THE TUNE OF SEVEN TOWERS

No one goes there now :
  For what is left to fetch away
From the desolate battlements all arow,
  And the lead roof heavy and grey ?
' *Therefore,*' *said fair Yoland of the flowers,*
' *This is the tune of Seven Towers.*'

No one walks there now ;
  Except in the white moonlight
The white ghosts walk in a row ;
  If one could see it, an awful sight,—   10
' *Listen !* ' *said fair Yoland of the flowers,*
' *This is the tune of Seven Towers.*'

But none can see them now,
   Though they sit by the side of the moat,
Feet half in the water, there in a row,
   Long hair in the wind afloat.
' *Therefore,' said fair Yoland of the flowers,*
' *This is the tune of Seven Towers.'*

If any will go to it now,
   He must go to it all alone,   20
Its gates will not open to any row
   Of glittering spears—will *you* go alone ?
' *Listen !' said fair Yoland of the flowers,*
' *This is the tune of Seven Towers.'*

By my love go there now,
   To fetch me my coif away,
My coif and my kirtle, with pearls arow,
   Oliver, go to-day !
' *Therefore,' said fair Yoland of the flowers,*
' *This is the tune of Seven Towers.'*   30

I am unhappy now,
   I cannot tell you why ;
If you go, the priests and I in a row
   Will pray that you may not die.
' *Listen !' said fair Yoland of the flowers,*
' *This is the tune of Seven Towers.'*

If you will go for me now,
   I will kiss your mouth at last ;
      [*She sayeth inwardly.*]
(*The graves stand grey in a row,*)
   Oliver, hold me fast !   40
' *Therefore,' said fair Yoland of the flowers,*
' *This is the tune of Seven Towers.'*

GOLDEN WINGS

MIDWAYS of a walled garden,
  In the happy poplar land,
  Did an ancient castle stand,
With an old knight for a warden.

Many scarlet bricks there were
  In its walls, and old grey stone ;
  Over which red apples shone
At the right time of the year.

On the bricks the green moss grew,
  Yellow lichen on the stone,   10
  Over which red apples shone ;
Little war that castle knew.

Deep green water fill'd the moat,
  Each side had a red-brick lip,
  Green and mossy with the drip
Of dew and rain ; there was a boat

Of carven wood, with hangings green
  About the stern ; it was great bliss
  For lovers to sit there and kiss
In the hot summer noons, not seen.   20

Across the moat the fresh west wind
  In very little ripples went ;
  The way the heavy aspens bent
Towards it, was a thing to mind.

The painted drawbridge over it
  Went up and down with gilded chains,
  'Twas pleasant in the summer rains   30
Within the bridge-house there to sit.

There were five swans that ne'er did eat
  The water-weeds, for ladies came
  Each day, and young knights did the same,
And gave them cakes and bread for meat.

They had a house of painted wood,
  A red roof gold-spiked over it,
  Wherein upon their eggs to sit
Week after week ; no drop of blood,

Drawn from men's bodies by sword-blows,
  Came over there, or any tear ;
  Most certainly from year to year
'Twas pleasant as a Provence rose.   40

The banners seem'd quite full of ease,
  That over the turret-roofs hung down ;
  The battlements could get no frown
From the flower-moulded cornices.

Who walked in that garden there ?
  Miles and Giles and Isabeau,
  Tall Jehane du Castel beau,
Alice of the golden hair,

Big Sir Gervaise, the good knight,
  Fair Ellayne le Violet,   50
  Mary, Constance fille de fay,
Many dames with footfall light.

Whosoever wander'd there,
  Whether it be dame or knight,
  Half of scarlet, half of white
Their raiment was ; of roses fair

Each wore a garland on the head,
  At Ladies' Gard the way was so :
  Fair Jehane du Castel beau
Wore her wreath till it was dead.   60

Little joy she had of it,
  Of the raiment white and red,
  Or the garland on her head,
She had none with whom to sit

In the carven boat at noon ;
  None the more did Jehane weep,
  She would only stand and keep
Saying, ' He will be here soon.'

Many times in the long day
  Miles and Giles and Gervaise past,   70
  Holding each some white hand fast,
Every time they heard her say :

' Summer cometh to an end,
  Undern cometh after noon ;
  Golden wings will be here soon,
What if I some token send ? '

Wherefore that night within the hall,
  With open mouth and open eyes,
  Like some one listening with surprise,
She sat before the sight of all.   80

Stoop'd down a little she sat there,
  With neck stretch'd out and chin thrown up,
  One hand around a golden cup ;
And strangely with her fingers fair

She beat some tune upon the gold ;
  The minstrels in the gallery
  Sung : ' Arthur, who will never die,
In Avallon he groweth old.'

And when the song was ended, she
  Rose and caught up her gown and ran ;   90
  None stopp'd her eager face and wan
Of all that pleasant company.

Right so within her own chamber
  Upon her bed she sat ; and drew
  Her breath in quick gasps ; till she knew
That no man follow'd after her :

She took the garland from her head,
  Loosed all her hair, and let it lie
  Upon the coverlit ; thereby
She laid the gown of white and red ;   100

And she took off her scarlet shoon,
  And bared her feet ; still more and more
  Her sweet face redden'd ; evermore
She murmur'd : ' He will be here soon ;

' Truly he cannot fail to know
    My tender body waits him here ;
    And if he knows, I have no fear
For poor Jehane du Castel beau.'

She took a sword within her hand,
    Whose hilts were silver, and she sung,   110
    Somehow like this, wild words that rung
A long way over the moonlit land :—

        Gold wings across the sea !
        Grey light from tree to tree,
        Gold hair beside my knee,
        I pray thee come to me,
        Gold wings !

                The water slips,
        The red-bill'd moorhen dips.
        Sweet kisses on red lips ;
        Alas ! the red rust grips,   120
        And the blood-red dagger rips,
        Yet, O knight, come to me !

        Are not my blue eyes sweet ?
        The west wind from the wheat
        Blows cold across my feet ;
        Is it not time to meet
        Gold wings across the sea ?

        White swans on the green moat,
        Small feathers left afloat
        By the blue-painted boat ;   130
        Swift running of the stoat ;
        Sweet gurgling note by note
        Of sweet music.

                O gold wings,
        Listen how gold hair sings,
        And the Ladies' Castle rings
        Gold wings across the sea.

I sit on a purple bed,
Outside, the wall is red,
Thereby the apple hangs,
And the wasp, caught by the fangs,   140

Dies in the autumn night.
And the bat flits till light,
And the love-crazed knight

Kisses the long wet grass :
The weary days pass,—
Gold wings across the sea !

Gold wings across the sea !
Moonlight from tree to tree,
Sweet hair laid on my knee,
O, sweet knight, come to me !   150

Gold wings, the short night slips,
The white swan's long neck drips,
I pray thee, kiss my lips,
Gold wings across the sea.

No answer through the moonlit night ;
  No answer in the cold grey dawn ;
  No answer when the shaven lawn
Grew green, and all the roses bright.

Her tired feet look'd cold and thin,
  Her lips were twitch'd, and wretched tears,   160
  Some, as she lay, roll'd past her ears,
Some fell from off her quivering chin.

Her long throat, stretch'd to its full length,
  Rose up and fell right brokenly ;
  As though the unhappy heart was nigh
Striving to break with all its strength.

And when she slipp'd from off the bed,
  Her cramp'd feet would not hold her ; she
  Sank down and crept on hand and knee,
On the window-sill she laid her head.   170

There, with crooked arm upon the sill,
   She look'd out, muttering dismally :
     There is no sail upon the sea,
No pennon on the empty hill.

' I cannot stay here all alone,
   Or meet their happy faces here,
     And wretchedly I have no fear ;
A little while, and I am gone.'

Therewith she rose upon her feet,
   And totter'd ; cold and misery   180
     Still made the deep sobs come, till she
At last stretch'd out her fingers sweet,

And caught the great sword in her hand ;
   And, stealing down the silent stair,
     Barefooted in the morning air,
And only in her smock, did stand

Upright upon the green lawn grass ;
   And hope grew in her as she said :
     ' I have thrown off the white and red,
And pray God it may come to pass   190

' I meet him ; if ten years go by
   Before I meet him ; if, indeed,
     Meanwhile both soul and body bleed,
Yet there is end of misery,

' And I have hope. He could not come,
   But I can go to him and show
     These new things I have got to know,
And make him speak, who has been dumb.'

O Jehane ! the red morning sun
   Changed her white feet to glowing gold,   200
     Upon her smock, on crease and fold,
Changed that to gold which had been dun.

O Miles, and Giles, and Isabeau,
   Fair Ellayne le Violet,
     Mary, Constance fille de fay !
Where is Jehane du Castel beau ?

O big Gervaise ride apace !
  Down to the hard yellow sand,
  Where the water meets the land.
This is Jehane by her face ;   210

Why has she a broken sword ?
  Mary ! she is slain outright ;
  Verily a piteous sight ;
Take her up without a word !

Giles and Miles and Gervaise there,
  Ladies' Gard must meet the war ;
  Whatsoever knights these are,
Man the walls withouten fear !

Axes to the apple trees,
  Axes to the aspens tall !   220
  Barriers without the wall
May be lightly made of these.

O poor shivering Isabeau ;
  Poor Ellayne le Violet,
  Bent with fear ! we miss to-day
Brave Jehane du Castel beau.

O poor Mary, weeping so !
  Wretched Constance fille de fay !
  Verily we miss to-day
Fair Jehane du Castel beau.   230

The apples now grow green and sour
  Upon the mouldering castle-wall,
  Before they ripen there they fall :
There are no banners on the tower.

The draggled swans most eagerly eat
  The green weeds trailing in the moat ;
  Inside the rotting leaky boat
You see a slain man's stiffen'd feet.

THE HAYSTACK IN THE FLOODS

HAD she come all the way for this,
To part at last without a kiss ?
Yea, had she borne the dirt and rain
That her own eyes might see him slain
Beside the haystack in the floods ?

Along the dripping leafless woods,
The stirrup touching either shoe,
She rode astride as troopers do ;
With kirtle kilted to her knee,
To which the mud splash'd wretchedly ;   10
And the wet dripp'd from every tree
Upon her head and heavy hair,
And on her eyelids broad and fair ;
The tears and rain ran down her face.
By fits and starts they rode apace,
And very often was his place
Far off from her ; he had to ride
Ahead, to see what might betide
When the roads cross'd ; and sometimes, when
There rose a murmuring from his men,   20
Had to turn back with promises ;
Ah me ! she had but little ease ;
And often for pure doubt and dread
She sobb'd, made giddy in the head
By the swift riding ; while, for cold,
Her slender fingers scarce could hold
The wet reins ; yea, and scarcely, too,
She felt the foot within her shoe
Against the stirrup : all for this,
To part at last without a kiss   30
Beside the haystack in the floods.

For when they near'd that old soak'd hay,
They saw across the only way
That Judas, Godmar, and the three
Red running lions dismally
Grinn'd from his pennon, under which,

In one straight line along the ditch,
They counted thirty heads.

So then,
While Robert turn'd round to his men,
She saw at once the wretched end,   40
And, stooping down, tried hard to rend
Her coif the wrong way from her head,
And hid her eyes ; while Robert said :
' Nay, love, 'tis scarcely two to one,
At Poictiers where we made them run
So fast—why, sweet my love, good cheer.
The Gascon frontier is so near,
Nought after this.'

But, ' O,' she said,
' My God ! my God ! I have to tread
The long way back without you ; then   50
The court at Paris ; those six men ;
The gratings of the Chatelet ;
The swift Seine on some rainy day
Like this, and people standing by,
And laughing, while my weak hands try
To recollect how strong men swim.
All this, or else a life with him,
For which I should be damned at last,
Would God that this next hour were past ! '

He answer'd not, but cried his cry,   60
' St. George for Marny ! ' cheerily ;
And laid his hand upon her rein.
Alas ! no man of all his train
Gave back that cheery cry again ;
And, while for rage his thumb beat fast
Upon his sword-hilts, some one cast
About his neck a kerchief long,
And bound him.

Then they went along
To Godmar ; who said : ' Now, Jehane,
Your lover's life is on the wane   70

So fast, that, if this very hour
You yield not as my paramour,
He will not see the rain leave off—
Nay, keep your tongue from gibe and scoff,
Sir Robert, or I slay you now.'

She laid her hand upon her brow,
Then gazed upon the palm, as though
She thought her forehead bled, and—' No.'
She said, and turn'd her head away,
As there were nothing else to say,   80
And everything were settled : red
Grew Godmar's face from chin to head :
' Jehane, on yonder hill there stands
My castle, guarding well my lands :
What hinders me from taking you,
And doing that I list to do
To your fair wilful body, while
Your knight lies dead ? '
                              A wicked smile
Wrinkled her face, her lips grew thin,
A long way out she thrust her chin :   90
' You know that I should strangle you
While you were sleeping ; or bite through
Your throat, by God's help—ah ! ' she said,
' Lord Jesus, pity your poor maid !
For in such wise they hem me in,
I cannot choose but sin and sin,
Whatever happens : yet I think
They could not make me eat or drink,
And so should I just reach my rest.'
' Nay, if you do not my behest,   100
O Jehane ! though I love you well,'
Said Godmar, ' would I fail to tell
All that I know.' ' Foul lies,' she said.
' Eh ? lies my Jehane ? by God's head,
At Paris folks would deem them true !
Do you know, Jehane, they cry for you,
" Jehane the brown ! Jehane the brown !
Give us Jehane to burn or drown ! "—

Eh—gag me Robert !—sweet my friend,
This were indeed a piteous end   110
For those long fingers, and long feet,
And long neck, and smooth shoulders sweet ;
An end that few men would forget
That saw it—So, an hour yet :
Consider, Jehane, which to take
Of life or death ! '

                  So, scarce awake,
Dismounting, did she leave that place,
And totter some yards : with her face
Turn'd upward to the sky she lay,
Her head on a wet heap of hay,   120
And fell asleep : and while she slept,
And did not dream, the minutes crept
Round to the twelve again ; but she,
Being waked at last, sigh'd quietly,
And strangely childlike came, and said :
' I will not.' Straightway Godmar's head,
As though it hung on strong wires, turn'd
Most sharply round, and his face burn'd.

For Robert—both his eyes were dry,
He could not weep, but gloomily   130
He seem'd to watch the rain ; yea, too,
His lips were firm ; he tried once more
To touch her lips ; she reach'd out, sore
And vain desire so tortured them,
The poor grey lips, and now the hem
Of his sleeve brush'd them.

                  With a start
Up Godmar rose, thrust them apart ;
From Robert's throat he loosed the bands
Of silk and mail ; with empty hands
Held out, she stood and gazed, and saw,   140
The long bright blade without a flaw
Glide out from Godmar's sheath, his hand
In Robert's hair ; she saw him bend
Back Robert's head ; she saw him send

The thin steel down ; the blow told well,
Right backward the knight Robert fell,
And moan'd as dogs do, being half dead,
Unwitting, as I deem : so then
Godmar turn'd grinning to his men,
Who ran, some five or six, and beat   150
His head to pieces at their feet.

Then Godmar turn'd again and said :
' So, Jehane, the first fitte is read !
Take note, my lady, that your way
Lies backward to the Chatelet ! '
She shook her head and gazed awhile
At her cold hands with a rueful smile,
As though this thing had made her mad.

This was the parting that they had
Beside the haystack in the floods.   160

TWO RED ROSES ACROSS THE MOON

THERE was a lady lived in a hall,
Large in the eyes, and slim and tall ;
And ever she sung from noon to noon,
Two red roses across the moon.

There was a knight came riding by
In early spring, when the roads were dry ;
And he heard that lady sing at the noon,
Two red roses across the moon.

Yet none the more he stopp'd at all,
But he rode a-gallop past the hall ;   10
And left that lady singing at noon,
Two red roses across the moon.

Because, forsooth, the battle was set,
And the scarlet and blue had got to be met,
He rode on the spur till the next warm noon :—
Two red roses across the moon.

But the battle was scatter'd from hill to hill,
From the windmill to the watermill ;
And he said to himself, as it near'd the noon.
Two red roses across the moon.   20

You scarce could see for the scarlet and blue,
A golden helm or a golden shoe ;
So he cried, as the fight grew thick at the noon,
Two red roses across the moon !

Verily then the gold bore through
The huddled spears of the scarlet and blue ;
And they cried, as they cut them down at the noon,
Two red roses across the moon !

I trow he stopp'd when he rode again
By the hall, though draggled sore with the rain ;   30
And his lips were pinch'd to kiss at the noon
Two red roses across the moon.

Under the may she stoop'd to the crown,
All was gold, there was nothing of brown ;
And the horns blew up in the hall at noon,
Two red roses across the moon.

WELLAND RIVER

FAIR Ellayne she walk'd by Welland river,
    Across the lily lee :
O, gentle Sir Robert, ye are not kind
    To stay so long at sea.

Over the marshland none can see
    Your scarlet pennon fair ;
O, leave the Easterlings alone,
    Because of my golden hair.

The day when over Stamford bridge
    That dear pennon I see   10
Go up toward the goodly street,
    'Twill be a fair day for me.

O, let the bonny pennon bide
　　At Stamford, the good town,
And let the Easterlings go free,
　　And their ships go up and down.

For every day that passes by
　　I wax both pale and green,
From gold to gold of my girdle
　　There is an inch between.　　　　　　20

I sew'd it up with scarlet silk
　　Last night upon my knee,
And my heart grew sad and sore to think
　　Thy face I'd never see.

I sew'd it up with scarlet silk,
　　As I lay upon my bed :
Sorrow ! the man I'll never see
　　That had my maidenhead.

But as Ellayne sat on her window-seat
　　And comb'd her yellow hair,　　　　30
She saw come over Stamford bridge
　　The scarlet pennon fair.

As Ellayne lay and sicken'd sore,
　　The gold shoes on her feet,
She saw Sir Robert and his men
　　Ride up the Stamford street.

He had a coat of fine red gold,
　　And a bascinet of steel ;
Take note his goodly Collayne sword
　　Smote the spur upon his heel.　　　40

And by his side, on a grey jennet,
　　There rode a fair lady,
For every ruby Ellayne wore,
　　I count she carried three,

Say, was not Ellayne's gold hair fine,
　　That fell to her middle free ?

But that lady's hair down in the street,
  Fell lower than her knee.

Fair Ellayne's face, from sorrow and grief,
  Was waxen pale and green :   50
That lady's face was goodly red,
  She had but little tene.

But as he pass'd by her window
  He grew a little wroth :
O, why does yon pale face look at me,
  From out the golden cloth ?

It is some burd, the fair dame said
  That aye rode him beside,
Has come to see your bonny face
  This merry summer-tide.   60

But Ellayne let a lily-flower
  Light on his cap of steel :
O, I have gotten two hounds, fair knight,
  The one has served me well.

But the other, just an hour agone,
  Has come from over sea,
And all his fell is sleek and fine,
  But little he knows of me.

Now, which shall I let go, fair knight,
  And which shall bide with me ?   70
O, lady, have no doubt to keep
  The one that best loveth thee.

O, Robert, see how sick I am !
  Ye do not so by me.
Lie still, fair love ! have ye gotten harm
  While I was on the sea ?

Of one gift, Robert, that ye gave,
  I sicken to the death,
I pray you nurse-tend me, my knight,
  Whiles that I have my breath.   80

Six fathoms from the Stamford bridge
　He left that dame to stand,
And whiles she wept, and whiles she cursed
　That she ever had taken land,

He has kiss'd sweet Ellayne on the mouth,
　And fair she fell asleep,
And long and long days after that
　Sir Robert's house she did keep.

RIDING TOGETHER [1]

For many, many days together
　The wind blew steady from the East ;
For many days hot grew the weather,
　About the time of our Lady's Feast.

For many days we rode together,
　Yet met we neither friend nor foe ;
Hotter and clearer grew the weather,
　Steadily did the East wind blow.

We saw the trees in the hot, bright weather,
　Clear-cut, with shadows very black,　　　　10
As freely we rode on together
　With helms unlaced and bridles slack.

And often, as we rode together,
　We, looking down the green bank'd stream,
Saw flowers in the sunny weather,
　And saw the bubble-making bream.

And in the night lay down together,
　And hung above our heads the rood,
Or watch'd night-long in the dewy weather,
　The while the moon did watch the wood.　　　20

[1] This poem had previously appeared in *The Oxford and Cambridge Magazine*, May 1856.

Our spears stood bright and thick together,
   Straight out the banners stream'd behind,
As we gallop'd on in the sunny weather,
   With faces turn'd towards the wind.

Down sank our threescore spears together,
   As thick we saw the pagans ride ;
His eager face in the clear fresh weather,
   Shone out that last time by my side.

Up the sweep of the bridge we dash'd together,
   It rock'd to the crash of the meeting spears,   30
Down rain'd the buds of the dear spring weather,
   The elm-tree flowers fell like tears.

There, as we roll'd and writhed together,
   I threw my arms above my head,
For close by my side, in the lovely weather,
   I saw him reel and fall back dead.

I and the slayer met together,
   He waited the death-stroke there in his place,
With thoughts of death, in the lovely weather,
   Gapingly mazed at my madden'd face.   40

Madly I fought as we fought together ;
   In vain : the little Christian band
The pagans drown'd, as in stormy weather,
   The river drowns low-lying land.

They bound my blood-stain'd hands together,
   They bound his corpse to nod by my side :
Then on we rode, in the bright March weather,
   With clash of cymbals did we ride.

We ride no more, no more together ;
   My prison-bars are thick and strong,   50
I take no heed of any weather,
   The sweet Saints grant I live not long.

FATHER JOHN'S WAR-SONG

The Reapers.

So many reapers, Father John,
So many reapers and no little son,
To meet you when the day is done,
With little stiff legs to waddle and run ?
Pray you beg, borrow, or steal one son.
Hurrah for the corn-sheaves of Father John !

Father John.

O maiden Mary, be wary, be wary !
And go not down to the river,
Lest the kingfisher, your evil wisher,
Lure you down to the river,   10
Lest your white feet grow muddy,
Your red hair too ruddy
With the river-mud so red :
But when you are wed
Go down to the river ;
O maiden Mary, be very wary,
And dwell among the corn !
See, this dame Alice, maiden Mary,
Her hair is thin and white,
But she is a housewife good and wary,   20
And a great steel key hangs bright
From her gown, as red as the flowers in corn ;
She is good and old like the autumn corn.

Maiden Mary.

This is knight Roland, Father John,
Stark in his arms from a field half-won ;
Ask him if he has seen your son :
Roland, lay your sword on the corn,
The piled-up sheaves of the golden corn.

KNIGHT ROLAND.
Why does she kiss me, Father John ?
She is my true love truly won ;   30
Under my helm is room for one,
But the molten lead-streams trickle and run
From my roof-tree, burning under the sun ;
No corn to burn, we had eaten the corn,
There was no waste of the golden corn.

FATHER JOHN.
Ho, you reapers, away from the corn,
To march with the banner of Father John !

THE REAPERS.
We will win a house for Roland his son,
And for maiden Mary with hair like corn,
As red as the reddest of golden corn.   40

OMNES.
Father John, you have got you a son,
Seven feet high when his helm is on !
Pennon of Roland, banner of John,
Star of Mary, march well on.

SIR GILES' WAR-SONG

Ho ! is there any will ride with me,
Sir Giles, le bon des barrières ?

The clink of arms is good to hear,
The flap of pennons fair to see ;
  Ho ! is there any will ride with me,
    Sir Giles, le bon des barrières ?

The leopards and lilies are fair to see,
' St. George Guienne ' right good to hear :
  Ho ! is there any will ride with me,
    Sir Giles, le bon des barrières ?   10

I stood by the barrier,
My coat being blazon'd fair to see ;
  Ho ! is there any will ride with me,
    Sir Giles, le bon des barrières ?

Clisson put out his head to see,
And lifted his basnet up to hear ;
  I pull'd him through the bars to ME,
    Sir Giles, le bon des barrières.

NEAR AVALON

A SHIP with shields before the sun,
Six maidens round the mast,
A red-gold crown on every one,
A green gown on the last.

The fluttering green banners there
Are wrought with ladies' heads most fair,
And a portraiture of Guenevere
The middle of each sail doth bear.

A ship with sails before the wind,
And round the helm six knights,
Their heaumes are on, whereby, half blind,
They pass by many sights.

The tatter'd scarlet banners there,
Right soon will leave the spear-heads bare,
Those six knights sorrowfully bear
In all their heaumes some yellow hair.

PRAISE OF MY LADY

My lady seems of ivory
Forehead, straight nose, and cheeks that be
Hollow'd a little mournfully.
          Beata mea Domina !

Her forehead, overshadow'd much
By bows of hair, has a wave such
As God was good to make for me.
          Beata mea Domina !

Not greatly long my lady's hair,
Nor yet with yellow colour fair,   10
But thick and crisped wonderfully :
          Beata mea Domina !

Heavy to make the pale face sad,
And dark, but dead as though it had
Been forged by God most wonderfully
          —Beata mea Domina !—

Of some strange metal, thread by thread,
To stand out from my lady's head,
Not moving much to tangle me.
          Beata mea Domina !   20

Beneath her brows the lids fall slow,
The lashes a clear shadow throw
Where I would wish my lips to be.
          Beata mea Domina !

Her great eyes, standing far apart,
Draw up some memory from her heart,
And gaze out very mournfully ;
          —Beata mea Domina !—

So beautiful and kind they are,
But most times looking out afar,   30
Waiting for something, not for me.
          Beata mea Domina !

I wonder if the lashes long
Are those that do her bright eyes wrong,
For always half tears seem to be
            —*Beata mea Domina !*—

Lurking below the underlid,
Darkening the place where they lie hid—
If they should rise and flow for me !
            Beata mea Domina !   40

Her full lips being made to kiss,
Curl'd up and pensive each one is ;
This makes me faint to stand and see.
            Beata mea Domina !

Her lips are not contented now,
Because the hours pass so slow
Towards a sweet time : (pray for me),
            —*Beata mea Domina !*—

Nay, hold thy peace ! for who can tell ;
But this at least I know full well,   50
Her lips are parted longingly,
            –*Beata mea Domina !*—

So passionate and swift to move,
To pluck at any flying love,
That I grow faint to stand and see.
            Beata mea Domina !

Yea ! there beneath them is her chin,
So fine and round, it were a sin
To feel no weaker when I see
            —*Beata mea Domina !*—   60

God's dealings ; for with so much care
And troublous, faint lines wrought in there,
He finishes her face for me.
            Beata mea Domina !

Of her long neck what shall I say ?
What thing about her body's sway,
Like a knight's pennon or slim tree
            —*Beata mea Domina !*—

Set gently waving in the wind ;
Or her long hands that I may find 70
On some day sweet to move o'er me ?
       Beata mea Domina !

God pity me though, if I miss'd
The telling, how along her wrist
The veins creep, dying languidly
      —Beata mea Domina !—

Inside her tender palm and thin.
Now give me pardon, dear, wherein
My voice is weak and vexes thee.
       Beata mea Domina ! 80

All men that see her any time,
I charge you straightly in this rhyme,
What, and wherever you may be,
      —Beata mea Domina !—

To kneel before her ; as for me,
I choke and grow quite faint to see
My lady moving graciously.
       Beata mea Domina !

SUMMER DAWN [1]

PRAY but one prayer for me twixt thy closed lips,
  Think but one thought of me up in the stars.
The summer night waneth, the morning light slips,
  Faint and grey 'twixt the leaves of the aspen, betwixt
    the cloud-bars,
That are patiently waiting there for the dawn :
  Patient and colourless, though Heaven's gold
Waits to float through them along with the sun.

---

[1] This poem had previously appeared in *The Oxford and Cambridge Magazine*, October 1856.

Far out in the meadows, above the young corn,
　The heavy elms wait, and restless and cold
The uneasy wind rises ; the roses are dun ;
Through the long twilight they pray for the dawn,
Round the lone house in the midst of the corn.
　Speak but one word to me over the corn,
　Over the tender, bow'd locks of the corn.

IN PRISON [1]

WEARILY, drearily,
Half the day long,
Flap the great banners
High over the stone ;
Strangely and eerily
Sounds the wind's song,
Bending the banner-poles.

While, all alone,
Watching the loophole's spark,
Lie I, with life all dark,
Feet tether'd, hands fetter'd
Fast to the stone,
The grim walls, square letter'd
With prison'd men's groan.

Still strain the banner-poles
Through the wind's song,
Westward the banner rolls
Over my wrong.

[1] This poem had previously appeared in ' Frank's Sealed Letter '
in *The Oxford and Cambridge Magazine*, April 1856.

THE LIFE AND DEATH OF JASON

A POEM

1867

(First published in 1867. Reprinted here from the second edition, revised, 1868. The alternate readings given at the foot of the page are those of the first edition).

ARGUMENT

JASON, the son of Æson, king of Iolchos, having come to man's estate, demanded of Pelias his father's kingdom, which he held wrongfully. But Pelias answered, that if he would bring from Colchis the golden fleece of the ram that had carried Phryxus thither, he would yield him his right. Whereon Jason sailed to Colchis in the ship Argo, with other heroes, and by means of Medea, the king's daughter, won the fleece : and carried off also Medea ; and so, after many troubles, came back to Iolchos again. There, by Medea's wiles, was Pelias slain ; but Jason went to Corinth, and lived with Medea happily, till he was taken with the love of Glauce, the king's daughter of Corinth, and must needs wed her ; whom also Medea destroyed, and fled to Ægeus at Athens ; and not long after Jason died strangely.

THE LIFE AND DEATH OF JASON

BOOK I

Jason having grown up to manhood in the woods, is warned
of what his life shall be.

In Thessaly, beside the tumbling sea,
Once dwelt a folk, men called the Minyæ ;
For, coming from Orchomenus the old,
Bearing their wives and children, beasts and gold,
Through many a league of land they took their way,
And stopped at last, where in a sunny bay
The green Anaurus cleaves the white sea-sand,
And eastward inland doth Mount Pelion stand,
Where bears and wolves the centaurs' arrows find ;
And southward is a gentle sea and kind,　　　　　　 10
Nigh landlocked, peopled with all kinds of fish,
And the good land yields all that man can wish.

   So there they built Iolchos, that each day
Grew great until all these were passed away,
With many another, and Cretheus the king
Had died, and left his crown and everything
To Æson, his own son by fair Tyro ;
Whom, in unhappy days and long ago,
A God had loved, whose son was Pelias.

   And so, within a while, it came to pass　　　　 20
This Pelias, being covetous and strong
And full of wiles, and deeming naught was wrong
That wrought him good, thrust Æson from his throne,
And over all the Minyæ reigned alone ;
While Æson, like a poor and feeble lord,
Dwelt in Iolchos still, nor was his word
Regarded much by any man therein,
Nor did men labour much his praise to win.

Now 'mid all this a fair young son he had ;
And when his state thus fell from good to bad 30
He thought, Though Pelias leave me now alone,
Yet he may wish to make quite sure his throne
By slaying me and mine, some evil day ;
Therefore the child will I straight send away,
Ere Pelias feels his high seat tottering,
And gets to know the terrors of a king,
That blood alone can deaden. Therewithal
A faithful slave unto him did he call,
And bade him from his nurses take the child
And bear him forth unto the forest wild 40
About the foot of Pelion : There should he
Blow loudly on a horn of ivory
That Æson gave him ; then would come to him
A Centaur, grave of face and large of limb,
Before whom he should fall upon his knees
And, holding forth the child, say words like these :
  ' O my lord Chiron, Æson sends me here
To say, if ever you have held him dear,
Take now this child, his son, and rear him up
Till we have fully drained the bitter cup 50
The fates have filled for us ; and if times change
While through the peaceful oakwood here you range,
And the crown comes upon the youngling's head,
Then, though a king right fair apparelled,
Yet unto you shall he be but a slave,
Since now from fear his tender years you save ; '
' And then,' quoth Æson, ' all these words being said,
Hold out this ring, set with a ruby red,
Adorned with dainty little images,
And this same horn, whereon, 'twixt carven trees, 60
Diana follows up the flying hart ;
They shall be signs of truth upon your part.
Then leave the child with him, and come to me,
Minding what words the Centaur saith to thee ;
Of whom thou needest have no whit of fear ;
And, ere thou goest, bring me the child here.'
  Then went the man and came again to him
With Jason, who was strong and large of limb

As for his years, and now upon his feet
Went firmly, and began to feel life sweet, 70
And longed for this and that, and on his tongue,
Bewildered, half articulate, speech hung.
　But Æson, when he saw the sturdy boy,
His bright round limbs and face lit up with joy
Of very life, sighed deeply, and he said :
' O child, I pray the Gods to spare thine head
The burden of a crown ; were it not good
That thou shouldst live and die within this wood
That clothes the feet of Pelion, knowing naught
Of all the things by foolish men so sought ; 80
For there, no doubt, is everything man needs,—
The quiver, with the iron-pointed reeds,
The cornel bow, the wood-knife at the side,
The garments of the spotted leopard's hide,
The bed of bear-skin in the hollow hill,
The bath within the pool of some green rill ;
There shall the quick-eyed centaurs be thy friends,
Unto whose hearts such wisdom great Jove sends
They know the past and future, and fear naught
That by the fates upon them may be brought. 90
And when the spring brings love, then mayst thou find
In some fair grassy place, the wood-nymphs kind,
And choose thy mate, and with her, hand in hand,
Go wandering through the blossoming sweet land ;
And naught of evil there shall come to thee,
But like the golden age shall all things be ;
And when upon thee falls the fated day,
Fearless and painless shalt thou pass away.'
　So spoke he foolishly, nor knew indeed
How many hearts his son should make to bleed, 100
How many griefs his head, whitened with care
Long ere its time, before his death should bear.
　Now, since the moonless night and dark was come,
Time was it that the child should leave his home ;
And saddled in the court the stout horse stood
That was to bear them to the Centaur's wood ;

74 bright] fair

And the tried slave stood ready by his lord,
With wallet on his back, and sharpened sword
Girt to his side ; to whom the horn and ring,
Fit for the belt and finger of a king,   110
Did Æson give, and therewith kissed the boy,
Who with his black beard played, and laughed for joy
To see the war-horse in the red torch-light.
At last, being mounted, forth into the night
They rode, and thus has Jason left his home.

All night they rode, and at the dawn, being come
Unto the outskirts of the forest wild,
They left the horse, and the still sleeping child
The slave bore in his arms, until they came
Unto the place where, living free from blame,   120
Chiron the old roamed through the oaken wood ;
There by a flowering thorn-bush the slave stood,
And set the little Jason on the ground ;
Who, waking from sweet sleep, looked all around
And 'gan to prattle ; but his guardian drew
The horn from off his neck, and thereon blew
A point of hunting known to two or three,
That sounded through the forest merrily,
Then waited listening.
                        And meantime the sun,
Come from Eubœan cliffs, had just begun   130
To light the high tips of the forest grass,
And in the thorn the blackbird singing was ;
But 'mid his noise the listening man could hear
The sound of hoofs, whereat a little fear
He felt within his heart, and heeded naught
The struggling of the child, who ever sought
To gain the horn all glittering of bright gold,
Wrought by the cunning Dædalus of old.
But louder still the noise he hearkened grew,
Until at last in sight the Centaur drew,   140
A mighty grey horse, trotting down the glade,
Over whose back the long grey locks were laid,

114 At last] Then
137 of bright gold] of gold

That from his reverend head abroad did flow ;
For to the waist was man, but all below
A mighty horse, once roan, now well-nigh white
With lapse of years ; with oak-wreaths was he dight
Where man joined unto horse, and on his head
He wore a gold crown, set with rubies red,
And in his hand he bare a mighty bow,
No man could bend of those that battle now.   150
   So, when he saw him coming through the trees,
The trembling slave sunk down upon his knees
And put the child before him ; but Chiron,
Who knew all things, cried : ' Man with Æson's son,
Thou needest not to tell me who thou art,
Nor will I fail to do to him my part :
A vain thing were it, truly, if I strove,
Such as I am, against the will of Jove.
Lo now, this youngling, set 'twixt thee and me,
In days to come a mighty man shall be,   160
Well-nigh the mightiest of all those that dwell
Between Olympus and Malea ; and well
Shall Juno love him till he come to die.
   ' Now get thee to thy master presently,
But leave with me the red ring and the horn,
That folk may know of whom this boy was born
In days to come, when he shall leave this wild :
And lay between my arms the noble child.'
   So the slave joyful, but still half afraid,
Within the mighty arms young Jason laid,   170
And gave up both the horn and the red ring
Unto the Centaur, who the horn did sling
About him ; on his finger, with a smile,
Setting the ring ; and in a little while
The slave departing, reached the open plain,
And straight he mounted on his horse again,
And rode on toward Iolchos all the day,
And as the sunset darkened every way,
He reached the gates, and coming to his lord,
Bid him rejoice, and told him every word   180
That Chiron said. Right glad was Æson then
That from his loins a great man among men

Should thus have sprung ; and so he passed his days
Full quietly, remote from fear or praise.
  And now was Pelias mindful of the day
When from the altar's horns he drew away
Sidero's cruel hands, while Neleus smote
The golden-hilted sword into her throat,
And without fire, or barley-cake, or cup,
No pleasing victim, she was offered up   190
In Juno's temple ; so he feared that he,
Though sprung from him who rules the restless sea,
Should meet an evil fate at Juno's hands :
Therefore he sent for men from many lands,
Marble and wood, and gold and brass enow,
And day by day, with many a sounding blow,
The masons wrought, until at last was reared
A temple to the Goddess that he feared ;—
A wonder among temples, for the stone
That made it, and the gold that therein shone.   200
And in the midst her image Pelias set,
Wrought cunningly of purest gold, which yet
Had served him better in his treasury,
So little store the Goddess set thereby.
  Moreover to Dodona, where the doves
Amid the oak-trees murmur of their loves,
He sent a messenger to know his fate ;
Who, up the temple steps, beneath the weight
Of precious things went bending ; and being come
Back from the north to his Thessalian home,   210
Gave forth this answer to the doubtful king :—
  ' O Pelias, fearful of so many a thing,
Sit merry o'er thy wine, sleep safe and soft,
Within thy golden bed ; for surely oft
The snows shall fall before the half-shod man
Can come upon thee through the water wan.'
  So at this word the king along the shore
Built many a tower, and ever more and more
Drew men unto him skilled in spear and bow ;
And through the streets full often would he go   220
Beset with guards, and for the rest began

218 ever] still

To be a terror unto every man.
   And yet indeed were all these things but vain,
For at the foot of Pelion grew his bane
In strength and comeliness from day to day,
And swiftly passed his childish years away :
Unto whom Chiron taught the worthy lore
Of elders who the wide world filled before ;
And how to forge his iron arrow-heads ;
And how to find within the marshy steads   230
The stoutest reeds, and from some slain bird's wing
To feather them, and make a deadly thing ;
And through the woods he took him, nor would spare
To show him how the just-awakened bear
Came hungry from his tree, or show him how
The spotted leopard's lurking-place to know ;
And many a time they brought the hart to bay,
Or smote the boar at hottest of the day.
   Now was his dwelling-place a fair-hewn cave,
Facing the south : thereto the herdsmen drave   240
Full oft to Chiron woolly sheep, and neat,
And brought him wine and garden-honey sweet,
And fruits that flourish well in the fat plain,
And cloth and linen, and would take again
Skins of slain beasts, and little lumps of gold,
Washed from the high crags : then would Chiron hold,
Upon the sunny lawns, high feast with them,
And garland all about the ancient stem
Of some great tree, and there do sacrifice
Unto the Gods, and with grave words and wise   250
Tell them sweet tales of elders passed away :
But for some wished thing every man would pray
Or ever in their hands the steel did shine,
And or the sun lit up the bubbling wine ;
Then would they fall to meat, nor would they leave
Their joyances, until the dewy eve
Had given good heart unto the nightingale
To tell the sleepy wood-nymphs all his tale.
   Moreover, Chiron taught him how to cast
His hand across the lyre, until there passed   260
Such sweetness through the woods, that all about

The wood-folk gathered, and the merry rout
That called on Bacchus, hearkening, stayed awhile.
And in the chase the hunter, with a smile,
From his raised hand let fall the noisy horn,
When to his ears the sweet strange sound was borne.

But in the night-time once did Jason wake,
And seem to see the moonlit branches shake
With huge, unwonted clamour of the chase ;
Then up he sprung, but ere he went one pace   270
Unto the cave's mouth, Chiron raised his arm
And drew him back, and said ; ' Surely, no charm
Thou hast, my son, against Diana's sight,
Who over Pelion goes abroad this night ;
Now let those go to her that she doth call,
Because no fenced town, brazen gate or wall,
No coat of mail, or seven-folded shield,
Can guard thee from the wound that ne'er is healed,
When she is angry. Sleep again, my son,
Nor wish to spoil great deeds not yet begun.'   280

Then Jason lay and trembled, while the sound
Grew louder through the moonlit woods around,
And died off slowly, going toward the sea,
Leaving the fern-owl wailing mournfully.

Thereafter wandering lonely did he meet
A maid, with girt-up gown and sandalled feet,
Who joyously through flowering grass did go,
Holding within her hand an unstrung bow ;
And, setting eyes on her, he thought, indeed,
This must be she that made Actæon bleed ;   290
For, certes, ere that day he had not seen
Within that wild, one made so like a queen.

So, doubtful, he held back, nor dared to love
Her rosy feet, or ivory knees above,
And, with half-lifted eyes, could scarcely dare
To gaze upon her eyes or golden hair,
Or hidden bosom : but she called aloud,—
' Tell me, fair youth, if thou hast seen a crowd
Of such as I go through these woods to-day ? '
And when his stammering tongue no word could say,
She smiled upon him, and said, ' Who art thou,   301

Who seemest fitter from some galley's prow
To lead the heroes on the merchant-town,
Than through the wilds to hunt the poor beasts down,
Or underneath the canopy to sit,
Than by the beech to watch the cushat flit ?
Speak out, and fear not.'

     O, my queen ! ' said he,
' Fair Goddess, as thou seemest well to be,
Give me good days and peace, and maiden's love,
And let great kings send out their sons to rove ; 310
But as for me, my name is little known,
I am but Jason, who dwell here alone
With Chiron in the hollow mountain-side,
Wishful for happy days, whate'er betide.'
 ' Jason,' she said, ' all folk shall know thy name,
For verily the Gods shall give thee fame,
Whatever they keep back from thee : behold
Restless thou shalt be, as thou now art bold ;
And cunning, as thou now art skilled to watch
The crafty bear, and in the toils to catch 320
The grey-maned yellow lion ; and now see
Thou doest my commands, for certainly
I am no mortal ; so to Chiron tell
No longer is it fitting thou shouldst dwell
Here in the wilds, but in a day or two,
Clad in Magnesian garments, shalt thou go
Unto Iolchos, and there claim thine own.
And unto thee shall Chiron first make known
The story of thy father and thy kin,
That thou mayst know what right thou hast herein.
And say to him, I bid him do this thing, 331
By this same token, that the silver ring
Upon mine altar, with Sidero's blood
Is spotted still, and that the half-charred wood
My priests had lighted early on that day,
Yet lies thereon, by no flame burnt away.'
Then Jason fell a trembling, and to him
The tall green stems grew wavering and dim ;

And when a fresh gust of the morning breeze
Came murmuring along the forest trees,   340
And woke him as from dreaming, all alone
He stood, and with no farewell she was gone,
Leaving no traces of her dainty feet.

But through the leaves ambrosial odours sweet
Yet floated as he turned to leave the place,
And with slow steps, and thinking on his case,
Went back to Chiron, whom at rest he found,
Half sleeping on the sunny thyme-strewn ground,
To whom he told the things that he had heard,
With flushed and eager face, for they had stirred   350
New thoughts within him of the days to come,
So that he longed to leave his woodland home.

Then Chiron said : ' O fair son, thou shalt go,
Since now, at last, the Gods will have it so :
And know that, till thou comest to the end
Of thy loved life, shall Juno be thy friend,
Because the lovely huntress thou did see
Late in the greenwood certainly was she
Who sits in heaven beside Almighty Jove,
And noble things they do that have her love.   360
    ' Now, son, to-day I rede thee not to go,
Nor yet to-morrow, for clouds great and slow
Are gathering round the hill-tops, and I think
The thirsty fields full many a draught will drink ;
Therefore to-day our cups shall not be dry,
But we will sit together, thou and I,
And tales of thy forefathers shalt thou hear,
And many another, till the heavens clear.'
    So was it as the Centaur said ; for soon
The woods grew dark, as though they knew no noon ;
The thunder growled about the high brown hills,   371
And the thin, wasted, shining summer rills
Grew joyful with the coming of the rain,
And doubtfully was shifting every vane
On the town spires, with changing gusts of wind ;
Till came the storm-blast, furious and blind,

347-8 Went back to Cheiron, whom he found laid there,
        Half sleeping on the thymy herbage fair,

'Twixt gorges of the mountains, and drove back
The light sea breeze ; then waxed the heavens black,
Until the lightning leapt from cloud to cloud,
With clattering thunder, and the piled up crowd   380
Began to turn from steely blue to grey,
And toward the sea the thunder drew away,
Leaving the north-wind blowing steadily
The rain clouds from Olympus ; while the sea
Seemed mingled with the low clouds and the rain ;
And one might think that never now again
The sunny grass would make a pleasant bed
For tired limbs, and dreamy, languid head
Of sandalled nymph, forewearied with the chase.

   Meantime, within a pleasant lighted place,   390
Stretched upon warm skins, did the Centaur lie,
And nigh him Jason, listening eagerly
The tales he told him, asking, now and then,
Strange questions of the race of vanished men :
Nor were the wine-cups idle ; till at last
Desire of sleep over their bodies passed,
And in their dreamless rest the wind in vain
Howled round about, with washing of the rain.   398

BOOK II

Jason claims his own—Pelias tells about the Golden
Fleece—Jason vows the quest thereof.

So there they lay until the second dawn
Broke fair and fresh o'er glittering glade and lawn ;
Then Jason rose, and did on him a fair
Blue woollen tunic, such as folk do wear
On the Magnesian cliffs, and at his thigh
An iron-hilted sword hung carefully ;
And on his head he had a russet hood ;
And in his hand two spears of cornel wood,
Well steeled and bound with brazen bands he shook.

   Then from the Centaur's hands at last he took   10
The tokens of his birth, the ring and horn,
And so stept forth into the sunny morn,

And bade farewell to Chiron, and set out
With eager heart, that held small care or doubt.
    So lightly through the well-known woods he passed,
And came out to the open plain at last,
And went till night came on him, and then slept
Within a homestead that a poor man kept ;
And rose again at dawn, and slept that night
Nigh the Anaurus, and at morrow's light   20
Rose up and went unto the river's brim ;
But fearful seemed the passage unto him,
For swift and yellow drave the stream adown
'Twixt crumbling banks ; and tree-trunks rough and
        brown
Whirled in the bubbling eddies here and there ;
So swollen was the stream a maid might dare
To cross, in fair days, with unwetted knee.
    Then Jason with his spear-shaft carefully
Sounded the depth, nor any bottom found ;
And wistfully he cast his eyes around   30
To see if help was nigh, and heard a voice
Behind him, calling out, ' Fair youth, rejoice
That I am here to help, or certainly
Long time a dweller hereby shouldst thou be.'
    Then Jason turned round quickly, and beheld
A woman, bent with burdens and with eld,
Grey and broad shouldered ; so he laughed, and said :
' O mother, wilt thou help me ? by my head,
More help than thine I need upon this day '
    ' O son ' she said, ' needs must thou on thy way ;   40
And is there any of the giants here
To bear thee through this water without fear ?
Take, then, the help a God has sent to thee,
For in mine arms a small thing shalt thou be.'
    So Jason laughed no more, because a frown
Gathered upon her brow, as she cast down
Her burden to the earth, and came a-nigh,
And raised him in her long arms easily,
And stept adown into the water cold.
    There with one arm the hero did she hold,   50
And with the other thrust the whirling trees

Away from them ; and laughing, and with ease
Went through the yellow foaming stream, and came
Unto the other bank ; and little shame
Had Jason that a woman carried him,
For no man, howsoever strong of limb,
Had dared across that swollen stream to go,
But if he wished the Stygian stream to know ;
Therefore he doubted not, that with some God
Or reverend Goddess that rough way he trod.   60

    So when she had clomb up the slippery bank
And let him go, well-nigh adown he sank,
For he was dizzy with the washing stream,
And with that passage mazed as with a dream.

    But, turning round about unto the crone,
He saw not her, but a most glorious one,
A lady clad in blue, all glistering
With something more than gold, crowned like the king
Of all the world, and holding in her hand
A jewelled rod. So when he saw her stand   70
With unsoiled feet scarce touching the wet way,
He trembled sore, but therewith heard her say :—
    ' O Jason, such as I have been to thee
Upon this day, such ever will I be ;
And I am Juno ; therefore doubt thou not
A mighty helper henceforth thou hast got
Against the swords and bitter tongues of men,
For surely mayst thou lean upon me, when
The turbulent and little-reasoning throng
Press hard upon thee, or a king with wrong   80
Would fain undo thee, as thou leanedst now
Within the yellow stream : so from no blow
Hold back thine hand, nor fear to set thine heart
On what thou deemest fits thy kingly part.
    ' Now to the king's throne this day draw anear,
Because of old time have I set a fear
Within his heart, ere yet thou hadst gained speech,
And whilst thou wanderedst beneath oak and beech
Unthinking. And, behold ! so have I wrought,
That with thy coming shall a sign be brought   90

86 have I] I have

Unto him ; for the latchet of thy shoe
Rushing Anaurus late I bade undo,
Which now is carried swiftly to the sea.
  ' So Pelias, this day setting eyes on thee,
Shall not forget the shameful trickling blood
Adown my altar-steps, or in my wood
The screaming peacocks scared by other screams,
Nor yet to-night shall he dream happy dreams.
  ' Farewell then, and be joyful, for I go,
Unto the people, many a thing to show,   100
And set them longing for forgotten things,
Whose rash hands toss about the crowns of kings.'
  Therewith before his eyes a cloud there came,
Sweet-smelling, coloured like a rosy flame,
That wrapt the Goddess from him ; who, indeed,
Went to Iolchos, and there sowed the seed
Of bitter change, that ruins kings of men ;
For, like an elder of threescore and ten,
Throughout the town she went, and, as such do,
Ever she blessed the old, and banned the new ;   110
Lamenting for the passed and happy reign
Of Cretheus, wishing there were come again
One like to him ; till in the market-place
About the king was many a doubtful face.
  Now Jason, by Anaurus left alone,
Found that, indeed, his right-foot shoe was gone,
But, as the Goddess bade him, went his way
Half shod, and by an hour before mid-day
He reached the city gates, and entered there,
Whom the folk mocked, beholding his foot bare,   120
And iron-hilted sword, and uncouth weed :
But of no man did he take any heed,
But came into the market-place, where thronged
Much folk about Him who his sire had wronged.
But when he stood within that busy stead,
Taller he showed than any by a head,
Great limbed, broad shouldered, mightier than all,
But soft of speech, though unto him did fall

124 Him] him

Full many a scorn upon that day to get.
So in a while he came where there was set   130
Pelias, the king, judging the people there ;
In scarlet was he clad, and o'er his hair,
Sprinkled with grey, he wore a royal crown,
And from an ivory throne he looked adown
Upon the suitors and the restless folk.

Now, when the yellow head of Jason broke
From out the throng, with fearless eyes and grey,
A terror took the king, that ere that day
For many a peaceful year he had not felt,
And his hand fell upon his swordless belt ;   140
But when the hero strode up to the throne,
And set his unshod foot upon the stone
Of the last step thereof, and as he stood,
Drew off the last fold of his russet hood,
And with a clang let fall his brass-bound spear,
The king shrunk back, grown pale with deadly fear ;
Nor then the oak-trees' speech did he forget,
Noting the one bare foot, and garments wet,
And something half remembered in his face.

And now nigh silent was the crowded place,   150
For through the folk remembrance Juno sent,
And soon from man to man a murmur went,
And frowning folk were whispering deeds of shame
And wrong the king had wrought, and Æson's name,
Forgotten long, was bandied all about,
And silent mouths seemed ready for a shout.

So, when the king raised up a hand, that shook
With fear, and turned a wrathful, timorous look
On his Ætolian guards, upon his ears
There fell the clashing of the people's spears ;   160
And on the house-tops round about the square
Could he behold folk gathered here and there,
And see the sunbeams strike on brass and steel.
But therewithal, though new fear did he feel,
He thought, ' Small use of arms in this distress,—
Needs is it that I use my wiliness ; '

132 o'er] on

Then spoke aloud : ' O man, what wouldst thou here,
That beardest thus a king with little fear ? '
  ' Pelias,' he said, ' I will not call thee king,
Because thy crown is but a stolen thing,   170
And with a stolen sceptre dost thou reign,
Which now I bid thee render up again,
And on his father's throne my father set,
Whom for long years the Gods did well forget,
But now, in lapse of time, remembering,
Have raised me, Jason, up to do this thing,
His son, and son of fair Alcimidé ;
Yet now, since Tyro's blood 'twixt thee and me
Still runs, and thou my father's brother art,
In no wise would I hurt thee, for my part,   180
If thou wilt render to us but our own,
And still shalt thou stand nigh my father's throne.'
  Then all the people, when aright they knew,
That this was Æson's son, about them drew,
And when he ended gave a mighty shout ;
But Pelias cleared his face of fear and doubt,
And answered Jason, smiling cunningly :—
  ' Yea, in good time thou comest unto me,
My nephew Jason ; fain would I lay down
This heavy weight and burden of a crown,   190
And have instead my brother's love again,
I lost, to win a troublous thing and vain ;
And yet, since now thou showest me such goodwill,
Fain would I be a king a short while still,
That everything in order I may set,
Nor any man thereby may trouble get.
And now I bid thee stand by me to-day,
And cast all fear and troublous thoughts away ;
And for thy father Æson will I send,
That I may see him as a much-loved friend,   200
Now that these years of bitterness are passed,
And peaceful days are come to me at last.'
   With that, from out the press grave Æson came,
E'en as he spoke ; for to his ears the fame
Of Jason's coming thither had been brought ;
Wherefore, with eager eyes his son he sought ;

But, seeing the mighty hero great of limb,
Stopped short, with eyes set wistfully on him,
While a false honied speech the king began :
   ' Hail, brother Æson, hail, O happy man !   210
To-day thou winnest back a noble son,
Whose glorious deeds this fair hour sees begun,
And from my hands thou winnest back the crown
Of this revered and many-peopled town ;
So let me win from thee again thy love,
Nor with long anger slight the Gods above.'
   Then Jason, holding forth the horn and ring,
Said to his father, ' Doubtest thou this thing ?
Behold the tokens Chiron gave to me
When first he said that I was sprung from thee.'   220
   Then little of those signs did Æson reck,
But cast his arms about the hero's neck,
And kissed him oft, remembering well the time
When as he sat beneath the flowering lime
Beside his house, the glad folk to him came
And said : ' O King, all honour to thy name
That will not perish surely, for thy son
His royal life this day has just begun.'
   Wherefore unto him, like an empty dream,
The busy place, the king and folk did seem,   230
As on that sight at last he set his eyes,
Prayed for so oft with many a sacrifice ;
And speechless for a while fain must he stand,
Holding within his hand the mighty hand ;
And as the wished-for son he thus beheld,
Half mournful thoughts of swiftly-gathering eld
Came thick upon him, till the salt tears ran
On to the raiment of the goodly man ;
Until at last he said : ' All honour now
To Jove and all the Gods ! Surely, I know,   240
Henceforth my name shall never perish ; yet
But little joy of this man shall I get,
For through the wide world where will be the king
Who will not fear him ; nor shall anything

212 this fair hour] this hour

Be strong against him ; therefore certainly
Full seldom will he ride afield with me,
Nor will he long bear at his father's board
To sit, well known of all, but with his sword
Will rather burst asunder banded throngs
Of evil men, healing the people's wrongs.   250
      ' And as for thee, O Pelias, as I may,
Will I be friend to thee from this same day ;
And since we both of us are growing old,
And both our lives will soon be as tales told,
I think perchance that thou wilt let me be,
To pass these few years in felicity
That this one brings me.'
                        Thereon Pelias said :—
' Yea, if I hurt thee ought, then on my head
Be every curse that thou canst ever think ;
And dying, of an ill draught may I drink,   260
For in my mind is naught but wish for rest.
      ' But on this day, I pray thee, be my guest,
While yet upon my head I wear the crown,
Which, ere this morning's flowers have fallen down,
Your head shall bear again ; for in the hall,
Upon the floor the fresh-plucked rushes fall,
Even as we speak, and maids and men bear up
The kingly service ; many a jewelled cup
And silver platter ; and the fires roar
About the stalled ox and the woodland boar ;   270
And wine we have, that ere this youngling's eyes
First saw the light, made tears and laughter rise
Up from men's hearts, making the past seem dull,
The future hollow, but the present full
Of all delights, if quick they pass away ;
And we, who have been foes for many a day,
Surely, ere evening sees the pitcher dry,
May yet be friends, and talking lovingly,
And with our laughter make the pillars ring,
While this one sits revolving many a thing,   280
Saddened by that, which makes us elders glad.'
      Such good words said he, but the thoughts were bad
      250 Of evil men, and heal some great king's wrongs.

Within his crafty breast ; and still he thought
How best he might be rid of him just brought,
By sentence of the Gods, upon his head.
  Then moved the kinsmen from the market-stead
Between a lane of men, who ever pressed
About the princes, and with loud words blessed
The hero and his race, and thought no shame
To kiss his skirts ; and so at last they came   290
Unto the house that rustling limes did shade,
And thereabout was many a slender maid,
Who welcomed them with music and sweet song,
And cast red roses as they went along
Before their feet ; and therewith brought the three
Into the palace, where right royally
Was Jason clad, and seemed a prince indeed.
  So while the harp-string and shrill-piping reed
Still sounded, trooped the folk unto the feast,
And all were set to meat, both most and least ;   300
And when with dainties they were fully fed,
Then the tall jars and well-sewn goat-skins bled,
And men grew glad, forgetting every care.
But first a golden chain and mantle fair
Pelias did on him ; and then, standing up,
Poured out red wine from a great golden cup,
Unto the Gods, and prayed to them : ' O ye
Who rule the world, grant us felicity
This hour, at least, nor let our sweet delight
Be marred by aught, until the silent night   310
Has come, and turned to day again, and we
Wake up once more to joy or misery,
Or death itself, if so it pleaseth you :
Is this thing, then, so great a thing to do ? '
  Thereon folk shouted, and the pipes again
Breathed through the hall a sweet heart-softening strain,
And up the hall came lovely damsels, dressed
In gowns of green, who unto every guest
Gave a rose garland, nor yet hasted they,
When this was done, to pass too quick away,   320
If here and there an eager hand still held
By gown or wrist, whom the young prince beheld
With longing eyes that roved about the hall.

Now longer did the cool grey shadows fall,
And faster drew the sun unto the west,
And in the field the husbandman, opprest
With twelve hours' labour, turned unto his home,
And to the fold the woolly sheep were come ;
And in the hall the folk began to tell
Stories of men of old, who bore them well,   330
And piteous tales. And Jason in mean while
Sat listening as his uncle, with a smile,
Kept pouring many a thing into his ears,
Now worthy laughter, and now meet for tears.
Until at last, when twilight was nigh gone,
And dimly through the place the gold outshone,
He bade them bring in torches, and while folk
Blinked on the glare that through the pillars broke,
He said to Jason : ' Yet have I to tell
One tale I would that these should hear as well   340
As you, O Prince.'   And therewith did he call
The herald, bidding him throughout the hall
Cry silence for the story of the king.

And this being done, and all men listening,
He rose and said, ' O noble Minyæ,
Right prosperous and honoured may ye be ;
When Athamas ruled over Thebes the great,
Upon his house there fell a heavy fate,
Making his name a mere byword ; for he,
Being wedded to the noble Nephele,   350
Gat on her a bold youth and tender maid,
Phryxus and Helle ; but, being naught afraid
Of what the righteous Gods might do to him,
And seeing Ino, fair of face and limb
Beyond all other, needs with her must wed,
And to that end drove from his royal bed
Unhappy Nephele, who now must be
A slave, where once she governed royally ;
While white-foot Ino smiling sat alone
By Athamas upon the ivory throne.   360

351 bold] fair   359 While the white-footed Ino sat alone

' And now, as time went on, did Ino bear
To Athamas two children hale and fair ;
Therefore, the more increased her enmity
Against those two erst born of Nephele,
Who yet, in spite of all things, day by day
Grew lovelier as their sad lives wore away ;
Till Ino thought, " What help will it have been,
That through these years I have been called a queen,
And set gold raiment on my children dear,
If Athamas should die and leave me here   370
Betwixt the people and this Nephele,
With those she bore ? What then could hap to me
But death or shame ? for then, no doubt, would reign
Over this mighty town the children twain ;
With her who once was queen still standing near,
And whispering fell words in her darlings' ear.
And then what profit would it be that they
Have won through me full many an evil day ;
That Phryxus base and servile deeds doth know,
Unmeet for lords ; that many a shame and woe,   380
Helle has borne, and yet is wont to stand,
Shrinking with fear, before some dreaded hand ;
If still the ending of it must be this,
That I must die while they live on in bliss,
And cherish her that first lay in my bed ?
Nor is there any help till they be dead."
  ' Then did she fall on many an evil thought,
And going thence, with threats and money brought
The women of the land to do this thing :
In the mid-winter, yea, before the spring   390
Was in men's minds, they took the good seed corn,
And while their husbands toiled in the dark morn,
And dreaded naught, they throughly seethed it all ;
Whereby this seeming portent did befall,
That neither the sweet showers of April tide,
Nor the May sunshine, gleaming far and wide
Over the meadows, made their furrows green,
Nor yet in June was any young shoot seen.

Then drew the country folk unto the king,
Weeping and wailing, telling of the thing,   400
And praying him to satisfy the God,
Whoe'er he was, who with this cruel rod
So smote his wretched people : whereon he
Bade all his priests inquire solemnly
What thing had moved the Gods to slay them thus ?
Who, hearing all this story piteous,
Because their hands had felt Queen Ino's gold,
And itched for more, this thing in answer told :—
    'That great Diana with Queen Nephele
Was wroth beyond all measure, for that she,   410
Being vowed unto the Goddess, none the less
Cast by the quiver and the girt-up dress,
To wed with Athamas, the mighty king,
Therefore must she pay forfeit for the thing,
And though she still should keep her wretched life,
Yet must she give her children to the knife,
Or else this dearth should be but happiness
To what should come, for she would so oppress
The land of Thebes, that folk who saw its name
In old records, would turn the page, and blame   420
The chronicler for telling empty lies,
And mingling fables with his histories.
    ' Therefore is Athamas a wretched man
To hear this tale, and doeth what he can
To save his flesh and blood, but all in vain ;
Because the people, cruel in their pain,
With angry words were thronging the great hall,
And crafty Ino at his feet did fall,
Saying, " Oh, King, I pray for these, and me,
And for my children." Therefore, mournfully   430
He called the priests again, and bade them say,
In few words, how his children they would slay,
And when the dreadful bearer of the bow
Would best be pleased to see their young blood flow.
Who said, " that if the thing were quickly done,
Seeing the green things were not wholly gone,
The ruined fields might give a little food,
And that high noon-tide the next day was good,

Above all other hours, to do the thing ; ''
And thereupon they prayed unto the king,   440
To take the younglings, lest, being fled away,
They still might live and leave an evil day
To Thebes and all its folk henceforth to bear.
  ' Then men were sent, who by the river fair
Found Phryxus casting nets into the stream,
Who, seeing them coming, little harm did deem
They meant him, and with welcome bade them share
The glittering heap of fishes that lay there.
But they with laughter fell at once on him,
Who, struggling wrathfully, broke here a limb   450
And there a head, but lastly on the ground
Being felled by many men, was straightly bound,
And in an iron-bolted prison laid,
While to the house they turned to seek the maid.
  ' Whom soon they found, within the weaving-room,
Bent earnestly above the rattling loom,
Working not like a king's child, but a slave
Who strives her body from the scourge to save.
On her they seized, speechless for very fear,
And dragged her trembling to the prison drear,   460
Where lay her brother, and there cast her in,
Giddy and fainting, wondering for what sin
She suffered this ; but, finding Phryxus laid
In the same dismal place, the wretched maid
Bewailed with him the sorrows of their life,
Praying the Gods to show the king's new wife
What sorrow was, nor let her hair grow grey
Ere in some hopeless place her body lay.
  ' Now in that court a certain beast there was,
The gift of Neptune to King Athamas,   470
A mighty ram, greater than such beasts be
In any land about the Grecian sea ;
And in all else a wonder to men's eyes,
For from his shoulders did two wings arise,
That seemed as they were wrought of beaten gold,
And all his fleece was such as in no fold
The shepherd sees, for all was gold indeed.
And now this beast with dainty grass to feed,

The task of Nephele had late been made,
Who, nothing of the mighty ram afraid,   480
Would bring him flowering trefoil day by day,
And comb his fleece ; and her the ram would pay
With gentle bleatings, and would lick her hand,
As in his well-built palace he did stand.
For all the place was made of polished wood,
Studded with gold ; and, when he thought it good,
Within a little meadow could he go,
Throughout the midst whereof a stream did flow,
And at the corners stood great linden-trees,
Hummed over by innumerable bees.   490
     ' So on the morning when these twain should die,
Stole Nephele to this place quietly
And loosed the ram, and led him straight away
Unto Diana's temple, where that day
Her heart should break unless the Gods were good.
There with the ram, close in a little wood,
She hid herself a-nigh the gates, till noon
Should bring those to the Lady of the Moon
She longed to see ; and as the time drew nigh,
She knelt, and with her trembling hands did tie   500
About the gold beast's neck a mystic thing,
And in his ears, meanwhile, was murmuring
Words taught her by the ever-changing God,
Who on the sands at noon is wont to nod
Beside the flock of Neptune ; till at last
Upon the breeze the sound of flutes went past ;
Then sore she trembled, as she held the beast
By the two golden horns, but never ceased
Her mystic rhyme ; and louder, and more loud
The music sounded, till the solemn crowd   510
Along the dusty road came full in sight.
First went the minstrels, clad in raiment white,
Both men and maids garlanded daintily ;
And then ten damsels, naked from the knee,
Who in their hands bare bows done round with leaves,
And arrows at their backs in goodly sheaves

        489 And at the corners were there great lime-trees,

Gaudily feathered, ready for the strife ;
Then came three priests, whereof one bore the knife,
One a great golden bowl to hold the blood,
And one a bundle of some sacred wood ;   520
And then was left a little vacant space,
And then came gold, and therewithal the face
Of beauteous Ino, flushed and triumphing,
And by her, moody and downcast, the king.
  ' And now her heart beat quick and fast indeed,
Because the two came, doomed that day to bleed
Over the grey bark of the hallowed wood,
Of whom went Phryxus in most manly mood,
Looking around, with mournful, steady eyes,
Upon the green fields and the braveries,   530
And all he never thought to see again.
But Helle, as she went, could not refrain
From bitter wailing for the days gone by,
When hope was mixed with certain misery ;
And, when the long day's task and fear was done,
She might take pleasure sometimes in the sun,
Whose rays she saw now glittering on the knife
That in a little time should end her life.
  ' Now she, who in coarse raiment had been clad
For many a year, upon her body had,   540
On this ill day, a golden pearl-wrought gown,
And on her drooping head a glittering crown,
And jewelled sandals on her fainting feet,
And on her neck and bosom jewels meet
For one who should be wedded to a king ;
Thus to her death went moaning this sweet thing.
  ' But when they drew a-nigh the temple gate
The trembling, weeping mother, laid in wait,
Let go the mighty beast upon the throng,—
Like as a hunter holds the gazehound long,   550
Until the great buck stalks from out the herd,
And then, with well-remembered hunting word,
Slips the stout leash,—so did she slip the beast,
Who dashed aside both singing-man and priest,

522 therewithal] she could see
527 *This line was not in the first edition.*   538 should] would
MORRIS
Z

And girded maiden, and the startled king,
And Ino, grown all pale to see the thing,
With rising horror in her evil heart.
And thereon Phryxus, seeing the close crowd part,
And this deliverer nigh him, with wings spread
Ready for flight, and eager threatening head,   560
Without more words, upon his broad back sprung,
And drew his sister after him, who clung
With trembling arms about him ; and straightway
They turned unto the rising of the day,
And over all rose up into the air
With sounding wings ; nor yet did any dare,
As fast they flew, to bend on them a bow,
Thinking some God had surely willed it so.

  ' Then went the king unto his house again,
And Ino with him, downcast that the twain   570
Had so escaped her, waiting for what fate
Should bring upon her doomed head, soon or late.
  ' Nor long she waited ; for, one evil day,
Unto the king her glittering gold array
And rosy flesh, half seen through raiment thin,
Seemed like the many-spotted leopard's skin ;
And her fair hands and feet like arméd paws,
The treacherous beast across the strained throat draws
Of some poor fawn ; and when he saw her go
Across the hall, her footsteps soft and slow   580
And the lithe motion of her body fair
But made him think of some beast from his lair
Stolen forth at the beginning of the night.
  ' Therefore with fear and anger at the sight
He shook, being maddened by some dreadful God ;
And stealthily about the place he trod,
Seeking his sword ; and, getting it to hand,
With flaming eyes and foaming mouth did stand
Awhile, then rushed at Ino as she stood
Trembling, with cheeks all drained of rosy blood ;   590
Who straightway caught her raiment up, and fled
Adown the streets, where once she had been led

558 the close crowd] the crowd

In triumph by the man whose well-known cheer
Close at her heels, now struck such deadly fear
Into her heart, the forge of many a woe.
'So, full of anguish, panting did she go
O'er rough and smooth, till field and wood were passed,
And on the border of the sea at last,
With raiment torn and unshod feet, she stood,
Reddening the flowering sea-pink with her blood. 600
'But when she saw the tireless hunter nigh,
All wild and shouting, with a dreadful cry
She stretched her arms out seaward, and sprung down
Over the cliff among the seaweed brown
And washing surf, neither did any one
See aught of her again beneath the sun.
'But Athamas, being come to where she stood,
Stared vacantly awhile upon the blood,
Then, looking seaward, drew across his eyes
His fevered hand ; and thronging memories 610
Came thick upon him, until dreamily
He turned his back upon the hungry sea,
And cast his sword down ; and so, weaponless,
Went back, half-waking to his sore distress.

'As for the twain,—perched on that dizzy height,
The white-walled city faded from their sight,
And many another place that well they knew ;
And over woods and meadows still they flew ;
And to the husbandmen seemed like a flame
Blown 'twixt the earth and the sky ; until they came
Unto the borders of the murmuring sea. 621
Nor stayed they yet, but flew unceasingly,
Till, looking back, seemed Pelion like a cloud ;
And they beheld the white-topped billows crowd
Unto the eastward, 'neath the following wind.
'And there a wretched end did Helle find
Unto her life ; for when she did behold,
So far beneath, the deep green sea and cold,
She shut her eyes for horror of the sight,
Turning the sunny day to murk midnight, 630

597 were] was
z 2

Through which there floated many an awful thing,
Made vocal by the ceaseless murmuring
Beneath her feet ; till a great gust of wind
Caught the beast's wings and swayed him round ; then,
    blind,
Dizzy, and fainting, did she grow too weak
To hold her place, though still her hands did seek
Some stay by catching at the locks of gold ;
And as she fell her brother strove to hold
Her jewelled girdle, but the treacherous zone
Broke in his hand, and he was left alone   640
Upon the ram, that, as a senseless thing,
Still flew on toward the east, no whit heeding
His shouts and cries ; but Helle, as she fell
Down through the depths, the sea-folk guarded well,
And kept her body dead, from scar or wound,
And laid it, in her golden robes enwound,
Upon the south side of the murmuring strait,
That still, in memory of her piteous fate,
Bears her sweet name ; her, in a little while,
The country folk beheld, and raised a pile   650
Of beech and oak, with scented things around,
And, lifting up the poor corpse from the ground,
Laid it thereon, and there did everything,
As for the daughter of a mighty king.

' But through the straits passed Phryxus, sad enow,
And fearful of the wind that by his brow
Went shrieking, as, without all stop or stay,
The golden wings still bore him on his way
Above the unlucky waves of that ill sea
That foamed beneath his feet unceasingly.   660
Nor knew he to what land he was being borne,
Whether he should be set, unarmed, forlorn,
In darksome lands, among unheard-of things,
Or, stepping off from 'twixt the golden wings,
Should set foot in some happy summer isle,
Whereon the kind unburning sun doth smile

635 did she grow] grew her limbs   636 her] their

For ever, and that knows no frost or drought ;
Or else, it seemed to him, he might be brought
Unto green forests where the wood-nymphs play
With their wild mates, and fear no coming day.   670
And there might he forget both crown and sword,
And e'en the names of slave, and king, and lord,
And lead a merry life, till all was done,
And 'mid the green boughs, marked by no carved stone,
His unremembered bones should waste away,
In dew, and rain, and sunshine, day by day.
  ' So, 'mid these thoughts, still clinging fearfully
Unto his dizzy seat, he passed the sea,
And reached a river opening into it,
Across the which the white-winged fowl did flit   680
From cliff to cliff, and on the sandy bar
The fresh waves and the salt waves were at war,
At turning of the tide.   Forth flew they then,
Till they drew nigh a strange abode of men,
Far up the river, white-walled, fair, and great,
And at each end of it a brazen gate,
Wide open through the daylight, guarded well ;
And nothing of its name could Phryxus tell,
But hoped the beast would stop, for to his eyes
The place seemed fair ; nor fell it otherwise.   690
There stayed the ram his course, and lighted down
Anigh the western gate of that fair town,
And on the hard way Phryxus joyfully
Set foot, full dizzy with the murmuring sea,
Numbed by the cold wind ; and, with little fear,
Unto the guarded gate he drew anear,
While the gold beast went ever after him.
  ' But they, beholding him so strong of limb,
And fair of face, and seeing the beast that trod
Behind his back, deemed him some wandering God,
So let the two-edged sword hang by the side,   701
And by the wall the well-steeled spear abide.
  ' But he called out to them, " What place is this ?
And who rules over you for woe or bliss ?

692 Anigh] Hard by   702 spear] spears

And will he grant me peace to-day or war ?
And may I here abide, or still afar
Must I to new abodes go wandering ? "
 ' Now as he spake those words, that city's king
Adown the street was drawing toward the gate,
Clad in gold raiment worthy his estate,   710
Therefore one said : " Behold, our king is here,
Who of all us is held both lief and dear ;
Æetes, leader of a mighty host,
Feared by all folk along the windy coast.
And since this city's name thou fain wouldst know,
Men call it Æa, built long years ago,
Holpen of many Gods, who love it well.
Now come thou to the king, and straightway tell
Thy name and country, if thou art a man,
And how thou camest o'er the water wan,   720
And what the marvel is thou hast with thee ;
But if thou art a God, then here will we
Build thee a house, and, reverencing thy name,
Bring thee great gifts and much-desired fame."
 ' Thus spake he, fearful ; but by this the king
Had reached the place, and stood there wondering
At that strange beast and fair man richly clad,
Who at his belt no sort of weapon had ;
Then spoke he : " Who art thou, in what strange wain
Hast thou crossed o'er the green and restless plain   730
Unharvested of any ? And this thing,
That like an image stands with folded wing,
Is he a gift to thee from any God,
Or hast thou in some unknown country trod,
Where beasts are such-like ? Howsoe'er it be,
Here shalt thou dwell, if so thou wilt, with me,
Unless some God is chasing thee, and then,
What wouldst thou have us do, who are but men,
Against the might of Gods ? "
                          Then answered he :
" O king, I think no God is wrath with me,   740
But rather some one loves me ; for, behold,
A while ago, just as my foe did hold

709 toward] towards   718 straightway] straightly

A knife against my throat, there came this ram,
Who brought me to the place where now I am
Safe from the sea and from the bitter knife.
And in this city would I spend my life,
And do what service seemeth good to thee,
Since all the Gods it pleases I should be
Outcast from friends and country, though alive ;
Nor with their will have I the heart to strive   750
More than thou hast ; and now as in such wise
I have been saved, fain would I sacrifice
This beast to Jove, the helper of all such,
As false friends fail, or foes oppress too much."
    " Yea," said Æetes, " so the thing shall be
In whatsoever fashion pleaseth thee ;
And long time mayst thou dwell with us in bliss,
Not doing any service worse than this,
To bear in war my royal banner forth,
When fall the wild folk on us from the north.   760
Come now this eve, and hold high feast with us,
And tell us all of strange and piteous
Thy story hath."
                So went he with the king,
And gladly told unto him everything
That had befallen him, and in a grove,
Upon the altar of the Saving Jove,
They offered up the ram the morrow morn
That thitherward the Theban prince had borne.
    ' And thenceforth Phryxus dwelt in Colchis long
In wealth and honour, and being brave and strong,
Won great renown in many a bloody fray,   771
And still grew greater ; and both night and day,
Within his pillared house, upon the wall
Hung the gold fell ; until it did befall
That in Æetes' heart a longing grew
To have the thing, yea, even if he slew
His guest to get it ; so, one evil night,
While the prince lay and dreamed about the fight,
With all armed men was every entry filled,
And quickly were the few doorkeepers killed ;   780

                743 A knife] The knife

And Phryxus, roused with clamour from his bed,
Half-armed and dizzy, with few strokes was dead.
And thus the king Æetes had his will,
And thus the GOLDEN FLEECE he keepeth still
Somewhere within his royal house of gold.

' And thus, O Minyæ, is the story told
Of things that happened forty years agone ;
Nor of the Greeks has there been any one
To set the Theban's bones within a tomb,
Or to Æetes mete out his due doom ;   790
And yet indeed, it seemeth unto me
That many a man would go right willingly,
And win great thanks of men and godlike fame,
If there should spring up some great prince of name
To lead them ; and I pray that such an one,
Before my head is laid beneath a stone,
Be sent unto us by the Gods above.'

    Therewith he ceased ; but all the hall did move
As moves a grove of rustling poplar trees
Bowed all together by the shifting breeze,   800
And through the place the name of Jason ran,
Nor, 'mid the feasters, was there any man
But toward the hero's gold-seat turned his eyes.
    Meanwhile, in Jason's heart did thoughts arise
That brought the treacherous blood into his cheek,
And he forgot his father, old and weak,
Left 'twixt the fickle people of the land
And wily Pelias, while he clenched his hand,
As though it held a sword, about his cup.
    Then, 'mid the murmuring, Pelias stood up   810
And said : ' O, leaders of the Minyæ,
I hear ye name a name right dear to me—
My brother's son, who in the oaken wood
Has grown up nurtured of the Centaur good,
And now this day has come again to us,
Fair faced and mighty limbed, and amorous
Of fame and glorious deeds ; nowise content
Betwixt the forest and the northern bent

To follow up the antlers of the deer,
Nor in his eyes can I see any fear   820
Of fire, or water, or the cleaving sword.
  ' Now, therefore, if ye take him for your lord
Across the sea then surely will ye get
Both fame and wealth, nor will men soon forget
To praise the noble city whence ye came,
Passing from age to age each hero's name.'
  Then all stood up and shouted, and the king,
While yet the hall with Jason's name did ring,
Set in his hands a gleaming cup of gold,
And said : ' O Jason, wilt thou well behold   830
These leaders of the people, who are fain
To go with thee and suffer many a pain
And deadly fear, if they may win at last
Undying fame when fleeting life is past ?
And now, if thou art willing to be first
Of all these men, of whom, indeed, the worst
Is like a God, pour out this gleaming wine
To him with whose light all the heavens shine
Almighty Jove.'
                    Then Jason poured, and said :
' O Jove, by thy hand may all these be led   840
To name and wealth ! and yet, indeed, for me,
What happy ending shall I ask from thee ?
What helpful friends ? what length of quiet years ?
What freedom from ill care and deadly fears ?
Do what thou wilt, but none the less believe
That all these things and more thou shouldst receive,
If thou wert Jason, I were Jove to-day.
  ' And ye who now are hot to play this play,
Seeking the fleece across an unknown sea,
Bethink ye yet of death, and misery,   850
And dull despair, before ye arm to go
Unto a savage king and folk none know,
Whence it may well hap none of ye to come
Again unto your little ones and home.
  ' And do thou, Pelias, ere we get us forth,
Send heralds out, east, west, and south, and north,

823 will ye] ye will

And with them cunning men, of golden speech,
Thy tale unto the Grecian folk to teach ;
That we may lack for neither strength nor wit,
For many a brave man like a fool will sit   860
Beside the council board ; and men there are
Wise-hearted who know little feats of war ;
Nor would I be without the strength of spears,
Or waste wise words on dull and foolish ears.
' Also we need a cunning artizan,
Taught by the Gods, and knowing more than man,
To build us a good ship upon this shore.
Then, if but ten lay hold upon the oar,
And I, the eleventh, steer them toward the east,
To seek the hidden fleece of that gold beast,   870
I swear to Jove that only in my hand
The fleece shall be, when I again take land
To see my father's hall, or the green grass
O'er which the grey Thessalian horses pass.
' But now, O friends, forget all till the morn
With other thoughts and fears is duly born ! '

He ceased, and all men shouted ; and again
They filled their cups, and many a draught did drain.
But Pelias gazed with heedful eyes at him,
Nor drank the wine that well-nigh touched the brim
Of his gold cup ; and, noting every word,   881
Thought well that he should be a mighty lord,
For now already like a king he spoke,
Gazing upon the wild tumultuous folk
As one who knows what troubles are to come
And in this world looks for no peaceful home,—
So much he dreaded what the Gods might do.
But Æson, when he first heard Pelias, knew
What wile was stirring, and he sat afeard,
With sinking heart, as all the tale he heard ;   890
But after, hearkening what his son did say,
He deemed a God spoke through him on that day,
And held his peace ; yet to himself he said :
' And if he wins all, still shall I be dead
Ere on the shore he stands beside the fleece,

The greatest and most honoured man in Greece.'
  But Jason, much rejoicing in his life,
Drank and was merry, longing for the strife ;
Though in his heart he did not fail to see
His uncle's cunning wiles and treachery ;   900
But thought, when sixty years are gone, at most,
Then will all pleasure and all pain be lost ;
Although my name, indeed, be cast about
From hall to temple, amid song and shout :
So let me now be merry with the best.
  Meanwhile, all men spoke hotly of the quest,
And healths they drank to many an honoured man,
Until the moon sank, and the stars waxed wan,
And from the east faint yellow light outshone
O'er the Greek sea, so many years agone.   910

BOOK III

The Argonauts called together.

Now the next morn, when risen was the sun,
Men 'gan to busk them for the quest begun ;
Nor long delay made Pelias, being in fear
Lest aught should stay them ; so his folk did bear
News of these things throughout the towns of Greece,
Moving great men to seek the golden fleece.
  Therefore, from many a lordship forth they rode,
Leaving both wife and child and loved abode,
And many a town must now be masterless,
And women's voices rule both more and less,   10
And women's hands be dreaded, far and wide,
This fair beginning of the summer-tide.

  Now, all the folk who went upon this quest
I cannot name, but fain would hope the best
In men's remembrance ancient tales did keep
Unto our time, letting the others sleep
In nameless graves—though, mayhap, one by one,
These grew to be forgotten 'neath the sun,

Being neither poor of heart, or weak of wit,
More than those others whose crowned memories sit
Enthroned amid the echoing minstrelsy   21
Sung of old time beside the Grecian sea.
  Howe'er it be, now clinging to the hem
Of those old singers, will I tell of them,
In weak and faltering voice, e'en as I can.

  Now was the well-skilled Argus the first man
Who through the gates into Iolchos passed
Whose lot in fertile Egypt first was cast,
The nurse of Gods and wonder-working men ;
His father's name was Danaus, who till then   30
Had held the golden rod above the Nile,
Feared by all men for force and deadly wile.
  So he, being brought to Jason, said : ' O King,
Me have the Gods sent here to do the thing
Ye need the most ; for truly have I seen,
'Twixt sleep and waking, one clad like a queen,
About whose head strange light shone gloriously,
Stand at my bed's foot, and she said to me :
" Argus, arise, when dawn is on the earth,
And go unto a city great of girth   40
Men call Iolchos, and there ask for one
Who now gets ready a great race to run
Upon a steed whose maker thou shalt be,
And whose course is the bitter trackless sea,—
Jason, the king's son, now himself a king ;—
And bid him hearken, by this tokening,
That I, who send thee to him, am the same
Who in the greenwood bade him look for fame
That he desired little ; and am she
Who, when the eddies rushed tumultuously   50
About us, bore him to the river side :—
And unto thee shall such-like things betide. "
  ' Therewith she told me many a crafty thing
About this keel that ye are now lacking,
Bidding me take thee for my king and lord,
And thee to heed my counsel as her word
As for this thing. So if ye would set forth

Before the winter takes us from the north,
I pray you let there be at my commands
Such men as are most skilful of their hands,   60
Nor spare to take lintel, rooftree, or post
Of ash or pine, or oak that helpeth most.
From whoso in this city lacketh gold ;
And chiefly take the post that now doth hold
The second rafter in the royal hall,
That I may make the good ship's prow withal,
For soothly from Dodona doth it come,
Though men forget it, the grey pigeons' home.
      ' So look to see a marvel, and forthright
Set on the smiths the sounding brass to smite,   70
For surely shall all ye your armour need
Before these close flower-buds have turned to seed.'
      Then Jason gave him thanks and gifts enow,
And through the town sought all who chanced to know
The woodwright's craft, by whom was much begun,
Whilst he took gifts of wood from many an one,
And getting timber with great gifts of gold,
Spared not to take the great post used to hold
The second rafter in the royal hall
To make the new ship's goodly prow withal.   80
      So Argus laboured, and the work was sped
Moreover, by a man with hoary head,
Whose dwelling and whose name no man could know,
Who many a secret of the craft did show,
And 'mid their work men gazed at him askance,
Half fearful of his reverend piercing glance,
But did his bidding ; yet knew not, indeed,
It was the Queen of Heaven, Saturn's seed.

      Meanwhile came many heroes to the town :—
Asterion, dweller on the windy down   90
Below Philæus, far up in the north ;
Slow-footed Polyphemus, late borne forth
In chariot from Larissa, that beholds
Green-winding Peneus cleaving fertile wolds ;

72 these close flower-buds] these flower-buds
84 secret] strange thing

Erginus, son of Neptune, nigh the sea
His father set him, where the laden bee
Flies low across Mæander, and falls down
Against the white walls of a merchant town
Men call Miletus.
                    Behind him there came
The winner of a great and dreaded name,   100
Theseus, the stayer of the fearful beast,
Who soon in winding halls should make his feast
On youths and maidens ; and with him there rode
The king Pirithous, who his loved abode
Amid the shady trees had left that tide
Where fly the centaurs' arrows far and wide.

Black-haired was Theseus, slim, and still his cheek
Lacked all but down, for yet he had to seek
The twisted ways of Dædalus the old ;
But long and twining locks of ruddy gold   110
Blew round the face of the huge forest king,
As carelessly he rode and feared no thing.

Great joy had Jason, gazing on the twain,
Young though they were, and thought that not in vain
His quest should be, if such as these had will
The hollow of his great black ship to fill.

Next, threading Argive ways and woody lanes,
Came Nauplius, son of Neptune, to those plains,
Crossing Anaurus dryshod, for his sire
With threats and blows drove up the land-stream higher,
And sucked the sea-waves back across the sands ;   121
With him came Idmon, mighty of his hands,
But mightier that he was skilled to know
The counsel of the God who bears the bow,
His very father, who bore not to see
Unloved, Cyrene wandering carelessly
Beside Peneus ; Iolaus came
From Argos, too, to win a deathless name ;
And if thenceforth came any heroes more
I know not, and their names have died of yore.   130

But from Arcadian forests came forth one
Who like a goddess 'mid the rowers shone,

127 Beside Peneus] Beside the Peneus

Swift-running Atalanta, golden-haired,
Grey-eyed, and simple ; with her white limbs bared,
And sandalled feet set firm upon the sand,
Amid the wondering heroes did she stand
A very maid, yet fearing not for aught
For she, with many a vow, had dearly bought
Diana's love, and in no flowery stead
Had borne to hear love-songs, or laid her head   140
On any trembling lover's heaving breast ;
Therefore of mortals was she loved the best
By Her, who through the forest goes a-nights,
And in return for never-tried delights,
Has won a name no woman else can have.
   Next through the gates his car Oileus drave,
The Locrian king, red-haired, with fierce grey eyes
Wandering from right to left, as though some prize
He sought for in the rich Thessalian land ;
Then Iphiclus beside the gates did stand,   150
His kine at all adventure left at home,
That on a doubtful voyage he might roam.
   Admetus from the well-walled Pheræ came,
Longing to add new glory to the fame
Of him whose flocks Apollo once did keep,
And then Echion, who would nowise sleep
Amid Ephesian roses, or behold
Betwixt gold cups and lovely things of gold
The white limbs of the dancing-girl, her hair
Swung round her dainty loins and bosom bare ;   160
But needs must try the hollow-sounding sea,
As herald of the heroes, nor was he
Left by his brother Eurytus the strong.
   Neither did Cæneus, the Magnesian, long
Less than the others strange new lands to see,
Though wondrous things were told of him,—that he,
Once woman, now was man by Neptune's aid,
And thus had won a long-desired maid.
   From nigh Larissa came Ætalides,
Leaving a plain well-watered, set with trees,   170
That feeds much woolly sheep and lowing neat

158 lovely] dainty

And knoweth well the dancing maiden's feet.
Mopsus, like Idmon, knew of things to come,
And had in Lipara a rocky home.
Eurydamas, tired of the peaceful lake
Of Xynias, was come for Jason's sake
To lay his well-skilled hands upon the oar,
Dealing with greater waves than heretofore.

Menœtius, son of Actor, from the land
Where swift Asopus runs through stones and sand,   180
Bridged by the street of Opus, next was seen.
Eribotes, who through the meadows green
Would wander oft to seek what helpeth man,
Yet cannot cure his lust, through waters wan
To seek for marvels, cometh after him.
Then a rich man, grown old, but strong of limb,
Eurytion, son of Iras, leaveth now
His husbandmen still following of the plough
In the fat Theban meadows, while he goes,
Driven by fate, to suffer biting woes.   190

From Œchalia, Clytius the king,
And Iphitus his brother, felt the sting
That drives great men through woes to seek renown,
And left their guarded city, looking down
From rocky heights on the well-watered plain.
Right wise they were, and men say, not in vain
Before Apollo's court they claimed to be
The first who strung the fatal cornel tree,
And loosed the twanging bowstring from the ear.

Then to the gate a chariot drew a-near,   200
Wherein two brothers sat, whereof the one
Who held the reins was mighty Telamon ;
And Peleus was the other's dreaded name.
And from an island both the heroes came,
Sunny Ægina, where their father's hand
Ruled o'er the people of a fruitful land ;
But they now young, rejoicing in their birth,
Dreamed not that, ere they lay beneath the earth,
Still greater heroes from their loins should come,
The doomsmen of the Trojan's godlike home.   210

Fair Athens, and the olive groves thereby,

Phalerus left, riding through deserts dry
And rocky passes where no sweet birds sing ;
And with him Butes, with the owlet's wing
Well-painted on his shield ; and he, at least,
Came back no more to share the joyous feast
And pour out wine for well accomplished days,
Who, all besotted with the Syren's lays,
Must leave his mates ; nor happier than he,
Tiphys the pilot came, although the sea   220
Dealt gently with the ship whose ashen helm
His hand touched ; in the rich Bœotian realm
He left outlandish merceries stored up
With many a brazen bowl and silver cup
His heirs should feast from in the days to come,
When men he knew not, went about his home.

　　Next Phlias came, forgetful of the hill
That bears his name, where oft the maidens fill
Their baskets with the coal-black clustering grapes,
Far on in autumn, when the parched earth gapes   230
For cool November rain and winter snow,
For there his house stood, on the shaded brow
Of that fair ridge that Bacchus loves so well.

　　Then through the gates one with a lion's fell
Hung o'er his shoulders, on a huge grey steed
Came riding, with his fair Phœnician weed
Glittering from underneath the tawny hair,
Who loosely in his dreadful hand did bear
A club of unknown wood bound round with brass,
And underneath his curled black hair did pass   240
A golden circlet o'erwrought cunningly
With running beasts ; so folk knew this was he
That in Amphytrion's palace first saw light,
And whose first hour began with deadly fight,
Alcmena's son, the dreadful Hercules ;
The man whose shout the close Nemean trees
Had stifled, and the lion met in vain ;
The ravisher of hell, the serpent's bane,
Whom neither Gods nor fate could overwhelm.

　　Now was he come to this Thessalian realm   250
To serve with Jason on the wandering seas,

Half seeking fame, half wishing to appease
The wrath of her who grudged him ease and rest,
Yet needs must see him of all men the best.
Laughing he went, and with him on each hand
There rode a squire from the Theban land ;
Hylas was first, whose sire, Theodamas,
Had given him worthy gifts of gold and brass,
And gold-wrought arms, that he should see no more
Glittering along the green Ismenian shore.   260
With him Ephebus came, who many a year
Had backed the steed and cast the quivering spear
In Theban meadows, but whose fathers came
From Argos, and thereby had left their name.
     So through the streets like Gods they rode, but he
Who rode the midmost of the glorious three
O'ertopped them by a head ; and looking down
With smiling face, whereon it seemed no frown
Could ever come, showed like the king of all.

     Now coming to the palace, by the wall   270
Sat Jason, watching while an armourer wrought
A golden crest according to his thought ;
And round about the heroes were at play,
Casting the quoit ; but on the well-paved way,
With clanging arms, leapt down Alcmena's son
Before the prince, and said : ' I who have won
Some small renown, O Jason, in this land,
Come now to put my hand within your hand
And be your man, if wide report says true,
That even now with cinnabar and blue   280
Men paint your long ship's prow, and shave the oars
With sharpened planes ; for soothly, other shores
I fain would see than this fair Grecian one,
Wherein great deeds already I have done :
And if thou willest now to hear my name,
A Theban queen my mother once became,
And had great honour ; wherefore some men say
That in Amphytrion's bed my mother lay
When I was gotten ; and yet other some
Say that a God upon that night did come   290

(Whose name I speak not), like unto the king,
With whom Alcmena played, but nought witting.
  ' Nor I, nor others know the certainty
Of all these things ; but certes, royally
My brother rules at Thebes, whom all men call
Amphytrion's son, in whose well-peopled hall,
Right little loved of him and his, I eat,
Nor does he grieve to see my empty seat,
Though, since my name is Hercules, the man
Who owes me hatred hides it if he can.   300
  ' And now, O prince, I bid thee take my hand,
And hear me swear that till unto this land
Thou hast borne back the fleece across the sea,
Thy liege-man and thy servant I will be.
Nor have I seen a man more like a king
Than thou art, of whom minstrel folk shall sing
In days to come when men sit by the wine.'
  Then Jason said : ' A happy lot is mine !
Surely the Gods must love me, since that thou
Art come, with me the rough green plain to plough   310
That no man reaps ; yet certes, thou alone
In after days shalt be the glorious one
Whom men shall sing of when they name the fleece,
That bore the son of Athamas from Greece,
When I and all these men have come to nought.'
  So spake he ; but the great-eyed Juno brought
His words to nothing, stooping to behold
Jason's fair head, whereon the locks of gold
Curled thick and close, and his grey eager eyes,
That seemed already to behold the prize   320
In far-off Colchis : like a God he stood,
No less than he that in the darksome wood
Slew the lake-haunting, many-headed beast.

  But on that day the Minyæ held a feast,
Praising the Gods, and those that they had sent
Across the sea to work out their intent.

297-8 *One line only in first edition :*
            Ever am I the least loved guest of all,
                       A a 2

Yea, ere the night, greater their joyance grew,
For to the throng of heroes came there two,
In nowise worse than any of the best,—
Castor and Pollux, who thought not to rest   330
In woody Lacedæmon, where the doves
Make summer music in the beechen groves,
But rather chose to hear the sea-fowl sing.
     Their mother wedded Tyndarus the king.
And yet a greater name their father had,
As men deem ; for that Leda, all unclad,
In cold Eurotas, on a summer morn,
Bathed her fair body, unto whom was borne,
Fleeing from seeming death, a milk-white swan,
Whom straight the naked queen, not fearing man,   340
Took in her arms, nor knew she fostered Jove,
Who rules o'er mortal men and Gods above.
     So in the hall of Pelias, in their place
The twain sat down ; and joy lit every face,
When both their names the sweet-voiced herald cried.
But the next morn into the town did ride
Lynceus and Idas, leaving far away
Well-walled Messene where the kestrels play
About the temples and the treasure-house.
But of these twain was Idas valorous   350
Beyond most men, and hasty of his blow ;
And unto Lynceus would the darkness show
That which he lacked ; and of all men was he
The luckiest to find the privity
Of gold or gems. And on the self-same day
Came Periclymenes, who folk did say
Had Proteus' gift to change from shape to shape.
     Next from Tegea, where the long green grape
Grows yellow in the dewy autumn night,
There came Ancæus, stubborn in the fight.   360
     Amphidamus and Apheus left the trees
Where sing the wood-doves to their mistresses
In the Arcadian forests ; and where oft,
If through the springing brake he treadeth soft,
The happy hunter may well chance to see
Beside a hidden stream some two or three

Of tired nymphs, stripping the silken weed
From off their limbs ; nor shall Actæon's meed
Betide him there among the oaken trees.
  Next came there Augeas, who at Elis sees   370
On his fat plains the sheep, and kine, and beeves,
Unnumbered as the rustling aspen leaves
Beside the river : from the grassy plain
Anigh Pellene, where the harvest wain
Scatters the grazing sheep, Amphion came,
In nowise skilled like him who bore his name,
The deathless singer, but right wise in war.
Then through the town there passed a brazen car
Bearing Euphemus, who had power to go
Dryshod across the plain no man doth sow.   380
By Tenarus he dwelt, beside the sea,
Anigh the temple of the deity
Whose son he was, the Shaker of the earth.
  Then came a fresh Ancæus, who had birth
In woody Samos, of the self-same sire
Whose heart white-footed Alta set on fire,
As on the yellow sands at dawn she went.
  Then Calydon the great a hero sent,
The fair-haired Meleager, who became,
In after-days, the glory of his name,   390
The greatest name of the Ætolian land ;
While yet on him fate laid her heavy hand,
In midst of all his glory so raised up,
Who nowise now dreaded the proffered cup
Of life and death she held for him to drain,
Nor thought of death and wishes wished in vain.
With him his uncle rode, Laocoon,
No longer young, teaching his brother's son
What 'longed to ruling men and unto war.
  From Lacedæmon, Iphiclus afar   400
Had travelled, till the rich embroidered weed
His father Thestius gave him at his need
Was stained with sun and dust, but still he came
To try the sea and win undying fame.
  Then came a man long-limbed, in savage weed,

383 Shaker] shaker

Arcas the hunter, to whose unmatched speed
All beasts that wander through the woods are slow.
In his right hand he bare the fatal bow
Of horn, and wood, and brass, but now unstrung,
And at his back a well-closed quiver hung,   410
Done round with silver bands and leopard's skin,
And fifty deaths were hidden well therein
Of men or beasts ; for whoso stood before
His bended bow and angry eyes, no more
Should see the green trees and the fertile earth.

Then came two brothers of a wondrous birth,
Zetes and Calaïs, sons of Boreas ;
For he beheld Erechtheus' daughter pass
Along Ilissus, one bright windy day,
Whom from amidst her maids he bore away   420
Unto the hills of Thrace to be his bride.
Now unto them this marvel did betide,
Like men in all else, from anigh the head
Of each sprung wings, wherewith at will they sped
From land to land, 'midst of the pathless air.

Next from Magnesia did roan horses bear
Phocus and Priasus, well skilled to cast
The whistling dart ; then o'er the drawbridge passed
Ætolian Palæmonius, who not yet
Had seen men armed in anger, or steel wet.   430
With blood of aught but beasts, but none the less
Was willing now to stand among the press
Of god-like men, who, with the Minyæ,
Were armed to bring the fleece across the sea.

Then came Asclepius, whom the far-darter
Saved living from the lifeless corpse of her
He once loved well, but slew for treason done,
Fair-haired Coronis, whose far-seeing son
He honoured much, and taught so many a thing,
That first he knew how man may ease the sting   440
Of sickening pain, because all herbs he knew,
And what the best and worst of them could do.
So many a bitter fight with death he had,
And made the heart of many a sick man glad,

423 That like fair men in all else, from the head

And gave new life to many a man who seemed
But dead already, wherefore people deemed
When he was dead that he was God indeed,
And on his altars many a beast did bleed.
    Acastus, Pelias' son, from wandering
Was come that self-same day unto the king,   450
And needs must go with Jason on his quest,
Careless of princely ease and golden rest.

    Next Neleus, growing grey, forgetting not
The double crime, had left the pleasant spot
Where wan Alpheus meets the green sea waves,
And twice a-day the walls of Pylos laves ;
For he was fain to expiate the sin
Pelias shared with him, long years past within
Queen Juno's temple, where the brothers slew
The old Sidero, crying out, who knew   460
Then first the bitterness of such a cry
As broke from Tyro in her agony
When helpless, bound, within the brazen hall,
She felt unthought-of torment on her fall,
With none to pity her, nor knew what end
The Gods unto such misery would send.
So might Sidero feel, when fell on her
Unlooked-for death and deadly, hopeless fear ;
And in their turn must Neleus o'er the sea
Go wandering now, and Pelias must be   470
A trembling liar till death seizes him.
    But now with Neleus, young but strong of limb,
His wise, far-seeing offspring, Nestor, went,
With eyes a little downward ever bent,
Thinking of this and that which he had seen ;
Who, when his youth was flourishing and green,
Saw many feats of arms and ways of men,
Yet lived so long to be well honoured, when
In Troy the old the princes shared the spoil.
    Next came Lærtes to share grief and toil   480
With these upon the sea ; yet had he not
An easy land in Ithaca the hot,

    451 his] this   455 Where wan] Where the wan

Though Bacchus loves the ledges of the land,
And weighs the peasant in his sunburnt hand
The heavy oozing bunches, in the time
When frosts draw nigh in the rough northern clime.

Next whom came Almenus, of naught afraid,
Well armed and hardy, whom a mortal maid
Bore unto Mars, for he, new-come from Thrace,
Beside Enipeus met her, and in chase   490
He held her long, who vainly fled from him,
Though light of foot she was, and strong of limb.

And last of all, Orpheus the singer came,
The son of King Œager, great of fame,
Yet happier by much in this, that he
Was loved by heavenly Calliope,
Who bore him Orpheus on a happy day.
And now, through many a rough and toilsome way,
Hither he came the Minyæ to please,
And make them masters of the threatening seas,   500
Cheering their hearts, and making their hands strong
With the unlooked-for sweetness of his song.
Now it was eve by then that Orpheus came
Into the hall, and when they heard his name,
And toward the high-seat of the prince he drew,
All men beholding him the singer knew,
And glad were all men there that he should be
Their mate upon the bitter, tuneless sea.
And loud they shouted, but Prince Jason said :—
' Now, may the Gods bring good things on thy head,
Son of Œager, but from me, indeed,   511
This gold Dædalian bowl shall be thy meed,
If thou wilt let us hear thy voice take wing
From out thine heart, and see the golden string
Quiver beneath thy fingers.   But by me
First sit and feast, and happy mayst thou be.'
Then, glad at heart, the hero took his place,
And ate and drank his fill, but when the space
Was cleared of flesh and bread, he took his lyre
And sung them of the building up of Tyre,   520

507 And glad they were, indeed, that he should be

And of the fair things stored up over sea,
Till there was none of them but fain would be
Set in the ship, nor cared one man to stay
On the green earth for one more idle day.

But Jason, looking right and left on them,
Took his fair cloak, wrought with a golden hem,
And laid it upon Orpheus, and thereto
Added the promised bowl, that all men knew
No hand but that of Dædalus had wrought,
So rich it was, and fair beyond all thought.   530
Then did he say unto the Minyæ :—
' Fair friends and well-loved guests, no more shall ye
Feast in this hall until we come again
Back to this land, well-guerdoned for our pain,
Bearing the fleece, and mayhap many a thing
Such as this god-like guest erewhile did sing,
Scarlet, and gold, and brass ; but without fail
Bearing great fame, if aught that may avail
To men who die ; and our names certainly
Shall never perish, wheresoe'er we lie.   540
' And now behold within the haven rides
Our good ship, swinging in the changing tides,
Gleaming with gold, and blue, and cinnabar,
The long new oars beside the rowlocks are,
The sail hangs flapping in the light west wind,
Nor aught undone can any craftsman find
From stem to stern ; so is our quest begun
To-morrow at the rising of the sun.
And may Jove bring us all safe back to see
Another sun shine on this fair city,   550
When elders and the flower-crowned maidens meet
With tears and singing our returning feet.'

So spake he, and so mighty was the shout,
That the hall shook, and shepherd-folk without
The well-walled city heard it as they went
Unto the fold across the thymy bent.

BOOK IV

The quest begun—The loss of Hylas and Hercules.

But through the town few eyes were sealed by sleep
When the sun rose ; yea, and the upland sheep
Must guard themselves for that one morn at least,
Against the wolf , and wary doves may feast
Unscared that morning on the ripening corn.
Nor did the whetstone touch the scythe that morn ;
And all unheeded did the mackerel shoal
Make green the blue waves, or the porpoise roll
Through changing hills and valleys of the sea.
For 'twixt the thronging people solemnly   10
The heroes went afoot along the way
That led unto the haven of the bay,
And as they went the roses rained on them
From windows glorious with the well-wrought hem
Of many a purple cloth ; and all their spears
Were twined with flowers that the fair earth bears ;
And round their ladies' tokens were there set
About their helmets, flowery wreaths, still wet
With beaded dew of the scarce vanished night.
So as they passed, the young men at the sight   20
Shouted for joy, and their hearts swelled with pride ;
But scarce the elders could behold dry-eyed
The glorious show, remembering well the days
When they were able too to win them praise,
And in their hearts was hope of days to come.
Nor could the heroes leave their fathers' home
Unwept of damsels, who henceforth must hold
The empty air unto their bosoms cold,
And make their sweet complainings to the night
That heedeth not soft eyes and bosoms white.   30
And many such an one was there that morn,
Who, with lips parted and grey eyes forlorn,
Stood by the window and forgot to cast
Her gathered flowers as the heroes passed,

But held them still within her garment's hem,
Though many a wingèd wish she sent to them.
  But on they went, and as the way they trod,
His swelling heart nigh made each man a god ;
While clashed their armour to the minstrelsy
That went before them to the doubtful sea.   40
  And now, the streets being passed, they reached the
    bay,
Where by the well-built quay long Argo lay,
Glorious with gold, and shining in the sun.
Then first they shouted, and each man begun
Against his shield to strike his brazen spear ;
And as along the quays they drew a-near,
Faster they strode and faster, till a cry
Again burst from them, and right eagerly
Into swift running did they break at last,
Till all the wind-swept quay being overpast,   50
They pressed across the gangway, and filled up
The hollow ship as wine a golden cup.

  But Jason, standing by the helmsman's side
High on the poop, lift up his voice and cried :—
  ' Look landward, heroes, once, before ye slip
The tough well-twisted hawser from the ship,
And set your eager hands to rope or oar ;
For now, behold, the king stands on the shore
Beside a new-built altar, while the priests
Lead up a hecatomb of spotless beasts,   60
White bulls and coal-black horses, and my sire
Lifts up the barley-cake above the fire ;
And in his hand a cup of ruddy gold
King Pelias takes ; and now may ye behold
The broad new-risen sun light up the God,
Who, holding in his hand the crystal rod
That rules the sea, stands by Dædalian art
Above his temple, set right far apart
From other houses, nigh the deep green sea.
  ' And now, O fellows, from no man but me   70
These gifts come to the God, that, ere long years
Have drowned our laughter and dried up our tears,

We may behold that glimmering brazen God
Against the sun bear up his crystal rod
Once more, and once more cast upon this land
This cable, severed by my bloodless brand.'

So spake he, and raised up the glittering steel,
That fell, and seaward straight did Argo reel,
Set free, and smitten by the western breeze,
And raised herself against the ridgy seas,   80
With golden eyes turned toward the Colchian land,
Still heedful of wise Tiphys' skilful hand.
But silent sat the heroes by the oar,
Hearkening the sounds borne from the lessening shore ;
The lowing of the doomed and flower-crowned beasts,
The plaintive singing of the ancient priests,
Mingled with blare of trumpets, and the sound
Of all the many folk that stood around
The altar and the temple by the sea.
So sat they pondering much and silently,   90
Till all the landward noises died away,
And, midmost now of the green sunny bay,
They heard no sound but washing of the seas
And piping of the following western breeze,
And heavy measured beating of the oars :
So left the Argo the Thessalian shores.

Now Neptune, joyful of the sacrifice
Beside the sea, and all the gifts of price
That Jason gave him, sent them wind at will,
And swiftly Argo climbed each changing hill,   100
And ran through rippling valleys of the sea ;
Nor toiled the heroes unmelodiously,
For by the mast sat great Œager's son,
And through the harp-strings let his fingers run
Nigh soundless, and with closed lips for a while ;
But soon across his face there came a smile,
And his glad voice brake into such a song
That swiftlier sped the eager ship along.

' O bitter sea, tumultuous sea,
Full many an ill is wrought by thee !—   110

Unto the wasters of the land
Thou holdest out thy wrinkled hand ;
And when they leave the conquered town,
Whose black smoke makes thy surges brown,
Driven betwixt thee and the sun,
As the long day of blood is done,
From many a league of glittering waves
Thou smilest on them and their slaves.
  ' The thin bright-eyed Phœnician
Thou drawest to thy waters wan,   120
With ruddy eve and golden morn
Thou temptest him, until, forlorn,
Unburied, under alien skies
Cast up ashore his body lies.
  ' Yea, whoso sees thee from his door,
Must ever long for more and more ;
Nor will the beechen bowl suffice,
Or homespun robe of little price,
Or hood well-woven of the fleece
Undyed, or unspiced wine of Greece ;   130
So sore his heart is set upon
Purple, and gold, and cinnamon ;
For as thou cravest, so he craves,
Until he rolls beneath thy waves.
Nor in some landlocked, unknown bay,
Can satiate thee for one day.

  ' Now, therefore, O thou bitter sea,
With no long words we pray to thee,
But ask thee, hast thou felt before
Such strokes of the long ashen oar ?   140
And hast thou yet seen such a prow
Thy rich and niggard waters plough ?
  ' Nor yet, O sea, shalt thou be cursed,
If at thy hands we gain the worst,
And, wrapt in water, roll about
Blind-eyed, unheeding song or shout,
Within thine eddies far from shore,
Warmed by no sunlight any more.
  ' Therefore, indeed, we joy in thee,

And praise thy greatness, and will we   150
Take at thy hands both good and ill,
Yea, what thou wilt, and praise thee still,
Enduring not to sit at home,
And wait until the last days come,
When we no more may care to hold
White bosoms under crowns of gold,
And our dulled hearts no longer are
Stirred by the clangorous noise of war,
And hope within our souls is dead,
And no joy is remembered.   160
    ' So, if thou hast a mind to slay,
Fair prize thou hast of us to-day ;
And if thou hast a mind to save,
Great praise and honour shalt thou have ;
But whatso thou wilt do with us,
Our end shall not be piteous,
Because our memories shall live
When folk forget the way to drive
The black keel through the heaped-up sea,
And half dried up thy waters be.'   170

    Then shouted all the heroes, and they drove
The good ship forth, so that the birds above,
With long white wings, scarce flew so fast as they.
And so they laboured well-nigh all the day;
And ever in their ears divine words rung,
For 'midmost of them still the Thracian sung
Stories of Gods and men ; the bitter life
Pandora brought to luckless men ; the strife
'Twixt Pallas and the Shaker of the Earth,
The theft of Bacchus, and the wondrous birth   180
Of golden Venus. Natheless, when the sun
To fall adown the heavens had begun,
They trimmed the sails, and drew the long oars up,
And, having poured wine from a golden cup
Unto the Gods, gladdened their hearts with food ;
Then having feasted as they thought it good,
Set hands upon the oars again, and so
Toiled on, until the broad sun, growing low,

Reddened the green sea ; then they held their hands
Till he should come again from unknown lands,   190
And fell to meat again, and sat so long
Over the wine-cups, cheered with tale and song,
That night fell on them, and the moon rose high,
And the fair western wind began to die,
Though still they drifted slowly towards the east ;
Then with sweet sleep the others crowned their feast,
But Tiphys and the leader of the rest,
Who watched till drew the round moon to the west,
And Jason could behold beneath her light,
Far off at first, a little speck of white,   200
Which, as the grey dawn stole across the sea,
And the wind freshened, grew at last to be
Grey rocks and great, and when they nigher drew,
The skilful helmsman past all doubting knew
The land of Lemnos ; therefore from their sleep
They roused their fellows, bidding them to keep
The good ship from that evil rocky shore.
  So each man set his hand unto the oar,
And, striking sail, along the coast they crept,
Till the sun rose, and birds no longer slept ;   210
Then as they went they saw a sandy beach
Under the cliff, that no high wave could reach,
And in the rock a deep cave cut, whereby
A man was standing, gazing earnestly
Upon their ship, and shouting words that, tost
Hither and thither by the wind, were lost
Amid the tumbling of the ridgy sea :
Natheless, they deemed that he still prayed to be
Their fellow, and to leave those rocky shores ;
Therefore, with backing of the ashen oars,   220
They stayed the ship, and beckoned unto him
To try the sea, if so be he could swim,
Because, indeed, they doubted there might be
A-nigh the place some hidden enemy ;
Nor cared they much to trust their oaken keel
Too near those rocks, as deadly as sharp steel,
That lay upon their lee ; but with a shout
He sprang into the sea, and beat about

The waters bravely, till he reached the ship ;
And clambering up, let the salt water drip   230
From off his naked limbs, nor spoke he ought
Until before the fair prince he was brought.
But Jason, when he set his eyes on him,
And saw him famished and so gaunt of limb,
Bade them to give him food and wine enow
Before he told his tale ; and still to row
Along the high cliffs eastward, nor to stay
For town or tower, or haven or deep bay.

Then being clothed and fed, the island man
Came back to Jason, and his tale began :—   240

' O Lord, or Prince, or whoso thou mayst be,
Great thanks I give thee ; yet, I pray, of me,
Ask not my name, for surely ere this day
Both name, and house, and friends have past away.
A Lemnian am I, who within the town
Had a fair house, and on the thymy down
Full many a head of sheep ; and I had too
A daughter, old enough for men to woo,
A wife and three fair sons ; of whom the first
For love and gold had now begun to thirst :   250
Full rich I was, and led a pleasant life,
Nor did I long for more, or doubt for strife.
' Know that in Lemnos were the Gods well served,
And duly all their awful rites observed,
Save only that no temple Venus had,
And from no altars was her heart made glad ;
Wherefore for us she wove a bitter fate,
For by her power she set an evil hate
Of man, like madness in each woman's heart,
And heavy sleep on us men, for our part,   260
From which few woke, or woke in time to feel
Against their throats the pitiless sharp steel.
' But that there might be one to tell the thing,
Nigh dawn I woke, and turning, thought to cling
Unto the warm side of my well-loved wife,
But found naught there but a keen two-edged knife.

238 tower, or haven] tower, haven

So, wondering much, I gat me from the bed,
And going thence, found all the floor be-bled
In my son's sleeping place, and nigh the door
His body, hacked and hewn, upon the floor :   270
Naked he was, but in his clenched right hand
Held tufts of woman's hair. Then did I stand
As in a dream a man stands, when draws nigh
The thing he fears with such wild agony,
Yet dares not flee from ; but the golden sun
Came forth at last and daylight was begun ;
Then trembling I took heart to leave at last
The lonely house, but, as I slowly passed
Into the porch, a dreadful noise I heard,
Nor shall I be again by aught so feared,   280
How long soe'er I live, as I was then,
Because that shout was worse than cries of men
Drunken with blood ; but yet as in a dream
I went to meet it, and heard many a scream
From dying men ; but, as I gained the street,
Men flying for their dear lives did I meet,
And turned and fled with them, I knew not why,
But looking back in running, could espy,
With shrinking horror, what kept up the chase.
   ' Because, indeed, the old familiar place,   290
From house-wall unto house-wall, was now filled
With frantic women, whose thin voices shrilled
With unknown war-cries ; little did they heed
If, as they tore along, their flesh did bleed
So that some man was slain, nor feared they now
If they each other smote with spear or bow,
For all were armed in some sort, and had set
On head or breast what armour they might get ;
And some were naked else, and some were clad
In such-like raiment as the slain men had,   300
And some their kirtles wore looped up or rent.
   ' So ever at us shafts and spears they sent,
And through the street came on like a huge wave,
Until at last against the gates they drave,
And we gained on them, till some two or three,
As still the others strove confusedly,

MORRIS   B b

Burst from the press, and, heading all the rest,
Ran mightily, and the last men, hard pressed,
Turned round upon them, and straightway were slain,
Unarmed and faint, and 'gan the crowd to gain　310
Upon the fleeing men, till one by one
They fell, and looked their last upon the sun,
And I alone was held in chase, until
I reached the top of a high thymy hill
Above the sea, bleeding from arm and back,
Wherein two huntsmen's arrows lightly stack,
Shot by no practised hands ; but nigh my death
I was indeed, empty of hope and breath.
　' Yet, ere their changed hands could be laid on me,
I threw myself into the boiling sea,　320
And they turned back, nor doubted I was dead ;
But I, though fearing much to show my head,
Got me, by swimming, to yon little beach,
And there the mouth of yon cave scarce could reach,
And lay there fainting till the sun was high.
Then I awoke, and, rising fearfully,
Gat into the dark cave, and there have been,
How long I know not, and no man have seen ;
And as for food and drink, within the cave
Good store of sweet clear water did I have,　330
And in the nights I went along the beach
And got me shell-fish, and made shift to reach
Some few birds' eggs ; but natheless, misery
Must soon have slain me, had not the kind sea
Sent you, O lords, to give me life again ;
Therefore, I pray, ye may not wish in vain
For aught, and that with goods and happiness
The Father of all folk your lives may bless.'

　Then said the prince : ' And be thou strong of heart,
For, after all thy woes, shalt thou have part　340
In this our quest, if so thou willest it ;
But if so be that thou wouldst rather sit
In rest and peace within a fair homestead,
That shall some king give to thee by my head,
For love of me ; or else for very fear

Shall some man give thee what thou countest dear.
' And if thou askest of us, know that we
Are children of the conquering Minyæ,
And make for Colchis o'er the watery plain,
And think we shall not fail to bring again   350
The fleece of Neptune's ram to Thessaly.'
' Prince ' said the Lemnian, ' I will go with thee
Whereso thou willest, neither have I will
To wait again for ruin, sitting still
Among such goods as grudging fate will give,
Even at the longest, only while I live.'
    Then Jason bade them bring him arms well wrought
And robes of price ; and when all these were brought,
And he was armed, he seemed a goodly man.

    Meanwhile, along the high cliffs Argo ran   360
Until a fresh land-wind began to rise,
Then did they set sail, and in goodly wise
Draw off from Lemnos, and at close of day
Again before them a new country lay,
Which when they neared, the helmsman Tiphys knew
To be the Mysian land ; being come thereto,
They saw a grassy shore and trees enow,
And a sweet stream that from the land did flow ;
Therefore they thought it good to land thereon
And get them water ; but, the day being gone,   370
They anchored till the dawn anigh the beach,
Till the sea's rim the golden sun did reach.
But when the day dawned, most men left the ship,
Some hasting the glazed water-jars to dip
In the fresh water ; others among these
Who had good will beneath the murmuring trees
To sit awhile, forgetful of the sea.
And with the sea-farers there landed three
Amongst the best, Alcmena's godlike son,
Hylas the fair, and that half-halting one,   380
Great Polyphemus. Now both Hercules
And all the others lay beneath the trees,
When all the jars were filled, nor wandered far ;
But Hylas, governed by some wayward star,

Strayed from them, and up stream he set his face.
And came unto a tangled woody place,
From whence the stream came, and within that wood
Along its bank wandered in heedless mood,
Nor knew it haunted of the sea-nymphs fair,
Whom on that morn the heroes' noise did scare　　390
From their abiding-place anigh the bay ;
But these now hidden in the water lay
Within the wood, and thence could they behold
The fair-limbed Hylas, with his hair of gold,
And mighty arms down-swinging carelessly,
And fresh face, ruddy from the wind-swept sea ;
Then straight they loved him, and, being fain to have
His shapely body in the glassy wave,
And taking counsel there, they thought it good
That one should meet him in the darksome wood,　　400
And by her wiles should draw him to some place
Where they his helpless body might embrace.

So from the water stole a fair nymph forth,
And by her art so wrought, that from the north
You would have thought her come, from where a queen
Rules over lands summer alone sees green ;
For she in goodly raiment, furred, was clad,
And on her head a golden fillet had,
Strange of its fashion, and about her shone
Many a fair jewel and outlandish stone.　　410
So in the wood, anigh the river side,
The coming of the Theban did she bide,
Nor waited long, for slowly pushing through
The close-set saplings, o'er the flowers blue
He drew nigh, singing, free from any care ;
But when he saw her glittering raiment fair
Betwixt the green tree-trunks, he stayed a space,
For she, with fair hands covering up her face,
Was wailing loud, as though she saw him not,
And to his mind came old tales half forgot,　　420
Of women of the woods, the huntsman's bane.

Yet with his fate indeed he strove in vain ;
For, going further forward warily,
From tree-trunk unto tree-trunk, he could see

Her ivory hands, with wrist set close to wrist,
Her cheek as fair as any God has kissed,
Her lovely neck and wealth of golden hair,
That from its fillet straggled here and there,
And all her body writhing in distress,
Wrapped in the bright folds of her golden dress.   430
　　Then forthwith he drew near her eagerly,
Nor did she seem to know that he was nigh,
Until almost his hand on her was laid ;
Then, lifting up a pale wild face, she said,
Struggling with sobs and shrinking from his hand :—
' O, fair young warrior of a happy land,
Harm not a queen, I pray thee, for I come
From the far northland, where yet sits at home
The king, my father, who, since I was wooed
By a rich lord of Greece, had thought it good   440
To send me to him with a royal train,
But they, their hearts being changed by hope of gain,
Seized on my goods, and left me while I slept ;
Nor do I know, indeed, what kind God kept
Their traitorous hands from slaying me outright ;
And surely yet, the lion-haunted night
Shall make an end of me, who erewhile thought
That unto lovelier lands I was being brought,
To live a happier life than heretofore.
　' But why think I of past times any more,   450
Who, a king's daughter once, am now grown fain
Of poorest living, through all toil and pain,
If so I may but live : and thou, indeed,
Perchance art come, some God, unto my need ;
For nothing less thou seemest, verily.
But if thou art a man, let me not die,
But take me as thy slave, that I may live.
For many a gem my raiment has to give,
And these weak fingers surely yet may learn
To turn the mill, and carry forth the urn   460
Unto the stream, nor shall my feet unshod,
Shrink from the flinty road and thistly sod.'

425 ivory] lovely

She ceased; but he stooped down, and stammering said:
' Mayst thou be happy, O most lovely maid,
And thy sweet life yet know a better day :
And I will strive to bring thee on thy way,
Who am the well-loved son of a rich man
Who dwells in Thebes, beside Ismenus wan.'
Therewith he reached his hand to her and she
Let her slim palm fall in it daintily ;   470
But with that touch he felt as through his blood
Strange fire ran, and saw not the close wood,
Nor tangled path, nor stream, nor aught but her
Crouching before him in her gold and fur,
With kind appealing eyes raised up to his,
And red lips trembling for the coming kiss.

But ere his lips met hers did she arise,
Reddening with shame, and from before his eyes
Drew her white hand, wherewith the robe of gold
She gathered up, and from her feet did hold,   480
Then through the tangled wood began to go,
Not looking round ; but he cared not to know
Whither they went, so only she was nigh.
So to her side he hurried fearfully,
She naught gainsaying, but with eyes downcast
Still by his side betwixt the low boughs past,
Following the stream, until a space of green
All bare of trees they reached, and there-between
The river ran, grown broad and like a pool,
Along whose bank a flickering shade and cool   490
Grey willows made, and all about they heard
The warble of the small brown river bird.
And from both stream and banks rose up a haze
Quivering and glassy, for of summer days
This was the chiefest day and crown of all.

There did the damsel let her long skirts fall
Over her feet, but as her hand dropped down,
She felt it stopped by Hylas' fingers brown,
Whereat she trembled and began to go
Across the flowery grass with footsteps slow,   500
As though she grew aweary, and she said,
Turning about her fair and glorious head :

' Soft is the air in your land certainly,
But under foot the way is rough and dry
Unto such feet as mine, more used to feel
The dainty stirrup wrought of gold and steel,
Or tread upon the white bear's fell, or pass
In spring and summer o'er such flowery grass
As this, that soothly mindeth me too much
Of that my worshipped feet were wont to touch,   510
When I was called a queen ; let us not haste
To leave this sweet place for the tangled waste,
I pray thee, therefore prince, but let us lie
Beneath these willows while the wind goes by,
And set our hearts to think of happy things,
Before the morrow pain and trouble brings.'
  She faltered somewhat as she spoke, but he
Drew up before her and took lovingly
Her other hand, nor spoke she more to him,
Nor he to her awhile, till, from the rim   520
Of his great shield, broke off the leathern band
That crossed his breast, whether some demon's hand
Snapped it unseen, or some sharp, rugged bough
Within the wood had chafed it even now ;
But clattering fell the buckler to the ground,
And, startled at the noise, he turned him round,
Then, grown all bold within that little space,
He set his cheek unto her blushing face,
And smiling, in a low voice said :
                                    ' O sweet,
Call it an omen that this, nowise meet   530
For deeds of love, has left me by its will,
And now by mine these toys that cumber still,
My arms shall leave me.'
                        And therewith he threw
His brass-bound spear upon the grass, and drew
The Theban blade from out its ivory sheath,
And loosed his broad belt's clasp, that like a wreath
His father's Indian serving-man had wrought,
And cast his steel coat off, from Persia brought ;
And so at last being freed of brass and steel,

               521 leathern] leather

Upon his breast he laid her hand to feel   540
The softness of the fine Phœnician stuff
That clad it still, nor yet could toy enough
With that fair hand ; so played they for a space,
Till softly did she draw him to a place
Anigh the stream, and they being set, he said :
 ' And what dost thou, O love ? art thou afraid
To cast thine armour off, as I have done,
Within this covert where the fiery sun
Scarce strikes upon one jewel of your gown ? '
    Then she spake, reddening, with her eyes cast down :
O prince, behold me as I am to-day,   551
But if o'er many a rough and weary way
It hap unto us both at last to come
Unto the happy place that is thine home,
Then let me be as women of thy land
When they before the sea-born goddess stand,
And not one flower hides them from her sight.'
    But with that word she set her fingers white
Upon her belt, and he said amorously :
' Ah, God, whatso thou wilt must surely be,   560
But would that I might die or be asleep
Till we have gone across the barren deep,
And you and I together, hand in hand,
Some day ere sunrise lights the quiet land,
Behold once more the seven gleaming gates.'
    ' O love,' she said, ' and such a fair time waits
Both thee and me ; but now to give thee rest,
Here, in the noontide, were it not the best
To soothe thee with some gentle murmuring song,
Sung to such notes as to our folk belong ;   570
Such as my maids awhile ago would sing
When on my bed a-nights I lay waking ? '
' Sing on,' he said, ' but let me dream of bliss
If I should sleep, nor yet forget thy kiss '
She touched his lips with hers, and then began
A sweet song sung not yet to any man.

    ' I know a little garden close
    Set thick with lily and red rose,

Where I would wander if I might
From dewy dawn to dewy night,   580
And have one with me wandering.
  ' And though within it no birds sing,
And though no pillared house is there,
And though the apple boughs are bare
Of fruit and blossom, would to God,
Her feet upon the green grass trod,
And I beheld them as before.
  ' There comes a murmur from the shore,
And in the place two fair streams are,
Drawn from the purple hills afar,   590
Drawn down unto the restless sea ;
The hills whose flowers ne'er fed the bee,
The shore no ship has ever seen,
Still beaten by the billows green,
Whose murmur comes unceasingly
Unto the place for which I cry.
  ' For which I cry both day and night,
For which I let slip all delight,
That maketh me both deaf and blind,
Careless to win, unskilled to find,   600
And quick to lose what all men seek.
  ' Yet tottering as I am, and weak,
Still have I left a little breath
To seek within the jaws of death
An entrance to that happy place,
To seek the unforgotten face
Once seen, once kissed, once reft from me
Anigh the murmuring of the sea.'

  She ceased her song, that lower for a while
And slower too had grown, and a soft smile   610
Grew up within her eyes as still she sung.
Then she rose up and over Hylas hung,
For now he slept ; wherewith the God in her
Consumed the northern robe done round with fur   ·
That hid her beauty, and the light west wind
Played with her hair no fillet now did bind,
And through her faint grey garment her limbs seemed

Like ivory in the sea, and the sun gleamed
In the strange jewels round her middle sweet,
And in the jewelled sandals on her feet.   620
  So stood she murmuring till a rippling sound
She heard, that grew until she turned her round
And saw her other sisters of the deep
Her song had called while Hylas yet did sleep,
Come swimming in a long line up the stream,
And their white dripping arms and shoulders gleam
Above the dark grey water as they went,
And still before them a great ripple sent.
  But when they saw her, toward the bank they drew,
And landing, felt the grass and flowers blue   630
Against their unused feet ; then in a ring
Stood gazing with wide eyes, and wondering
At all his beauty they desired so much.
And then with gentle hands began to touch
His hair, his hands, his closed eyes ; and at last
Their eager naked arms about him cast,
And bore him, sleeping still, as by some spell,
Unto the depths where they were wont to dwell ;
Then softly down the reedy bank they slid,
And with small noise the gurgling river hid   640
The flushed nymphs and the heedless sleeping man.
  But ere the water covered them, one ran
Across the mead and caught up from the ground
The brass-bound spear, and buckler bossed and round,
The ivory-hilted sword, and coat of mail,
Then took the stream ; so what might tell the tale,
Unless the wind should tell it, or the bird
Who from the reed these things had seen and heard ?

  Meanwhile, the ship being watered, and the day
Now growing late, the prince would fain away ;   650
So from the ship was blown a horn to call
The stragglers back, who mustered one and all,
But Theban Hylas ; therefore, when they knew
That he was missing, Hercules withdrew
From out the throng, if yet perchance his voice
Hylas might hear, and all their hearts rejoice

With his well-known shout in reply thereto ;
With him must Polyphemus likewise go,
To work out the wise counsel of the fates,
Unhappy, who no more would see the gates   660
Of white-walled fair Larissa, or the plain
Burdened by many an overladen wain.

  For, while their cries and shouts rang through the wood,
The others reached the ship, and thought it good
To weigh the anchor, and anigh the shore,
With loosened sail, and run-out ready oar,
To trim the ship for leaving the fair bay ;
And therefore, Juno, waiting for that day,
And for that hour, had gathered store of wind
Up in the hills to work out all her mind,   670
Which, from the Mysian mountains now let slip,
Tearing along the low shore, smote the ship
In blinding clouds of salt spray mixed with rain.

  Then vainly they struck sail, and all in vain
The rowers strove to keep her head to wind,
And still they drifted seaward, drenched and blind.

  But, 'mid their struggling, suddenly there shone
A light from Argo's high prow, and thereon
Could their astonished, fearful eyes behold
A figure standing, with wide wings of gold,   680
Upright, amid the weltering of the sea,
Calm 'midst the noise and cries, and presently
To all their ears a voice pierced, saying : ' No more,
O Jove-blessed heroes, strive to reach the shore,
Nor seek your lost companions, for of these
Jove gives you not the mighty Hercules
To help you forward on your happy way,
But wills him in the Greek land still to stay,
Where many a thing he has for him to do,
With whom awhile shall Polyphemus go,   690
Then build in Mysia a fair merchant-town,
And when long years have passed, there lay him down :
And as for Hylas, never think to see
His body more, who yet lies happily
Beneath the green stream where ye were this morn,
And there he praises Jove that he was born,

Forgetting the rough world, and every care ;
Not dead, nor living, among faces fair,
White limbs, and wonders of the watery world.
    ' And now I bid ye spread the sail ye furled,   700
And make on towards the straits while Juno sends
Fair wind behind you, calling you her friends.'
    Therewith the voice ceased, and the storm was still,
And afterward they had good wind at will,
To help them toward the straits, but all the rest,
Rejoicing at the speeding of their quest,
Yet wondered much whence that strange figure came,
That on the prow burnt like a harmless flame ;
Yea, some must go and touch the empty space
From whence those words flew from the godlike face ;
But Jason and the builder, Argus, knew   711
Whereby the prow foretold things strange and new,
Nor wondered aught, but thanked the Gods therefore,
As far astern they left the Mysian shore.

BOOK V

The death of Cyzicus—Phineus freed from the Harpies.

Now, driven by the oar, and feeling well
The wind that made the fair white sail outswell,
Thessalian Argo flew on toward the place
Where first the rude folks saw dead Helle's face ;
There, fearful of the darkness of the night,
Without the rocks they anchored till the light,
And when the day broke, sped them through the straits
With oars alone, and through the narrow gates
Came out into Propontis, where with oar
And sail together, within sight of shore,   10
They went, until the sun was falling down,
And then they saw the white walls of a town,
And made thereto, and soon being come anigh,
They found that on an isle the place did lie,
And Tiphys called it Cyzicum, a place
Built by a goodly man of a great race,

13 and soon being] and being

Himself called Cyzicus, Euzorus' son,
Who still in peace ruled over many an one,
Merchants and other, in that city fair.
    Therefore, they thought it good to enter there,   20
And going softly, with sails struck, at last
Betwixt the two walls of a port they passed,
And on the quays beheld full many a man
Buying and selling, nigh the water wan.
    So, as they touched the shore, an officer
Drew nigh unto them, asking who they were ;
And when he knew, he cried : ' O heroes, land,
For here shall all things be at your command ;
And here shall you have good rest from the sea.'
Therewith he sent one to go speedily   30
And tell the king these folks were landed there.
    Then passed the heroes forth upon the fair
Well builded quays ; and all the merchant folk
Beholding them, from golden dreams awoke,
And of the sword and clattering shield grew fain,
And glory for awhile they counted gain.
    But Jason and his fair folk passing these,
Came to a square shaded about by trees,
Where they beheld the crowned king glorious stand
To wait them, who took Jason by the hand   40
And led him through the rows of linden trees
Unto his house, the crown of palaces ;
And there he honoured them with royal feast
In his fair hall, hung round with man and beast
Wrought in fair Indian cloths, and on soft beds,
When they grew weary, did they lay their heads.
    But he, when on the morn they would away,
Full many a rich gift in their keel did lay,
And while their oars were whitening the green sea,
Within his temple he prayed reverently   50
For their good hap to Jove the Saving God.
Hapless himself that these had ever trod
His quiet land ; for, sailing all the day,
Becalmed at last at fall of night they lay ;
And lying there, an hour before midnight
A black cloud rose that swallowed up the light

Of moon and stars, and therefrom leapt a wind
That drave the Argo, tottering and blind,
Back on her course, and, as it died, at last
They heard the breakers roaring, and so cast   60
Their anchors out within some shallow bay,
They knew not where, to wait until the day.

There, as they waited, they saw beacons flame
Along the coast, and in a while there came
A rout of armed men thereto, as might seem
By shouts and clash of arms that now 'gan gleam
Beneath the light of torches that they bore.
Then could the heroes see that they from shore
Were distant scarce a bowshot, and the tide
Had ebbed so quick the sands were well-nigh dried   70
Betwixt them and the foremost of the foe,
Who, ere they could push off, began to go
Across the wet beach, and with many a cry
The biting arrows from their bows let fly.
Nor were the heroes slow to make return,
Aiming where'er they saw the torches burn.

So passed the night with little death of men ;
But when the sky at last grew grey, and when
Dimly the Argo's crew could see their foes,
Then overboard they leapt, that they might close   80
With these scarce seen far-fighting enemies,
And so met man to man, crying their cries,
In deadly shock, but Jason, for his part,
Rushing before the rest, put by a dart
A tall man threw, and closing with him, drave
His spear through shield and breast-plate weak to save
His heart from such an arm ; then straight he fell
Dead on the sands, and with a wailing yell
The others, when they saw it, fled away,
And gat them swiftly to the forest grey   90
The yellow sands fringed like a garment's hem,
Nor gave the seafarers much chase to them,
But on the hard sand all together drew.

And now, day growing, they the country knew
And found it Cyzicum, and Jason said :
' Fellows, what have we done ? by likely-head

An evil deed, and luckless, but come now,
Draw off the helmet from this dead man's brow
And name him.' So when they had done this thing
They saw the face of Cyzicus the king. 100

But Jason, when he saw him, wept, and said :
' Ill hast thou fared, O friend, that I was led
To take thy gifts and slay thee ; in such guise,
Blind and unwitting, do fools die and wise,
And I myself may hap to come to die
By that I trusted, and like thee to lie
Dead ere my time, a wonder to the world.
But, O poor king, thy corpse shall not be hurled
Hither and thither by the heedless wave,
But in an urn thine ashes will I save, 110
And build a temple when I come to Greece
A rich man, with the fair-curled golden fleece,
And set them there, and call it by thy name,
That thou mayst yet win an undying fame.'
Then hasted all the men, and in a while,
'Twixt sea and woodland, raised a mighty pile,
And there they burned him, but for spices sweet
Could cast thereon but wrack from 'neath their feet,
And wild wood flowers and resin from the pine ;
And when the pile grew low, with odorous wine 120
They quenched the ashes, and the king's they set
Within a golden vessel, that with fret
Of twining boughs and gem-made flowers was wrought
That they from Pelias' treasure-house had brought.
Then, since the sun his high meridian
Had left, they pushed into the waters wan,
And so, with hoisted sail and stroke of oar,
Drew off from that unlucky fateful shore.

Now eastward with a fair wind as they went,
And towards the opening of the ill sea bent 130
Their daring course, Tiphys arose and said :
' Heroes, it seems to me that hardihead
Helps mortal men but little, if thereto
They join not wisdom ; now needs must we go

Into the evil sea through blue rocks twain,
No keel hath ever passed, although in vain
Some rash men trying it of old, have been
Pounded therein, as poisonous herbs and green
Are pounded by some witch-wife on the shore
Of Pontus,—for these two rocks evermore   140
Each against each are driven, and leave not
Across the whole strait such a little spot
Safe from the grinding of their mighty blows,
As that through which a well-aimed arrow goes
When archers for a match shoot at the ring.
  ' Now, heroes, do I mind me of a king
That dwelleth at a sea-side town of Thrace
That men call Salmydessa, from this place
A short day's sail, who hidden things can tell
Beyond all men ; wherefore, I think it well   150
That we for counsel should now turn thereto,
Nor headlong to our own destruction go.'
  Then all men said that these his words were good,
And turning, towards the Thracian coast they stood,
Which yet they reached not till the moonlit night
Was come, and from the shore the wind blew light ;
Then they lay to until the dawn, and then
Creeping along, found an abode of men
That Tiphys knew to be the place they sought.
Thereat they shouted, and right quickly brought   160
Fair Argo to the landing-place, and threw
Grapnels ashore, and landing forthwith drew
Unto the town, seeking Phineus the king.
But those they met and asked about this thing
Grew pale at naming him, and few words said ;
Natheless, they being unto the palace led,
And their names told, soon were they bidden in
To where the king sat, a man blind and thin,
And haggard beyond measure, who straightway
Called out aloud : ' Now blessed be the way   170
That led thee to me, happiest of all
Who from the poop see the prow rise and fall
And the sail bellying, and the glittering oars ;
And blessed be the day whereon our shores

First felt thy footsteps, since across the sea
My hope and my revenge thou bring'st with thee.'
Then Jason said : ' Hail, Phineus, that men call
Wisest of men, and may all good befall
To thee and thine, and happy mayst thou live ;
Yet do we rather pray thee gifts to give,   18o
Than bring thee any gifts, for, soothly, we
Sail, desperate men and poor, across the sea.'
Then answered Phineus : ' Guest, I know indeed
What gift it is that on this day ye need,
Which I will not withhold ; and yet, I pray,
That ye will eat and drink with me to-day,
Then shall ye see how wise a man am I,
And how well-skilled to scape from misery.'
Therewith he groaned, and bade his folk to bring
Such feast as 'longed unto a mighty king,   190
And spread the board therewith ; who straight obeyed.
Trembling and pale, and on the tables laid
A royal feast most glorious in show.
Then said the king : ' I give you now to know
That the Gods love me not, O guests ; therefore,
Lest your expected feast be troubled sore,
Eat by yourselves alone, while I sit here
Looking for that which scarcely brings me fear
This day, since I so long have suffered it.'
So, wondering at his words, they all did sit   200
At that rich board, and ate and drank their fill ;
But yet with little mirth indeed, for still
Within their wondering ears the king's words rang,
And his blind eyes, made restless by some pang,
They still felt on them, though no word he said.
At last he called out : ' Though ye be full fed,
Sit still at table and behold me eat,
Then shall ye witness with what royal meat
The Gods are pleased to feed me, since I know
As much as they do both of things below   210
And things above.'
　　　　　　　Then, hearkening to this word,
The most of them grew doubtful and afeard

197 Eat] Feast   203 wondering ears] ears   rang] harshly rang,

Of what should come ; but now unto the board
The king was led, and nigh his hand his sword,
Two-edged and ivory-hilted, did they lay,
And set the richest dish of all that day
Before him, and a wine-crowned golden cup,
And a pale, trembling servant lifted up
The cover from the dish ; then did they hear
A wondrous rattling sound that drew anear,   220
Increasing quickly : then the gilded hall
Grew dark at noon, as though the night did fall,
And open were all doors and windows burst,
And such dim light gleamed out as lights the cursed,
Unto the torments behind Minos' throne :
Dim, green, and doubtful through the hall it shone,
Lighting up shapes no man had seen, before
They fell, awhile ago, upon that shore.

For now, indeed, the trembling Minyæ
Beheld the daughters of the earth and sea,   230
The dreadful snatchers, who like women were
Down to the breast, with scanty coarse black hair
About their heads, and dim eyes ringed with red,
And bestial mouths set round with lips of lead,
But from their gnarled necks there began to spring
Half hair, half feathers, and a sweeping wing
Grew out instead of arm on either side,
And thick plumes underneath the breast did hide
The place where joined the fearful natures twain.
Grey feathered were they else, with many a stain   240
Of blood thereon, and on birds' claws they went.
These through the hall unheard-of shrieking sent,
And rushed at Phineus, just as to his mouth
He raised the golden cup to quench his drouth,
And scattered the red wine, and buffeted
The wretched king, and one, perched on his head,
Laughed as the furies laugh, when kings come down
To lead new lives within the fiery town,
And said : ' O Phineus, thou art lucky now
The hidden things of heaven and hell to know ;   250
Eat, happy man, and drink.' Then did she draw

From off the dish a goblet with her claw,
And held it nigh his mouth, the while he strove
To free his arm, that one hovering above,
Within her filthy vulture-claws clutched tight,
And cried out at him : ' Truly, in dark night .
Thou seest, Phineus, as the leopard doth.'
   Then cried the .third : ' Fool, who would fain have
     both
Delight and knowledge, therefore, with blind eyes
Clothe thee in purple, wrought with braveries,   260
And set the pink-veined marble 'neath thy throne ;
Then on its golden cushions sit alone,
Hearkening thy chain-galled slaves without singing
For joy, that they behold so many a thing.'
   Then shrieked the first one in a dreadful voice :—
' And I, O Phineus, bid thee to rejoice,
That 'midst thy knowledge still thou know'st not this—
Whose flesh the lips, wherewith thy lips I kiss,
This morn have fed on.' Then she laughed again,
And fawning on him, with her sisters twain   270
Spread her wide wings, and hid him from the sight,
And mixed his groans with screams of shrill delight.
   Now trembling sat the seafarers, nor dared
To use the weapons from their sheaths half-bared,
Fearing the Gods, who there, before their eyes,
Had shown them with what shame and miseries
They visit impious men : yet from the board
There started two, with shield and ready sword,
The Northwind's offspring, since, upon that day,
Their father wrought within them in such way,   280
They had no fear : but now, when Phineus knew,
By his divine art, that the godlike two
Were armed to help him, then from 'twixt the wings
He cried aloud : O, heroes, more than kings,
Strike, and fear not, but set me free to-day,
That ye within your brazen chests may lay
The best of all my treasure-house doth hold,
Fair linen, scarlet cloth, and well-wrought gold.'
   Then shrieked the snatchers, knowing certainly

252 goblet a misprint ; read gobbet as in first edition.

C c 2

That now the time had come when they must fly   290
From pleasant Salmydessa, casting off
The joys they had in shameful mock and scoff.
So gat they from the blind king, leaving him
Pale and forewearied in his every limb ;
And, flying through the roof, they set them down
Above the hall-doors, 'mid the timbers brown,
Chattering with fury. Then the fair dyed wings
Opened upon the shoulders of the kings,
And on their heels, and shouting, they uprose,
And poised themselves in air to meet their foes.   300
   Then here and there those loathly things did fly
Before the brazen shields, and swords raised high,
But as they flew unlucky words they cried.

   The first said : ' Hail, O folk who wander wide,
Seeking a foolish thing across the sea,
Not heeding in what case your houses be,
Where now perchance the rovers cast the brand
Up to the roof, and leading by the hand
The fair-limbed women with their fettered feet
Pass down the sands, their hollow ship to meet.'   310
   ' Fair hap to him who weds the sorceress,'
The second cried, ' and may the just Gods bless
The slayer of his kindred and his name.'
   ' Luck to the toilsome seeker after fame,'
The third one from the open hall-door cried,
' Fare ye well, Jason, still unsatisfied,
Still seeking for a better thing than best,
A fairer thing than fairest, without rest ;
Good speed, O traitor, who shall think to wed
Soft limbs and white, and find thy royal bed   320
Dripping with blood, and burning up with fire ;
Good hap to him who henceforth ne'er shall tire
In seeking good that ever flies his hand
Till he lies buried in an alien land ! '

   So screamed the monstrous fowl, but now the twain
Sprung from the north-wind's loins to be their bane,
Drew nigh unto them ; then, with huddled wings,

Forth from the hall they gat, but evil things
In flying they gave forth with weakened voice,
Saying unto them : ' O ye men, rejoice, 330
Whose bodies worms shall feed on soon or late,
Blind slaves, and foolish of unsparing fate,
Seeking for that which ye can never get,
Whilst life and death alike ye do forget
In needless strife, until on some sure day,
Death takes your scarcely tasted life away.'
    Quivering their voices ceased as on they flew
Before the swift wings of the godlike two
Far over land and sea, until they were
Anigh the isles called Strophades, and there, 340
With tired wings, all voiceless did they light,
Trembling to see anigh the armour bright
The wind-born brothers bore, but as these drew
Their gleaming swords and towards the monsters flew,
From out the deep rose up a black-haired man,
Who, standing on the white-topped waves that ran
On towards the shore, cried : ' Heroes, turn again,
For on this islet shall ye land in vain,
But without sorrow leave the chase of these
Who henceforth 'mid the rocky Strophades 350
Shall dwell for ever, servants unto me,
Working my will, therefore rejoice that ye
Win gifts and honour for your deed to-day.'
    Then, even as he spoke, they saw but grey,
White headed waves rolling where he had stood,
Whereat they sheathed their swords, and through their
        blood
A tremor ran, for now they knew that he
Was Neptune, shaker of the earth and sea ;
Therefore they turned them back unto the hall
Where yet the others were, and ere nightfall 360
Came back to Salmydessa and the king,
And lighting down they told him of the thing.
    Who, hearing them, straight lifted up his voice,
And 'midst the shouts cried : ' Heroes, now rejoice
With me who am delivered on this day

344 towards] to

From that which took all hope and joy away ;
Therefore to feast again, until the sun
Another glad day for us has begun,
And then, indeed, if ye must try the sea,
With gifts and counsel shall ye go from me ;   370
Such as the Gods have given me to give,
And happy lives and glorious may ye live.'
 Then did they fall to banqueting again,
Forgetting all forebodings and all pain ;
And when that they had ate and drank enow,
With songs and music, and a goodly show,
Their hearts were gladdened, for before their eyes
Played youths and damsels with strange fantasies,
Clad as in Saturn's time folk used to be,
With green leaves gathered from the summer tree,   380
When all the year was summer everywhere,
And every man and woman blest and fair.
 So, set 'twixt pleasure and some soft regret,
All cares of mortal men did they forget,
Except the vague desire not to die,
The hopeless wish to flee from certainty,
That sights and sounds we love will bring on us
In this sweet fleeting world and piteous.

BOOK VI

The passage of the Symplegades—The heroes come to Æa.

But on the morrow did they get them gone,
Gifted with gold and many a precious stone,
And many a bale of scarlet cloth and spice,
And arms well wrought, and goodly robes of price.
But chiefly to the wind-born brothers strong
Did gifts past telling on that morn belong.
 Now as they stood upon the windy quay,
Ready their hands upon the ropes to lay,
Phineus, who 'midst his mighty lords was there,
Set high above them in a royal chair,   10
Said : ' Many a gift ye have of me to-day
Within your treasuries at home to lay,

If so it be that through hard things and pain
Ye come to the horse-nurturing land again ;
Natheless, one more gift shall ye have of me,
For lacking that, beneath the greedy sea,
The mighty tomb of mariners and kings,
Doubt not to lay down these desired things,
Nor think to come to Thessaly at all.'
And therewith turning, he began to call   20
Unto his folk to bring what they had there.
Then one brought forward a cage great and fair,
Wherein they saw a grey, pink-footed dove.
    Then said the king : ' The very Gods above
Can scantly help you more than now I do,
For listen ; as upon this day ye go
Unto the narrow ending of the sea,
Anigh the clashing rocks lie patiently,
And let the keenest-eyed among you stand
Upon the prow, and let loose from his hand   30
This dove, who from my mouth to-day has heard
So many a mystic and compelling word,
He cannot choose, being loosed, but fly down straight
Unto the opening of that dreadful gate ;
So let the keen-eyed watch, and if so be
He comes out safe into the evil sea,
Then bend unto the oars, nor fear at all
Of aught that from the clashers may befall ;
But if he perish, then turn back again,
And know the Gods have made your passage vain.   40
Thereafter, if ye will, come back to me,
And if ye find nought in my treasury
That ye desire, yet ye at least shall have
A king and a king's son to be your slave ;
And all things here still may ye bind and loose,
And from our women freely may ye choose,
Nor spare the fairest or most chaste to kiss,
And in fair houses shall ye live in bliss.'
    ' O king,' said Jason, ' know that on this day
I will not be forsworn, but by some way   50
Will reach the oak-grove and the Golden Fleece,
Or, failing, die at least far off from Greece,

Not unremembered ; yet great thanks we give
For this thy gift and counsel, and will strive
To come to Colchis through the unknown land
And whatso perils wait us, if Jove's hand
Be heavy on us, and the great blue gates
Are shut against us by the unmoved fates.
Farewell, O king, and henceforth, free from ill,
Live happy as thou mayest, and honoured still.'   60
    Then turned he, shouting, to the Minyæ,
Who o'er the gangways rushed tumultuously,
And from the land great Argo straightway thrust,
And gat them to their work, hot with the lust
Of fame and noble deeds, and happy prize.
But the bird Lynceus took, unto whose eyes
The night was as the day, and fire as air.

    Then back into his marble palace fair
The king turned, thinking well upon the way
Of what had happed since morn of yesterday.   70
    Now from the port passed Argo, and the wind
Being fair for sailing, quickly left behind
Fair Salmydessa, the kind, gainful place ;
And so, with sail and oar, in no long space
They reached the narrow ending of the sea,
Where the wind shifted, blowing gustily
From side to side, so that their flapping sail
But little in the turmoil could avail ;
And now at last did they begin to hear
The pounding of the rocks ; but nothing clear   80
They saw them ; for the steaming clouds of spray,
Cast by the meeting hammers every way,
Quite hid the polished bases from their sight ;
Unless perchance the eyes of Lynceus might
Just now and then behold the deep blue shine
Betwixt the scattering of the silver brine ;
But sometimes 'twixt the clouds the sun would pass
And show the high rocks glittering like glass,
Quivering, as far beneath the churned-up waves
Were ground together the strong arched caves,   90
Wherein none dwelt, no, not the giant's brood,

Who fed the green sea with his lustful blood,
Nor were sea-devils even nurtured there,
Nor dared the sea-worm use them for its lair.
  And now the Minyæ, as they drew anear,
Had been at point to turn about for fear,
Each man beholding his pale fellow's face,
Whose speech was silenced in that dreadful place
By the increasing clamour of the sea
And adamantine rocks ; then verily   100
Was Juno good at need, who set strange fire
In Jason's heart, and measureless desire
To be the first of men, and made his voice
Clear as that herald's, whose sweet words rejoice
The Gods within the flowery fields of Heaven,
And gave his well-knit arm the strength of seven.
So then, above the crash and thundering,
The Minyæ heard his shrill, calm voice, crying :—
' Shall this be, then, an ending to our quest ?
And shall we find the worst, who sought the best ?   110
Far better had ye sat beside your wives,
And 'mid the wine-cups lingered out your lives,
Dreaming of noble deeds, though trying none,
Than as vain boasters, with your deed undone,
Come back to Greece, that men may sing of you.
Are ye all shameless ?—are there not a few
Who have slain fear, knowing the unmoved fates
Have meted out already what awaits
The coward and the brave ? Ho ! Lynceus ! stand
Upon the prow, and let slip from your hand   120
The wise king's bird ; and all ye note, the wind
Is steady now, and blowing from behind
Drives us on toward the clashers, and I hold
The helm myself ; therefore, lest we be rolled
Broadside against these horrors, take the oar,
And hang here, half a furlong from the shore,
Nor die of fear, until at least we know
If through these gates the Gods will let us go :
And if so be they will not, yet will we
Not empty-handed come to Thessaly,   130

101 need] heed

But strike for Æa through this unknown land,
Whose arms reach out to us on either hand.'

Then they for shame began to cast off fear,
And, handling well the oars, kept Argo near
The changing, little-lighted, spray-washed space
Whereunto Lynceus set his eager face,
And loosed the dove, who down the west wind flew ;
Then all the others lost her, dashing through
The clouds of spray, but Lynceus noted how
She reached the open space, just as a blow   140
Had spent itself, and still the hollow sound
Of the last clash was booming all around ;
And eagerly he noted how the dove
Stopped 'mazed, and hovered for a while above
The troubled sea, then stooping, darted through,
As the blue gleaming rocks together drew ;
Then scarce he breathed, until a joyous shout
He gave, as he beheld her passing out
Unscathed, above the surface of the sea,
While back again the rocks drew sluggishly.   150
   Then back their poised oars whirled, and straight they
       drave
Unto the opening of the spray-arched cave ;
But Jason's eyes alone, of all the crew,
Beheld the sunny sea and cloudless blue,
Still narrowing, but bright from rock to rock.
   Now as they neared, came the next thundering shock,
That deafened all, and with an icy cloud
Hid man from man ; but Jason, shouting loud,
Still clutched the tiller ; and the oars, grasped tight
By mighty hands, drave on the ship forthright   160
Unto the rocks, until, with blinded eyes,
They blinked one moment at those mysteries
Unseen before, the next they felt the sun
Full on their backs, and knew their deed was done.

Then on their oars they lay, and Jason turned,
And o'er the rocks beheld how Iris burned
In fair and harmless many-coloured flame,

And he beheld the way by which they came
Wide open, changeless, of its spray-clouds cleared ;
And though in his bewildered ears he heard   170
The tumult yet, that all was stilled he knew,
While in and out the unused sea-fowl flew
Betwixt them, and the now subsiding sea
Lapped round about their dark feet quietly.
   So, turning to the Minyæ, he cried :—
' See ye, O fellows, the gates opened wide,
And chained fast by the Gods, nor think to miss
The very end we seek, or well-earned bliss
When once again we feel our country's earth,
And 'twixt the tears of elders, and the mirth   180
Of young men grown to manhood since we left,
And longing eyes of girls, the fleece, once reft
From a king's son of Greece, we hang again
In Neptune's temple, nigh the murmuring main.'
   Then all men, with their eyes now cleared of brine,
Beheld the many-coloured rainbow shine
Over the rocks, and saw it fade away,
And saw the opening cleared of sea and spray,
And saw the green sea lap about the feet
Of those blue hills, that never more should meet,   190
And saw the wondering sea-fowl fly about
Their much-changed tops ; then, with a mighty shout,
They rose rejoicing, and poured many a cup
Of red wine to the Gods, and hoisting up
The weather-beaten sail, with mirth and song,
Having good wind at will, they sped along.

   Three days with good hap and fair wind they went,
That ever at their backs Queen Juno sent,
But on the fourth day, about noon, they drew
Unto a new-built city no man knew ;   200
No, not the pilot ; so they thought it good
To arm themselves, and thus in doubtful mood
Brought Argo to the port, and being come nigh,
A clear-voiced herald from the land did cry :
' Whoso ye be, if that ye come in peace,

King Lycus bids you hail, but if from Greece
Ye come, and are the folk of whom we hear
Who make for Colchis, free from any fear
Then doubly welcome are ye, here take land,
For everything shall be at your command.'   210
  So without fear they landed at that word,
And told him who they were, which when he heard,
Through the fair streets he brought them to the king,
Who feasted them that night with everything
That man could wish ; but when on the next day
They gathered at the port to go away,
The wind was foul and boisterous, so perforce
There must they bide, lest they should come to worse.
  And there for fourteen days did they abide,
And for their pastime oft would wander wide   220
About the woods, for slaying of the beasts
Whereby to furnish forth the royal feasts ;
But on a day, a closely-hunted boar,
Turning to bay, smote Idmon very sore
So that he died ; poor wretch, who could foresee
Full many an unknown thing that was to be,
And yet not this, whose corpse they burnt with fire
Upon a purple-covered spice-strewn pyre,
And set his ashes in a marble tomb.
Neither could Tiphys there escape his doom,   230
Who, after suffering many a bitter storm,
Died bitten of a hidden crawling worm,
As through the woods he wandered all alone.
Now he being burned, and laid beneath a stone,
The wind grew fair for sailing, and the rest
Bade farewell to the king, and on their quest
Once more were busied, and began to plough
The unsteady plain ; for whom Erginus now,
Great Neptune's son, the brass-bound tiller held.

  Now leaving that fair land, nought they beheld   240
For seven days but sea and changeful sky,
But on the eighth, keen could Lynceus espy
A land far off, and nigher as they drew
          242 But on the eighth day could Lynceus espy

A low green shore, backed up by mountains blue,
Cleft here and there, all saw, 'twixt hope and fear,
For now it seemed to them they should be near
The wished-for goal of Æa, and the place
Where in the great sea Phasis ends his race.
  Then, creeping carefully along the beach,
The mouth of a green river did they reach, 250
Cleaving the sands, and on the yellow bar
The salt waves and the fresh waves were at war,
As Phryxus erst beheld them, but no man
Among them ere had sailed that water wan,
Now that wise Tiphys lay within his tomb.
  Natheless they, wrapt in that resistless doom
The fates had woven, turned from off the sea
Argo's fair head, and rowing mightily
Drave her across the bar, who with straight keel
The eddying stream against her bows did feel. 260
  So, with the wind behind them, and the oars
Still hard at work, they went betwixt the shores
Against the ebb, and now full oft espied
Trim homesteads here and there on either side,
And fair kine grazing, and much woolly sheep,
And skin-clad shepherds, roused from mid-day sleep,
Gazing upon them with scared wondering eyes.
So now they deemed they might be near their prize ;
And at the least knew that some town was nigh,
And thought to hear new tidings presently, 270
Which happed indeed, for on the turn of tide,
At ending of a long reach, they espied
A city wondrous fair, which seemed indeed
To bar the river's course ; but, taking heed
And drawing nigher, soon found out the case,
That on an island builded was the place
The more part of it ; but four bridges fair
Set thick with goodly houses everywhere,
Crossed two and two on each side to the land,
Whereon was built, with walls on either hand, 280
A towered outwork, lest that war should fall
Upon the land, and midmost of each wall

249 Then] So

A noble gate ; moreover did they note
About the wharves full many a ship and boat.
And they beheld the sunlight glistering
On arms of men and many a warlike thing,
As nigher to the city they were borne,
And heard at last some huge deep booming horn
Sound from a tower o'er the watery way,
Whose last loud note was taken up straightway   290
By other watchers further and more near.
  Now when they did therewith loud shouting hear,
Then Jason bade them arm for what might come,
' For now,' quoth he, ' I deem we reach the home
Of that great marvel we are sworn to seek,
Nor do I think to find these folk so weak
That they with few words and a gift or two
Will give us that for which they did forego
Fair fame, the love of Gods, and praise of men ;
Be strong and play the man, I bid you then,   300
For certes in none other wise shall ye
Come back again to grassy Thessaly.'
  Then loud they shouted, clean forgetting fear,
And strong Erginus Argo straight did steer
On to the port ; but through the crowded waist
Ran Jason to the high prow, making haste
To be the first to look upon that throng.
Shieldless he was, although his fingers strong
About a sharpened brass-bound spear did meet,
And as the ashen oars swept on, his feet   310
Moved lightly to their cadence under him ;
So stood he like a God in face and limb.

  Now drawing quickly nigh the landing-place,
Little by little did they slack their pace,
Till half a bowshot from the shore they lay,
Then Jason shouted : ' What do ye to-day
All armed, O warriors ? and what town is this
That here by seeming ye have little bliss
Of quiet life, but, smothered up in steel,
Ye needs must meet each harmless merchant keel   320

That nears your haven, though perchance it bring
Good news, and many a much-desired thing
That ye may get good cheap ? and such are we,
But wayfarers upon the troublous sea,
Careful of that stored up within our hold,
Phœnician scarlet, spice, and Indian gold,
Deep dying-earths, and woad and cinnabar,
Wrought arms and vessels, and all things that are
Desired much by dwellers in all lands ;
Nor doubt us friends, although indeed our hands   330
Lack not for weapons, for the unfenced head,
Where we have been, soon rests among the dead.'
   So spake he with a smiling face, nor lied ;
For he, indeed, was purposed to have tried
To win the fleece neither by war or stealth ;
But by an open hand and heaps of wealth,
If so it might be, bear it back again,
Nor with a handful fight a host in vain.
   But being now silent, at the last he saw
A stir among those folk, who 'gan to draw   340
Apart to right and left, leaving a man
Alone amidst them, unarmed, with a wan
And withered face, and black beard mixed with grey
That swept his girdle, who these words did say :—
   ' O seafarers, I give you now to know
That on this town oft falleth many a foe,
Therefore not lightly may folk take the land
With helm on head, and naked steel in hand ;
Now, since indeed ye folk are but a few,
We fear you not, yet fain would that we knew   350
Your names and countries, since within this town
Of Æa may a good man lay him down
And fear for nought, at least while I am king,
Æetes, born to heed full many a thing.'
   Now Jason, hearing this desired name
He thought to hear, grown hungrier yet for fame,
With eager heart, and fair face flushed for pride,
Said : ' King Æetes, if not over wide
My name is known, that yet may come to be,   .

   332 rests] lies   356 hungrier yet for] hungrier for

For I am Jason of the Minyæ,   360
And through great perils have I come from Greece.
And now, since this is Æa, and the fleece
Thou slayedst once a guest to get, hangs up
Within thine house, take many a golden cup,
And arms, and dyestuffs, cloth, and spice, and gold,
Yea, all the goods that lie within our hold ;
Which are not mean, for neither have we come
Leaving all things of price shut up at home,
Nor have we seen the faces of great kings
And left them giftless ; therefore take these things
And be our friend ; or, few folk as we are,   371
The Gods and we may bring thee bitter care.'
    Then spake Æetes : ' Not for any word,
Or for the glitter of thy bloodless sword,
O youngling, will I give the fleece to thee,
Nor yet for gifts,—for what are such to me ?
Behold, if all thy folk joined hand to hand
They should not, striving, be enough to stand
And girdle round my bursting treasure-house ;
Yet, since of this thing thou art amorous,   380
And I love men, and hold the Gods in fear,
If thou and thine will land, then mayst thou hear
What great things thou must do to win the fleece ;
Then, if thou wilt not dare it, go in peace.
But come now, thou shalt hear it amidst wine
And lovely things, and songs well-nigh divine,
And all the feasts that thou hast shared erewhile
With other kings, to mine shall be but vile.
Lest thou shouldst name me, coming to thy land,
A poor guest-fearing man, of niggard hand.'   390
    So spake he outwardly, but inly thought,
' Within two days this lading shall be brought
To lie amongst my treasures with the best,
While 'neath the earth these robbers lie at rest.'
    But Jason said : ' King, if these things be such
As man may do, I shall not fear them much,
And at thy board will I feast merrily
To-night, if on the morrow I must die ;
And yet, beware of treason, since for nought

Such lives as ours by none are lightly bought.   400
   ' Draw on, O heroes, to the shore, if ye
Are willing still this great king's house to see.'
   Thereat was Argo brought up to the shore,
And straight all landed from her, less and more,
And the king spake to Jason honied words,
And idle were all spears, and sheathed all swords,
As toward the palace they were gently brought.
But Jason, smiling outwardly, yet thought
Within his heart : ' All this is fair enow,
Yet do I think it but an empty show ;   410
Natheless, until the end comes, will not I,
Like a bad player, spoil the bravery
By breaking out before they call my turn,
And then of me some mastery they may learn.'

   Amidst these thoughts, between the fair streets led,
He noted well the size and goodly-head
Of all the houses, and the folk well clad,
And armed as though good store of wealth they had,
Peering upon them with a wondering gaze.
At last a temple, built in ancient days   420
Ere Æa was a town, they came unto ;
Huge was it, but not fair unto the view
Of one beholding from without, but round
The ancient place they saw a spot of ground
Where laurels grew each side the temple door,
And two great images set up before
The brazen doors, whereof the one was She,
Who draws this way and that the fitful sea ;
The other the great God, the Life of man,   429
Who makes the brown earth green, the green earth wan,
From spring to autumn, through quick following days,
The lovely archer with his crown of rays.
   Now over against this temple, towering high
Above all houses, rose majestically
Æetes' marble house ; silent it stood,
Brushed round by doves, though many a stream of
   blood
Had trickled o'er its stones since it was built,

But now, unconscious of all woe and guilt,
It drank the sunlight that fair afternoon.
  Then spake Æetes : ' Stranger, thou shalt soon   440
Hear all thou wouldst hear in my house of gold ;
Yet ere thou enterest the door, behold
That ancient temple of the Far Darter,
And know that thy desire hangeth there,
Against the gold wall of the inmost shrine,
Guarded by seven locks, whose keys are thine
When thou hast done what else thou hast to do,
And thou mayst well be bold to come thereto.'
  ' King,' said the prince, ' fear not, but do thy part,
Nor look to see me turn back faint of heart,   450
Though I may die as my forefathers died,
Who, living long, their loved souls failed to hide
From death at last, however wise they were.
But verily, O King, thy house is fair,
And here I think to see full many a thing
Men love ; so, whatso the next day may bring,
Right merrily shall pass these coming hours
Amidst fair things and wine-cups crowned with flowers.'
  ' Enter, O guests,' the king said, ' and doubt not
Ye shall see things to make the heart grow hot   460
With joy and longing.'
                        As he spoke, within
Blew up the horns, as when a king doth win
His throne at last, and from behind, the men
Who hedged the heroes in, shouted as when
He stands up on his throne, hidden no more.
Then those within threw open wide the door,
And straight the king took Jason by the hand,
And entered, and the Minyæ did stand
In such a hall as there has never been
Before or afterwards, since Ops was queen.   470
  The pillars, made the mighty roof to hold,
The one was silver and the next was gold,
All down the hall ; the roof, of some strange wood
Brought over sea, was dyed as red as blood,
Set thick with silver flowers, and delight
Of intertwining figures wrought aright.

With richest webs the marble walls were hung,
Picturing sweet stories by the poets sung
From ancient days, so that no wall seemed there,
But rather forests black and meadows fair,   480
And streets of well-built towns, with tumbling seas
About their marble wharves and palaces ;
And fearful crags and mountains ; and all trod
By changing feet of giant, nymph and God,
Spear-shaking warrior and slim-ankled maid.
    The floor, moreover, of the place was laid
With coloured stones, wrought like a flowery mead ;
And ready to the hand for every need,
Midmost the hall, two fair streams trickled down
O'er wondrous gem-like pebbles, green and brown,   490
Betwixt smooth banks of marble, and therein
Bright-coloured fish shone through the water thin.
    Now, 'midst these wonders were there tables spread,
Whither the wondering seafarers were led,
And there with meat and drink full delicate
Were feasted, and strange dainty things they ate,
Of unused savour, and drank godlike wine ;
While from the golden galleries, divine,
Heart-softening music breathed about the place ;
And 'twixt the pillars, at a gentle pace,   500
Passed lovely damsels, raising voices sweet
And shrill unto the music, while their feet
From thin dusk raiment now and then would gleam
Upon the polished edges of the stream.

    Long sat the Minyæ there, and for their parts
Few words they said, because, indeed, their hearts,
O'er-burdened with delight, still dreaded death ;
Nor did they think that they might long draw breath
In such an earthly Paradise as this,
But looked to find sharp ending to their bliss.   510

     484 By many a changing foot of nymph and God,

BOOK VII

Jason first sees Medea—The magic potion of Medea.

So long they sat, until at last the sun
Sank in the sea, and noisy day was done.
Then bade Æetes light the place, that they
Might turn grim-looking night into the day ;
Whereon, the scented torches being brought,
As men with shaded eyes the shadows sought,
Turning to Jason, spake the king these words :—
    ' Dost thou now wonder, guest, that with sharp swords
And mailèd breasts of men I fence myself,
Not as a pedlar guarding his poor pelf,   10
But as a God shutting the door of heaven.
Behold ! O Prince, for threescore years and seven
Have I dwelt here in bliss, nor dare I give
The fleece to thee, lest I should cease to live ;
Nor dare I quite this treasure to withhold,
Lest to the Gods I seem grown over-bold ;
For many a cunning man I have, to tell
Divine foreshowings of the oracle,
And thus they warn me. Therefore shalt thou hear
What well may fill a hero's heart with fear ;   20
But not from my old lips ; that thou mayst have,
Whether thy life thou here wilt spill or save,
At least one joy before thou comest to die :—
Ho ye, bid in my lady presently ! '
    But Jason, wondering what should come of this,
With heart well steeled to suffer woe or bliss,
Sat waiting, while within the music ceased,
But from without a strain rose and increased,
Till shrill and clear it drew anigh the hall,
But silent at the entry did it fall ;   30
And through the place there was no other sound
But falling of light footsteps on the ground,
For at the door a band of maids was seen,
Who went up towards the dais, a lovely queen
Being in their midst, who, coming nigh the place
Where the king sat, passed at a gentle pace

Alone before the others to the board,
And said : ' Æetes, father, and good lord,
What is it thou wouldst have of me to-night ? '
  ' O daughter,' said Æetes, ' tell aright   40
Unto this king's son here, who is my guest,
What things he must accomplish, ere his quest
Is finished, who has come this day to seek
The golden fell brought hither by the Greek,
The son of Athamas, the unlucky king,
That he may know at last for what a thing
He left the meadowy land and peaceful stead.'
  Then she to Jason turned her golden head,
And reaching out her lovely arm, took up
From off the board a rich fair-jewelled cup,   50
And said : ' O prince, these hard things must ye do :—
First, going to their stall, bring out the two
Great brazen bulls, the king my father feeds
On grass of Pontus and strange-nurtured seeds ;
Nor heed what they may do, but take the plough
That in their stall stands ever bright enow,
And on their gleaming necks cast thou the yoke,
And drive them as thou mayst, with cry and stroke,
Through the grey acre of the God of War.
  ' Then, when turned up the long straight furrows
    are,   60
Take thou the sack that holds the serpents' teeth
Our fathers slew upon the sunless heath ;
There sow those evil seeds, and bide thou there
Till they send forth a strange crop, nothing fair,
Which garner thou, if thou canst 'scape from death.
  ' But if thereafter still thou drawest breath,
Then shalt thou have the seven keys of the shrine
Wherein the beast's fair golden locks yet shine ;
But yet sing not the song of triumph then,
Or think thyself the luckiest of men ;   70
For just within the brazen temple-gates
The guardian of the fleece for ever waits,—
A fork-tongued dragon, charmed for evermore
To writhe and wallow on the precious floor,
Sleepless, upon whose skin no steel will bite.

' If then with such an one thou needs must fight,
Or knowest arts to tame him, do thy worst,
Nor, carrying off the prize, shalt thou be curst
By us or any God. But yet, think well
If these three things be not impossible   80
To any man ; and make a bloodless end
Of this thy quest, and as my father's friend
Well gifted, in few days return in peace,
Lacking for nought, forgetful of the fleece.'

Therewith she made an end ; but while she spoke
Came Love unseen, and cast his golden yoke
About them both, and sweeter her voice grew,
And softer ever, as betwixt them flew,
With fluttering wings, the new-born, strong desire ;
And when her eyes met his grey eyes, on fire   90
With that that burned her, then with sweet new shame
Her fair face reddened, and there went and came
Delicious tremors through her. But he said :—
' A bitter song thou singest, royal maid,
Unto a sweet tune ; yet doubt not that I
To-morrow this so certain death will try ;
And dying, may perchance not pass unwept,
And with sweet memories may my name be kept,
That men call Jason of the Minyæ.'
    Then said she, trembling : ' Take, then, this of me,
And drink in token that thy life is passed,   101
And that thy reckless hand the die has cast.'
    Therewith she reached the cup to him, but he
Stretched out his hand, and took it joyfully,
As with the cup he touched her dainty hand,
Nor was she loth, awhile with him to stand,
Forgetting all else in that honied pain.
    At last she turned, and with head raised again
He drank, and swore for nought to leave that quest
Till he had reached the worst end or the best ;   110
And down the hall the clustering Minyæ
Shouted for joy his godlike face to see.
But she, departing, made no further sign
Of her desires, but, while with song and wine

They feasted till the fevered night was late,
Within her bower she sat, made blind by fate.

But, when all hushed and still the palace grew,
She put her gold robes off, and on her drew
A dusky gown, and with a wallet small
And cutting wood-knife girt herself withal,   120
And from her dainty chamber softly passed
Through stairs and corridors, until at last
She came down to a gilded watergate,
Which with a golden key she opened straight,
And swiftly stept into a little boat,
And, pushing off from shore, began to float
Adown the stream, and with her tender hands
And half-bared arms, the wonder of all lands,
Rowed strongly through the starlit gusty night
As though she knew the watery way aright.   130
So, from the city being gone apace,
Turning the boat's head, did she near a space
Where, by the water's edge, a thick yew wood
Made a black blot on the dim gleaming flood :
But when she reached it, dropping either oar
Upon the grassy bank, she leapt ashore
And to a yew-bough made the boat's head fast.
Then here and there quick glances did she cast
And listened, lest some wanderer should be nigh.
Then by the river's side she tremblingly   140
Undid the bands that bound her yellow hair
And let it float about her, and made bare
Her shoulder and right arm, and, kneeling down,
Drew off her shoes, and girded up her gown,
And in the river washed her silver feet
And trembling hands, and then turned round to meet
The yew-wood's darkness, gross and palpable,
As though she made for some place known full well.

Beneath her feet the way was rough enow,
And often would she meet some trunk or bough,   150
And draw back shrinking, then press on again
With eager steps, not heeding fear or pain ;

116 bower she sat] chamber sat

At last an open space she came unto,
Where the faint glimmering starlight, shining through,
Showed in the midst a circle of smooth grass,
Through which, from dark to dark, a stream did pass,
And all around was darkness like a wall.
  So, kneeling there, she let the wallet fall,
And from it drew a bundle of strange wood
Wound all about with strings as red as blood ;   160
Then breaking these, into a little pyre
The twigs she built, and swiftly kindling fire,
Set it alight, and with her head bent low
Sat patiently, and watched the red flames grow
Till it burned bright and lit the dreary place ;
Then, leaving it, she went a little space
Into the shadow of the circling trees
With wood-knife drawn, and whiles upon her knees
She dropt, and sweeping the sharp knife around,
Took up some scarce-seen thing from off the ground 170
And thrust it in her bosom, and at last
Into the darkness of the trees she passed.
  Meanwhile, the new fire burned with clear red flame,
Not wasting aught ; but when again she came
Into its light, within her caught-up gown
Much herbs she had, and on her head a crown
Of dank night-flowering grasses, known to few.
  But, casting down the mystic herbs, she drew
From out her wallet a bowl polished bright,
Brazen, and wrought with figures black and white, 180
Which from the stream she filled with water thin,
And, kneeling by the fire, cast therein
Shreddings of many herbs, and setting it
Amidst the flames, she watched them curl and flit
About the edges of the blackening brass.
But when strange fumes began therefrom to pass,
And clouds of thick white smoke about her flew,
And colourless and sullen the fire grew,
Unto her fragrant breast her hand she set,
And drew therefrom a bag of silken fret, 190
And into her right palm she gently shook

    173 the new fire] the fire   188 sullen] dull

Three grains of something small that had the look
Of millet seeds, then laid the bag once more
On that sweet hidden place it kissed before.
And, lifting up her right hand, murmured low :—

O Three-formed, Venerable, dost thou know
That I have left to-night my golden bed
On the sharp pavement of thy wood to shed
Blood from my naked feet, and from mine eyes
Intolerable tears ; to pour forth sighs   200
In the thick darkness, as with footsteps weak
And trembling knees I prowl about to seek
That which I need forsooth, but fear to find ?
What wouldest thou, my Lady ? art thou blind,
Or sleepest thou, or dost thou, dread one, see
About me somewhat that misliketh thee ?
What crown but thine is on mine unbound hair,
What jewel on my arms, or have I care
Against the flinty windings of thy wood
To guard my feet ? or have I thought it good   210
To come before thee with unwashen hands ?
   ' And this my raiment : Goddess, from three lands
The fleeces it was woven with were brought
Where deeds of thine in ancient days were wrought,
Delos, and Argos, and the Carian mead ;
Nor was it made, O Goddess, with small heed ;
By unshod maidens was the yarn well spun,
And at the moonrise the close web begun,
And finished at the dawning of the light.
   ' Nought hides me from the unseen eyes of night   220
But this alone, what dost thou then to me,
That at my need my flame sinks wretchedly,
And all is vain I do ? Ah, is it so
That to some other helper I must go
Better at need ; wilt thou then take my part
Once more, and pity my divided heart ?
For never was I vowed to thee alone,
Nor didst thou bid me take the tight-drawn zone,
And follow through the twilight of the trees
The glancing limbs of trim-shod huntresses.   230

Therefore, look down upon me, and see now
These grains of what thou knowest, I will throw
Upon the flame, and then, if at my need
Thou still wilt help me, help ; but if indeed
I am forsaken of thee utterly,
The naked knees of Venus will I try ;
And I may hap ere long to please her well
And one more story they may have to tell
Who in the flowery isle her praises sing.'

So speaking, on the dulled fire did she fling   240
The unknown grains ; but when the Three-formed heard
From out her trembling lips that impious word,
She granted all her asking, though she knew
What evil road Medea hurried to
She fain had barred against her on that night.
So, now again the fire flamed up bright,
The smoke grew thin, and in the brazen bowl,
Boiling, the mingled herbs did twine and roll,
And with new light Medea's wearied eyes
Gleamed in the fireshine o'er those mysteries ;   250
And, taking a green twig from off the ground,
Therewith she stirred the mess, that cast around
A shower of hissing sparks and vapour white,
Sharp to the taste, and 'wildering to the sight ;
Which when she saw, the vessel off she drew,
As though the ending of her toil she knew,
And cooling for awhile she let it stand,
But at the last therein she laid her hand,
And when she drew it out she thrust the same
Amidst the fire, but neither coal or flame   260
The tender rosy flesh could harm a whit,
Nor was there mark or blemish left on it.
    Then did she pour whatso the bowl did hold
Into a fair gemmed phial wrought of gold
She drew out from the wallet, and straightway
Stopping the mouth, in its own place did lay
The well-wrought phial, girding to her side
The wallet that the precious thing did hide ;

        240 the dulled fire] the fire   261 flesh] hand

Then all the remnants of the herbs she cast
On to the fire, and straight therefrom there passed   270
A high white flame, and when that sunk, outright
The fire died into the voiceless night.
    But toward the river did she turn again,
Not heeding the rough ways or any pain,
But running swiftly came unto her boat,
And in the mid-stream soon was she afloat,
Drawn onward toward the town by flood of tide.

    Nor heeded she that by the river side
Still lay her golden shoes, a goodly prize
To some rough fisher in whose sleepy eyes   280
They first should shine, the while he drew his net
Against the yew wood of the Goddess set.

    But she, swept onward by the hurrying stream,
Down in the east beheld a doubtful gleam
That told of dawn ; so bent unto the oar
In terror lest her folk should wake before
Her will was wrought ; nor failed she now to hear
From neighbouring homesteads shrilly notes and clear
Of waking cocks, and twittering from the sedge
Of restless birds about the river's edge ;   290
And when she drew between the city walls,
She heard the hollow sound of rare footfalls
From men who needs must wake for that or this
While upon sleepers gathered dreams of bliss,
Or great distress at ending of the night,
And grey things coloured with the gathering light.
    At last she reached the gilded water-gate,
And though nigh breathless, scarce she dared to wait
To fasten up her shallop to the stone,
Which yet she dared not leave ; so this being done,   300
Swiftly by passages and stairs she ran,
Trembling and pale, though not yet seen by man,
Until to Jason's chamber door she came.

    And there awhile indeed she stayed, for shame
Rose up against her fear ; but mighty love

And the sea-haunting rose-crowned seed of Jove
O'ermastered both ; so trembling, on the pin
She laid her hand, but ere she entered in
She covered up again her shoulder sweet,
And dropped her dusky raiment o'er her feet ;   310
Then entering the dimly-lighted room,
Where with the lamp dawn struggled, through the gloom,
Seeking the prince she peered, who sleeping lay
Upon his gold bed, and abode the day
Smiling, still clad in arms, and round his sword
His fingers met ; then she, with a soft word,
Came nigh him, and from out his slackened hand
With slender rosy fingers drew the brand,
Then kneeling, laid her hand upon his breast,
And said : ' O Jason, wake up from thy rest,   320
Perchance from thy last rest, and speak to me.'
      Then fell his light sleep from him suddenly,
And on one arm he rose, and clenched his hand,
Raising it up, as though it held the brand,
And on this side and that began to stare.
      But bringing close to him her visage fair,
She whispered : ' Smite not, for thou hast no sword,
Speak not above thy breath, for one loud word
May slay both thee and me. Day grows apace ;
What day thou knowest ! Canst thou see my face ?
Last night thou didst behold it with such eyes,   331
That I, Medea, wise among the wise,
The safeguard of my father and his land,
Who have been used with steady eyes to stand
In awful groves alone with Hecate,
Henceforth must call myself the bond of thee,
The fool of love ; speak not, but kiss me, then,
Yea, kiss my lips, that not the best of men
Has touched ere thou. Alas, quick comes the day !
Draw back, but hearken what I have to say,   340
For every moment do I dread to hear
Thy wakened folk, or our folk drawing near ;
Therefore I speak as if with my last breath,
Shameless, beneath the shadowing wings of death,

        317 Came] Drew

That still may let us twain again to meet,
And snatch from bitter love the bitter sweet
That some folk gather while they wait to die.
  ' Alas, I loiter, and the day is nigh !
Soothly I came to bring thee more than this,
The memory of an unasked fruitless kiss   350
Upon thy death-day, which this day would be
If there were not some little help in me.'
  Therewith from out her wallet did she draw
The phial, and a crystal without flaw
Shaped like an apple, scored with words about,
Then said : ' But now I bid thee have no doubt.
With this oil hidden by these gems and gold
Anoint thine arms and body, and be bold,
Nor fear the fire-breathing bulls one whit,
Such mighty virtue have I drawn to it,   360
Whereof I give thee proof.' Therewith her hand
She thrust into the lamp-flame that did stand
Anigh the bed, and showed it him again
Unscarred by any wound or drawn with pain,
Then said : ' Now, when Mars' plain is ploughed at last
And in the furrows those ill seeds are cast,
Take thou this ball in hand and watch the thing ;
Then shalt thou see a horrid crop upspring
Of all-armed men therefrom to be thy bane,
Were I not here to make their fury vain.   370
Draw not thy sword against them as they rise,
But cast this ball amid them, and their eyes
Shall serve them then but little to see thee,
And each of others' weapons slain shall be.
  ' Now will my father hide his rage at heart,
And praise thee much that thou hast played thy part,
And bid thee to a banquet on this night,
And pray thee wait until to-morrow's light
Before thou triest the Temple of the Fleece.
Trust not to him, but see that unto Greece   380
The ship's prow turns, and all is ready there.
And at the banquet let thy men forbear
The maddening wine, and bid them arm them all
For what upon this night may chance to fall.

' But I will get by stealth the keys that hold
The seven locks which guard the Fleece of Gold ;
And while we try the fleece, let thy men steal,
How so they may, unto thy ready keel,
Thus art thou saved alive with thy desire.
  ' But what thing will be left to me but fire ?   390
The fire of fierce despair within my heart,
The while I reap my guerdon for my part,
Curses and torments, and in no long space
Real fire of pine-wood in some rocky place,
Wreathing around my body greedily,
A dreadful beacon o'er the leaden sea.'

  But Jason drew her to him, and he said :—
' Nay, by these tender hands and golden head,
That saving things for me have wrought to-night,
I know not what ; by this unseen delight   400
Of thy fair body, may I rather burn,
Nor may the flame die ever if I turn
Back to my hollow ship, and leave thee here,
Who in one minute art become so dear,
Thy limbs so longed for, that at last I know
Why men have been content to suffer woe
Past telling, if the Gods but granted this,
A little while such lips as thine to kiss,
A little while to drink such deep delight.
  ' What wouldst thou ?   Wilt thou go from me ?   The
    light   410
Is grey and tender yet, and in your land
Surely the twilight, lingering long, doth stand
'Twixt dawn and day.'
                    ' O Prince,' she said, ' I came
To save your life. I cast off fear and shame
A little while, but fear and shame are here.
The hand thou holdest trembles with my fear,
With shame my cheeks are burning, and the sound
Of mine own voice : but ere this hour comes round,
We twain will be betwixt the dashing oars,

The ship still making for the Grecian shores. 420
Farewell, till then, though in the lists to-day
Thyself shalt see me, watching out the play.'

Therewith she drew off from him, and was gone,
And in the chamber Jason left alone,
Praising the heavenly one, the Queen of Jove,
Pondered upon this unasked gift of love,
And all the changing wonder of his life.
But soon he rose to fit him for the strife,
And ere the sun his orb began to lift
O'er the dark hills, with fair Medea's gift 430
His arms and body he anointed well,
And round about his neck he hung the spell
Against the earth-born, the fair crystal ball
Laid in a purse, and then from wall to wall,
Athwart the chamber paced full eagerly,
Expecting when the fateful time should be.
Meanwhile, Medea coming to her room
Unseen, lit up the slowly parting gloom
With scented torches : then bound up her hair,
And stripped the dark gown from her body fair, 440
And laid it with the brass bowl in a chest,
Where many a day it had been wont to rest,
Brazen and bound with iron, and whose key
No eye but hers had ever happed to see.
Then wearied, on her bed she cast her down,
And strove to think ; but soon the uneasy frown
Faded from off her brow, her lips closed tight
But now, just parted, and her fingers white
Slackened their hold upon the coverlet,
And o'er her face faint smiles began to flit, 450
As o'er the summer pool the faint soft air :
So instant and so kind the God was there.

BOOK VIII

The taming of the brazen bulls—The destruction of the Earth-born.

Now when she woke again the bright sun glared
In at the window, and the trumpets blared,
Shattering the sluggish air of that hot day,
For fain the king would be upon his way.
Then straight she called her maidens, who forthright
Did due observance to her body white,
And clad her in the raiment of a queen,
And round her crown they set a wreath of green.

But she descending, came into the hall,
And found her father clad in royal pall,   10
Holding the ivory rod of sovereignty,
And Jason and his folk were standing by.

Now was Æetes saying : ' Minyæ,
And you, my people, who are here by me,
Take heed, that by his wilful act to-day
This man will perish, neither will I slay
One man among you. Nay, Prince, if you will,
A safe return I give unto you still '

But Jason answered, smiling in his joy :—
' Once more, Æetes, nay. Against this toy   20
My life is pledged, let all go to the end.'
Then, lifting up his eyes, he saw his friend,
Made fresh, and lovelier by her quiet rest,
And set his hand upon his mailèd breast,
Where in its covering lay the crystal ball.

But the king said : ' Then let what will fall, fall !
Since time it is that we were on the way ;
And thou, O daughter, shalt be there to-day,
And see thy father's glory once more shown
Before our folk and those the wind has blown   30
From many lands to see this play played out.'

Then raised the Colchians a mighty shout,
And doubtful grew the Minyæ of the end,
Unwitting who on that day was their friend.
But down the hall the king passed, who did hold

Medea's hand, and on a car of gold
They mounted, drawn anigh the carven door,
And spearmen of the Colchians went before
And followed after, and the Minyæ
Set close together followed solemnly,   40
Headed by Jason, at the heels of these.
  So passed they through the streets and palaces
Thronged with much folk, and o'er the bridges passed,
And to the open country came at last,
Nor there went far, but turning to the right,
Into a close they came, where there were dight
Long galleries about the fateful stead,
Built all of marble fair and roofed with lead,
And carved about with stories of old time,
Framed all about with golden lines of rhyme.   5c
Moreover, midmost was an image made
Of mighty Mars who maketh kings afraid,
That looked down on an altar builded fair,
Wherefrom already did a bright fire glare
And made the hot air glassy with its heat.
  So in the gallery did the king take seat
With fair Medea, and the Colchians stood
Hedging the twain in with a mighty wood
Of spears and axes, while the Minyæ
Stood off a space the fated things to see.   60
  Ugly and rugged was that spot of ground,
And with an iron wall was closed around,
And at the further end a monstrous cage
Of iron bars, shut in the stupid rage
Of those two beasts, and therefrom ever came
The flashing and the scent of sulphurous flame,
As with their brazen, clangorous bellowing
They hailed the coming of the Colchian king ;
Nor was there one of the seafaring men
But trembled, gazing on the deadly pen,   70
But Jason only, who before the rest
Shone like a star, having upon his breast
A golden corslet from the treasury

    50 Framed all about with] And all around them
    54 a bright fire] a fire

Of wise King Phineus by the doubtful sea,
By an Egyptian wrought who would not stay
At Salmydessa more than for a day,
But on that day the wondrous breast-plate wrought,
Which, with good will and strong help, Jason bought ;
And from that treasury his golden shoe
Came, and his thighs the king's gift covered too ;   80
But on his head his father's helm was set
Wreathed round with bay leaves, and his sword lay yet
Within the scabbard, while his ungloved hand
Bore nought within it but an olive wand.

  Now King Æetes well beholding him,
Fearless of mien and so unmatched of limb,
Trembled a little in his heart as now
He bade the horn-blowers the challenge blow,
But thought, ' what strength can help him, or what art,
Or which of all the Gods be on his part ? '   90
Impious, who knew not through what doubtful days,
E'en from his birth, and perilous rough ways
Juno had brought him safely, nor indeed
Of his own daughter's quivering lips took heed,
And restless hands wherein the God so wrought,
The wise man seeing her had known her thought.

  Now Jason, when he heard the challenge blow,
Across the evil fallow 'gan to go
With face beyond its wont in nowise pale,
Nor footstep faltering, if that might avail   100
The doomed man aught : so to the cage he came,
Whose bars now glowed red hot with spouted flame,
In many a place ; nor doubted any one
Who there beheld him that his days were done,
Except his love alone, and even she,
Sickening with doubt and terror, scarce could see
The hero draw the brazen bolt aside
And throw the glowing wicket open wide.

  But he alone, apart from his desire,
Stood unarmed, facing those two founts of fire,   110
Yet feared not aught, for hope and fear were dead

89 art] heart

Within his heart, and utter hardihead
Had Juno set there ; but the awful beasts
Beholding now the best of all their feasts,
Roared in their joy and fury, till from sight
They and the prince were hidden by the white
Thick rolling clouds of sulphurous pungent smoke,
Through which upon the blinded man they broke.
    But when within a yard of him they came,
Baffled they stopped, still bellowing, and the flame   120
Still spouting out from nostril and from mouth,
As from some island mountain in the south
The trembling mariners behold it cast ;
But still to right and left of him it passed,
Breaking upon him as cool water might,
Nor harming more, except that from his sight
All corners of the cage were hidden now,
Nor knew he where to seek the brazen plough ;
As to and fro about the quivering cage
The monsters rushed in blind and helpless rage.   130
    But as he doubted, to his eyes alone
Within the place a golden light outshone,
Scattering the clouds of smoke, and he beheld
Once more the Goddess who his head upheld
In rough Anaurus on that other tide ;
She, smiling on him, beckoned, and 'gan glide
With rosy feet across the fearful floor,
Breathing cool odours round her, till a door
She opened to him in the iron wall,
Through which he passed, and found a grisly stall   140
Of iron still, and at one end of it,
By glimmering lamps with greenish flame half lit,
Beheld the yoke and shining plough he sought ;
Which, seizing straight, by mighty strength he brought
Unto the door, nor found the Goddess there,
    Who in the likeness of a damsel fair,
Colchian Metharma, through the spearmen passed,
Bearing them wine, and causeless terror cast
Into their foolish hearts, nor spared to go
And 'mid the close seafaring ranks to sow   150

      130 blind and helpless] helpless and blind

Good hope of joyful ending, and then stood
Behind the maid unseen, and brought the blood
Back to her cheeks and trembling lips and wan,
With thoughts of things unknown to maid or man.
  Meanwhile upon the foreheads of the twain
Had Jason cast the yoke with little pain,
And drove them now with shouts out through the door
Which in such guise ne'er had they passed before,
For never were they made the earth to till,
But rather, feeding fat, to work the will   160
Of some all-knowing man ; but now they went
Like any peasant's beasts, tamed by the scent
Of those new herbs Medea's hand had plucked,
Whose roots from evil earth strange power had sucked.
  Now in the open field did Jason stand
And to the plough-stilts set his unused hand,
And down betwixt them lustily he bent ;
Then the bulls drew, and the bright ploughshare sent
The loathly fallow up on the right side,
Whilst o'er their bellowing shrilly Jason cried :—   170
' Draw nigh, O King, and thy new ploughman see,
Then mayst thou make me shepherd, too, to thee ;
Nor doubt thou, doing so, from out thy flock
To lose but one, who ne'er shall bring thee stock,
Or ram or ewe, nor doubt the grey wolf, King,
Wood-haunting bear, dragon, or such like thing.
Ah the straight furrow ! how it mindeth me
Of the smooth parting of the land-locked sea
Over against Eubœa, and this fire
Of the fair altar where my joyful sire   180
Will pour out wine to Neptune when I come
Not empty-handed back unto my home.'

  Such mocks he said ; but when the sunlight broke
Upon his armour through the sulphurous smoke,
And showed the lengthening furrow cutting through
The ugly farrow as anigh they drew,
The joyful Minyæ gave a mighty shout ;
But pale the king sat with brows knit for doubt,
          186 farrow, *a misprint ; read* fallow *as in first edition*

Muttering : ' Whose counsel hast thou taken, then,
To do this thing, which not the best of men   190
Could do unholpen of some sorcery ?
Whoso it is, wise were he now to die
Ere yet I know him, since for many a day
Vainly for death I hope to hear him pray.'
    Meanwhile, askance Medea eyed the king,
Thinking nought safe until that everything
Was finished in the Colchian land, and she
No more beheld its shores across the sea ;
But he, beholding her pale visage, thought
Grief like to his such paleness on her brought,   200
And turning to her, said : ' How pale thou art !
Let not this first foil go unto thine heart
Too deeply, since thou knowest certainly,
One way or other this vain fool must die.'
' Father,' she said, ' a doubt is on me still,
Some God this is come here our wealth to spill ;
Nor is this first thing easier than the rest.'
Then stammering, she said : ' Were it not best
To give him that which he must have at last,
Before he slays us.' But Æetes cast   210
A sharp glance at her, and a pang shot through
His weary heart as half the truth he knew.
But for one moment, and he made reply
In passionate words : ' Then, daughter, let me die !
And, ere I die, behold thee led along
A wretched slave to suffer grief and wrong
In far-off lands, and Æa at thy back
Nought but a huge flame hiding woe and wrack,
Before from out my willing open hand
This wonder, and the safeguard of my land   220
A God shall take ; and such this man is not.
What ! dost thou think because his eyes are hot
On tender maidens he must be a God ?
Or that because firmly this field he trod
Well-fenced with magic ? Were he like to me,
Grey-haired and lean, what Godhead wouldst thou see
In such an one ? Hold, then, thy peace of this,

    202 Yet let not this first foil go to thine heart   213 and] as

And thou shalt see thy God full widely miss
The mark he aims at, when from out the earth
Spring up those brothers of an evil birth.'   230
　　And therewithal he gazed at her, and thought
To see the rosy flush by such words brought
Across her face ; as in the autumn eve,
Just as the sun's last half begins to leave
The shivering world, both east and west are red.—
But calm and pale she turned about her head,
And said : ' My father, neither were these words
My words, nor would I struggle with my lords ;
Thou art full wise ; whatso thine heart would have
That do, and heed me not, who fain would save   240
This glory of thy kingdom and of thee.
But now look up, and soothly thou shalt see
Mars' acre tilled : the field is ready then,
Bid them bring forth the seed that beareth men.'
　　Again with her last words the shouts out-broke
From the seafearers, for, beside the yoke,
Before Mars' altar did Prince Jason stand,
Holding the wand of olive in his hand,
And on the new-turned furrow shone the sun
Behind him, and his half-day's work was done   250

　　And now another marvel : for, behold,
As at the furrow's end he slacked his hold
Upon the plough-stilts, all the bellowing
Wherewith the beasts had made the grim close ring,
Fell suddenly, and all the fire died
That they were wont erewhile to scatter wide
From mouth and nostril, and their loins and knees
Stiffened, and they grew nought but images
Lifelike but lifeless, wonderful but dead,
Such as he makes, who many a day hath fed   260
His furnace with the beechwood, when the clay
Has grown beneath his deft hands day by day
And all is ready for the casting, then
Such things as these he makes for royal men.

　　245 out-broke] broke out
　　246 seafearers, *a misprint ; read* seafarers *as in first edition*

But 'mid the shouts turned Jason to the king,
And said : ' Fair sir, behold a wondrous thing,
And since these beasts have been content to stay
Before Mars' altar, from this very day
His should they be if they were mine to give.'
   ' O Jason,' said the king, ' well mayst thou live   270
For many a day, since thou this deed hast done,
But for the Gods, not unto any one
Will I give gifts ; but let them take from me
What once they gave, if so the thing must be.
But do thou take this sack from out my hand
And cast its seed about the new-tilled land,
And watch the issue ; and keep words till then,
I counsel thee, O luckiest of men.'

   Then Jason took the sack, and with it went
About that field new turned, and broadcast sent   280
The white teeth scattering, but or ere he came
Back to the altar, and the flickering flame,
He heard from 'neath the earth a muttered sound
That grew and grew, till all that piece of ground
Swelled into little hillocks, like as where
A stricken field was foughten, but that there
Quiet the heroes' bones lie underneath
The quivering grasses and the dusky heath ;
But now these heaps the labouring earth upthrew
About Mars' acre, ever greater grew,   290
And still increased the noise, till none could hear
His fellow speak, and paleness and great fear
Fell upon all ; and Jason only stood
As stands the stout oak in the poplar wood
When winds are blowing.
                 Then he saw the mounds
Bursten asunder, and the muttered sounds
Changed into loud strange shouts and warlike clang,
As with freed feet at last the earth-born sprang
On to the tumbling earth, and the sunlight
Shone on bright arms clean ready for the fight.   300
   But terribly they showed, for through the place
Not one there was but had his staring face,

With great wide eyes, and lips in a set smile,
Turned full on Jason, who, for a short while,
Forgot indeed Medea's warning word,
And from its golden sheath half drew his sword,
But then, remembering all, cried valiantly :
' New born ye are—new slain too shall ye be,
Take this, and round about it read your doom,
And bid them make new dwellings in the tomb,   310
Wherefrom ye came, nor ever should have passed.'
      Therewith the ball among the host he cast,
Standing to watch what next that folk would do.
But he the ball had smitten turned unto
The one who stood by him and like a cup
Shattered his head ; then the next lifted up
His axe and slew the slayer, and straightway
Among the rest began a deadly fray.
      No man gave back a foot, no breathing space
One took or gave within that dreadful place,   320
But where the vanquished stood there was he slain,
And straight the conquering arm was raised again
To meet its match and in its turn to fall,
No tide was there of fainting and recall,
No quivering pennon o'er their heads to flit,
Nor name or eager shout called over it,
No groan of pain, and no despairing cry
From him who knows his time has come to die,
But passionless each bore him in that fight,
Scarce otherwise than as a smith might smite   330
On sounding iron or bright glittering brass.
      So, little by little, did the clamour pass
As one by one each fell down in his place,
Until at last, midmost the bloody space,
One man was left, alive but wounded sore,
Who, staring round about and seeing no more
His brothers' spears against him, fixed his eyes
Upon the queller of those mysteries.
Then dreadfully they gleamed, and with no word,
He tottered towards him with uplifted sword.   340
But scarce he made three paces down the field,
Ere chill death reached his heart, and on his shield

Clattering he fell. So satiate of fight
Quickly the earth-born were, and their delight
With what it fed on perished, and one hour
Ripened the deadly fruit of that fell flower.
    Then, Jason, mocking, cried unto the king :—
' O wonderful, indeed, must be the thing
Thou guardest with such wondrous guards as these ;
Make no delay, therefore, but bring the keys   350
That I may see this dear delight of all.'
    But on Æetes' face a change did fall,
As though a mask had been set over it,
And smiles of little meaning 'gan to flit
O'er his thin lips, as he spake out at last :—
' No haste, dear guest, for surely now is passed
All enmity from 'twixt us, since I know
How like a God thou art ; and thou shalt go
To-morrow to thy ship, to make for Greece ;
And with no trial more, bear back the fleece   360
Along our streets, and like no conquered thing,
But with much scattered flowers and tabouring,
Bearing with it great gifts and all my love ;
And in return, I pray thee, pray to Jove,
That I may have a few more years of life,
And end at last in honour, free from strife.
And now to-night be merry, and let time
Be clean forgotten, and bring Saturn's clime
And golden days upon our flower-crowned brows,
For of the unseen future what man knows ? '   370
    ' O King,' said Jason, ' for these words I praise
Thy wisdom much, and wish thee happy days.
And I will give thee honour as I can,
Naming thee ever as a noble man
Through all the lands I come to : and will take
Thy gifts, indeed, and thou, for Jason's sake,
Shalt have gifts too, whatso thy soul may wish,
From out our keel that has escaped the fish.'
    So spake those wary foes, fair friends in look,
And so in words great gifts they gave and took,   380
And had small profit, and small loss thereby.
Nor less Medea feigned, but angrily

Regarded Jason, and across her brow
Drew close her veil, nor doubted the king now
Her faith and loyalty.
                    So from the place
Back toward the town they turned at a soft pace,
In guise of folk that hold high festival,
Since straightly had Æetes bid that all
Should do the strangers pleasure on that day.
But warily went Jason on the way,   390
And through his folk spread words, to take good heed
Of what might come, and ready be at need,
Nor yet to take Æetes for their friend,
Since even then he plotted how to end
Their quest and lives : therefore he bade them spare
The wine that night, nor look on damsels fair ;
But that, the feast done, all should stealthily
Get to the quay, and round about to sea
Turn Argo's head, and wait like hounds in slip,
Holding the oars, within the hollow ship.   400
    ' Nor doubt,' said he, ' that good and glorious
The end shall be, since all the Gods for us
Are fighting certainly : but should death come
Upon me in this land, then turn back home,
Nor wait till they shall lay your bones with mine,
Since now I think to go unto the shrine,
The while ye wait, and take therefrom the fleece,
Not all unholpen, and depart in peace,
While yet the barbarous king beholds us dead
In dreams alone, or through his waking head   410
The vile plots chase each other for our death.'
    These things he said, but scarce above his breath,
Unto wise Nestor, who beside him went,
Who unto Butes straight the message sent,
And he to Phlias, so the words at last
Throughout the wondering seafarers had passed,
And so were all made ready for the night.

    But on that eve, with manifold delight,
Æetes feasted them in his fair hall ;
But they, well knowing what might chance to fall,   420

Sat saying little, nor drank deep of wine ;
Until at last the old king gave the sign
To break the feast up, and within a while
All seemed asleep throughout the mighty pile
　　All seemed asleep, but now Medea went
With beating heart to work out her intent,
Scarce doubtful of the end, since only two
In all the world, she and Æetes, knew
Where the keys were, far from the light of day,
Beneath the palace. So, in garments grey,　　430
Like the soft creeping twilight did she go,
Until she reached a passage far below
The river, past whose oozing walls of stone
She and the king alone had ever gone.
　　Now she, who thus far had come through the dark,
Stopped, and in haste striking a little spark
From something in her hand, lit up a lamp,
Whose light fell on an iron door, with damp
All rusted red, which with a key of brass
She opened, and there through made haste to pass,　　440
Shuddering a little, as her feet 'gan tread
Upon a dank cold floor, though overhead
High-arched the place was, fairly built enow.
　　But she across the slippery floor did go
Unto the other wall, wherein was built
A little aumbrye, with a door o'er-gilt,
That with the story of King Athamas,
And Phryxus, and the ram all carven was.
There did she draw forth from her balmy breast
A yellow flowering herb, that straight she pressed　　450
Upon the lock, low muttering the while ;
But soon across her face there passed a smile,
As backward in the lock the bolts did turn,
And the door opened ; then a golden urn
She saw within the aumbrye, whereon she
Drew out the thing she sought for eagerly,
The seven keys with sere-cloth done about.
Then through the dreary door did she pass out,
And made it fast, and went her way once more
Through the black darkness on from floor to floor.　　460

And so, being come to Jason, him she found
All armed, and ready ; therefore, with no sound,
She beckoned him to follow, and the twain
Passed through the brazen doors, locked all in vain,
Such virtue had the herb Medea bore,
And passing, did they leave ajar each door,
To give more ease unto the Minyæ.
 So out into the fresh night silently
The lovers passed, the loveliest of the land ;
But as they went, neither did hand touch hand,   470
Or face seek face ; for, gladsome as they were,
Trembling with joy to be at last so near
The wished-for day, some God yet seemed to be
'Twixt the hard past and their felicity.

BOOK IX

The Fleece taken from the temple—The departure of Argo—
The death of Absyrtus

But when they reached the precinct of the God,
And on the hallowed turf their feet now trod,
Medea turned to Jason, and she said :—
' O love, turn round, and note the goodlihead
My father's palace shows beneath the stars.
Bethink thee of the men grown old in wars,
Who do my bidding ; what delights I have,
How many ladies lie in wait to save
My life from toil and carefulness, and think
How sweet a cup I have been used to drink,   10
And how I cast it to the ground for thee.
Upon the day thou weariest of me,
I wish that thou mayst somewhat think of this,
And 'twixt thy new-found kisses, and the bliss
Of something sweeter than thine old delight,
Remember thee a little of this night
Of marvels, and this starlit, silent place,
And these two lovers standing face to face.'
 ' O love,' he said, ' by what thing shall I swear,

That while I live thou shalt not be less dear   20
Than thou art now ? '
      ' Nay, sweet,' she said, ' let be ;
Wert thou more fickle than the restless sea,
Still should I love thee, knowing thee for such ;
Whom I know not, indeed, but fear the touch
Of Fortune's hand when she beholds our bliss,
And knows that nought is good to me but this.

  ' But now be ready, for I long full sore
To hear the merry dashing of the oar,
And feel the freshness of the following breeze
That sets me free, and sniff the rough salt seas.   30
Look ! yonder thou mayst see armed shadows steal
Down to the quays, the guiders of thy keel ;
Now follow me, though little shalt thou do
To gain this thing, if Hecate be true
Unto her servant. Nay, draw not thy sword,
And, for thy life, speak not a single word
Until I bid thee, else may all be lost,
And of this game our lives yet pay the cost.'
  Then toward the brazen temple-door she went,
Wherefrom, half-open, a faint gleam was sent ;   40
For little need of lock it had forsooth,
Because its sleepless guardian knew no ruth,
And had no lust for precious things or gold,
Whom, drawing near, Jason could now behold,
As back Medea thrust the heavy door,
For prone he lay upon the gleaming floor,
Not moving, though his restless, glittering eyes
Left them no hope of wile or of surprise.
Hideous he was, where all things else were fair ;
Dull-skinned, foul-spotted, with lank rusty hair   50
About his neck ; and hooked yellow claws
Just showed from 'neath his belly and huge jaws,
Closed in the hideous semblance of a smile.
Then Jason shuddered, wondering with what guile
That fair king's daughter such a beast could tame,
And of his sheathed sword had but little shame.

   48 Gave unto them no least hope of surprise   54 guile] wile

But being within the doors, both mantle grey
And heavy gown Medea cast away,
And in thin clinging silk alone was clad,
And round her neck a golden chain she had,   60
Whereto was hung a harp of silver white.
Then the great dragon, at that glittering sight,
Raised himself up upon his loathly feet,
As if to meet her, while her fingers sweet
Already moved amongst the golden strings,
Preluding nameless and delicious things ;
But now she beckoned Jason to her side,
For slowly towards them 'gan the beast to glide,
And when close to his love the hero came,
She whispered breathlessly : ' On me the blame   70
If here we perish ; if I give the word,
Then know that all is lost, and draw thy sword,
And manlike die in battle with the beast ;
So dying shalt thou fail to see at least
This body thou desiredst so to see,
In thy despite here mangled wretchedly.
Peace, for he cometh, O thou Goddess bright,
What help wilt thou be unto me this night ? '
    So murmured she, while ceaselessly she drew
Her fingers through the strings, and fuller grew   80
The tinkling music, but the beast drawn nigh
Went slower still, and turning presently
Began to move around them in a ring.
And as he went, there fell a strange rattling
Of his dry scales ; but as he turned, she turned,
Nor failed to meet the eyes that on her burned
With steadfast eyes, and, lastly, clear and strong
Her voice broke forth in sweet melodious song :—

        ' O evil thing, what brought thee here
        To be a wonder and a fear
        Unto the river-haunting folk ?   90
        Was it the God of Day that broke
        The shadow of thy windless trees,
        Gleaming from golden palaces,

And shod with light and armed with light,
Made thy slime stone, and day thy night,
And drove thee forth unwillingly
Within his golden house to lie ?
  ' Or was it the slim messenger,
Who, treading softly, free from fear,   100
Beguiled thee with his smiling face
From out thy dim abiding place,
To follow him and set thee down
Midst of this twice-washed royal town ?
  ' Or, was it rather the dread Lord
Who slayeth without spear or sword,
And with the flower-culling maid
Of Enna, dwelleth in the shade,
Who, with stern voice compelling thee,
Hath set thee here, our bane to be ?   110
  ' Or was it Venus, seeking far
A sleepless guard 'gainst grief and war,
Who, journeying through thy dismal land,
Beside the heavy lake did stand,
And with no word, but very sight
Of tender limbs and bosom white,
Drew forth thy scaly feet and hard,
To follow over rock and shard ?
  ' Or rather, thy dull, waveless lake
Didst thou not leave for her dread sake,   120
Who, passing swift from glade to glade,
The forest-dwellers makes afraid
With shimmering of her silver bow
And dreadful arrows ?   Even so
I bid thee now to yield to me,
Her maid, who overmastered thee,
The three-formed dreadful one who reigns
In heaven and the fiery plains,
But on the green earth best of all.
  ' Lo, now thine upraised crest let fall,   130
Relax thy limbs, let both thine eyes
Be closed, and bestial fantasies
Fill thy dull head till dawn of day
And we are far upon our way.'

As thus she sung the beast seemed not to hear
Her words at first, but ever drew anear,
Circling about them, and Medea's face
Grew pale unto the lips, though still the place
Rung with the piercing sweetness of her song ;
But slower soon he dragged his length along,   140
And on his limbs he tottered, till at last
All feebly by the wondering prince he passed,
And whining to Medea's feet he crept,
With eyes half closed, as though well-nigh he slept,
And there before her laid his head adown ;
Who, shuddering, on his wrinkled neck and brown
Set her white foot, and whispered : ' Haste, O love !
Behold the keys ; haste ! while the Gods above
Are friendly to us ; there behold the shrine
Where thou canst see the lamp of silver shine.   150
Nay, draw not death upon both thee and me
With fearless kisses ; fear, until the sea
Shall fold green arms about us lovingly,
And kindly Venus to thy keel be nigh.'
Then lightly from her soft side Jason stept,
While still upon the beast her foot she kept,
Still murmuring gently many an unknown word,
As when through half-shut casements the brown bird
We hearken when the night is come in June,
And thick-leaved woods are 'twixt us and his tune.   160

But Jason, going swiftly with good heart,
Came to the wished-for shrine built all apart
Midmost the temple, that on pillars stood
Of jasper green, and marble red as blood,
All white itself and carven cunningly
With Neptune bringing from the wavy sea
The golden shining ram to Athamas ;
And the first door thereof of silver was,
Wrought over with a golden glittering sun
That seemed well-nigh alike the heavenly one.   170
Such art therein the cunningest of men
Had used, which little Jason heeded then,

157 gently] softly

But thrusting in the lock the smallest key
Of those he bore, it opened easily ;
And then five others, neither wrought of gold,
Or carved with tales, or lovely to behold,
He opened ; but before the last one stayed
His hand, wherein the heavy key he weighed,
And pondering, in low muttered word, he said :—
   ' The prize is reached, which yet I somewhat dread
To draw unto me ; since I know indeed,   181
That henceforth war and toil shall be my meed.—
Too late to fear, it was too late, the hour
I left the grey cliffs and the beechen bower,
So here I take hard life and deathless praise,
Who once desired nought but quiet days,
And painless life, not empty of delight ;
I, who shall now be quickener of the fight,
Named by a great name—a far-babbled name,
The ceaseless seeker after praise and fame.   190
   ' May all be well, and on the noisy ways
Still may I find some wealth of happy days.'
   Therewith he threw the last door open wide,
Whose hammered iron did the marvel hide,
And shut his dazzled eyes, and stretched his hands
Out toward the sea-born wonder of all lands,
And plunged them deep within the locks of gold,
Grasping the fleece within his mighty hold.

   Which when Medea saw, her gown of grey
She caught up from the ground, and drew away   200
Her wearied foot from off the rugged beast,
And while from her soft strain she never ceased,
In the dull folds she hid her silk from sight,
And then, as bending 'neath the burden bright,
Jason drew nigh, joyful, yet still afraid,
She met him, and her wide grey mantle laid
Over the fleece, whispering : ' Make no delay ;
He sleeps, who never slept by night or day
Till now ; nor will his charmed sleep be long.
Light foot am I, and sure thine arms are strong ;   210

   197 plunged them deep within] buried them deep in

Haste, then !   No word !   nor turn about to gaze
At me, as he who in the shadowy ways
Turned round to see once more the twice-lost face.'

Then swiftly did they leave the dreadful place,
Turning no look behind, and reached the street,
That with familiar look and kind did greet
Those wanderers, mazed with marvels and with fear.
And so, unchallenged, did they draw anear
The long white quays, and at the street's end now
Beheld the ships' masts standing row by row   220
Stark black against the stars : then cautiously
Peered Jason forth, ere they took heart to try
The open starlit place ; but nought he saw
Except the night-wind twitching the loose straw
From half-unloaded keels, and nought he heard
But the strange twittering of a caged green bird
Within an Indian ship, and from the hill
A distant baying : yea, all was so still,
Somewhat they doubted, natheless forth they passed,
And Argo's painted sides they reached at last.   230
   On whom down-looking, scarce more noise they heard
Than from the other ships ; some muttered word,
Some creaking of the timbers, as the tide
Ran gurgling seaward past her shielded side.
Then Jason knelt, and whispered : ' Wise be ye,
O fair companions on the pathless sea,
But come, Erginus, Nestor, and ye twain
Of Lacedæmon, to behold my gain ;
Take me amongst you, neither be afraid
To take withal this gold, and this fair maid.   240
Yare !—for the ebb runs strongly towards the sea,
The east wind drives the rack to Thessaly,
And lightly do such kings as this one sleep
If now and then small watch their servants keep.'
   Then saw Medea men like shadows grey
Rise from the darksome decks, who took straightway
With murmured joy, from Jason's outstretched hands,
The conquered fleece, the wonder of all lands,

While with strong arms he raised the royal maid,
And in their hold the precious burthen laid, 250
And scarce her dainty feet could touch the deck,
Ere down he leapt, and little now did reck
That loudly clanged his armour therewithal.
    But, turning townward, did Medea call :—
' O noble Jason, and ye heroes strong,
To sea, to sea ! nor pray ye loiter long ;
For surely shall ye see the beacons flare
Ere in mid stream ye are, and running fair
On toward the sea with tide, and oar, and sail.
My father wakes, nor bides he to bewail 260
His loss and me ; I see his turret gleam
As he goes towards the beacon, and down stream
Absyrtus lurks before the sandy bar
In mighty keel well manned and dight for war.'
    But as she spoke, rattling the cable slipped
From out the hawse-hole, and the long oars dipped
As from the quays the heroes pushed away,
And in the loosened sail the wind 'gan play ;
But e'en as they unto the stroke leaned back,
And Nauplius, catching at the main-sheet slack 270
Had drawn it taut, out flared the beacon wide,
Lighting the waves, and they heard folk who cried :
' Awake, awake, awake, O Colchian folk ! '
And all about the blare of horns outbroke,
As watch-tower answered watch-tower down the stream,
Where far below they saw the bale-fires gleam ;
And galloping of horses now they heard,
And clang of arms, and cries of men afeard,
For now the merchant mariners who lay
About the town, thought surely an ill day 280
Had dawned upon them while they slept at ease,
And, half awake, pushed madly from the quays
With crash of breaking oars and meeting ships,
And cries and curses from outlandish lips ;
So fell the quiet night to turmoil sore,
While in the towers, over the uproar,
Melodiously the bells began to ring.

        249 raised] took   278 afeard] afeared
                            F f 2

But Argo, leaping forward to the swing
Of measured oars, and leaning to the breeze,
Sped swiftly 'twixt the dark and whispering trees ;   290
Nor longer now the heroes silence kept,
So joyously their hearts within them leapt,
But loud they shouted, seeing the gold fell
Laid heaped before them, and longed sore to tell
Their fair adventure to the maids of Greece ;
And as the mingled noises did decrease
With added distance, and behind them night
Grew pale with coming of the eastern light,
Across the strings his fingers Orpheus drew,
And through the woods his winged music flew :—   300

   ' O surely, now the fisherman
Draws homeward through the water wan
Across the bay we know so well,
And in the sheltered chalky dell
The shepherd stirs ; and now afield
They drive the team with white wand peeled
Muttering across the barley-bread
At daily toil and dreary-head.
   ' And midst them all, perchance, my love
Is waking, and doth gently move   310
And stretch her soft arms out to me,
Forgetting thousand leagues of sea ;
And now her body I behold,
Unhidden but by hair of gold,
And now the silver water kiss,
The crown of all delight and bliss.
And now I see her bind her hair
And do upon her raiment fair,
And now before the altar stand,
With incense in her outstretched hand,   320
To supplicate the Gods for me ;
Ah, one day landing from the sea,
Amid the maidens shall I hear
Her voice in praise, and see her near,
Holding the gold-wrapt laurel crown,
'Midst of the shouting, wondering town ! '

298 pale] wan

So sung he joyously, nor knew that they
Must wander yet for many an evil day
Or ever the dread Gods should let them come
Back to the white walls of their long-left home.　330
But on the shouting heroes gazed adown
The foundress of their triumph and renown,
And to her lover's side still drew anear,
With heart now swelled with joy, now sick with fear,
And cheeks now flushed with love, now pale and wan,
As now she thought upon that goodly man,
And now on the uncertain, dreadful Gods,
And now upon her father, and the odds
He well might raise against the reckless crew,
For all his mighty power full well she knew ;　340
No wonder therefore if her heart grew cold,
And if her wretched self she did behold,
Led helpless through some old familiar place,
With none to turn on her a pitying face,
Unto the death in life, she still might win ;
And yet, if she should 'scape the meed of sin
This once, the world was fair and bright enough,
And love there was to lead her o'er the rough
Of life, and love to crown her head with flowers,
And fill her days and nights with happy hours.　350

Now swift beneath the oar-strokes Argo flew,
While the sun rose behind them, and they drew
Unto the river's mouth, nor failed to see
Absyrtus' galley waiting watchfully
Betwixt them and the white-topped turbid bar.
Therefore they gat them ready now for war
With joyful hearts, for sharp they sniffed the sea,
And saw the great waves tumbling green and free
Outside the bar upon the way to Greece,
The rough green way to glory and sweet peace.　360
Then to the prow gat Jason, and the maid
Must needs be with him, though right sore afraid,

340 power full well] power well
341-2 And at that thought well might her heart grow cold,
　　　 And well might she her wretched self behold,

As nearing now the Colchian ship, they hung
On balanced oars ; but the wild Arcas strung
His deadly bow, and clomb into the top.

Then Jason cried : ' Absyrtus, will ye stop
Our peaceful keel, or let us take the sea ?
Soothly, have we no will to fight with thee
If we may pass unfoughten, therefore say,
What is it thou wilt have this dawn of day ? '   370

Now on the other prow Absyrtus stood,
His visage red with eager wrathful blood,
And in his right hand shook a mighty spear,
And said : ' O seafarers, ye pass not here,
For gifts or prayers, but if it must be so,
Over our sunken bulwarks shall ye go ;
Nor ask me why, for thus my father wills,
Yet, as I now behold you, my heart thrills
With wrath indeed ; and hearken for what cause,
That ye against all friendship and good laws   380
Bear off my sister with you ; wherefore now
Mars give you courage and a brazen brow !
That ye may try this dangerous pass in vain,
For soothly, of your slaughter am I fain.'

Then Jason wrathfully threw up his head,
But ere the shout came, fair Medea said,
In trembling whisper thrilling through his ear :—
' Haste, quick upon them ! if before is fear,
Behind is death ! ' Then Jason turning, saw
A tall ship staggering with the gusty flaw,   390
Just entering the long reach where they were,
And heard her horns through the fresh morning air.

Then lifted he his hand, and with a cry
Back flew the balanced oars full orderly,
And toward the doomed ship mighty Argo passed ;
Thereon Absyrtus shouted loud, and cast
His spear at Jason, that before his feet
Stuck in the deck ; then out the arrows fleet
Burst from the Colchians ; and scarce did they spare
Medea's trembling side and bosom fair ;   400
But Jason, roaring as the lioness
When round her helpless whelps the hunters press,

Whirled round his head his mighty brass-bound spear,
That flying, smote the Prince beneath the ear,
As Arcas' arrow sunk into his side.
Then falling, scarce he met the rushing tide,
Ere Argo's mighty prow had thrust apart
The huddled oars, and through the fair ship's heart
Had thrust her iron beak, and the green wave
Rushed in as rush the waters through a cave   410
That tunnels half a sea-girt lonely rock.
Then drawing swiftly backward from the shock,
And heeding not the cries of fear and woe,
They left the waters dealing with their foe ;
And at the following ship threw back a shout,
And seaward o'er the bar drave Argo out.
   Then joyful felt all men as now at last
From hill to green hill of the sea they passed ;
But chiefly joyed Medea, as now grew
The Colchian hills behind them faint and blue,   420
And like a white speck showed the following ship.
There 'neath the canopy, lip pressed to lip,
They sat and told their love, till scarce he thought
What precious burden back to Greece he brought
Besides the maid, nor for his kingdom cared,
As on her beauty with wet eyes he stared,
And heard her sweet voice soft as in a dream,
When all seems gained, and trouble dead does seem.
   So passed this day, and she no less forgot
That wreck upon the bar, the evil spot,   430
Red with a brother's blood, where long was stayed
The wrathful king as from the stream he weighed
The bleeding body of his well-loved son.
   Lo in such wise their journey was begun,
And so began short love and long decay,
Sorrow that bides and joy that fleets away.

409 and] then

After l. 428 *the first edition inserts :*

And on his face her red lips he could feel,
And round her panting sides his fingers steal.

BOOK X

Argo cut off from the straits—The entry of the river—
The passage northward.

NIGHT came, but still on by the stars they sailed
Before the wind, till at the dawn it failed,
And faded soon the sunrise hue away,
Leaving the heavens colourless and grey,
And dull and lightless the decreasing swell
About the watery ways now rose and fell,
And Lynceus, looking back, no more beheld
The galley that so long the chase had held.
Then were all glad, and toiled on at the oar,
When now the drooping sails would help no more.   10
    But soon before their way it seemed as though
A curtain hung they needs must journey through,
A low black mist so brooded o'er the sea.
Then did they hold their hands, but presently,
Moving to meet them, did it hide from sight
The dog-vane and the maintop gilded bright,
Yea in heart-chilling waves it so enwound
The seafarers, that each man gazed around
And saw but shadows where his fellows were.
So with the windless swell did Argo fare   20
Two days with furled sails purposeless and blind,
And bearing heavy hearts ; the third, the wind
Sprung up at daybreak, and straight drove away
That hideous mist, that after sunrise lay
A heavy purple bank down in the west.

    Then by the sun his way Erginus guessed,
For on no side could they see any land ;
But as upon the helm he set his hand
Such mighty light blazed out upon the prow,
That faint and yellow did the sunlight show   30
Beside it, and amidst it they beheld
The figure that ere now their hands had held
Anigh the Mysian shore ; and now it said :—
    ' O heroes, wherefore haste ye to be dead ?

Behold, while through the heart of yonder fog
I, Argo, drifted as an unsteered log,
Æetes passed us going towards the straits,
And now is lying ready by the gates ;
Nor with one ship alone, but with ten keels,
Raised from his subject kings and commonweals,   40
Abides your coming, hoping soon to see
Your bodies on the shore lie wretchedly,
While to the Gods he offers bulls and sheep ;
But your fair helper and your joy will keep,
That she in Æa unavenged may burn.
  ' But now the Gods, taking your swift return
Away from you, yet will not let you die ;
But bid you, taking heart, turn presently
Unto the northern shore of this ill sea ;
There by a mighty river shall ye be,   50
Along whose sides dwell the Sarmatian folk,
Knowing no arts, untaught to bear the yoke
Of equal laws ; into this river's mouth
Straight must ye enter, and forget the south,
And many unknown lands and unknown seas,
And deadly forests, vocal with no breeze,
Shall ye go wandering through, but long time past,
Unto the seas ye know shall come at last,
And passing by the western garden fair
Toward the Italian shore, shall ye find there   60
Circe the wise, the wonder of all lands,
Thy father's sister, lady, at whose hands
Of late-wrought guilt shall ye be purified.
  ' And so, by many troubles being tried,
Unto Iolchos shall ye all come back
Except some few ; nor there find any lack
Of much-desired wealth and babbling praise,
And so each man depart unto such days
As the fates grant him, be they good or ill,
With death at last according to their will.'   70
  With these last words she vanished quite away,
And these, left floating on that dawn of day
Felt severed utterly from hoped-for things ;
Like some caged eagle that, with fluttering wings,

Beats at his bars, beholding far away
His windy eyrie up the mountain grey.
—A while ago, and every man nigh saw
The long white walls rise sunny without flaw
From out the curled white edges of the sea ;
Yea, almost felt as if they well might be   80
In fair Iolchos that same afternoon.
And now how many and many a glittering moon
Must fill her horns up, while their lives are spent
In unknown lands mid helpless drearyment !

But as his fellows, speechless and amazed,
Upon the weary sea so stood and gazed,
Spake Jason to them : ' Heroes, tell me where
Your hearts are gone, since helpless thus ye stare
On that which helpeth not ? in no such wise
A while ago, before Æetes' eyes   90
Ye smote the Colchian ship ; with other heart
Ye drave the dark blue clashers far apart ;
No eyes I saw like these upon the day,
When with the Colchian spears on every way,
Unto Mars' acre on a doubtful quest
We passed, and dared the worst to get the best.
  ' What will ye ? Is it then so hard a thing
That we, through many countries wandering,
Shall see unheard-of things, nor fail to come
When yet our blood is warm, back to our home ?   100
Be merry, think upon the lives of men,
And with what troubles threescore years and ten
Are crowded oft, yea, even unto him
Who sits at home, nor fears for life and limb,
But trembles the base slave unto a slave ;
Or holding trifles he is fain to save,
Sits pleasureless and wearing out his life,
Or with vain words wages disgraceful strife
That leads nowhither, till forgotten death
Seizes the babbler, choking out his breath.   110
  ' But ye—forget all—get ye to the oar,
And steer rejoicing to the northern shore,

              83 are] were   84 mid] and

Since we shall win such glory and renown,
That, coming home again to our fair town,
Those left behind shall count us all for lords,
And tremble, gazing at our sheathed swords.
Fair is the wind, the sunny dawn is clear,
Nor are we bound for Pluto's kingdom drear,
But for fair forests, plentiful of beasts,
Where, innocent of craft, with joyous feasts   120
The wise folk live as in the golden age,
Not reddening spears and swords in useless rage ;
Nor need they houses, but in fair-wrought cave
Their bodies from the winter's cold they save ;
Nor labour they at all, or weave, or till,
For everything the kind land bears at will.
Doubt not at all that they will welcome us
As very Gods, with all things plenteous.'

     So spake he, knowing nought of that same land ;
Natheless, they noting him as he did stand   130
Beside Erginus, with unclouded face,
Took heart again, and to the oars apace
They gat and toiled, forgetting half the word
That from great Argo's sprite ere now they heard,
Nor thinking of the ills that they might meet,
But of the day when their returning feet
Should bear them, full of knowledge, wealth, and fame,
Up to the royal hall wherefrom they came.
     But Jason in his heart thought : ' Now, indeed,
Of home and fame full little is my need,   140
The days will change, and time will bring a day
When through my beard are sprinkled locks of grey,
And love no more shall be enough for me,
And no fair woman much delight shall be ;
But little do we want when we are young,
The bended knee and flattering double tongue,
Which we, grown old, and drained of half our fire,
Knowing them false, do yet so much desire '
     But for his love, she, set quite free from fear
Of frightful death, held life itself so dear,   150

146 double] false

That where she went she scarcely heeded yet,
For still she seemed to see the black pile set
For her undoing by the temple-gate ;
And seemed to see the thronging people wait
For her, who there to make the tragedy
Alone was wanting : then she saw anigh
His face, and with her fingers felt him toy,
And therewithal trembled for very joy,
And set aside for that time all her care,
So sweet was love, and life so blithe and fair.   160

Now northward Argo steered for two days more,
Until at last they came in sight of shore,
And creeping on, they found a river-mouth,
That a long spit of land fenced from the south,
And turned due west ; and now, at ebb, full strong
Turbid and yellow rolled its stream along,
That scarce could Argo stem it ; wherefore they,
It being but early, anchored till mid-day,
And as they waited, saw an eddy rise
Where sea joined river, and before their eyes   170
The battle of the waters did begin.
So, seeing the mighty ocean best therein,
Weighing their anchor, they made haste to man
Both oars and sails, and therewith plying, ran
With the first wave of the great conquering flood
Far up the stream, on whose banks forests stood,
Darkening the swirling water on each side.
And now between them swiftly did they glide,
And now no more they smelt the fresh salt sea,
Or heard the steady wind pipe boisterously   180
Through the strained rigging, neither with their feet
Set wide, the pitching of their ship to meet,
Went to and fro ; for all was quiet now
But gurgling of the stream beside the prow,
And flapping of the well-nigh useless sail,
And from the black woods some faint dismal wail,
Whether of man or beast they knew not well.

Then o'er their hearts a melancholy fell,
And they began to think they might forget

The quest whereon their hearts had once been set,   190
Now half accomplished, and all wealth and fame,
All memory of the land wherefrom they came,
Their very names indeed, to wander on,
Unseen, unheard of till their lives were done.
　In such-like thoughts they anchored for the night,
Nor slept they much, but wishing for daylight,
About the deck they paced, or sat them down
In longing thought of some fair merchant-town.
　So sadly passed the weary night away,
That, dreary, yet was noisier than the day ;   200
For all about them evil beasts 'gan stir
At nightfall, and great soft-winged bats would whirr
About their raiment and their armour bright.
And when the moon rose, and her crescent white
Made the woods blacker, then from either shore
They heard the thundering of the lion's roar,
Now coming nigher, dying now away ;
And once or twice, as in the stream they lay
A spear-cast from the shore, could they behold
The yellow beast stalk forth, and, stark and bold,   210
Stand in the moonlight on the muddy beach.
Then, though they doubted not their shafts could reach
His kingly heart, they held their hands, for here
All seemed as in a dream, where deadly fear
Is mingled with the most familiar thing ;
And in the cup we see the serpent's sting,
And common speech we answer with a scream.
Moreover, sounds they heard they well might deem
To be men's voices ; but, whatso they were,
Unto the river side they drew not near,   220
Nor yet of aught like man did they have sight.
　So dawned the day ; but like another night
Unto their wearied eyes it seemed to be,
Amid that solitude, where tree joined tree
For ever, as it seemed ; and natheless, they
Ran out the oars and gat them on their way
Against the ebb, and little help the flood
Gave them that day ; but yet for bad or good

202 would] to

They laboured on, though still with less intent
More hopeless past the changeless woods they went.   230
　　But every day, more and more sluggishly
And shorter time, the water from the sea
Ran up, and failed ere eve of the third day,
Though slower took the downward stream its way,
Grown wide and dull, and here and there the wood
Would draw away and leave some dismal rood
Of quaggy land about the river's edge,
Where 'mid the oozes and decaying sedge
There wallowed ugly, nameless, dull-scaled things.
　　These now the weary company of kings,   240
As they passed by, could not endure to see
Unscathed of arrows, turning lazily
Blue-gleaming slimy sides up in the sun,
Whose death swift Atalanta first begun.
For as anigh the prow she chanced to stand,
Unto her bow did she set foot and hand,
And strung it, and therefrom an arrow sent
That through the belly of a monster went,
Legged like a lizard, maned with long lank hair.
He, screaming, straight arose from out his lair,   250
With many another of his kith and kin,
And swiftly getting to the water thin,
Made for the ship ; and though upon the way
Some few among them lost the light of day,
Smit by Thessalian arrows, yet the most
The narrow strip of water fairly crossed,
And scaled the ship's sides, and therewith began
A fearful battle betwixt worm and man.
Not long it dured ; though Ceneus through the mail
Was bitten, and one monster's iron tail   260
Smote down Asterion, whom Eribotes
Made shift to save ; but chiefly amid these
She who had been the first to raise the strife
Was hard bested, and scarce escaped with life.
　　One worm 'twixt ship and shore her arrow slew,
But ere her amazonian axe she drew,
Another monster had got slimy hold
Of her slim ankles and cast fold on fold

About her legs, and binding thigh to thigh,
Wrapt round her sides, enfolding mightily   270
Her foiled right hand, then raised aloft his crest
Against her unembraced tender breast ;
But she, with one unarmed hand yet left free,
Still strove to ward the blow, but giddily,
Because the deadly rings still tighter grew
About her heart ; yet as she fell, there flew
A feathered javelin swiftly from the left,
By Arcas desperately cast, that cleft
The monster's head, and dulled his glittering eyes.
    Then the glad Minyæ with joyous cries   280
Cleared Argo's decks of all the monstrous things,
As from the maiden's limbs the slimy rings
Slacked and fell off : but she, so saved from death,
Sat weary by the mast, and drew glad breath,
And vowed the grey and deadly thing should shine,
Wrought all of gold, within Diana's shrine,
In woody fair Arcadia. But the rest,
When they with poured-out wine the Gods had blest,
And flayed the slain worms, gat them to the oar,
And 'gainst the sluggish stream slid past the shore.   290
    But swifter the next day the river ran
With higher banks, and now the woods began
To be of trees that in their land they knew,
And into clumps of close-set beeches grew,
And oak-trees thinly spread, and there-between
Fair upland hillocks well beset with green ;
And 'neath the trees great herds of deer and neat,
And sheep, and swine, fed on the herbage sweet,
Seeming all wild as though they knew not man,
For quite untented here and there they ran,   300
And while two great bucks raised the armed brow
Each against each (since time of fight was now)
About them would the swine squeal, and the sheep
In close-drawn flock their faint republic keep,
With none to watch : nor saw they fence or fold,
Nor any husbandry did they behold,
But the last men their wearied eyes had seen
Were those strong swimmers in the Phasis green.

So seeing now these beasts in such plenty,
It seemed good unto the Minyæ   310
To make provision thereof for their need.
And drawing Argo up through sedge and reed,
They made her fast, while divers took the land.
Arcas the hunter, Idas strong of hand,
White Atalanta, wise Eurytion,
Far-seeing Lynceus, and the Sminthian's son,
Keen Theseus, with Pirithous his mate,
Clitius, whose swift shaft smote as sure as fate,
Ætalides, the runner of the plain,
Phocus, whose sling was seldom whirled in vain,   320
Cæneus the cragsman, Periclimenes,
And Apheus, haunter of the close-set trees.
So forth these set, and none of them had lack
Of spear or bow, or quiver at the back,
As through the land they went with wary mirth,
For they rejoiced once more to feel the earth
Beneath their feet, while on their heads fell down
The uncupped acorn, and the long leaves brown,
For on that land the sad mid-autumn lay,
And earlier came the sunset day by day.   330
But now unto their hunting gave they heed,
And of the more part happy was the speed,
And soon to Argo did they turn again,
Laden with that they had set forth to gain,
Of deer and beasts the slaughtered carcases
Upborne on interwoven boughs of trees,
With whom came Theseus not, nor Arcus came,
Nor yet Ætalides (who had the fame
Next Atalanta among all the rest
For swiftness, she being easily the best)   340
There waiting till the night, yet none the more
Came down those three unto the river's shore,
Nor through the night : but swift Ætalides
At dawn they saw come running through the trees,
With Arcas far behind, and Theseus slim
The last of all, but straining every limb
To be their equal : empty-handed they

312 And] So

Came back to Argo on that dawn of day,
And on being asked, a short tale had to tell.
   Unto their part to chase a great buck fell,   350
That led them far, and he at last being lost,
They sat them down with nought to pay the cost
Of all their travail, so being set, they heard
A hubbub of strange voices, and afeard
Leapt to their feet, and presently they saw
Strange folk, both men and women, toward them draw,
Who spread about them as to stop their flight
On all hands more than they durst lightly fight.
   So being thus trapped they fain had spoke them fair,
But knowing not their tongue, they yet had care   360
To speak with smiles as though they feared not aught,
Asking for food by signs, which soon was brought ;
No flesh, but roots and nuts, whereof they ate,
And so by signs until the day grew late
They dealt together, making clear indeed
Each unto each but little of their need ;
At last of their departure were they fain,
But, being stayed, they durst not strive in vain
For fear of worse ; but now, the night being come,
The wild folk seemed to think that place their home
Just as another, and there gat to sleep,   371
Nor yet upon the Greeks a watch did keep
To stop their going ; ' So,' said Arcas, ' we,
An hour after midnight, warily
Stole from among them, neither gave they chase,
Being still asleep like beasts, in that same place ;
And for their semblance, neither were they clad,
Nor in their hands a spear or sword they had,
Or any brass or iron, but long slings,
And scrips of stones, and ugly stone-set things   380
Most like to knives, and clubs of heavy wood ;
Soft-voiced they were, and gentle of their mood,
And goodly made as such wild folk may be,
But tanned with sun and wind ; there did we see
Old men and young, and women old and young,
With many children scattered there among,
All naked, and with unshorn yellow hair

MORRIS

G g

Blowing about ; and sooth we deem they were
Houseless and lawless, without town or king,
Knowing no Gods, and lacking everything.'   390
  So said he, but Medea spoke, and said :—
' O heroes, surely by all likelihead
These are the folk of whom I erst heard tell
In Æa, where to me it oft befell
To speak with many men from many lands,
Long ere ye crossed the Phasis' yellow sands.
  ' Of these I learned more tongues of speaking men
Than ye might deem men spoke, who told me then
Of such as these, that ye have seen but now.
And yet indeed some Gods these folk do know,   400
The Sun, the Moon, the mother of the earth,
And more perchance, and days they have of mirth
When these they honour ; yea, and unto these
Within their temples, groves of ancient trees,
Clad but in leaves, and crowned in solemn wise,
They offer strangers up in sacrifice,
Which was your doom had not the Gods been kind,
Who for your bodies other graves will find.'

  But when they heard her, glad they were indeed
That they from such a bondage had been freed.   410
And, day being fully come, they loosed from shore,
And 'gainst the stream all bent unto the oar.
All day they toiled, and every mile of way
Still swifter grew the stream, so on that day
Few leagues they made ; and still the banks were fair,
But rising into scarped cliffs here and there,
Where screamed the great ger-falcon as they passed,
And whence the sooty swifts about the mast
Went sweeping, with shrill cries at that new sight. 419
  Nought happed that day worth record, but at night,
When they were moored, and sound of splashing oars
Had ceased, and stiller grew the upland shores,
Another sound they heard besides the stream
That gurgled past them, that to them did seem
Like sound of feet of men who pass to war,

Rising and falling as the wind from far
Would bear it on or drop it in the dark.
So, while with strained ears, they stood to hark
The murmur, as folk use, scarce sure they heard
That which already inward fear had stirred,   430
Erginus spoke : ' O heroes, fear ye nought,
This is not death, though ye to toil are brought ;
This noise is but the river as it falls
Over its mountainous and iron walls,
Which, being once passed, both calm and deep will be
The pent-up stream, and Argo easily
Will stem it ; but or ere we come thereto,
Needs must we heave her up and make her go
Over the hard earth, till the falls are past.
Eat therefore now, and sleep, that ye may last   440
Through this and other toils, and so may come,
Through many labours, back unto your home.'
    So, landing, many a pine-torch did they light,
And made the dusky evening strange and bright,
And there a mighty fire did they pile,
And set the flesh thereto, and in a while,
When all was ready, did they offer up
That which the Gods claimed, pouring out a cup
Of red wine to them from a new-pierced skin.
Then in that lonely land did they begin   450
Their feast, and first the flesh to Jason gave,
And next to her who all their souls did save
Far up the Phasis on that other day,
And then unto the swift Arcadian May
The guarded treasure of the trim-shod queen.
Then to the godlike singer, set between
The twin Laconian stars, and then to these ;
And then to Arcas, haunter of the trees,
Theseus, Pirithous, Erginus true,
The north-wind's sons, the cleavers of the blue ;   460
And all the kings being satisfied in turn,
With vain desires 'gan their hearts to burn,
So stirred within them wine and changing speech.
    But unto him his harp did Orpheus reach,

435 being once passed] being passed

And smote the strings, and through the ancient trees
Rang the heart-piercing honied melodies :—
    ' Alas ! for Saturn's days of gold,
Before the mountain men were bold
To dig up iron from the earth
Wherewith to slaughter health and mirth,   470
And bury hope far underground.
When all men needed did abound
In every land ; nor must they toil,
Nor wear their lives in strife to foil
Each other's hands, for all was good,
And no man knew the sight of blood.
    ' With all the world man had no strife,
No element against his life
Was sworn and bitter ; on the sea,
Dry shod, could all walk easily ;   480
No fire there was but what made day,
Or hidden in the mountains grey ;
No pestilence, no lightning flash,
No over-mastering wind, to dash
The roof upon some trembling head.
    ' Then the year changed, but ne'er was dead,
Nor was the autumn-tide more sad
Than very spring ; and all unclad
Folk went upon the harmless snow,
For not yet did mid-winter know,   490
The biting frost and icy wind,
The very east was soft and kind.
    ' And on the crown of July days,
All heedless of the mid-day blaze,
Unshaded by the rosy bowers,
Unscorched beside the tulip flowers,
The snow-white naked girl might stand ;
Or fearless thrust her tender hand
Amidst the thornless rose-bushes.
    ' Then, 'mid the twilight of the trees   500
None feared the yellow beast to meet ;
Smiling to feel their languid feet
Licked by the serpent's forkèd tongue.
For then no clattering horn had rung

Through those green glades, or made afraid
The timid dwellers in the shade.
No lust of strength nor fear of death
Had driven men, with shortened breath,
The stag's wide-open eyes to watch ;
No shafts to slay, no nets to catch,   510
Were yet ; unyoked the neat might play
On untilled meads, and mountains grey,
Unshorn, the silly sheep might rove.
  ' Nor knew that world consuming love,
Mother of hate, or envy cold,
Or rage for fame, or thirst for gold,
Or longing for the ways untried,
That ravening and unsatisfied,
Draw shortened lives of men to Hell.

  ' Alas ! what profit now to tell   520
The long unweary lives of men
Of past days—threescore years and ten,
Unbent, unwrinkled, beautiful,
Regarding not death's flower-crowned skull,
But with some damsel intertwined
In such love as leaves hope behind.
  ' Alas, the vanished days of bliss !
Will no God send some dream of this,
That we may know what it has been ?

  ' Oh, thou, the chapleted with green,   530
Thou purple-stained, but not with blood,
Who on the edge of some cool wood
Forgettest the grim Indian plain,
And all the strife and all the pain,
While in thy sight the must foams out,
And maid and man, with cry and shout,
Toil while thou laughest, think of us,
And drive away these piteous,
Formless and wailing thoughts, that press
About our hour of happiness.   540
  ' Lyæus, King ! by thee alone
To song may change our tuneless moan,

The murmur of the bitter sea
To ancient tales be changed by thee.
By thee the unnamed smouldering fire
Within our hearts turns to desire
Sweet, amorous, half satisfied ;
Through thee the doubtful years untried
Seem fair to us and fortunate,
In spite of death, in spite of fate.'   550

He ceased, and bent his head above the wine :
Then, as he raised his eyes they saw them shine
In the red torchlight with unwilling tears,
And their hearts too, with thoughts of vanished years
Were pensive, as at ending of his song
They heard the bubbling river speed along,
Nor did they miss that doubtful noise to hear
The rising night-wind through the branches bear,
Till sleep fell on them, and the watch alone
Waked in that place, and heard the distant moan   560
Grow louder as the dead night stiller grew,
And fuller of all fear, till daylight drew
A faint wan streak between the thinner trees,
And in their yellowing foliage the breeze
Made a new sound, that through their waking dream
Like to the surging sea well-nigh did seem.

But the full day being come, all men awake,
Fresh hold upon the oars began to take,
Stemming the stream, that now at every mile
Swifter and shallower ran, and in a while   570
Above all noises did they hear that roar,
And saw the floating foam borne past the shore,
So but ten leagues they made upon that day,
And on the morrow, going on their way,
They went not far, for underneath their keel
Some once or twice the hard rock did they feel,
And looking on ahead, the stream could see
White with the rapids ; therefore warily
Some mile or two they went at a slow pace
And stayed their course where they beheld a place   580

Soft-sloping to the river ; and there all,
Half deafened by the noises of the fall
And bickering rapids, left the ashen oar,
And spreading over the well-wooded shore
Cut rollers, laying on full many a stroke,
And made a capstan of a mighty oak,
And so drew Argo up, with hale and how,
On to the grass, turned half to mire now.
    Thence did they toil their best, in drawing her
Beyond the falls, whereto being come anear,   590
They trembled when they saw them, for from sight
The rocks were hidden by the spray-clouds white,
Cold, wretched, chilling, and the mighty sound
Their heavy-laden hearts did sore confound ;
For parted from all men they seemed, and far
From all the world, shut out by that great bar.
    Moreover, when with toil and pain, at last
Unto the torrent's head they now had passed,
They sent forth swift Ætalides to see
What farther up the river there might be.   600
Who going twenty leagues, another fall
Found, with great cliffs on each side, like a wall,
But 'twixt the two, another unbarred stream
Joined the main river ; therefore did they deem,
When this they heard, that they perforce must try
This smoother branch ; so somewhat heavily
Argo they launched again, and gat them forth
Still onward toward the winter and the north.

BOOK XI

The passage northward continued—Argo drawn overland—
The winter by the northern river.

Now might the Minyæ hoist up to the breeze
Their well-wrought sail, for barren of all trees
The banks were now become, not rising high
Above the deep green stream that sluggishly
Strove with the strenuous Argo's cleaving stem.
    So after all their toil was rest to them

A little while, and on the deck they sat,
Not wholly sad, and talked of this and that,
Or watched the restless fishes turn and wind,
Or the slim kestrel hanging in the wind,   10
Or the wild cattle scouring here and there
About the plain ; for in a plain they were,
Edged round with hills, with quaggy brooks cleft through,
That 'mid their sedges toward the river drew,
And harboured noisome things, and death to man.
But looking up stream, the green river ran
Unto their eyes, from out the mountains high,
For 'twixt no pass could they behold the sky,
Though at the mountain's foot, far through the plain,
They saw the wandering river shine again,   20
Then vanish wholly, therefore through their ease,
With fear did they the jealous Gods appease.

Natheless, for two days did they speed along,
Not toiling aught, and cheered with tale and song,
But the third noonday, bringing them anear
The mountains, turned to certain grief their fear,
For now they saw the stream, grown swift but deep,
Come from a cavern in the mountain steep,
Nor would it help them aught upon that tide
To heave the swift ship out on either side,   30
For all that plain the mountain ridge bestrode,
And scarcely could a horseman find a road
Through any pass into the farther land.

Then 'mid the downcast men did Jason stand,
And lifting up his voice, said : ' Minyæ,
Why right and left upon this plain look ye,
Where dwell but beasts or beast-like men alone ?
Look rather to that heap of rugged stone,
Pierced with the road that leadeth to the north.
Yea, if from very hell this stream runs forth,   40
Let us go thither, bearing in our hands
This golden, hard-won marvel of all lands.
Yet, since not death it bears, but living things,
Shall we not reach thereby the sea that rings
The whole world round, and so make shift to reach
Sunny Eubœa, and fair Argo beach

Before Iolchos, having lost no whit
Of all our gains ? Or else here must we sit
Till hunger slays us on some evil day,
Or wander till our raiment falls away   50
From off our bodies, and we, too, become
Like those ye saw, not knowing any home,
Voiceless, desiring nought but daily food,
And seeking that like beasts within the wood,
Each for himself. And all our glory gone,
Our names but left upon some carven stone
In Greece, still growing fainter day by day.
And this work wrought within the sunny bay,
Nor yet without the help of Gods, shall lie
A wonder to the wild beasts passing by,   60
While on her fallen masts the sedge-birds sing,
Unseen of men, a clean forgotten thing.'
  So spake he, setting courage in their hearts
To try the unknown dark, and to their parts
All gat them swiftly, and they struck the mast,
And deftly steered from out the sunlight passed
Into the cold, bat-haunted cavern low,
And, thrusting out with poles, made shift to go
Against the stream, that with a hollow sound
Smote Argo's stem. Then Jason, looking round,   70
Trembled himself, for now, indeed, he thought,
Though to the toiling heroes he said nought :—
' What do we, if this cavern narrows now,
Or over falls these burrowing waters flow,
And drive us back again into the sun,
Cursing the day this quest was first begun,
Or somewhat traps us here, as well it may,
And ends us all, far from the light of day ? '
  Therewith he bade them light the torches up,
And to the mountain Gods to pour a cup,   80
And one unto the river Gods, and pray
That they might come into the light of day,
When they had pierced the mountain through and through.
So from the torches trains of sparkles flew,
And strangely flashed their arms in that dark place,
And white and haggard showed each anxious face

Against those dripping walls of unknown stone.
  But now in Jason's hand the cup outshone,
Full of red wine, pressed by the Grecian sea,
And lifting high his hand, he cried : ' O ye,   90
Both Gods and nymphs who in this wild land dwell,
In hill or river, henceforth may ye tell
How through your midst have passed the Minyæ ;
And if, ye helping, the cold northern sea
We safely reach, and our desired home,
Thither the fame and fear of you shall come,
And there a golden-pillared house shall stand,
Unto our helpers in this savage land.
Nor when we reach the other side of this
Grim cavern, due observance shall ye miss,   100
For whatso on the teeming plain we snare,
Slain with due rites shall smoke before you there.'
  So spake he, and twice poured the fragrant wine ;
But they, well-pleased to have the gift divine,
And noting well his promises, took heed
Unto his prayers, and gave the heroes speed.
Then Jason straightway bade more torches light,
And Argo pushed along flared through the night
Of the dank cavern, and the dull place rang
With Grecian names, as loud the heroes sang,   110
For hope had come into their hearts at last.
  So through the winding cave three days they passed.
But on the fourth day Lynceus gave a cry,
Smiting his palms together, who could spy,
Far off, a little white speck through the dark,
As when the 'lated traveller sees the spark
Of some fair-lighted homestead glitter bright.
But soon to all men's eyes the joyous sight
Showed clear, and with redoubled force they pushed
Swift Argo forth, who through the water rushed   120
As though she longed for daylight too and air.
And so within an hour they brought her there,
And on the outer world the sun shone high.
For it was noon ; so mooring presently,
On the green earth they clean forgot their pain,
For joy to feel the sweet soft grass again,

And see the fair things of the world, and feel
The joyous sunlight that the sick can heal,
And soft tormenting of the western wind.

And there for joy about their heads they twined   130
The yellow autumn flowers of the field,
And of untimely sorrow were they healed
By godlike conquering wine ; nor yet forgot
Their promise to the Gods, but on that spot,
Of turf and stones they built up altars twain,
And sent the hunters forth, and not in vain ;
For Atalanta, swifter than a man,
Arcas, and mighty Theseus, overran
A white high-crested bull, and tough cords threw
About his horns, and so by main force drew   140
The great beast to the altars, where the knife
Of wise Asclepius ended his hot life
And there they feasted far into the night.

But when their toil the next returning light
Brought back to them, they gat unto the oar,
While Jason anxiously scanned either shore ;
For now the stream was narrowing apace,
And little more than just enough of space
Was left the oars ; but deep it ran and slow,
And through a like flat grassy plain did go   150
As that which ere its burrowing it had cleft ;
But lower were the hills, and on the left
So low they grew, they melted quite away
To woody swells before the end of day.

Full many a league upon that day they made,
And the next day the long oars down they laid,
For at their back the steady south-west blew,
And low anigh their heads the rain-clouds flew ;
Therefore they hoisted up their sail to it,
And idle by the useless oars did sit,   160
Watching the long wave from their swift sea-plough
Sweep up the low green bank, for soothly now,
A pebble ill-thrown by a stripling's hand
From Argo's deck had lighted on the land ;
And yet far inland still they seemed to be,
Nor noted aught to tell them of the sea.

So on that night, for thought of many things,
Full little sleep fell on the troubled kings ;
But Argus slept, and at the dawn he dreamed,
Not wholly sleeping, and to him it seemed   170
That one said to him : ' Where is now become
The cunning that thou learnedst in thine home,
O wise artificer ? What dost thou here,
While in thy fellows' hearts is gathering fear ?
Now from the north thou seest this river flow,
Why doubtest thou to find another go
Into the cold green icy northern sea ?
Lo ! if thou willest well to trust in me,
About the noontide of this very day,
At the wood's end I bid thee Argo stay,   180
And from her straightway let the Minyæ land
And take the adze and wood-axe in the hand,
And let them labour hard, with thee to guide,
Until on wheels thy well-built keel shall glide ;
And this being done as pleases thy wise mind,
Doubt not a northern-flowing stream to find,
For certainly some God shall show it thee.
And if thou wishest now to ask of me,
No dream I am, but lovely and divine,
Whereof let this be unto thee a sign,   .   190
That when thou wak'st the many-coloured bow
Across the world the morning sun shall throw,
But me indeed thine eyes shall not behold.'

Then he awaking in the morning cold,
A sprinkle of fine rain felt on his face,
And leaping to his feet, in that wild place,
Looked round and saw the morning sunlight throw
Across the world the many-coloured bow,
And trembling knew that the high Gods indeed
Had sent the Messenger unto their need.   200
And when the Minyæ, running out the oars
That windless morning, found them touch the shores
On either side, then ere one said a word,
He cried, and said : ' O Jason, chief and lord,
And ye, fair fellows, to no bitter end

Our quest is come ; but this sharp keel shall send
A glittering foam-heap up in the wide sea,
If ye will hear my words and trust in me.'
    Therewith he told them of that dream divine,
And of the many-coloured arched sign,   210
And gladdened all their hearts, for well they knew
That some God helped them, and straightway they threw
Hawsers ashore, wherewith their keel to tow,
And swiftly through the water made her go,
Until they reached the ending of the wood,
Just at the noonday, and there thought it good
To rest till morning : but at dawn of day
Gat forth, and mighty blows began to lay
On many a tree, making the tall trunks reel,
That ne'er before had felt the woodman's steel.   220
    So many days they laboured, cutting down
The smooth grey beeches, and the pine-trees brown,
And cleft them into planks and beams foursquare.
And so, with Argus guiding all things there,
A stage with broad wheels nigh the stream they made,
And then from out the water Argo weighed
Little by little, dealing cunningly,
Till on the stage the great black ship did lie,
And all things waited for the setting forth
Unto some river flowing toward the north.   230
    But midst all this, as painfully they wrought,
Passed twenty days, and on their heads was brought
The first beginning of the winter cold ;
For now the wind-beat twigs had lost their hold
Of the faint yellow leaves, and thin and light
The forest grew, and colder night by night,
Or soaked with rain, and swept with bitter wind,
Or with white creeping mist made deaf and blind.
    Meanwhile for long there came no sign at all,
Nor yet did sight of man to them befall,   240
To guide them on their way, though through the trees,
Singly at times, at times in twos and threes,
Both for their daily flesh they hunted oft,
And also fain of fells to clad them soft,

                207 foam-heap] furrow

And guard their bodies from the coming cold
Yet never any man did they behold,
Though underneath the shaft and hunting-spear,
Fell many a stag, and shuffling crafty bear,
And strange the Minyæ showed in shaggy spoil.
But now, at ending of their woodwright's toil,   250
It chanced Argus' self alone to go,
One bitter day, when the first dusty snow
Was driven through the bare boughs from the east,
In hot chase of the honey-loving beast
Far from his fellows : him he brought to bay
Nigh to the dusk of that quick-darkening day,
Deep in the forest 'mid a clump of yews,
And ere the red-eyed beast again could choose
To fight or flee, ran in, and thrust his spear
Into his heart ; then fell the shaggy bear,   260
As falls a landslip by the mining sea,
With grass and bracken, and wind-bitten tree,
And Argus, drawing out his two-edged knife,
Let out the last spark of his savage life ;
But as he arose, he heard a voice that said :—
' Good luck, O huntsman, to thine hardihead,
Well met thou art to me, who wander far
On this first winter night that shows no star.'

Then looking up, he saw a maid draw nigh,
Like those who by Thermodon live and die ;   270
Her legs and arms with brazen scales were clad,
Well-plated shoes upon her feet she had,
And fur-lined, gold-wrought raiment to the knee,
And on her head a helm wrought royally ;
In her slim hand a mighty bow she bore,
And at her back well-feathered shafts good store,
And in her belt a two-edged cutting sword.
Then straightly answered Argus to her word :—
' Lady, not far hence are my fellows stayed,
But on hard earth this night will they be laid,   280
And eat the flesh of beasts their hands have slain.
For from the sea we come, to meet again
The ocean that the round world rings about,
Still wandering on, in trouble and in doubt.'

'Nay,' said she, 'let us set on through the wood,
For food and fire alone to me are good,
And guarded sleep among such folk as thee,
For being alone, I fear the enemy,
The savage men our bands are wont to chase
Through these wild woods, from tangled place to place.'
Then Argus swiftly flayed off the bear's hide,   291
And through the wood went with her side by side ;
But long ere they could reach the skirts of it,
Across the world the wings of night 'gan flit ;
Then blindly had he stumbled through the place,
But still the damsel went before a pace,
Leading him on ; and as she went, she shed
A faint light round, but no word Argus said,
Because he deemed she was a thing divine,
And in his heart still thought upon the sign.   300

So went the twain till nigh the woods were past,
And the new-risen moon slim shadows cast
Upon the thin snow, and the windless sky
Was cleared, and all the stars shone frostily.
Therewith she stopped, and turned about on him,
And with the sight his dazzled eyes did swim,
So was she changed, for from her raiment light
Her rosy limbs showed 'gainst the wintry white,
Not shrinking from the snow ; her arms were bare,
Her head unarmed set round with yellow hair,   310
And starred with unnamed dainty glimmering things ;
From her two shoulders many-coloured wings
Rose up, and fanning in the frosty night,
Shone as they moved with sparkles of strange light ;
And on an ivory rod within her hand
A letter bound round by a golden band
He saw. Then to the dazed man she said :—
'Argus, be glad, and lifting up thine head,
Look through these few last trees upon the plain,
Smooth and unseamed, though never crossed by wain,
And thank the Gods that led you here at last,   321
For in no long time shall the leagues be passed
'Twixt you and a swift river running north.
But now next morn at daybreak get ye forth,

And labour all ye may, for see the sky
How clear it is—the few light clouds are high,
And from the east light blows the frosty wind ;
Firm will the way be now, nor ill to find,
But surely in few days will come the snow,
And all the plain so smooth and even now,   330
Shall be swept into drifts impassable.
And now I bid thee heed the great downs well
Thou seest bar the northern way to thee ;
Left of the moon a wide pass thou mayst see ;
Look—where the yew-trees o'er the whitened grass
Mix with the dark sky : make ye for that pass,
While yet endures the east wind and the frost,
And in your journey shall ten days be lost,
If that ye labour hard : but coming there,
Shall ye behold a clear green river fair,   340
Unfrozen yet, swift-running, that will hold
Great Argo well : now at my word be bold,
And set her therein, and the black ship tow
Adown the stream, though not far shall ye go,
But reaching a great forest, bide ye there,
And there the coming unknown winter bear.
The days shall darken, the north-wind shall blow,
And all about shall swirl the drifting snow,
And your astonished eyes shall soon behold
Firm earth and river one with binding cold,   350
And in mid-winter then shall ye be shut ;
But ere that haps shall ye build many an hut,
And dwell there as ye may, until the spring
Unchains the streams, and quickens everything.
Then get ye down the river to the sea.
  ' Nor doubt thou aught since thou beholdest me,
For I indeed am Iris ; but farewell,
For of my finished message must I tell
To her that sent me to this dreary place.'
    Thus spake she, and straightway before his face   360
She spread her fair wings wide, and from the earth
Rose upwards toward the place that gave her birth,
Still growing faint and fainter 'neath the moon,

360 Thus] So

Till from his wondering eyes she vanished soon.
But she being gone, he gat him straight away
Unto his fellows, bidding them 'gainst day
Be ready to set forth, and told his tale.
And they, not fearing that his word should fail,
Gat them to sleep, and ere the late dawn came,
By the faint starlight, and the flickering flame   370
Of their own watch-fires were upon the way.
    So at the cables toiled all men that day
In bands of twenty, and strong shoulders bore
The unused yoke, and laboured very sore,
And yet with all their toil few miles they made,
Though 'gainst that bitter labour sweet hope, weighed,
Was found the heavier, and their hearts were cheered
With wine and food ere the noontide they neared ;
Nor as they laboured did the Thracian spare
To cast his music on the frosty air,   380
That therewith ringing, gladdened every heart.
So till the evening did each man his part,
When all that night they slept, and at daybreak
The twisted cables in strong hands did take
And laboured on, not earning warriors' meed,
But like some carl's unkempt and rugged steed,
That to the town drags his corn-laden wain.

    But neither was the heavenly word in vain,
For as the yew-clad hill they drew anear
The grey-eyed keen Messenian could see clear,   390
From the bare top of a great ashen-tree,
The river running to the northern sea,
Showing all dull and heavy 'gainst the snow,
And when the joyful tidings they did know,
Light grew their hearts indeed, and scarcely less
They joyed than he who, lying all helpless
In dreary prison, sees his door ope wide,
And half-forgotten friends stand by his side.
    So on the tenth day through the pass they drew
Their strange ship-laden wain, and came unto   400
A deep dark river, their long-promised road ;

383 that] the

MORRIS

H h

Then from the car they slipped its heavy load,
And when safe in the stream the keel had slid,
They with strong axes their own work undid,
And to the Goddess a great altar made
Of planks and beams, foursquare, and thereon laid
A white wild bull, and barley cakes, and spice,
Not sparing gold and goodly things of price ;
And fire being set thereto, and all things done
That they should do, by a faint mid-day sun,   410
Seaward they turned, and some along the shore
With lightened hearts the hempen tow-ropes bore,
And some on Argo's deck abode their turn.

But now did Jason's heart within him burn
To show his deeds to other men than these,
Nor did he quite forget the palaces
Of golden Æa, long left, as a dream,
Or Æson's beauteous house, whose oaken beam
Cleft the dark wintry river, as they went
With longing eyes and hearts still northward bent,   420
And fain he was to see his dainty bride,
That wrapt in muffling furs sat by his side,
Sit 'neath some heavy rustling summer tree,
Thin clad, to drink the breezes from the sea.

Now the next day the great oak-wood they reached,
And as the Goddess bade them, there they beached
Their sea-beat ship, on which from side to side
They built a roof against the snowy tide,
And round about her, huts wherein to dwell,
When on their heads the full midwinter fell,   430
And round the camp a wooden wall they made,
That by no men or beasts they might be frayed.
Meanwhile, the frost increased, and the thin snow
From off the iron ground the wind did blow,
And in the cold, dark stream, from either bank
The ice stretched forth ; at last, ere the sun sank,
One bitter day, low grew the clouds and dun
A little northward of the setting sun,
Wherefrom, at nightfall, sprung a furious blast,
That, ere the middle of the night was past,   440
Brought up the snow from some untrodden land,

Joyless and sunless, where in twilight stand,
Amid the fleecy drift with faces wan,
Giants immovable by God or man.
  So 'mid the many changes of the night,
The silent snow fell till the world was white,
And to those southland folk entrapped, forlorn
The waking was upon the morrow morn,
And few were light of foot enough to go
Henceforth about the woods their darts to throw   450
At bird or beast, though, as the wild-fowl passed
South o'er their camp, yet flew they not so fast
As Arcas' arrows, and the elk at bay
Deep in the forest, seldom found a way
To 'scape from Jason's mighty well-steeled spear,
And Atalanta's feet outran the deer
And slew him, tangled in the wreathed drift.
  Nor for the rest, did they yet lack the gift
Of sunny Bacchus, but by night and day,
By firelight passed the snowy time away,   460
Forgetting not their fathers, or the time
When all the world still dwelt in equal clime,
But each to each amid the wine-cups told
Unwritten, half-forgotten tales of old.

BOOK XII

The heroes reach the northern sea : and pass unknown lands, and
seas without land, till they come at last to the pillars of Hercules.

MOST pitiless and stark the winter grew
Meanwhile, beneath a sky of cloudless blue,
And sun that warmed not, till they nigh forgot
The green lush spring, the summer rich and hot,
The autumn fragrant with slow-ripening fruit ;
Till each grew listless, dull to the heart's root ;
For day passed day, and yet no change they saw
In the white sparkling plain without a flaw,
No cloud, no change within the sunny sky,
Or in the wind, that rose at noon, to die   10
Before the sunset, and no change at all

In the drear silence of the dead nightfall.
  Ten weeks they bode there, longing for the spring,
And to the hearts of some the thought would cling
That thus they should be till their lives were past,
And into hopeless bonds that land was cast ;
But on a day the wind, that rose at noon,
Died not at night, and the white, sharp-edged moon,
Just as the west had given it to sight,
Was hidden from the watchers of the night   20
By fleecy clouds, and the next dawn of day
Broke o'er the Minyæ colourless and grey,
With gusts of fitful wind 'twixt south and east,
That with the day grew steadier and increased,
Until a south-west gale blew o'er the snow,
And northward drove the steel-blue clouds and low.
And on that night the pattering of the rain
Roused them from sleep, and next they saw the plain
Made grey and ugly with quick-coming thaw,
And all the sky beset with fowl they saw,   30
Who sniffed the wind and hastened from the sea
Unto the floods now coming certainly.
  For from their camp the Minyæ beheld
How the swift river from the high ground swelled,
And still tormented by the wind and rain,
Burst from the ice and covered all the plain
With breadth of turbid waters, while around
Their high-raised camp again they saw the ground
Freed from the swathing snow ; nor was it long
Ere in the woods the birds began their song,   40
For March was come and life to everything,
Nor did the buds fear much the doubtful spring.
  Now in few days the sun shone out again,
The waters drew from off the flooded plain,
And all was bright and soft as it might be,
Though bank-high rolled the river to the sea,
Made perilous with trees and heavy drift ·
Natheless on rollers Argo did they lift,
And drew her toward the stream in spite of all
The ills they saw, and chances that might fall ;   50
And there they launched her, being now most fain

Once more to try the green and shifting plain,
And for the praise of other men they yearned
And all the goods of life so dearly earned,
Nor failed desire and longing love to come
That spring-tide to those rovers far from home.
  Therefore with joy they shouted, when once more
They felt great Argo move, and saw the shore
Keep changing as they swept on toward the sea,
With cheerful hearts still rowing steadily ;   60
For now the ashen oars could they thrust forth
Into the widened stream, that toward the north
Ran swiftly, and thenceforward day by day
Toiling, they made full many a league of way.
Nor did they see great hills on either hand,
When they had fairly passed the woody land
Where they abode the winter ; neither heard
The sound of falls to make their hearts afeared,
But through great woods the gentle river ran,
And plains where fed the herds unowned of man ;   70
Though sometimes in the night-time did they hear
Men's voices calling out, far-off and near,
But in some tongue not one among them knew,
No, not the Queen : but Lynceus, passing through
The woods with Idas, following up a bear,
A sudden clamour of men's tongues did hear,
And in a cleared space came upon a throng
Of naked men and women, fair and strong,
About a fire, just at point to eat,
But at the flash of arms they to their feet   80
Rose suddenly, and swiftly gat away,
Nor durst the twain give chase to them that day,
But coming to that fire, laid their hands
On a brass cauldron, and three woollen bands,
That seemed like belts or fillets for their heads,
Set thick with silver knots and amber beads.
Now round the brazen cauldron, graven well,
Were uncouth letters, that some tale might tell,
If any them could read ; so when the fleece
Was offered up unto the Gods of Greece,   90
This thing in fair Messene Idas hung

In the white fane where deeds of war are sung.
   But through all this the wearied Minyæ
Were drawing nigh unto the northern sea,
And marshier grew the plain as on they went,
And eastward the still-widening river bent,
Until one day at eve, with chilling rain,
The north-wind blew across the marshy plain
Most cold and bitter, but to them as sweet
As the rose-scented zephyr those do meet   100
Who near the happy islands of the blest ;
For as upon their eager brows it pressed,
They sniffed withal the odour of the sea,
And going on a mile, they seemed to be
Within some eddy rippling languidly,
And when the stream they tasted that went by
Their shielded bulwark, better was the draught
Than any wine o'er which a king has laughed,
For still it savoured of the bitter sea.
   So fell the night, and next day joyously   110
They met the full flood, whose first toppling wave
Against the sturdy prow of Argo drave,
And with good heart, as 'midst the sweeping oars
It tossed and foamed, and swept the muddy shores,
They toiled, and felt no weariness that day.
But though right well they gat them on their way
They failed ere dark the open sea to reach ;
But in the night the murmur of the beach,
Tormented by the changeful dashing seas,
Came to their ears upon the fitful breeze.   120
Then sore they longed for dawn, and when it broke
Again the waters foamed beneath their stroke,
Till they had gained that river's utmost reach,
Which from the sea by a low sandy beach
Was guarded well, all but a little space,
Through which now rushed in headlong, foaming race,
The huddled waters of the flowing tide.
So there the Minyæ thought it good to bide
And wait the ebb, dreading some hidden bank ;
And while they waited to good hap they drank,   130

93 But] So

And poured out wine unto the deity
Who dwelt between the river and the sea,
Forgetting not the great Earth-shaking One,
Nor Her by whose help thus far they had run
Their happy course unto that river's mouth.
And now the wind had changed, and from the south
Blew softly, and the hot sun shining forth,
Made lovely land of that once bitter north,
And filled their hearts with longing thoughts of love,
And worship of the sea-born seed of Jove.   140
   But as they waited thus, with hearts that burned
To try the sea, the tide grew high and turned,
And seaward through the deepened channel ran
In gentle ripple 'gainst the breakers wan.
Then thither gat the joyous Minyæ,
And shouting, drave out Argo to the sea.

   But when the first green ridge swept up her bow,
Then Jason cried : ' And who shall stop us now ?
And who shall drive us unto other end,
Than that we will ? Let whoso be our friend,   150
Whoso our foe, henceforth, until the earth
Forgets of changeful men the death and birth,
We shall not be forgotten anywhere,
But our deeds told shall free sad folk from care.'
   So spake he, and his love beholding him,
Trembled for joy and love in every limb,
And inwardly she saw an ivory throne,
And Jason sitting with her there alone,
High o'er wise men and warriors worshipping.
For they were young, nor yet had felt the sting   160
Of poisonous fear, nor thought of coming age
And bitter death, the turning of the page
By those who quite forget what they have read,
Taking no heed of living folk or dead.

   Now hoisting sail, and labouring with the oar,
They passed along the amber-bearing shore,
A low coast, backed by pine-woods : none the less
Some days they needs must pass in idleness,
And lie-to, 'midst white rolling mist and blind,

Lest Argo on some shallow death should find ;   170
Yet holpen by the steersman's mighty sire,
Safely they sailed until the land rose higher,
And through a narrow strait at last they went,
Brushing the unknown coast, where, with bows bent,
They saw a skin-clad folk awaiting them,
Who stood to watch the well-built Argo stem
The rushing tide upon the shingly beach,
And thence, as knowing that they could not reach
The heroes with their arrows, shook their spears,
And shouted unknown threats to careless ears.   180
   But when against the midst of them they came,
Forth strode a huge man, with red hair like flame,
And his huge bow against them strongly drew,
Wherefrom a swift shaft straight to Argo flew,
And whistling over Jason's head, stuck fast
Over the barb-points in the gleaming mast.
Then all men praised that archer ; but the man
Who in Arcadian woods all beasts outran,
Straight drew his bow unto the arrow-head,
And no man doubted that wild king was dead :   190
Natheless, unmoved they saw the archer stand,
And toward the Arcadian arrow stretch his hand,
That midmost of his skin-clad body smote,
But bounded back as from an iron coat.
Then loud his people shouted, and all drew
Their feeble bows, but short their arrows flew,
And through the straits the wondering Minyæ
Passed out unscathed into the open sea,
While still of wizardry and charms they spoke.
   But Jason from the mast the arrow broke,   200
That erewhile had so scantly missed his life,
And found it scored as by a sharp-edged knife,
From barb to notch, with what seemed written words,
In tongue unknown to aught but beasts and birds.
So when Medea saw it, straight she said :
   ' Fair love, now praise some God thou art not dead,
For from the Cimbrian folk this arrow came,
And its sharp barbs within a wizard's flame
Were forged with peril, and the shaft of it

Was carved by one who in great fear did sit   210
Within the haunted places of the wood,
And tears are on its feathers, and red blood :
Nor ask me now the name of her who taught
This wisdom to me : but two arrows brought
From this same folk to Æa have I seen,
By one whose wounds will evermore be green
While on the earth he dwells.' So spoke the maid,
But Jason, wondering at the words she said,
Gazed on her fair face, smiling lovingly,
Nor cared to think that he must one day die.   220

    Now rose a south-east gale, and Argo lost
All sight of land, and the vexed Minyæ, tost
From sea to sea, began to feel a fear
They yet might pass into some ocean drear,
Beyond the circling sea that rings the world,
And down a bottomless abyss be hurled,
To fall for ever : then the winged twain,
That erst had been the loathly harpies' bane,
Came forth, and on the prow with wings spread wide,
Half stood, half floated, while aloud they cried :—   230
    ' What dost thou, Father ? art thou sleeping then,
And does it not suffice that trading men
Float up and down, dead corpses on the sea,
While all their wealth is lying wretchedly
On Nereus' pavement ; but must we too drive
Before this south wind, hopeless though alive,
Until the farthest gulfs shall suck us down,
And land our battered keel at Pluto's town ? '
    So spake they ; but still blew the south the same
Until the starless night upon them came,   240
But then a little did its fury lull,
And when the rain-beat night was at its full,
Fell to a light breeze, though still many a sea
Swept Argo's deck, and still the Minyæ
Had dread of some returning hideous blast.
But when the doubtful night from them had past,
Barefoot upon the prow Medea stood,
226 a bottomless] some bottomless

And burning in a censer hallowed wood,
With muttered words she swung it, nor took heed
Of how the wind was dealing with her weed.   250
Nor with firm-planted feet one whit did reck
Of washing of the brine about the deck,
But swung her censer till a bright red flame
From out the piercings of its cover came ;
Then round she turned and said : ' O Minyæ,
Fear not to die within the northern sea,
For on my head hither the north wind comes,
And ye some day shall surely see your homes.
But since upon us yet lies heavily
My brother's death, forget not we must see   260
My father's godlike sister, who one day
With all due rites that blood shall wash away.
    ' And now, behold the sun shines through the clouds,
And ye may hear across the well-strained shrouds
The longed-for wind, therefore make no delay,
For time it is that we were on our way,
So let Erginus to the south-west steer ;—
    ' But sleep to me of all things now is dear,
For with two mighty ones but for your sake
Have I contended. He who still doth shake   270
The firm-set earth, and She who draws the sea
This way and that, the while in majesty
She sits, regarding little but her will ;—
The fear of these my heavy heart doth fill.'
    So said she, and with pale and languid face
And half-shut eyes, unto the guarded place,
Where was her golden bed, the maiden came.
And in her dreams at first saw blood and flame
O'er all the world, and nothing green or fair ;
Then in a snowy land, with body bare,   280
Went wandering long, be-mocked of uncouth things ;
Then stood before the judgement-seat of kings,
Knowing no crime that she was charged withal,
Until at last deep sleep on her did fall
Like death itself, wherein the troublous past
And fearsome future in one tomb are cast.

       281 wandering long,] wandering

Meanwhile the Minyæ, joyful at her tale,
Ran out the oars and hoisted up the sail,
And toward the south with good hearts 'gan to go,
While still they felt the favouring north wind blow, 290
And the third day again they saw the land,
That in white cliffs rose up on the right hand,
Coasting whereby, they came into a strait,
Or so they deemed, for as the day grew late,
Beneath a frosty light-blue sky and cold
Another country could they now behold
Dim o'er the glittering sea ; but in the night
They by the moon past the high cliff and white
Ceased not to sail, and lost the other shore
When the day broke, nor saw it any more, 300
As the first land they coasted, that changed oft
From those high cliffs to meadows green and soft,
And then to other cliffs, some red, some grey,
Till all the land at noon of the fourth day
They left astern, sailing where fate might lead,
Of sun or stars scarce taking any heed,—
Such courage in their hearts the White-armed set,
Since, clad in gold, was Pelias living yet.
    But to the Gods now did they sacrifice
As seafarers may do, and things of price 310
Gave to the tumbling billows of the sea,
That for their lives still cried out hungrily,
And though for many days they saw no shore,
Yet fainted not their hearts as heretofore,
For as along the pathless plain they went,
The white-foot messenger the Goddess sent,
Who, unseen, whispered in the helmsman's ear,
And taught him how the goodly ship to steer ;
And on a time it chanced as the day broke,
And to their life the longing Minyæ woke, 320
Across the risen sun the west wind blew
A thin light rain, that He, just shining through,
Showed to them all the many-coloured sign ;
Then to the Goddess did they pour out wine,
Right glad at heart ; but she the live-long day
By Argo's prow flew o'er the shifting way

Unseen of all, and turned them still to land ;
And as they went the Thracian's cunning hand
Stole o'er the harp-strings till Arion's steeds
Gat them from 'twixt the tangled water-weeds,   330
And lifted listening heads above the sea,
And sea-birds, pensive with the harmony,
About the mast, above the singer hung,
With quivering wings, as from full heart he sung :—

    ' O death, that maketh life so sweet,
O fear, with mirth before thy feet,
What have ye yet in store for us,
The conquerors, the glorious ?
    ' Men say : " For fear that thou shouldst die
To-morrow, let to-day pass by   340
Flower-crowned and singing ; " yet have we
Passed our to-day upon the sea,
Or in a poisonous unknown land,
With fear and death on either hand,
And listless when the day was done
Have scarcely hoped to see the sun
Dawn on the morrow of the earth,
Nor in our hearts have thought of mirth.
And while the world lasts, scarce again
Shall any sons of men bear pain   350
Like we have borne, yet be alive.
    ' So surely not in vain we strive
Like other men for our reward ;
Sweet peace and deep, the chequered sward
Beneath the ancient mulberry-trees,
The smooth-paved gilded palaces,
Where the shy thin-clad damsels sweet
Make music with their gold-ringed feet.
The fountain court amidst of it,
Where the short-haired slave maidens sit,   360
While on the veined pavement lie
The honied things and spicery
Their arms have borne from out the town.
    ' The dancers on the thymy down
In summer twilight, when the earth

Is still of all things but their mirth
And echoes borne upon the wind
Of others in like way entwined.
  ' The merchant towns' fair market-place,
Where over many a changing face   370
The pigeons of the temple flit,
And still the outland merchants sit
Like kings above their merchandise,
Lying to foolish men and wise.
  ' Ah ! if they heard that we were come
Into the bay, and bringing home
That which all men have talked about,
Some men with rage, and some with doubt,
Some with desire, and some with praise,
Then would the people throng the ways,   380
Nor heed the outland merchandise,
Nor any talk, from fools or wise,
But tales of our accomplished quest.
  ' What soul within the house shall rest
When we come home ? The wily king
Shall leave his throne to see the thing ;
No man shall keep the landward gate,
The hurried traveller shall wait
Until our bulwarks graze the quay,
Unslain the milk-white bull shall be   390
Beside the quivering altar-flame ;
Scarce shall the maiden clasp for shame
Over her breast the raiment thin
The morn that Argo cometh in.
  ' Then cometh happy life again
That payeth well our toil and pain
In that sweet hour, when all our woe
But as a pensive tale we know,
Nor yet remember deadly fear ;
For surely now if death be near,   400
Unthought-of is it, and unseen
When sweet is, that hath bitter been.'
Thus sung the Thracian, and the rowing-folk
Sent Argo quivering with the well-timed stroke

379 desire, and some] desire, some   403 Thus] So

Over the green hills, through great clouds of spray,
And as they went upon their happy way
About the deck the longing men would stand
With wistful eyes still gazing for the land ;
Which yet they saw not, till the cool fresh night
Had come upon them, with no lack of light,   410
For moon and stars shone brightly overhead,
Nor through the night did Iris fail to lead
The wave-tossed Argo o'er the glittering sea.
     So as the moon set, did there seem to be
Upon their larboard, banks of high-piled cloud,
Which from their sight the last dark hour did shroud,
Then came the twilight, and those watchers fain
Against the eastern light beheld again
The clouds unchanged, and as the daylight grew,
Lynceus cried out : ' Some land we draw unto !   420
Look forth, Erginus, on these mountains grey,
If thou, perchance, hast seen them ere to-day.'
     Therewith all turned about, and some men ran
To hear what words the God-begotten man
Would say, who answered : ' Lynceus, and all ye,
The man we left erewhile across the sea
Might tell us this, the godlike Hercules ;
Yet I myself think that the landless seas
No more shall vex us now, but that we come
Unto the gates that look into our home :   430
So trim the sails, for thither will I steer,
Seeking what lies beyond with little fear,
Since surely now I see the Iberian land
That 'gainst the shore of Africa doth stand,
To break these mighty billows, ever pressed
Each against each from out the landless west.'
     So with glad hearts all men his bidding did,
And swiftly through the water Argo slid,
Till as the sun rose were they near the strait,
At whose mouth but a little did they wait   440
Till they had eaten, pouring honied wine
Unto the Gods, then biding no new sign,
They cried aloud, and running out the oars,
They swept great Argo midmost 'twixt the shores

Of either land, and as her gilded prow
Cleft the new waters, clean forgotten now
Grew all the wasteful washing of the main,
And clean forgotten the dull hopeless pain,
In the great swirling river left so long,
And in all hearts the memory was strong   450
Of the bright Grecian headlands and the bay
They left astern upon a glorious day.

BOOK XIII

Medea sees Circe, and has good counsel from her.

BUT as along the shore they sailed next day,
Full many a headland on their lucky way
Erginus knew, but said no towns there were
Within that land, but that from year to year
Well-nigh untilled the earth her produce gave,
And many a herd the houseless people drave,
And using neither roof nor sheltering wall,
Dwelt but in tents, and had no want at all.

With that he bade them trim the bellying sail,
For from the land now blew a gentle gale,   10
Spice-laden, warm, that made their full hearts yearn
For unseen things, but soon they left astern
That fruitful place, the lion-haunted land,
Nor saw but tumbling seas on either hand.

Three days they sailed, and passed on the third day
A rock-bound coast upon their left that lay,
But on the morrow eve made land again,
Stretched right ahead across the watery plain,
Whereto ere nightfall did they draw anear,
And so lay-to till dawn with little fear ;   20
For from the shore a light, soft land-wind blew.

But as the dead night round about them drew,
The ceaseless roar of savage beasts they heard,
Mingled with sounds like cries of men afeared,

24 afeared] afeard

And blare of horns, and clank of heavy chains,
And noise of bells, such as in moonlit lanes
Rings from the grey team on the market-night.
    And with these noises did they see a light,
That seemed to light some crown of palaces,
Shining from out a grove of thickset trees.   30
Then did the Minyæ doubt if they were come
Unto some great king's well-adorned home,
Or if some temple of a God were there,
Or if, indeed, the spirits of the air
Haunted that place : so slowly passed away
The sleepless night, and at the dawn of day
Their longing eyes beheld a lovely land,
Green meadows rising o'er a yellow strand,
Well-set with fair fruit-bearing trees, and groves
Of thick-leaved elms, all populous of doves,   40
And watered by a wandering clear green stream ;
And through the trees they saw a palace gleam
Of polished marble, fair beyond man's thought.
    There as they lay, the sweetest scents were brought
By sighing winds across the bitter sea,
And languid music breathed melodiously,
Steeping their souls in such unmixed delight,
Their hearts were melted, and all dim of sight
They grew, and scarce their hands could grip the oar,
And as they slowly neared the happy shore,   50
The young men well-night wept, and e'en the wise
Thought they had reached the gate of Paradise.
    But 'midst them all Medea thoughtfully
Gazed landward o'er the ripple of the sea,
And said no word, till from her precious things
She drew a casket full of chains and rings,
And took therefrom a chaplet brown and sere,
And set it on her head : and now being near
The yellow strand, high on the poop she stood,
And said : ' O heroes, what has chilled your blood,   60
That in such wise ye gaze upon this land
With tearful eye, and nerveless, languid hand,

53 But 'midst them stood Medea, and thoughtfully

And heaving breast, and measureless desire ?
Be wise, for here the never-dying fire,
The God begotten wonder, Circe, lights,
The wise of women, framer of delights
That being of man once felt, he ne'er shall cease
To long for vainly, as the years increase
On his dulled soul, shut in some bestial form.
  ' And good it had been that some bitter storm   70
Were tossing Argo's planks from sea to sea,
Than ye had reached this fair land, but for me,
Who amid tears and prayers, and nameless pain,
Some little wisdom have made shift to gain :
Look forth upon the green shore, and behold
Those many beasts, all collared with fine gold,
Lions and pards, and small-eyed restless bears,
And tusked boars, who from uneasy lairs
Are just come forth ; nor is there 'mongst them one
But once walked upright underneath the sun,   80
And had the name of man : such shall ye be,
If from the ship ye wander heedlessly,
But safely I my kinswoman may meet,
And learn from her the bitter and the sweet
That waits us ere ye come to Greece again,
And see the wind-swept green Thessalian plain.
  ' Meanwhile, let nothing tempt you to the land,
Nor unto anything stretch forth the hand
That comes from shore, for all ye may see there
Are but lost men and their undoers fair.'   90
  But with that word they furrowed the wet sand,
And straight they ran the gangway out to land,
O'er which, with girded raiment, passed the queen ;
But now another marvel was there seen,
For to the shore, from many a glade and lawn,
The golden-collared sad-eyed beasts were drawn
In close-set ranks above the sea-beat shore,
And open-mouthed, with varying moan and roar,
White-foot Medea did they seem to threat ;
Whereat the Minyæ on their bow-strings set   100
The notches of their arrows, but the maid
Turned round about, with calm face unafraid,

And said : ' O Minyæ, lay your weapons down,
Nor fear for me ; behold this chaplet brown,
Whose withered leaves rest lightly on my head,
This is the herb that Gods and mortals dread,
The Pontic Moly, the unchanging charm.'
Then up the beach she passed, and her white arm
This way and that the leopards thrust aside,
And 'mid the grisly swine her limbs did glide,   110
And on a lion's mane her hand she laid ;
But still with moans they thronged about the maid,
As she passed onward to the palace white,
Until the elm-groves hid her from the sight.
Then they with fearful hearts did sacrifice
Unto the Gods in their seafaring wise,
But of the lovely land were they so fain
That their return they scarcely counted gain,
Unto the green plain dotted o'er with folds
And that fair bay that Pelion beholds.   120

Meanwhile Medea through the thick-leaved grove
Passed underneath the moaning of the dove,
Not left by those strange beasts ; until at last
Her feet from off the sparse long grasses passed
Unto a sunny space of daisied sward,
From which a strange-wrought silver grate did guard
A lovely pleasance, set with flowers, foursquare,
On three sides ending in a cloister fair
That hid the fair feet of a marble house,
Carved thick with flowers and stories amorous.   130
And midmost of the slender garden trees
A gilded shrine stood, set with images,
Wherefrom the never-dying fire rose up
Into the sky, and a great jewelled cup
Ran over ever from a runlet red
Of fragrant wine, that 'mid the flowers shed
Strange scent that grapes yield not to any man,
While round about the shrine four streamlets ran
From golden founts to freshen that green place.
So there Medea stayed a little space,   140
Gazing in wonder through the silver rail

That fenced that garden from the wooded vale ;
For damsels wandered there in languid wise
As though they wearied of that Paradise,
Their jewelled raiment dragging from its stalk
The harmless daisy in their listless walk.
But though from rosy heel to golden head
Most fair they were and wrought with white and red,
Like to the casket-bearer who beguiled
The hapless one, and though their lips still smiled,   150
Yet to the Colchian, heavy-eyed they seemed,
And each at other gazed as though she dreamed ;
Not noting aught of all the glorious show
She joined herself, nor seeming more to know
What words she spoke nor what her fellows sung,
Nor feeling arms that haply round her clung.

For here and there the Colchian maid could see
Some browned seafarer kissing eagerly
White feet or half-bared bosom, and could hear
A rough voice stammering 'twixt love and fear   160
Amid the dreamy murmur of the place,
As on his knees, with eager upturned face,
Some man would pour forth many a fruitless word,
That did but sound like song of a wild bird
Unto his love ; while she for all reply,
Still gazing on his flushed face wearily,
Would undo clasp and belt, and show to him
Undreamed-of loveliness of side or limb.

And in such guise of half-stripped jewelled weed,
The men entrapped, Medea saw them lead   170
Into the dark cool cloister, whence again
They came not forth, but four-foot, rough of mane,
Uncouth with spots and dangerous of claw.
But when the sad-eyed beasts about her saw
These draw towards them and beheld the gate
Open and shut, and fellows to that state
New come, they whined, and brushing round her feet
Prayed for return unto that garden sweet,
Their own undoing once, that yet shall be
Death unto many a toiler of the sea,   180
Because all these outside the silver grate

Were men indeed though inarticulate,
And, spite of seeming, in none otherwise,
Did longing torture them, than when in guise
Of men they stood before that garden green,
And first their eyes the baneful place had seen.

But now the queen grew wrath, for in her way,
Before the gate a yellow lion lay,
A tiger-cat her raiment brushed aside,
And o'er her feet she felt a serpent glide,   190
The swine screamed loud about her, and a pard
Her shining shoulder of her raiment bared
With light swift clutch ; then she from off her head
Took the sere moly wreath, and therewith said :—
' What do ye, wretches, know ye not this sign,
That whoso wears is as a thing divine ?
Get from this place, for never more can ye
Become partakers of the majesty
That from man's soul looks through his eager eyes.
Go—wail that ever ye were made so wise   200
As men are made ; who chase through smooth and rough
Their own undoing, nor can have enough
Of bitter trouble and entangling woe.'

Then slowly from her did those monsters go,
In varied voices mourning for their lot
And that sweet poison ne'er to be forgot.

But straight with serious face the Colchian maid
Her slender fingers on the latchet laid
That held the silver gate, and entered in ;
Nor did those weary images of sin   210
Take any heed of her as she passed by,
But, if they met her eyes, stared listlessly,
Like those who walk in sleep, and as they dream
Turn empty faces to the lightning's gleam,
And murmur softly while the thunder rolls.

Swiftly she passed those bodies void of souls,
And through the darkling corridor she passed,
And reached a huge adorned hall at last,
Where sat alone the deathless sorceress,
Upon whose knees an open book did press,   220

Wherein strange things the Gods knew not, she read ;
A golden vine-bough wreathed her golden head,
And her fair body a thin robe did touch
With silken folds, but hid it not so much
As the cool ripple hides Diana's feet,
When through the brook the roe-deer, slim and fleet,
She follows at the dawning of the day.
   Smiling, she put the wondrous book away
As the light footsteps fell upon her ear,
She raised her head, and when the queen drew near, 230
She said : ' O wanderer from dark sea to sea,
I greet thee well, and dear thou art to me ·
Though verily if I could wish for aught,
I could have wished thou hadst been hither brought
Ere that had happed to thee that haps to all,
Into the troublous sea of love to fall,
Then like unto the gods shouldst thou have been,
Nor ever died, but sitting here have seen
The fashion of the foolish world go by,
And drunk the cup of power and majesty.   240
   ' But now it may not be, and thou must come
With him thou boughtedst, to a troublous home ;
But since indeed the fates will have it so,
Take heed thou dost the things I bid thee do.
And, first, since thou wouldst have me purify
Your hands of his blood that thou sawest die
'Twixt yellow Phasis and the green-ridged sea,
Behold, this is not possible to me,
Nor ever must another altar stand
In this green nook of the Italian land,   250
To aught but me, no, not unto my Sire ;
But unto him shall ye light ruddy fire,
When, drawing nigh to your desired home,
Unto the headland of Malea ye come ;
And then, indeed, I bid you not to spare
Spices and golden things and raiment fair,
But to the country folk give things of price,
And from them take wherewith to sacrifice,
A hundred milkwhite bulls, a hundred kine,

231 from dark sea] from sea

And many a jar of unmixed honied wine,   260
And, crowned with olive, round the altars sing
Unto the God who gladdens everything,
Thy father's father, the all-seeing Sun.
And then the deed thy Jason's spear has done
Mayst thou forget, it shall not visit thee.
Moreover, sailing hence across the sea,
A waste of yellow sand shall ye pass by
'Neath the Trinacrian cliffs, whereon shall lie
Fair women, fairer than thine eyes have seen.
And if thou still wouldst be a Grecian queen,   270
When to that deadly place ye draw anear,
And sweetest music ye begin to hear,
Bid your bold love steer Argo from the land,
While Thracian Orpheus takes his harp in hand,
And sings thereto some God-delighting strain.
And surely else shall all your toil be vain,
For deadlier than my gardens are those sands ;
And when the mariner's toil-hardened hands
Reach out unto those bodies fair and white,
They clasp but death instead of their delight.   280
      ' But, doing as I bid, Malea reach,
And after, nigh Iolchos Argo beach,
Yet at the city haste ye not to land,
For still the sceptre presses Pelias' hand,
And Æson is at rest for evermore ;
Bid then thy folk lurk by some wooded shore,
And to the white-walled city straightly wend
Thyself alone, and safely there make end
Of the King's life ; nor need I teach thee how,
For deep unfailing wiles thy soul doth know.   290
      ' What more ? what more ? I see thy grey eyes ask,
What course, what ending to the tangled task
The Gods have set before me, ere I die ?
O child, I know all things, indeed, but why
Shouldst thou know all, nor yet be wise therefore,
Me knowledge grieves not, thee should it grieve sore ;
Nor knowing, shouldst thou cease to hope or fear.
What ! do men think of death ere it draws near ?
Not so, else surely would they stint their strife,

For lengthening out their little span of life,   300
But where each found himself there should he sit,
Not moving hand or foot for thought of it.
Wherefore the Gods, wishing the earth to teem
With living wills like theirs, nor as a dream
To hold but beauty and the lives of beasts,
That they may have fair stories for their feasts,
Have given them forgetfulness of death,
Longings and hopes, and joy in drawing breath,
And they live happy, knowing nought at all,
Nor what death is, where that shall chance to fall.   310
For while he lives, few minutes certainly
Does any man believe that he shall die.
Ah, what ? thou hang'st thine head, and on thy feet
Down rain the tears from thy grey eyes and sweet ;
Weep not, nor pity thine own life too much :
Not painless shall it be, indeed, or such
As the Gods live in their unchanged abode,
And yet not joyless ; no unmeasured load
Of sorrows shall thy dull soul learn to bear,   319
With nought to keep thee back from death but fear,
Of what thou know'st not, knowing nought but pain.
  ' But though full oft thou shalt lift hands in vain,
Crying to what thou know'st not in thy need,
And blind with agony, yet oft, indeed,
Shalt thou go nigh to think thyself divine,
For love of what thou deemest to be thine,
For joy of what thou dreamest cannot die.

  ' Live then thy life, nor ask for misery,
Most certain if thou knewest what must be,
And then, at least, this shall not hap to thee,   330
To be like those who people my sad groves,
Beneath the moaning of the grey-winged doves.
And midst all pain and joy, and wrong and right,
Thy name to all shall be a dear delight
While the world lasts, if this avail thee aught.

  ' Farewell, O child, whose feet alone have brought
An earthly damsel to my house of gold,
For surely those thou didst erewhile behold

These hands have made, and can unmake again,
Nor know they aught of love, or fear, or pain.   340
Go, loiter not, this place befits thee nought,
Thou knowest many things full dearly bought,
And well I love thee, being so wise and fair,
But what is knowledge in this deadly air,
That floats about thee, poisoning hearts of man.
Behold I see thy cheeks, that erst were wan,
Flaming with new desire, and in thine eyes
Shine out new thoughts that from thine heart arise ;
Gird up thy raiment, nor run slower now
Than from the amorous bearer of the bow   350
Once Daphne ran ; nor yet forget the word
That thou from deadly lips this day hast heard.'

So said she, and thereat the Colchian maid
Turned from her fair face shuddering and afraid,
With beating heart, and flushed face like the rose
That in the garden of Damascus grows,
And catching up her raiment, hurried through
The mighty hall, where thick the pillars blue
Stood like a dream to hold the roof aloft ;
But as she left it, musky odours soft   360
Were cast about her by the dallying breeze,
That through the heavy-fruited garden-trees
Blew o'er those golden heads and bodies white,
And limbs well made for manifold delight,
From 'twixt whose fingers and the strings, did flow
Sweet music such as Helicon might know.

But dizzied, hurrying through the place she past,
Nor any look upon their beauty cast,
Nor any thought unto the music gave,
But set herself her own vext soul to save   370
From that dread place ; beginning now to run
Like to a damsel of the lightfoot One,
Who oft from twilight unto twilight goes
Through still dark woods, where never rough wind blows.

So, the grove passed, she made good speed to reach
The edges of the sea, the wind-swept beach ;
But as she ran, afar the heroes saw

362 through] 'twixt

Her raiment fluttering, and made haste to draw
Their two-edged swords, and their strong bows to string,
Doubting that she was chased of some dread thing ;
And Jason leapt ashore, and toward her ran,   381
And with him went the arrow-loving man,
The wise Arcadian, and the Minyæ
Got ready shielded Argo for the sea.

But ere these met her, with uplifted hand,
She cried : ' Turn back, nor deeper in this land
Thrust ye your souls ; nought chases me but fear,
And all is well if on the sea we were ;
Yea, if we once were free from fear and spell,
Then, truly, better were all things than well.'   390

Thereat they stayed, but onward still she ran
Until she reached them, and the godlike man
Took by the arm, and hurrying him along,
Stayed not until their feet were set among
The last faint ripples of the gentle sea,
Wherefrom they boarded Argo speedily,
And Jason bid all men unto the oar.

With that they left the fair death-bearing shore,
Not gladlier than some fair young man may leave
His love, upon the odorous summer eve,   400
When she turns sighing to her father's house,
And leaves him there alone and amorous,
Heartsick with all that shame has let him see,
Grieved that no bolder he has dared to be.

BOOK XIV

The Sirens—The Garden of the Hesperides—The heroes
do sacrifice at Malea.

Now o'er the open sea they took their way,
For three days, and at dawning of the day,
Upon the fourth, saw the Trinacrian shore,
And there-along they coasted two days more.
Then first Medea warned them to take heed,
Lest they should end all memory of their deed

Where dwell the Sirens on the yellow sand,
And folk should think some tangled poisonous land
Had buried them, or some tumultuous sea
O'er their white bones was tossing angrily ;   10
Or that some muddy river, far from Greece
Drove seaward o'er the ringlets of the fleece.
But when the Minyæ hearkened to this word,
With many a thought their wearied hearts were stirred,
And longing for the near-gained Grecian land,
Where in a little while their feet should stand ;
Yet none the less like to a happy dream,
Now, when they neared it, did their own home seem,
And like a dream the glory of their quest,
And therewithal some thought of present rest   20
Stole over them, and well-nigh made them sigh
To hear the sighing restless wind go by.
    But now, nigh even on the second day,
As o'er the gentle waves they took their way,
The orange-scented land-breeze seemed to bear
Some other sounds unto the listening ear
Than all day long they had been hearkening—
The land-born signs of many a well-known thing.
Thereat Medea trembled, for she knew
That nigh the dreadful sands at last they drew,   30
For certainly the Sirens' song she heard,
Though yet her ear could shape it to no word,
And by their faces could the queen behold
How sweet it was, although no tale it told,
To those worn toilers o'er the bitter sea.
    Now, as they sped along, they presently,
Rounding a headland, reached a little bay,
Walled from the sea by splintered cliffs and grey,
Capped by the thymy hills' green wind-beat head,
Where 'mid the whin the burrowing rabbits fed.   40
And 'neath the cliff they saw a belt of sand,
'Twixt Nereus' pasture and the high scarped land,
Whereon, yet far off, could their eyes behold
White bodies moving, crowned and girt with gold,
Wherefrom it seemed that lovely music welled.

41 belt] waste

So when all this the grey-eyed queen beheld,
She said : ' O Jason, I have made thee wise
In this and other things ; turn then thine eyes
Seaward, and note the ripple of the sea,
Where there is hope as well as fear for thee.   50
Nor look upon the death that lurketh there
'Neath the grey cliff, though sweet it seems and fair ;
For thou art young upon this day to die.
Take then the helm, and gazing steadily
Upon the road to Greece, make strong thine hand
And steer us toward the lion-haunted land :
And thou, O Thracian ! if thou e'er hast moved
Men's hearts, with stories of the Gods who loved,
And men who suffered, move them on this day,
Taking the deadly love of death away,   60
That even now is stealing over them,
While still they gaze upon the ocean's hem,
Where their undoing is if they but knew.'

But while she spake, still nigher Argo drew
Unto the yellow edges of the shore,
And little help she had of ashen oar,
For as her shielded side rolled through the sea,
Silent with glittering eyes the Minyæ
Gazed o'er the surge, for they were nigh enow
To see the gusty wind of evening blow   70
Long locks of hair across those bodies white,
With golden spray hiding some dear delight ;
Yea, nigh enow to see their red lips smile,
Wherefrom all song had ceased now for a while,
As though they deemed the prey was in the net,
And they no more had need a bait to set,
But their own bodies, fair beyond man's thought,
Under the grey cliff, hidden not of aught
But of such mist of tears as in the eyes
Of those seafaring men might chance to rise.   80
A moment Jason gazed, then through the waist
Ran swiftly, and with trembling hands made haste
To trim the sail, then to the tiller ran,
And thrust aside the skilled Milesian man,

Who with half-open mouth, and dreamy eyes,
Stood steering Argo to that land of lies ;
But as he staggered forward, Jason's hand
Hard on the tiller steered away from land,
And as her head a little now fell off
Unto the wide sea, did he shout this scoff   90
To Thracian Orpheus : ' Minstrel, shall we die,
Because thou hast forgotten utterly
What things she taught thee that men call divine,
Or will thy measures but lead folk to wine,
And scented beds, and not to noble deeds ?
Or will they fail as fail the shepherd's reeds
Before the trumpet, when these sea-witches
Pipe shrilly to the washing of the seas ?
I am a man, and these but beasts, but thou
Giving these souls, that all were men ere now   100
Shall be a very God and not a man ! '
     So spake he ; but his fingers Orpheus ran
Over the strings, and sighing turned away
From that fair ending of the sunny bay ;
But as his well-skilled hands were preluding
What his heart swelled with, they began to sing
With pleading voices from the yellow sands,
Clustered together, with appealing hands
Reached out to Argo as she turned away,
While o'er their white limbs flew the flakes of spray,
Since they spared not to set white feet among   111
The cold waves heedless of their honied song.
     Sweetly they sung, and still the answer came
Piercing and clear from him, as bursts the flame
From out the furnace in the moonless night ;
Yet, as their words are no more known aright
Through lapse of many ages, and no man
Can any more across the waters wan
Behold those singing women of the sea,
Once more I pray you all to pardon me,   120
If with my feeble voice and harsh I sing
From what dim memories may chance to cling
About men's hearts, of lovely things once sung
Beside the sea, while yet the world was young.

The Sirens.

O happy seafarers are ye,
 And surely all your ills are past,
And toil upon the land and sea,
 Since ye are brought to us at last.

To you the fashion of the world,
 Wide lands laid waste, fair cities burned, 130
And plagues, and kings from kingdoms hurled,
 Are nought, since hither ye have turned.

For as upon this beach we stand,
 And o'er our heads the sea-fowl flit,
Our eyes behold a glorious land,
 And soon shall be ye kings of it.

Orpheus.

A little more, a little more,
 O carriers of the Golden Fleece,
A little labour with the oar,
 Before we reach the land of Greece. 140

E'en now perchance faint rumours reach
 Men's ears of this our victory,
And draw them down unto the beach
 To gaze across the empty sea.

But since the longed-for day is nigh,
 And scarce a God could stay us now,
Why do ye hang your heads and sigh,
 Hindering for nought our eager prow ?

The Sirens.

Ah, had ye chanced to reach the home
 Your fond desires were set upon, 150
Into what troubles had ye come,
 What barren victory had ye won.

148 And still go slower and more slow ?

But now, but now, when ye have lain
　　Asleep with us a little while
Beneath the washing of the main,
　　How calm shall be your waking smile !

For ye shall smile to think of life
　　That knows no troublous change or fear,
No unavailing bitter strife,
　　That ere its time brings trouble near.　　160

ORPHEUS.

Is there some murmur in your ears,
　　That all that we have done is nought,
And nothing ends our cares and fears,
　　Till the last fear on us is brought ?

THE SIRENS.

Alas ! and will ye stop your ears,
　　In vain desire to do aught,
And wish to live 'mid cares and fears,
　　Until the last fear makes you nought ?

ORPHEUS.

Is not the May time now on earth,
　　When close against the city wall　　170
The folk are singing in their mirth,
　　While on their heads the May-flowers fall ?

THE SIRENS.

Yes, May is come, and its sweet breath
　　Shall well-nigh make you weep to-day,
And pensive with swift-coming death,
　　Shall ye be satiate of the May.

ORPHEUS.

Shall not July bring fresh delight,
　　As underneath green trees ye sit,
And o'er some damsel's body white
　　The noontide shadows change and flit ?　　180

THE SIRENS.
No new delight July shall bring,
But ancient fear and fresh desire,
And, spite of every lovely thing,
Of July surely shall ye tire.

ORPHEUS.
And now when August comes on thee,
And 'mid the golden sea of corn
The merry reapers thou mayst see,
Wilt thou still think the earth forlorn ?

THE SIRENS.
Set flowers on thy short-lived head,
And in thine heart forgetfulness
Of man's hard toil, and scanty bread,
And weary of those days no less.

190

ORPHEUS.
Or wilt thou climb the sunny hill,
In the October afternoon,
To watch the purple earth's blood fill
The grey vat to the maiden's tune ?

THE SIRENS.
When thou beginnest to grow old,
Bring back remembrance of thy bliss
With that the shining cup doth hold,
And weary helplessly of this.

200

ORPHEUS.
Or pleasureless shall we pass by
The long cold night and leaden day,
That song, and tale, and minstrelsy
Shall make as merry as the May ?

THE SIRENS.
List then to-night, to some old tale
Until the tears o'erflow thine eyes ;
But what shall all these things avail,
When sad to-morrow comes and dies ?

ORPHEUS.

And when the world is born again,
　　And with some fair love, side by side,　　210
Thou wanderest 'twixt the sun and rain,
　　In that fresh love-begetting tide ;

Then, when the world is born again,
　　And the sweet year before thee lies,
Shall thy heart think of coming pain,
　　Or vex itself with memories ?

THE SIRENS.

Ah ! then the world is born again
　　With burning love unsatisfied,
And new desires fond and vain,
　　And weary days from tide to tide.　　220

Ah ! when the world is born again,
　　A little day is soon gone by,
When thou, unmoved by sun or rain,
　　Within a cold straight house shall lie.

Therewith they ceased awhile, as languidly
The head of Argo fell off toward the sea,
And through the water she began to go,
For from the land a fitful wind did blow,
That, dallying with the many-coloured sail,
Would sometimes swell it out and sometimes fail,　　230
As nigh the east side of the bay they drew ;
Then o'er the waves again the music flew.

THE SIRENS.

Think not of pleasure, short and vain,
Wherewith, 'mid days of toil and pain,
With sick and sinking hearts ye strive
To cheat yourselves that ye may live
With cold death ever close at hand,
Think rather of a peaceful land,
The changeless land where ye may be
Roofed over by the changeful sea.　　240

ORPHEUS.

And is the fair town nothing then,
The coming of the wandering men
With that long talked of thing and strange,
And news of how the kingdoms change,
The pointed hands, and wondering
At doers of a desperate thing ?
Push on, for surely this shall be
Across a narrow strip of sea.

THE SIRENS.

Alas ! poor souls and timorous,
Will ye draw nigh to gaze at us   250
And see if we are fair indeed,
For such as we shall be your meed,
There, where our hearts would have you go.
And where can the earth-dwellers show
In any land such loveliness
As that wherewith your eyes we bless,
O wanderers of the Minyæ,
Worn toilers over land and sea ?

ORPHEUS.

Fair as the lightning thwart the sky,
As sun-dyed snow upon the high   260
Untrodden heaps of threatening stone
The eagle looks upon alone,
O fair as the doomed victim's wreath,
O fair as deadly sleep and death,
What will ye with them, earthly men,
To mate your three-score years and ten ?
Toil rather, suffer and be free,
Betwixt the green earth and the sea.

THE SIRENS.

If ye be bold with us to go,
Things such as happy dreams may show   270
Shall your once heavy eyes behold
About our palaces of gold ;

MORRIS   K k

Where waters 'neath the waters run,
And from o'erhead a harmless sun
Gleams through the woods of chrysolite.
There gardens fairer to the sight
Than those of the Phæacian king
Shall ye behold ; and, wondering,
Gaze on the sea-born fruit and flowers,
And thornless and unchanging bowers,   280
Whereof the May-time knoweth nought.

So to the pillared house being brought,
Poor souls, ye shall not be alone,
For o'er the floors of pale blue stone
All day such feet as ours shall pass,
And, 'twixt the glimmering walls of glass,
Such bodies garlanded with gold,
So faint, so fair, shall ye behold,
And clean forget the treachery
Of changing earth and tumbling sea.   290

ORPHEUS.

O the sweet valley of deep grass,
Where through the summer stream doth pass,
In chain of shallow, and still pool,
From misty morn to evening cool ;
Where the black ivy creeps and twines
O'er the dark-armed, red-trunked pines,
Whence clattering the pigeon flits,
Or, brooding o'er her thin eggs, sits,
And every hollow of the hills
With echoing song the mavis fills.   300
There by the stream, all unafraid,
Shall stand the happy shepherd maid,
Alone in first of sunlit hours ;
Behind her, on the dewy flowers,
Her homespun woollen raiment lies,
And her white limbs and sweet grey eyes
Shine from the calm green pool and deep,
While round about the swallows sweep,
Not silent ; and would God that we,
Like them, were landed from the sea.   310

The Sirens.

Shall we not rise with you at night,
Up through the shimmering green twilight,
That maketh there our changeless day,
Then going through the moonlight grey,
Shall we not sit upon these sands,
To think upon the troublous lands
Long left behind, where once ye were,
When every day brought change and fear ?
There, with white arms about you twined,
And shuddering somewhat at the wind   320
That ye rejoiced erewhile to meet,
Be happy, while old stories sweet,
Half understood, float round your ears,
And fill your eyes with happy tears.
  Ah ! while we sing unto you there,
As now we sing, with yellow hair
Blown round about these pearly limbs,
While underneath the grey sky swims
The light shell-sailor of the waves,
And to our song, from sea-filled caves   330
Booms out an echoing harmony,
Shall ye not love the peaceful sea ?

Orpheus.

Nigh the vine-covered hillocks green,
In days agone, have I not seen
The brown-clad maidens amorous,
Below the long rose-trellised house,
Dance to the querulous pipe and shrill,
When the grey shadow of the hill
Was lengthening at the end of day ?
Not shadowy or pale were they,   340
But limbed like those who 'twixt the trees,
Follow the swift of Goddesses.
Sunburnt they are somewhat, indeed,
To where the rough brown woollen weed
Is drawn across their bosoms sweet,
Or cast from off their dancing feet ;
                K k 2

But yet the stars, the moonlight grey,
The water wan, the dawn of day,
Can see their bodies fair and white
As Hers, who once, for man's delight,   350
Before the world grew hard and old,
Came o'er the bitter sea and cold ;
And surely those that met me there,
Her handmaidens and subjects were ;
And shame-faced, half-repressed desire
Had lit their glorious eyes with fire,
That maddens eager hearts of men.
O would that I were with them when
The risen moon is gathering light,
And yellow from the homestead white   360
The windows gleam ; but verily
This waits us o'er a little sea.

The Sirens.

Come to the land where none grows old,
And none is rash or over-bold,
Nor any noise there is or war,
Or rumour from wild lands afar,
Or plagues, or birth and death of kings ;
No vain desire of unknown things
Shall vex you there, no hope or fear
Of that which never draweth near ;   370
But in that lovely land and still
Ye may remember what ye will,
And what ye will, forget for aye.
So while the kingdoms pass away,
Ye sea-beat hardened toilers erst,
Unresting, for vain fame athirst,
Shall be at peace for evermore,
With hearts fulfilled of Godlike lore,
And calm, unwavering Godlike love,
No lapse of time can turn or move.   380
There, ages after your fair fleece
Is clean forgotten, yea, and Greece

Is no more counted glorious,
Alone with us, alone with us,
Alone with us, dwell happily,
Beneath our trembling roof of sea.

ORPHEUS.

Ah ! do ye weary of the strife
And long to change this eager life
For shadowy and dull hopelessness,
Thinking indeed to gain no less   390
Than far from this grey light to lie,
And there to die and not to die,
To be as if ye ne'er had been,
Yet keep your memory fresh and green,
To have no thought of good or ill
Yet feed your fill of pleasure still ?
O idle dream ! Ah, verily
If it shall happen unto me
That I have thought of anything,
When o'er my bones the sea-fowl sing,   400
And I lie dead, how shall I pine
For those fresh joys that once were mine,
On this green fount of joy and mirth,
The ever young and glorious earth ;
Then, helpless, shall I call to mind
Thoughts of the sweet flower-scented wind,
The dew, the gentle rain at night,
The wonder-working snow and white,
The song of birds, the water's fall,
The sun that maketh bliss of all   410
Yea, this our toil and victory,
The tyrannous and conquered sea.

THE SIRENS.

Ah, will ye go, and whither then '
    Will ye go from us, soon to die,
To fill your three-score years and ten,
    With many an unnamed misery ?

391 *This line was not in the first edition.*
392 And there] Than this,
396 Yet keep some thrilling pleasure still ?
406 the sweet flower-scented] the flower-scented

And this the wretchedest of all
　　That when upon your lonely eyes
　The last faint heaviness shall fall
　　Ye shall bethink you of our cries,　　　　420

Come back, nor grown old seek in vain
　　To hear us sing across the sea.
Come back, come back, come back again,
　　Come back, O fearful Minyæ !

ORPHEUS.
Ah, once again, ah, once again,
　　The black prow plunges through the sea,
Nor yet shall all your toil be vain
　　Nor ye forgot, O Minyæ.

In such wise sang the Thracian in such wise
Out gushed the Sirens' deadly melodies ;　　　430
But long before the mingled song was done,
Back to the oars the Minyæ, one by one,
Slunk silently ; though many an one sighed sore,
As his strong fingers met the wood once more,
And from his breast the toilsome breathing came
　But as they laboured, some for very shame
Hung down their heads, and yet amongst them some
Gazed at the place whence that sweet song had come ;
But round the oars and Argo's shielded side
The sea grew white, and she began to glide　　　440
Swift through the waters of that deadly bay ;
But when a long wake now behind her lay,
And still the whistle of the wind increased,
Past shroud and mast, and all the song had ceased,
Butes rose up, the fair Athenian man,
And with wild eyes betwixt the rowers ran
Unto the poop and leapt into the sea ;
Then all men rested on their oars, but he
Rose to the top, and towards the shore swam fast ;
While all eyes watched him, who had well-nigh past
The place where sand and water 'gan to meet　　　451
In wreaths and ripples round the ivory feet,

When sun-burnt swimmer, snow-white glancing limb,
And yellow sand unto their eyes grew dim,
Nor did they see their fellow any more.
  But when they once again beheld the shore
The wind sung o'er the empty beach and bare,
And by the cliff uprose into the air
A delicate and glittering little cloud,
That seemed some many-coloured sun to shroud ;   460
But as the rugged cliff it drew above
The wondering Minyæ beheld it move
Westward, toward Lilybæum and the sun.
  Then once more was their seaward course begun,
And soon those deadly sands were far astern,
Nor ever after could the heroes learn
If Butes lived or died ; but old tales tell
That while the tumbling waves he breasted well,
Venus beheld him, as unseen she drew
From sunny Cyprus to the headland blue   470
Of Lilybæum, where her temple is ;
She, with a mind his sun-burnt brows to kiss,
E'en as his feet were dropping nigh the beach,
And ere his hand the deadly hands could reach,
Stooped, as the merlin stoops upon the dove,
And snatched him thence to be awhile her love,
Betwixt the golden pillars of her shrine,
That those who pass the Ægades see shine
From high-raised Lilybæum o'er the sea.

  But far away the sea-beat Minyæ   480
Cast forth the foam, as through the growing night
They laboured ever, having small delight
In life all empty of that promised bliss,
In love that scarce can give a dying kiss,
In pleasure ending sweet songs with a wail,
In fame that little can dead men avail,
In vain toil struggling with the fateful stream,
In hope, the promise of a morning dream.
  Yet as night died, and the cold sea and grey
Seemed running with them toward the dawn of day,

468 while] as

Needs must they once again forget their death,   491
Needs must they, being alive and drawing breath,
As men who of no other life can know
In their own minds again immortal grow.
   But toward the south a little now they bent,
And for awhile o'er landless sea they went
But on the third day made another land
At dawn of day, and thitherward did stand ;
And since the wind blew lightly from the shore,
Somewhat abeam, they feared not with the oar   500
To push across the shallowing sea and green,
That washed a land the fairest they had seen,
Whose shell-strewn beach at highest of the tide
'Twixt sea and flowery shore was nowise wide,
And drawn a little backward from the sea
There stood a marble wall wrought cunningly,
Rosy and white, set thick with images,
And over-topped with heavy-fruited trees,
Which by the shore ran, as the bay did bend,
And to their eyes had neither gap nor end ;   510
Nor any gate : and looking over this,
They saw a place not made for earthly bliss,
Or eyes of dying men, for growing there
The yellow apple and the painted pear,
And well-filled golden cups of oranges
Hung amid groves of pointed cyprus trees ;
On grassy slopes the twining vine-boughs grew,
And hoary olives 'twixt far mountains blue,
And many-coloured flowers, like as a cloud
The rugged southern cliffs did softly shroud ;   520
And many a green-necked bird sung to his mate
Within the slim-leaved, thorny pomegranate,
That flung its unstrung rubies on the grass,
And slowly o'er the place the wind did pass
Heavy with many odours that it bore
From thymy hills down to the sea-beat shore,
Because no flower there is, that all the year,
From spring to autumn, beareth otherwhere,

519 like as a] like a   521 sung to his mate] they saw alight

But there it flourished ; nor the fruit alone
From 'twixt the green leaves and the boughs outshone,
For there each tree was ever flowering.   531
  Nor was there lacking many a living thing
Changed of its nature, for the roe-deer there
Walked fearless with the tiger, and the bear
Rolled sleepily upon the fruit-strawn grass,
Letting the coneys o'er his rough hide pass,
With blinking eyes, that meant no treachery.
Careless the partridge passed the red fox by ;
Untouched the serpent left the thrushes brown,
And as a picture was the lion's frown.   540
  But in the midst there was a grassy space,
Raised somewhat over all the flowery place,
On marble terrace-walls wrought like a dream ;
And round about it ran a clear blue stream,
Bridged o'er with marble steps, and midmost there
Grew a green tree, whose smooth grey boughs did bear
Such fruit as never man elsewhere had seen,
For 'twixt the sunlight and the shadow green
Shone out fair apples of red gleaming gold.
Moreover round the tree, in many a fold,   550
Lay coiled a dragon, glittering little less
Than that which his eternal watchfulness
Was set to guard ; nor yet was he alone,
For from the daisied grass about him shone
Cold raiment wrapping round two damsels fair,
And one upon the steps combed out her hair,
And with shut eyes sung low as in a dream ;
And one stood naked in the cold blue stream,
While on the bank her golden raiment lay ;
But on that noontide of the quivering day,   560
She only, hearing the seafarers' shout,
Her lovely golden head had turned about,
And seen their white sail flapping o'er the wall,
And as she turned had let her tresses fall,
Which the thin water rippling round her knee
Bore outward from her toward the restless sea.
  Not long she stood, but looking seaward yet,

535 fruit-strawn] fruit-strown   547 had] has

From out the water made good haste to get,
And catching up her raiment hastily,
Ran up the marble stair, and 'gan to cry :   570
' Wake, O my sisters, wake, for now are come
The thieves of Æa to our peaceful home.'
    Then at her voice they gat them to their feet,
And when her raiment all her body sweet
Once more had hidden, joining hand to hand,
About the sacred apples did they stand,
While coiled the dragon closer to the tree,
And raised his head above them threateningly.

    Meanwhile, from Argo many a sea-beat face
Gazed longingly upon that lovely place,   580
And some their eager hands already laid
Upon the gangway. Then Medea said :—
' Get back unto the oars, O Minyæ,
Nor loiter here, for what have such as we
To do herein, where, 'mid undying trees,
Undying watch the wise Hesperides,
And where the while they watch, scarce can a God
Set foot upon the fruit-besprinkled sod
That no snow ever covers ? therefore haste,
Nor yet in wondering your fair lives waste ;   590
For these are as the Gods, nor think of us,
Nor to their eyes can aught be glorious
That son of man can do ; would God that I
Could see far off the misty headland lie,
Where we the guilt of blood shall wash away,
For I grow weary of the dashing spray,
And ceaseless roll of interwoven seas,
And fain were sitting 'neath the whispering trees
In homely places, where the children play,
Who change like me, grow old, and die some day.'   600
    She ceased, and little soothly did they grieve,
For all its loveliness, that land to leave,
For now some God had chilled their hardihead,
And in their hearts had set a sacred dread,
They knew not why ; but on their oars they hung,
A little longer as the sisters sung.

' O ye, who to this place have strayed,
That never for man's eyes was made,
Depart in haste, as ye have come,
And bear back to your sea-beat home   610
This memory of the age of gold,
And for your eyes, grown over-bold,
Your hearts shall pay in sorrowing,
For want of many a half-seen thing.

' Lo, such as is this garden green,
In days past, all the world has been,
And what we know all people knew,
But this, that unto worse all grew.
' But since the golden age is gone,
This little place is left alone,   620
Unchanged, unchanging, watched of us,
The daughters of wise Hesperus.
' Surely the heavenly Messenger
Full oft is fain to enter here,
And yet without must he abide,
Nor longeth less the dark king's bride
To set red lips unto that fruit
That erst made nought her mother's suit.
Here would Diana rest awhile,
Forgetful of her woodland guile,   630
Among these beasts that fear her nought.
Nor is it less in Pallas' thought,
Beneath our trees to ponder o'er
The wide, unfathomed sea of lore ;
And oft-kissed Citheræa, no less
Weary of love, full fain would press
These flowers with unsandalled feet.

' But unto us our rest is sweet,
Neither shall any man or God
Or lovely Goddess touch the sod   640
Where-under old times buried lie,
Before the world knew misery.
Nor will we have a slave or king,
Nor yet will we learn anything
But that we know, that makes us glad ;

While oft the very Gods are sad
With knowing what the Fates shall do
  ' Neither from us shall wisdom go
To fill the hungering hearts of men,
Lest to them threescore years and ten   650
Come but to seem a little day,
Once given, taken soon away.
Nay, rather let them find their life
Bitter and sweet, fulfilled of strife,
Restless with hope, vain with regret,
Trembling with fear, most strangely set
'Twixt memory and forgetfulness ;
So more shall joy be, troubles less,
And surely when all this is past,
They shall not want their rest at last.   660
  ' Let earth and heaven go their way,
While still we watch from day to day,
In this green place left all alone,
A remnant of the days long gone.'
There in the wind they hung, as word by word
The clear-voiced singers silently they heard ;
But when the air was barren of their song,
Anigh the shore they durst not linger long,
So northward turned forewearied Argo's head,
And dipping oars, from that fair country sped,   670
Fulfilled of new desires and pensive thought,
Which that day's life unto their hearts had brought.
  Then hard they toiled upon the bitter sea,
And in two days they did not fail to be
In sight of land, a headland high and blue,
Which straight Milesian Erginus knew
To be the fateful place which now they sought,
Stormy Malea, so thitherward they brought
The groaning ship, and, casting anchor, lay
Beneath that headland's lee, within a bay,   680
Wherefrom the more part landed, and their feet
Once more the happy soil of Greece did meet.
  Therewith they failed not to bring ashore
Rich robes of price and of fair arms good store,
And gold and silver, that they there might buy

What yet they lacked for their solemnity ;
Then, while upon the highest point of land
Some built an altar, Jason, with a band
Of all the chiefest of the Minyæ,
Turned inland from the murmur of the sea.   690
  Not far they went ere by a little stream
Down in a valley they could see the gleam
Of brazen pillars and fair-gilded vanes,
And, dropping down by dank dark-wooded lanes
From off the hill-side, reached a house at last
Where in and out men-slaves and women passed,
And guests were streaming fast into the hall
Where now the oaken boards were laid for all.
With these the Minyæ went, and soon they were
Within a pillared hall both great and fair,   700
Where folk already sat beside the board,
And on the dais was an ancient lord.
  But when these saw the fearless Minyæ
Glittering in arms, they sprang up hastily,
And each man turned about unto the wall
To seize his spear or staff : then through the hall
Jason cried out : ' Laconians, fear ye not,
Nor leave the flesh-meat while it yet is hot
For dread of us, for we are men as ye,
And I am Jason of the Minyæ,   710
And come from Æa to the land of Greece,
And in my ship bear back the Golden Fleece,
And a fair Colchian queen to fill my bed.
And now we pray to share your wine and bread,
And other things we need, and at our hands
That ye will take fair things of many lands.'
  ' Sirs,' said the ancient lord, ' be welcome here,
Come up and sit by me, and make such cheer
As here ye can : glad am I that to me
The first of Grecian men from off the sea   720
Ye now are come.'
          Therewith the great hall rang
With joyful shouts, and as, with clash and clang
Of well-wrought arms, up to the dais they went,

723] Of well-wrought arms] Of brass and steel

All eyes upon the Minyæ were bent,
Nor could they have enough of wondering
At this or that sea-tossed victorious king.
　So with the strangers there they held high feast,
And afterwards the slaves drove many a beast
Down to the shore, and carried back again
Great store of precious things in pack and wain ;　　730
Wrought gold and silver, gems, full many a bale
Of scarlet cloth, and fine silk, fit to veil
The perfect limbs of dreaded Goddesses ;
Spices fresh-gathered from the outland trees,
And arms well-wrought, and precious scarce-known wine,
And carven images well-nigh divine.
　So when all folk with these were satisfied,
Back went the Minyæ to the water-side,
And with them that old lord, fain to behold
Victorious Argo and the Fleece of Gold,　　740
And so aboard amid the oars he lay
Throughout the night, and at the dawn of day
Did all men land, nor spared that day to wear
The best of all they had of gold-wrought gear,
And every one, being crowned with olive grey,
Up to the headland did they take their way,
Where now already stood the crowned priests
About the altars by the gilt-horned beasts.
There as the fair sun rose, did Jason break
Over the altar the thin barley-cake,　　750
And cast the salt abroad, and there were slain
The milk-white bulls, and there red wine did rain
On to the fire from out the ancient jar,
And high rose up the red flame, seen afar
From many another headland of that shore,
And through its fitful crackling and its roar,
From time to time in pleading song and prayer,
Swept by the wind about the summer air,
Clear rung the voices of the Minyæ
Unto the dashing of the conquered sea,　　760
That far below thrust on by tide and wind
The crumbling bases of the headland mined.

BOOK XV

Argo in ambush—Medea goes to Iolchos, and by her wiles
brings Pelias to his death.

BUT on the morrow did the Minyæ
Turn Argo's head once more to Thessaly,
And surely now the steersman knew his way,
As island after island every day
They coasted, with a soft land-wind abeam ;
And now at last like to a troubled dream
Seemed all the strange things they had seen erewhile,
Now when they knew the very green sea's smile
Beneath the rising and the setting sun,
And their return they surely now had won   10
To those familiar things long left behind,
When on their sails hard drave the western wind.
    So past Eubœa did they run apace,
And swept with oars the perilous green race
Betwixt Cerinthus and the islands white ;
But, when they now had doubled that dread height,
The shields that glittered upon Argo's side
They drew inboard, and made a shift to hide
Her golden eye and gleaming braveries,
And heaped the deck with bales of merchandize,   20
And on their yard sails patched and brown they bent,
And crawling slowly, with six oars they went,
Till Argo seemed like some Phœnician
Grown old and leaky, on the water wan.
    Now at the entering of their own green bay
There lies an island that men call to-day
Green Cicynethus, low, and covered o'er
With close-set trees, and distant from the shore
But some five furlongs, and a shallow sea
'Twixt main and island ripples languidly,   30
And on the shore there dwells not any man
For many a mile ; so there Erginus ran
Argo disguised, and steering skilfully,
Cast anchor with the island on his lee ;

Hid from the straits, and there struck sail and mast ;
Then to the island shore the heroes past,
And with their wide war-axes 'gan to lop
Full many a sapling with green-waving top
And full-leaved boughs of spreading maple-trees,
And covered Argo's seaward side with these.   40
And then the shipmen did Medea bid
To hold a shallop ready, while she hid
Her lovely body in a rough grey gown
And heavy home-spun mantle coarse and brown,
And round about her a great wallet slung,
And to her neck an uncouth image hung
Of Tauric Artemis, the cruel maid.

Then, all being ready, to the prince she said :—
' O well-beloved, amongst our foes I go
Alone and weak, nor do I surely know   50
If I shall live or die there ; but do thou
Let one watch ever, who from off the prow
Shall look towards white Iolchos o'er the bay,
And watching, wait until the seventh day,
And if no sign thou hast from me by then,
Believe me slain at hands of wicked men,
Or shut in some dark prison at the least,
While o'er my head thy foe holds royal feast.
      ' Then soothly if it lieth in thine heart
To leave this land untouched, do thou thy part ;   60
Yet do I think thou wilt be man enow
Unto the white-walled town to turn thy prow,
And either die a man or live a king,
Honoured of all, nor lacking anything
But me thy love—whom thou wilt soon forget,
When with thy tears my lone tomb has been wet
A little space ;—so be it, do thy will.
And of all good things mayst thou have thy fill
Before thou comest to the shadowy land
Where thou wilt strive once more to touch mine hand,
And have no power e'en to meet these eyes   71
That for thy love shall see such miseries.'

                52 Let one] Keep a

She ceased, nigh weeping, but he wept indeed,
Such tears as come to men in utmost need,
When all words fail them, and the world seems gone,
And with their love they fill the earth alone,
Careless of shame, and not remembering death.
But she clung round about him, with her breath
Shortened with sobs, as she began to say :—
' Weep not, O love, for surely many a day   80
May we be merry and forget all ill,
Nor have I yet forgotten all my skill,
And ere the days are gone thou well mayst see
Thy deadly foe brought unto nought by me.
And if indeed the Gods give me the day,
Then shall thy wakeful watch see o'er the bay
Smoke in the day-time, red flame in the night,
Rise o'er Iolchos' well-built walls and white ;
Then linger not, but run out every oar,
And hasten toward the many-peopled shore   90
That is thine own henceforth, as I am thine.'
Therewith from him she turned her face divine,
And reached the shallop over Argo's side,
That o'er the shallows soon began to glide,
Driven by arms of strong Eurydamas ;
But when the keel dragged on the rank sea-grass,
She stepped ashore, and back the hero turned
Unto his fellows, who, with hearts that burned
Unto the quays to bring great Argo's stem,
And gain the glory that was waiting them,   100
Watched ever for the sign across the bay,
Till nigh the dawning of the seventh day.

But from the shore unto a thick-leaved wood
Medea turned, drawing both cloak and hood
Right close about her, lest perchance some man,
Some hind, or fisher of the water wan,
Should wonder at her visage, that indeed
Seemed little worthy of that wretched weed.
In that thick wood a little stream there was,
That here was well-nigh hidden of the grass,   110
And there swelled into pools both clear and deep,

Wherein the images of trees did sleep,
For it was noontide of the summer day.
To such a pool Medea took her way,
And reaching it, upon the grass laid down
Her rough grey homespun cloak and wallet brown ;
And when her eyes had swept the space around,
Undid her tunic, that upon the ground
Fell huddled round her feet ; nor did she spare
To strip the linen from her body fair,   120
And shoes from off her feet ; then she drew near
The flowery edges of the streamlet clear,
And gazing down upon her image, stood,
Hearkening the drowsy murmur of the wood ;
And since the wind was hushed that noon of day,
And moveless down her back the long locks lay,
Her very self an image seemed to be,
Wrought in some wondrous faint-hued ivory,
Carved by a master among cunning men.

So still she stood, that the quick water-hen   130
Noted her not, as through the blue mouse-ear
He made his way ; the conies drew anear,
Nibbling the grass, and from an oak-twig nigh
A thrush poured forth his song unceasingly.

But in a while, sighing, she turned away,
And, going up to where the wallet lay,
She opened it, and thence a phial drew
That seemed to be well wrought of crystal blue,
Which when she had unstopped, therefrom she poured
Into the hollow of an Indian gourd,   140
A pale green liquor, wherefrom there arose
Such scent as o'er some poisonous valley blows,
Where nought but dull-scaled twining serpents dwell,
Nor any more now could the Colchian smell
The water-mint, the pine-trees, or the flower
Of the heaped-up sweet odorous virgin's bower.

But shuddering, and with lips grown pale and wan,
She took the gourd, and with shut eyes began
Therefrom her body to anoint all o'er ;
And this being done, she turned not any more   150
Unto the woodland brook, but hurrying,

Drew on her raiment, and made haste to sling
Her wallet round about her, nor forgot
The Tauric image, ere the lovely spot
She left unto the rabbit and the roe.

And now straight toward Iolchos did she go,
But as she went, a hideous, fearful change
Had come on her ; from sunken eyes and strange
She gazed around ; white grew her golden hair,
And seventy years her body seemed to bear ;   160
As though the world that coppice had passed by
For half an age, and caught her presently,
When from its borders once her foot had passed.
Then she began to murmur, as she cast
From changed eyes glances on her wrinkled hands :
' O Jason ! surely not for many lands,
Rich and gold-bearing lands, would I do this ;
But yet with thee to gain good peace and bliss
Far greater things would I have done to-day.'
So saying, she made haste upon her way,   170
Until at last, when it was well-nigh night,
She reached the city crowned with towers white,
And passing by the brazen gates of it,
Forewearied, by the fountain did she sit ;
Where, as she waited, came an ancient crone,
Who, groaning, set her pitcher on the stone,
And seeing the Colchian, asked her what she was.
' Mother,' Medea said, ' I strive to pass
Unto fair Athens, where dwelt long ago
My fathers, if perchance folk yet may know   180
Where they lie buried, that on that same stone
I may lie down and die ; a hapless one,
Whom folk once called Aglaia, once called fair ;
For years, long years agone, my golden hair
Went down the wind, as carelessly I strayed
Along the wet sea-beach, of nought afraid,
And there my joy was ended suddenly,
For on me fell the rovers of the sea,
And bore me bound into the land of Thrace,

And thence to some unnamed, far northern place,   190
Where I, a rich man's daughter, learned to bear
Fetters and toil and scourging year by year ;
Till it has happed unto me at the last,
Now that my strength for toil is overpast,
That I am free once more, if that is aught,
Whom in all wretched places death has sought,
And surely now will find—but wilt thou give
Some resting-place to me, that I may live
Until I come to Athens and my grave ?
And certainly, though nought of gold I have,   200
In the far northland did I gather lore
Of this and that amid my labour sore ;
And chiefly of this Goddess, rites I know,
Whose image round my neck thou seest now,
Well-shod Diana—and a whispered word
Within her inmost temple once I heard
Concerning this : how men may grow to be
E'en as the Gods, and gain eternity,
And how the work of years may be undone.'
    When she had finished, the Thessalian crone,   210
Filling her jar with water, turned and said :—
    ' Surely, Athenian, I am sore afraid,
Ere thou hast learned thy lesson utterly,
And gained that new life, thou thyself wilt die ;
Nor will it profit me, who am a slave
Wishing for death, a wretched life to save :
But hearken now, if thou art wise and bold,
Then will I show thee how thou mayst earn gold
And thanks enow, by telling this thy tale
Unto rich folk, for them will it avail   220
To know thy secret ; rise, and come with me,
And the king's daughters surely shalt thou see ;
For on my road from nothing unto hell
His palace is the last lodge where I dwell,
And I am well aweary of it now,
And of my toil, thanked with hard word and blow.'
    ' I thank thee, mother,' said the Colchian maid,
'' Nor of king's daughters shall I be afraid,
Whose ears Latona's daughter erst have heard,

Nor trembled at the heavy dreadful word.' 230
   Then on they passed, and as they went, the crone
Told her how Æson unto death was done,
And of the news that thither had been brought
Of those that o'er the sea that glory sought.
Namely, that when Æetes had been fain
To trap the Argo, all had been in vain,
Yet had he gone back well-nigh satisfied ;
For in the night to him a voice had cried
Louder and clearer than a mortal can :—
' Go back to Æa, sun-begotten man, 240
And there forget thy daughter and thy fleece,
But yet be merry, for the thieves of Greece
Shall live no longer than a poor wretch may
Who lies unholpen on a lonely way
Wounded, possessing nought but many woes,—
Lo, thus it happeneth now unto thy foes ! '
   This, said the crone, a Colchian had told
To Pelias, dweller in the house of gold,
And had large gifts from him ; who when he knew
The certainty of this, old Æson slew 250
With all his house who at Iolchos were.
   ' So,' said she, ' if, for quieting his fear
Of the sea-rover, such things he did give,
What would his gifts be if thou mad'st him live
His life again, with none of all his name
Alive, to give him fear of death or shame ? '
With that they came unto the royal house
Where Pelias dwelt, grown old and timorous,
Oppressed with blood of those that he had slain,
Desiring wealth and longer life in vain. 260
   So there a court low-built the old crone sought,
And to her lodging the tired Colchian brought,
Where she might sleep, and gave her food and drink.
Then into sleep did wise Medea sink,
And dreamed that she herself, made ever young,
Gold-robed within some peaceful garden sung,
Like that where dwelt the wise Hesperides.
But as she walked between the smooth-stemmed trees

267 dwelt] sung

She saw the sea rise o'er the marble wall,
And rolling o'er, drown grass and flowers and all,   270
And draw on towards her, who no whit could move,
Though from the high land Jason, her own love,
Was shouting out to her, so then, at last,
She dreamed the waters over all had passed
And reached her feet, and o'er her coldly swept,
And still undrowned, beneath the waves she wept,
And still was Jason shouting to her there.
    Therewith she woke, and felt the morning air
Cold on her face, because the ancient crone
Over her couch the casement had undone.   280
And as she oped her eyes, she heard her say :—
' Awake, O guest, for yet another day
We twain must bear before we gain our rest.
But now indeed I think it to be best
That to my ladies I alone should show
That prayers, and rites, and wonders thou dost know,
Which thou wilt tell for gold ; for sure I deem
That to us dying folk nought good doth seem,
But hoarding for the years we shall not see.
So bide thou there, and I will come to thee   290
And bring thee word of what the queens may say.'
    Then with these words she went upon her way,
While in her place alone Medea sat,
With eager heart, thinking of this and that,
And wishing that the glorious day were come,
When she should set her love within his home,
A king once more. So 'mid these thoughts, there came
Back to the place the wise Thessalian dame,
Who bade her rise and after her to go,
That she those marvels to the queens might show.   300
    Therewith she brought her to a chamber where
Abode the royal maidens slim and fair,
All doing well-remembered works ; of whom
White-armed Alcestis sat before the loom,
Casting the shuttle swift from hand to hand.
The while Eradne's part it was to stand
Amongst the maids who carded out the wool

294 and] or

And filled the gleaming ivory shuttles full.
Amphinome, meantime, her golden head
Bent o'er the spinners of the milk-white thread,   310
And by the growing web still set aside
The many-coloured bundles newly dyed,
Blood-red, and heavenly blue, and grassy green,
Yea, and more colours than man yet has seen
In flowery meadows midmost of the May.
   Then to the royal maids the crone 'gan say :—
' Behold the woman, O my mistresses,
Who 'midst the close-set gloomy northern trees
Has late learned that I told you of ; and ye
Who in this royal house live happily,   320
May well desire such life for evermore,
Which unto me were but a burden sore '
   Therewith she left them, but folk say, indeed,
That she who spoke was nought but Saturn's seed,
In very likeness of that woman old,
Whose body soon folk came on, dead and cold,
Within the place where she was wont to dwell.
Now how these things may be, I cannot tell,
But certainly Queen Juno's will was good
To finish that which, in the oaken wood   330
Anigh the Centaur's cave, she first began,
Giving good heart to the strange-nurtured man.

   But, she being gone, fair-limbed Amphinome
Said : ' Reverend mother, welcome here ye be,
And in return for thy so hard-earned lore
That thou wilt teach us, surely never-more
Shalt thou do labour whilst thou dwellest here,
But unto us shalt thou be lief and dear
As though thou wert the best of all our blood.'
   But, pondering awhile, Medea stood,   340
Then answered : ' Lady, I am now grown old,
And but small gifts to me were heaps of gold,
Or rest itself, for that the tomb shall give ;
I say all things are nought, unless I live
So long henceforward, that I need not think
               321 desire such life] desire life

When into nothing I at last must sink ;
But take me now unto the mighty king
That rules this land, and there by everything
That he holds sacred, let him swear to me
That I shall live in peace and liberty   350
Till quiet death upon my head is brought ;
But this great oath being made, things shall be wrought
By me, that never can be paid with gold ;
For I will make that young which has grown old,
And that alive that ye have seen lie dead.'

    Then much they wondered at the words she said,
And from the loom did fair Alcestis rise,
And tall Amphinome withdrew her eyes
From the fair spinners, and Eradne left
The carding of the fine wool for the weft.   360
Then said Eradne : ' Mother, fear not thou,
Surely our father is good man enow,
And will not harm thee : natheless, he will swear
By whatsoever thing he holdeth dear,
Nor needst thou have a doubt of him at all.
Come, for he sitteth now within the hall.'
With that, she took her shoes from off the ground
And round her feet the golden strings she bound,
As did her sisters, and fair cloaks they threw
About them, and their royal raiment drew   370
Through golden girdles, gemmed and richly wrought,
And forth with them the Colchian maid they brought.
But as unto the royal hall they turned,
Within their hearts such hot desire burned
For lengthening out the life they knew so sweet,
That scarce they felt the ground beneath their feet,
And through the marble court long seemed the way.

    But when they reached the place, glittering and gay
With all the slain man's goods, and saw the king
Wearing his royal crown and mystic ring,   380
And clad in purple, and his wearied face,
Anxious and cruel, gaze from Æson's place,
A little thing it seemed to slay him there,
As one might slay the lion in his lair,
Bestrewn with bones of beast, and man, and maid.

Then as he turned to them, Alcestis said :—
' O lord and father, here we bring to thee
A wise old woman, come from over sea,
Who 'mid the gloomy, close-set northern trees
Has heard the words of reverend Goddesses   390
I dare not name aloud ; therefore she knows
Why this thing perishes, and that thing grows,
And what to unborn creatures must befall,
And this, the very chiefest thing of all,
To make the old man live his life again,
And all the lapse of years but nought and vain ;
But we, when these strange things of her we heard,
Trembled before her, and were sore afeard,
In 'midst of all our measureless desire
Within thy veins and ours to set new fire,   400
And with thee live for many a happy day,
Whilst all about us passes soon away.'
    Now paler grew the king's face at this word,
And 'mid strange hopes he, too, grew sore afeard,
As sighing, he began to think of days
Now long gone by, when he was winning praise,
And thought : ' If so be I should never die,
Then would I lay aside all treachery,
And here should all folk live without alarm,
For to no man would I do any harm,   410
Whatso might hap, but I would bring again
The golden age, free from all fear and pain.'
    But through his heart there shot a pang of fear,
As to the queen he said : ' Why art thou here,
Since thou hast mastered this all-saving art,
Keeping but vagrant life for thine own part
Of what thou boastest with the Gods to share ?
Thou, but a dying woman, nowise fair.'
    ' Pelias,' she said, ' far from the north I come,
But in Erectheus' city was my home,   420
Where being alone, upon a luckless day,
By the sea-rovers was I snatched away,
And in their long-ship, with bound, helpless hands,
Was brought to Thrace, and thence to northern lands,
Of one of which I scarcely know the name,

Nor could your tongue the uncouth letters frame.
There had I savage masters, and must learn
With aching back to bend above the quern ;
There must I learn how the poor craftsman weaves,
Nor earn his wages ; and the barley-sheaves   430
Must bind in August ; and across the snow,
Unto the frozen river must I go,
When the white winter lay upon the land,
And therewithal must I dread many a hand,
And writhe beneath the whistle of the whip.
    ' 'Mid toils like these my youth from me did slip,
Uncomforted, through lapse of wretched years,
Till I forgot the use of sobs and tears,
And like a corpse about my labour went,
Grown old before my time, and worn and bent.   440
And then at last this good to me betid,
That my wise mistress strove to know things hid
From mortal men, and doubted all the rest,
Babblers and young, who in our fox's nest
Dwelt through the hideous changes of the year :
Then me she used to help her, and so dear
I grew, that when upon her tasks she went,
Into all dangerous service was I sent ;
And many a time, within the woods alone,
Have I sat watching o'er the heaps of stone   450
Where dwell the giants dead ; and many a time
Have my pale lips uttered the impious rhyme
That calls the dead from their unchanged abode ;
Till on my soul there lay a heavy load
Of knowledge, not without reward, for I
No longer went in rags and misery,
But in such bravery as there they had
My toil-worn body now was fairly clad,
And feared by man and maid did I become,
And mistress of my mistress' dreary home.   460
    ' Moreover, whether that, being dead to fear,
All things I noted, or that somewhat dear
I now was grown to those dread Goddesses,
I know not, yet amidst the haunted trees
More things I learned than my old mistress did,

Yea, some things surely from all folk else hid,
Whose names once spoken would unroof this hall,
And lay Iolchos underneath a pall
Of quick destruction ; and when these were learned,
At last my mistress all her wage had earned,   470
And to the world was dead for evermore.
  ' But me indeed the whole house hated sore,
First for my knowledge, next that, sooth to say,
I, when I well had passed my evil day,
And came to rule, spared not my fellows aught ;
Whereby this fate upon my head was brought,
That flee I must lest worse should hap to me ;
So on my way unto the Grecian sea
With weary heart and manifold distress,
My feet at last thy royal pavement press.   480
My lips beseech thy help, O mighty King !
Help me, that I myself may do the thing
I most desire, and this great gift may give
To thee and thine, from this time forth to live
In youth and beauty while the world goes by
With all its vain desires and misery.
  ' And if thou doubtest still, then hear me say
The words thou spakst upon a long-past day,
When thou wert fearful, and the half-shod man
Had come upon thee through the water wan.'   490

    She ceased awhile, and therewith Pelias,
With open mouth and eyes as fixed as glass,
Stared at her, wondering. Then again she said :—
' Awhile ago, when he thou knowest dead,
And he thou thinkest dead, were by thy side,
A crafty wile thou forgedst ; at that tide
Telling the tale of Theban Athamas,
And how that Phryxus dead at Æa was.
Thinking (and not in vain) to light the fire
Of glorious deeds, and measureless desire   500
Of fame within the hearts of men o'erbold.
  ' For thus thou saidst : " So is the story told
Of things that happened forty years agone,
                483 gift may give] gift givo

Nor of the Greeks has there been any one
To set the bones of Phryxus in a tomb,
Or mete out to the Colchian his due doom."
　　' So saidst thou then, and by such words didst drive
Thy nephew in a hopeless game to strive,
Wherefore thou deemest wisely he is dead,
And all the words that he can say are said.'　　510
　　She ceased again, while pale and shuddering,
Across his eyes the crafty, fearful king
Drew trembling hands.　But yet again she spoke :—
' What if the Gods by me the strong chain broke
Of thy past deeds, ill deeds wrought not in vain,
And thou with new desires lived again ?
Durst I still trust thee with my new-gained life ?
Who for the rest am not thy brother's wife,
Thy nephew, or thy brother.　Be it so.
Yet since the foolish hearts of men I know,　　520
Swear on this image of great Artemis
That unto me thy purpose harmless is,
Nor wilt thou do me hurt, or more or less.
Then while thy lips the ivory image press,
Will I call down all terrors that I know
Upon thine head if thou shouldst break thy vow.
　　' Yet for thyself dost thou trust what I say,
Or wilt thou still be dying day by day ? '

　　' Yea,' said the king, ' yea, whosoe'er thou art,
Needs must I trust thee, in such wise my heart　　530
Desires life again when this is done.
Give me the image, O thou fearful one,
Who knowest all my life, who in the breath
Wherein thou prayest help still threatenest death.'
　　Then on the image did she swear the king,
But while he spoke was she still muttering,
With glittering eyes fixed on him ;　but at last,
When from his lips the dreadful word had passed,
She said : ' O King, pray that thou mayst not die
Before the fifth day's sun has risen high ;　　540
Yet on to-morrow morn shalt thou behold
This hair of mine all glittering bright as gold,

542 glittering bright as] glittering as

My tottering feet firm planted on the ground,
My grey and shrivelled arms grown white and round,
As once, when by Ilissus' side I trod,
A snare of beauty to a very God,
To young men's eyes a fierce consuming fire.'
   So saying, did she kindle fresh desire
In the king's fainting heart, until he thought—
' Nay, if new life hereby to me is brought,   550
Withal there may be brought a lovely mate
To share my happy days and scorn of fate.'
Then did he bid his daughters straight to go
With that wise woman, nor spare aught to do
That she might bid them, and they wondering,
But in their hearts yet fearful of the thing,
Unto the women's chamber led her back,
And bade her say what matters she might lack.
   Then little did she ask unto her need,
But fair cold water, and some fitting weed,   560
And in a close-shut place to be alone,
Because no eye must see the wonder done.
   And ' Oh,' she said, ' fair women, haste ye now,
For surely weaker every hour I grow,
And fear to die ere I can live again.'
Then through the house they hastened, and with pain
A brazen caldron their fair hands bore up,
As well wrought over as a king's gold cup.
Which in a well-hung chamber did they set,
And filled with clear cold water, adding yet   570
New raiment wrought about with ruddy gold,
And snowy linen wrapped in many a fold.
   Then did Medea turn unto the three,
And said : ' Farewell, for no more shall ye see
These limbs alive, or hear this feeble voice,
For either shall my changed lips rejoice
In my new beauty, or else stark and cold
This wretched body shall your eyes behold.
Wait now until six hours are over-passed,
And if ye still shall find the door shut fast,   580
Then let the men bring hammers, neither doubt
That thence my corpse alone shall they bear out.

But if the door is open or ajar,
Draw nigh and see how great my helpers are,
And greet what there ye see with little fear,
For whatsoever may have touched me here,
By then, at least, shall no one be with me,
And nought but this old sorceress shall ye see
Grown young again ; alas ! grown young again !
Would God that I were past the fear and pain ! '   590
    So said the Colchian ; but their fearful eyes
Turned hastily from such hid mysteries
As there might lurk ; and to their bower they gat,
And well-nigh silent o'er the weaving sat,
And did what things they needs must do that day,
Until that six hours' space had passed away.

    Then had the sun set, and the whitening moon
Shone o'er the gardens where the brown bird's tune
Was quivering through the roses red and white,
And sweeter smelt the sweet flowers with the night ;
But to the chamber where there lay alone   601
The wise Medea, up the faint grey stone
Two rose-trees climbed, along a trellis led,
And with their wealth of blossoms white and red
Another garden of the window made.
    So now the royal sisters, sore afraid,
Each with a taper in her trembling hand,
Before the fateful chamber-door did stand
And heard no noise ; whereon Amphinome
Pushed at the door, that yielded, and the three   610
Passing with beating hearts the oaken door,
Pressed noiseless feet upon the polished floor,
Reddening the moonshine with their tapers' light.
    There they beheld the caldron gleaming bright,
And on the floor the heap of raiment rent
That erst had hid the body old and bent ;
And there a crystal phial they beheld
Empty, that once some wondrous liquor held ;
And by the window-side asleep they saw
The Colchian woman, white without a flaw   620

600 the sweet flowers] the flowers   604 blossoms] flowers

From head to heel ; her round arms by her side,
Her fair face flushed with sweet thoughts, as a bride
Who waits the coming of some well-loved man.
Softly she breathed, the while the moonlight ran
In silver ripples o'er her hair of gold.

But when that loveliness they did behold,
They cried aloud for wonder, though not yet
Her happy dreaming thoughts would she forget,
But into spoken words her murmuring grew,
Though of their purport nought the sisters knew,   630
Since in the outland Colchian tongue she spoke ;
Then, while they waited, slowly she awoke,
And looking round her, still with half-shut eyes,
She said : ' O damsels, fain would I arise,
I hear the morning murmur of the birds
And lowing of released and hungry herds
Across the meadows, sweet with vetch and bean,
And the faint ripple of the Phasis green.'
But with that last word did she start upright,
Shading her grey eyes from the tapers' light,   640
And said : ' O queens, and are ye come to me
This eve, my triumph over time to see ?
And is my boast for nought ? behold me made
Like the fair casket-bearer who betrayed
The luckless man while yet the world was young.'
So saying did she speak as one who sung,
So sweet her voice was ; then she stepped adown
From off the silken couch, and rough and brown
They seemed beside her, fair maids though they were.
But silently they stood, and wondered there,   650
And from their hearts had flown all thoughts at last
But that of living while the world went past.
Then at her feet Alcestis knelt and prayed :—
' O, who can see thee, Goddess, unafraid ?
Yet thou thyself hast promised life to us,
More than man's feeble life, and perilous,
And if thy promise now thou makest vain,
How can we live our thoughtless life again ?
Then, would thou ne'er hadst left thine heavenly home,

And o'er the green Thessalian meadows come ! '   660
   Then spoke Medea : ' Young as ye see me
The king, your father, in few days shall be,
And when that he has gained his just reward,
Your lives from death and danger will I guard.
Natheless no Goddess am I, but no more
Than a poor wanderer from shore to shore,
Though loved by her the swift of Goddesses,
Who now is glancing 'twixt the dark grey trees.
E'en while we speak. Now leave me to my rest,
For this new-changèd body is oppressed   670
By all the thoughts that round my heart will throng
Of ancient days, and hopes forgotten long ;
Go, therefore, but come hither with the sun
To do my bidding ; then shall there be done
Another marvel ere the morn comes round,
If yet ye three are dwelling above ground.'
   Then, trembling, they unto their chamber passed,
But, they being gone, she made the strong door fast,
And soon in deep sleep on the couch she lay
Until the golden sun brought back the day ;   680
Nor could she fail arising to be glad
That once again her own fair form she had,
And as the fresh air met her pleasantly,
She smiled, her image in the bath to see
That had been lost since at the noon she stood
Beside the still pool in the lonely wood ;
And she rejoiced her combed-out hair to bind,
And feel the linen in the morning wind
Fluttering about, in kissing side and limb,
And it was sweet about her ankles slim   690
To make the gemmed thongs of the sandals meet,
With rosy fingers touching her soft feet.
   But she being clad, there came the ladies three,
Who seemed by her but handmaidens to be ;
And such indeed they were, as dumb with awe
In the fresh morn that loveliness they saw.
   Then said Medea : ' Fair queens well be ye !
Surely in happy hour ye come to me,
Who, if I might, would do the whole world good.

But now take heed ; is there some close dark wood   700
Anigh the town ?—thither will we to-night,
And in that place, hidden from all men's sight,
Shall ye see wonders passing human thought.
But thither, by your hands there must be brought
Some ancient beast at very point to die,
That ye may see how loved an one am I
By dreadful Gods ; there, too, must ye convey
A brazen caldron ere the end of day,
And nigh the place there must not fail to be
Some running stream to help our mystery.   710
Yet more ; take heed that She who helpeth me,
Whose name I name not, willeth not to see
The robes of kings and queens upon her slaves ;
Therefore, if ye would please the one who saves,
This night must ye be clad in smocks of black,
And all adornment must your bodies lack,
Nor must there be a fillet on your hair,
And the hard road must feel your feet all bare.'
   ' Lady,' Eradne said, ' all shall be done,
Nor wilt thou yet have had beneath the sun   720
More faithful servants than we are to thee ;
But wilt thou not the king my father see,
And gladden him, that he may give thee things
Such as the heart desires—the spoil of kings ? '
   ' Nay,' said Medea, ' much have I to think
Ere the hot sun beneath the sea shall sink,
And much to call to mind, and for your sake
Unto my Helper many a prayer to make.'
   With that they went, and she, being left alone,
Took up the image of the swift-foot one,   730
Which for a hidden casket served her well,
And wherein things were laid right strange to tell.
So this and that she looked at, and the while
She muttered charms learned in the river isle.
   But at the noontide did they bring her food,
Saying that all was ready in the wood,
And that the night alone they waited now,
Ere unto them those marvels she might show.
Therefore Medea bade them come again
MORRIS   M m

When all the house of peaceful sleep was fain,   740
And nought was stirring :   so at dead of night
They came to her in black apparel dight,
Bearing like raiment for the Colchian,
Who did it on before their faces wan
And troubled eyes ;   then out of gates they stole,
Setting their faces to the wished-for goal.
   Now nigh Anaurus a blind pathway leads
Betwixt the yellow corn and whispering reeds,
The home of many a shy, quick-diving bird ;
Thereby they passed, and as they went they heard   750
Splashing of fish, and ripple of the stream ;
And once they saw across the water's gleam
The black boat of some fisher of the night,
And from the stream had drawn back in affright,
But that the Colchian whispered :   ' Wise be ye,
Thessalian sisters, yet with certainty
Make onward to the wood, for who indeed,
Beholding our pale faces and black weed,
Would come the nigher to us ?   Would not he
Think that some dread things we must surely be,   760
And tremble till we passed ?   Haste, for the night
Is waning now, and danger comes with light.'
Then on they passed, and soon they reached the wood,
And straight made for the midst of it, where stood
An old horned ram bound fast unto a tree,
Which the torch-bearer, tall Amphinome,
Showed to Medea, and not far therefrom
Unto a brazen caldron did they come,
Hidden with green boughs ;   then Medea bade
That by their hands a high pile should be made   770
Of fallen wood, and all else fit to burn ;
Which done, unto the caldron did they turn
And bore it to the river, and did strain
Their fair round arms to bear it back again
When it was filled, and raised it on the pile.
And then with hands unused to service vile
Lit up the fire, while Medea took
Dried herbs from out her wallet, which she shook
Into the caldron ;   till at last a cloud

Rose up therefrom and the dark trees did shroud.   780
  Then did she bid them the old ram to lead
Up to the caldron's side, and with good heed
To quench his just departing feeble life ;
So in his throat Eradne thrust the knife,
While in the white arms of Amphinome
And fair Alcestis, bleating piteously,
Feebly he struggled ; so being slain at last,
Piecemeal his members did the sisters cast
Into the seething water : then drew back
And hid their faces in their raiment black,   790
The while Medea midst the flickering light
Still sprinkled herbs from out her fingers white,
And in a steady voice at last did say :—
  ' O thou that turnest night into the day,
O thou the quencher of unhallowed fire,
The scourge of hot, inordinate desire,
Hast thou a mind to help me on this night,
That wrong may still be wrong, and right be right
In all men's eyes ? A little thing I ask
Before I put an ending to my task.'   800
  Scarce had she finished, ere a low black cloud
Seemed closing o'er the forest, and aloud
Medea cried : ' Oh, strong and terrible !
I fear thee not, do what may please thee well.'
Then as the pale Thessalians with affright
Crouched on the earth, forth leapt the lightning white
Over their shrinking heads, and therewithal
The thunder crashed, and down the rain did fall,
As though some angry deity were fain
To make a pool of the Thessalian plain.   810
  Till in a while it ceased, and all was stilled
Except the murmur of some brook new-filled,
And dripping of the thick-leafed forest trees
As they moved gently in the following breeze.
Yet still King Pelias' daughters feared to rise,
And with wet raiment still they hid their eyes,
And trembled, and white-armed Amphinome
Had dropped the long torch of the resin-tree,
That lay half-charred among the tall wet grass.

But unto them did wise Medea pass,   820
And said : ' O daughters of the sea-born man,
Rise up, for now the stars are growing wan,
And the grey dawn is drawing near apace ;
Nor need ye fear to see another face
Than this of mine, and all our work is done
We came to do.'
                    Then slowly, one by one,
The sisters rose, and, fearful, drew anigh
The place where they had seen the old ram die ;
And there beheld, by glimmering twilight grey,
Where on its side the brazen caldron lay,   830
And on the grass and flowers that hid the ground,
Half-charred extinguished brands lay all around,
But yet no token of the beast was there ;
But 'mid the brands a lamb lay, white and fair,
That now would raise his new-born head and bleat,
And now would lick the Colchian's naked feet,
As close he nestled to her : then the three
Drew nigh unto that marvel timidly,
And gazed at him with wide eyes wondering.
    Thereat Medea raised the new-changed thing   840
In her white arms, and smiled triumphantly,
And said : ' What things the Gods will do for me
Ye now behold ; take, then, this new-born beast,
And hope to sit long ages at the feast,
And this your youth and loveliness to keep
When all that ye have known are laid asleep.
Yet steel your hearts to do a fearful thing,
Ere this can happen, for unto the king
Must your hands do what they have done to-night
To this same beast. And now, to work aright   850
What yet is needful to this mystery,
Will be four days' full bitter toil for me.
Take heed that silence, too, on this ye keep,
Or else a bitter harvest shall ye reap.'
    So said she, willing well indeed to know,
Before the promised sign she dared to show,
What honour Pelias in Iolchos had,
And if his death should make his people sad.

        858 And if his death would make folk glad or sad.

But now they turned back on their homeward way,
Fleeing before the coming of the day ;   860
Nor yet the flinty way their feet did feel,
Nor their wet limbs the wind, that 'gan to steal
From out the north-west ere the sun did rise.
And swiftly though they went, yet did their eyes
Behold no more than eyes of those that dream
The crumbling edges of the swirling stream,
Or fallen tree-trunks or the fallow rough.
But Juno sent them feeling just enough
By the lone ways to come unto the town
And fair-walled palace, and to lay them down   870
Upon their fragrant beds, that stood forlorn
Of their white bodies, waiting for the morn
In chambers close-shut from the dying night.

But since Medea fain would know aright
What the folk willed to Pelias in the town,
Early next day she did on her the brown
And ragged raiment, and the sisters told
That she must find the place where herbs were sold,
And there buy this and that ; therewith she went
About the town, seeming crook-backed and bent ;   880
And, hidden in her mantle and great hood,
Within the crowded market-place she stood,
And marked the talk of all the busy folk,
And ever found that under Pelias' yoke
All people groaned : and therefore with good heart
She set herself to work out all her part.
For, going back, till the fifth day was gone
She dwelt within her chamber all alone,
Except that now and then the sisters came
To bring her food ; and whiles they saw a flame,   890
Strange-coloured, burning on the hearth, while she
Was bending o'er it, muttering wearily,
And whiles they saw her bent o'er parchment strange,
And letters that they knew not ; but no change
They ever saw upon her lovely face.
But at the last, she, mindful of the place
Where lay fair Argo's glorious battered keel,

And that dread hidden forest of bright steel,
Said to Eradne, when her food she brought
Upon the sixth morn : ' Sister, I have thought   900
How best to carry out the mystery
That is so dear at heart to thee and me,
And find that this night must the thing be done,
So seek a place where we may be alone,
High up, and looking southward o'er the bay ;
Thither ere midnight must ye steal away,
And under a huge caldron set dry brands.
And that being done, take sharp swords in your hands,
And while I watch the sea, and earth, and air,
Go ye to Pelias' well-hung chamber fair ;   910
There what ye will ye may most surely do,
If ye will work the way I counsel you.'
Therewith a phial in her hand she set,
And said : ' Who tasteth this will soon forget
Both life and death, and for no noise will wake
In two days' space ; therefore this phial take,
And with the king's drink see ye mingle it,
As well ye may, and let his servants sit
O'er wine so honied at the feast to-night.
Then certes shall their sleep not be so light,   920
That bare feet pattering quick across the floor,
Or unused creaking of an open door,
Shall rouse them ; though no deadly drug it is,
But bringer of kind sleep and dreamy bliss.
      ' But now, what think'st thou ? Are your hearts so
            good,
That ye will dare to shed your father's blood
That he may live for ever ?—then is he
The luckiest of all men. But if ye
Draw back now, after all my prayers and tears,
Then were it best that ye should end your fears   930
By burning me with quick fire ere to-night.
And yet not thus should ye lead lives aright,
And free from fear ; because the sandalled queen
Doth ever keep a memory fresh and green
For all her faithful servants—ye did see
Late in the green-wood how she loveth me.—

         921 pattering quick across] pattering across

'Therefore be wise, and when to-night ye draw
The sharp-edged steel, glittering without a flaw,
Cast fear and pity from you. Pity him
I bid you rather, who with shrunken limb   940
And sunken eyes, remembers well the days
When in the ranks of war he garnered praise,
Which unarmed, feeble, as his last year ends,
Babbling amongst the elders now he spends.
Such shall not Pelias be, but rather now
The breath of new life past misdeeds shall blow
Adown the wind, and, taught by his old life,
Shall he live honoured, free from fear or strife.'
    'Fear not,' Eradne said, 'our will to-night,
For all thy bidding will we do outright,   950
Since still a Goddess thou dost seem to be
To us poor strugglers with mortality.
And for the secret spot this night we need,
Close to the sea a place I know indeed,
Upon the outskirts of this palace fair ;
And on this night of all nights, close by there
My father sleeps, as oft his custom is,
When he is fain a Mysian girl to kiss,
Sea-rovers sold to him three months agone.
There after midnight we shall be alone   960
Beyond all doubt, since this place by the sea
A temple is of some divinity,
Whose very name men now have clean forgot,
And, as folk think, ill spirits haunt the spot :
So all men fear it sore, but soothly we
Fear nought of all these things, being led by thee.'
    She ceased, and from the Colchian won much praise,
And promises of many happy days.
    Then as upon the door she laid her hand,
Medea said : 'When midnight hides the land,   970
Come here to me, and bring me to that place ;
Then look the last upon your father's face
As ye have known it for these eighteen years,
Furrowed by eld and drawn by many fears ;
But when ye come, in such guise be ye clad
As in the wood that other night ye had.'

Then did Eradne leave her, and the day
Through sunshine and through shadow passed away.

But with the midnight came the sisters three,
To lead her to that temple by the sea,   980
And in black raiment had they hurried there,
With naked feet, and unadorned loose hair,
E'en as the other night Medea bade,
Except that each one had a trenchant blade
Slung round her neck, wherewith to do the deed.
Of these Alcestis trembled like the reed
Set midmost of some quickly running stream,
But with strange fire Eradne's eyes did gleam,
And a bright flush was burning on her cheek,
As still her fingers the sharp steel did seek ;   990
While tall Amphinome, grown pale and white
Beyond all measure, gazed into the night
With steady eyes, as with the queen they went
To that lone place to work out their intent.
So when all courts and corridors were passed,
Unto the ancient fane they came at last,
And found it twofold ; for below there stood
Square marble pillars, huge, and red as blood,
And wrought all o'er with fretting varying much ;
Heavy they were, and nowise like to such   1000
As men built in the lands Medea knew,
Or in the countries fate had led her through :
But they, set close and thick, aloft did hold
A well-wrought roof, where still gleamed scraps of gold,
That once told tales of Gods none living praise ;
And on this roof some king of later days
Had built another temple long before
The Minyæ came adown unto that shore
From fair Orchomenus, of whose rites indeed
And to what Gods the victim then did bleed,   1010
Men knew but little ; but therein there rose
Fair slim white pillars set in goodly rows,
And garlanded with brazen fruit and flowers,
That gleaming once, through lapse of many hours,
Now with black spirals wrapt the pillars white.

But this fair fane was open to the night
On one side only, toward the restless sea ;
And there a terrace, wrought full cunningly,
Clear of the pillars hung above the sand.

Now went those maids, groping with outstretched hand
Betwixt the pillars of the undercroft,   1021
Until they reached a stair that led aloft
Into the windy, long-deserted fane
Of younger days ; but when their feet did gain
The open space above the murmuring sea,
In whispers did the queens of Thessaly
Show to the Colchian where the great pile was,
Built 'neath a vessel of bright polished brass,
And many water-jars there stood around ;
And as they spoke, to them, the faint low sound   1030
Of their own whispered voices seemed as loud
As shouts that break from out the armed crowd
Of warriors ready for the fight.

                                    But she
Spoke with no lowered voice, and said : ' O ye !
Be brave to-night, and thenceforth have no fear
Of God or man since ye to me are dear.
Light up the torches, because certainly
Those that may see them gleaming o'er the sea
Will think they light but spirits of the air '
Then presently the torches out did flare,   1040
And lighted up the smile upon her face
And the tall pillars of the holy place,
And the three sisters gazing at her there,
Wild-looking, with the sea-wind in their hair,
And scant black raiment driven from their feet.

But when her eyes their fearful eyes did meet,
With wild appealing glances as for aid,
Some little pity touched the Colchian maid,
Some vague regret for their sad destiny.
But to herself she said : ' So must it be,   1050
And to such misery shall such a king
Lead wife and child, and every living thing
That trusts him.' Then she said, ' Leave me alone,
And go and do that which were better done

Ere any streak of dawn makes grey the sky.
And come to me when ye have seen him lie
Dead to his old life of misdeeds and woe.'

Then voiceless from the torchlight did they go
Into the darkness, and she, left alone,
Set by the torches till the deed was done   1060
Within the pillars, and turned back again
With eager eyes to gaze across the main,
But nothing she beheld by that starlight
But on the beach the line of breakers white,
And here and there, above the unlit grey,
Some white-topped billow dotting the dark bay.
    Then, sighing, did she turn herself around
And looked down toward the plot of unused ground,
Whereby they passed into that fateful place,
And gazed thereon with steadfast wary face,   1070
And there the pavement, whitened by the wind,
Betwixt the turf she saw, and nigh it, twined
About a marble image carelessly,
A white wild-rose, and the grey boundary
Of wind-beat stone, through whose unhinged door
Their stealthy feet had passed a while before.
    Nought else she saw for a long dreary hour,
For all things lay asleep in bed or bower,
Or in the little-lighted mountain caves,
Or 'neath the swirling streams and toppling waves
    She trembled then, for in the eastern sky   1081
A change came, telling of the dawning nigh,
And with swift footsteps she began to pace
Betwixt the narrow limits of the place ;
But as she turned round toward the close once more
Her eyes beheld the pavement by the door
Hid by some moving mass ; then joyfully
She waved her white arms toward the murmuring sea,
And listened trembling, and although the sound
Of breakers that the sandy sea-beach ground   1090
Was loud in the still night, yet could she hear
Sounds like the shuffling steps of those that bear
Some heavy thing, and as she gazed, could see

The thin black raiment of the sisters three
Blown out, and falling backward as they bent
Over some burden, and right slowly went ;
And 'twixt their arms could she behold the gleam
Of gold or gems, or silver-broidered seam,
Till all was hidden by the undercroft.
And then she heard them struggling bear aloft   1100
That dreadful burden, and then went to meet,
With beating heart, their slow ascending feet,
Taking a half-burnt torch within her hand.

   There by its light did she behold them stand
Breathless upon the first stone of that fane,
And with no word she beckoned them again
To move on toward the terrace o'er the sea,
And, turning, went before them silently.

   And so at last the body down they laid
Close by the caldron, and Eradne said :—   1110
' O thou, our life and saviour ! linger not,
We pray thee now ! because our hearts are hot
To see our father look with other eyes
Upon the sea, the green earth, and the skies,
And praise us for this seeming impious deed.'

   Not heeding her, Medea saw the weed
She erst beheld all glittering in the hall,
And that same mantle as a funeral pall
Which she had seen laid over either knee,
The wonder of King Æson's treasury,   1120
Which wise Phœnicians for much coined gold,
And many oxen, years agone had sold
To Æson, when folk called him king and lord.
Then to the head she went, and with no word
The white embroidered linen drew away
Over the face of the dead man, that lay
As though she doubted yet what thing it was,
And saw indeed the face of Pelias.

   Then o'er her pale face a bright flush there came,
And, turning, did she set the torches' flame   1130
Unto the dry brands of the well built pyre,
And, standing back, and waving from the fire

The shuddering girls, somewhat thereon she cast,
Like unto incense : then with furious blast
Shot up a smokeless flame into the air,
Quivering and red, nor then did she forbear
To cry aloud, in her old Colchian tongue,
Proud words, and passionate, that strangely rung
Within the poor bewildered sisters' ears,
Filling their hearts with vague and horrid fears.   1140
  ' O love ! ' she said, ' O love ! O sweet delight !
Hast thou begun to weep for me this night,
Dost thou stretch out for me thy mighty hands—
The feared of all, the graspers of the lands ?
Come then, O love, across the dark seas come,
And triumph as a king in thine own home,
While I, the doer of a happy deed,
Shall sit beside thee in this wretched weed ;
That folk may know me by thine eyes alone
Still blessing me for all that I have done.   1150
Come, king, and sit upon thy father's seat,
Come, conquering king, thy conqueror love to meet ! '

  But as she said these words the luckless three
Stared at her glowing face all helplessly,
Nor to their father's corpse durst turn their eyes,
While in their hearts did fearful thoughts arise.
But now Medea, ceasing, fed the fire
With that same incense, and the flame rose higher,
A portent to the dwellers in the town,
Unto the shepherd waking on the down,   1160
A terror telling of ill things to be.
  But from the God-built tower of Thessaly,
Grey Pelion, did the centaur Cheiron gaze,
And when he saw that ruddy flame outblaze,
He smiled, and said : ' So comes to pass the word
That in the forests of the north I heard,
And in such wise shall love be foiled, and hate,
And hope of gain, opposing steadfast fate.'
  So to the flowery eastern slopes he gat,
Waiting the dawn, nor hoped for this or that.   1170
      1147 a happy] this happy

BOOK XVI

The landing of the heroes—Jason is made king in Iolchos, and
the Argonauts go to their own homes.

BUT other watchers were there on that night,
Who saw the birth of that desired light
From nigh green Cicynethus' woody shore.
  For in mid-channel there, with every oar
Run out, and cable ready for the slip,
Did Jason hold his glorious storm-tossed ship,
While in the top did keen-eyed Lynceus stand,
And every man had ready to his hand
Sharp spear, and painted shield, and grinded sword.
Thus as they waited, suddenly the word   10
Rang out from Jason's mouth, and in the sea
The cable splashed, and straight the Minyæ
Unto their breasts the shaven ash-trees brought,
And, as the quivering blades the water caught,
Shouted for joy, and quickly passed the edge
Of Cicynethus, green with reed and sedge.
And whitening the dark waters of the bay,
Unto Iolchos did they take their way.
  Meanwhile the Colchian queen triumphantly
Watched the grey dawn steal forth above the sea,   20
Still murmuring softly in the Colchian tongue,
While o'er her head the flickering fire yet hung,
And in the brazen caldron's lips did gleam ;
Wherefrom went up a great white cloud of steam,
To die above their heads in that fresh air.
But Pelias' daughters, writhing in despair,
Silent for dread of her, she noted nought,
Nor of the dead man laid thereby she thought
  At last came forward tall Amphinome,
And said : ' O Queen, look o'er the whitening sea,   30
And tell us now what thing it is we lack
To bring our father's vanished breathing back

22 fire yet hung] fire hung

With that new life, whereof thou spak'st to us.'
So in a broken voice and piteous
She spoke ; but when no answer came at all,
Nor did Medea's grey eyes on her fall,
She cried again : ' O, art thou pitiless ?
Wilt thou not note our measureless distress ?
Wilt thou not finish that thou hast begun ?
Lo, in a little while the piercing sun   40
Shall find us slayers of our father here.
Then if thou hast no pity, hast thou fear ?
We are king's daughters still, and with us still
Are men who heed nought but to do our will ;
And if thou fall'st into the hands of these,
Thou shalt lament the gloomy northern trees
And painless death of threescore years and ten,
And little shall thy beauty help thee then.'
    So cried she shrilly in her gathering ire ;
But when Medea answered not, the fire   50
Burnt out within her heart, and on her knees
She fell, and cried : ' O crown of Goddesses,
Forgive these impious words, and answer me,
Else shall I try if the green heaving sea
Will hide from all these impious blood-stained hands,
Or bear them far away to savage lands,
That know no good or evil ; O speak, speak !
How can I pray thee when all words are weak ?
What gifts, what worship, shall we give to thee ? '
    E'en as she spoke, Medea seemed to see   60
A twinkling light far off amidst the bay,
Then from the suppliant hand she drew away,
Nor turned to her ; but looking seaward still,
She cried : ' O love ! yet shalt thou have thy fill
Of wealth, and power, and much desired fame,
Nor shall the Grecian folk forget my name
Who dearly bought these for thee ; therefore come,
And with the sun behold thy wished-for home.'
    So spoke she, and no less the wretched three
Beheld that light grow greater o'er the sea,   70
And therewithal the grey dawn coming fast,
And from them now well-nigh all hope had passed.

But fair Alcestis, grovelling on the ground,
And crying out, cast both her arms around
Medea's knees, and panting, and half-dead,
Poured forth wild words, nor knew the words she said.
While the two others, mad with their despair,
Ran wailing through the pillars here and there,
Nor knew indeed what thing had come on them,
For now, at last, fair Argo's plunging stem   80
Medea saw in the still gathering light,
And round about her the sea beaten white
With steady oars ; then she looked down, and said :
' What ! art thou praying for the newly dead,
For him who yesterday beheld the sun ?
And dost thou think that I am such an one
That what the Gods have unmade I can make ?
Lo ! with the dead shall Pelias awake,
And see such things as dead men's eyes may see.'

    Then as Alcestis, moaning wretchedly,   90
Fell back upon the pavement, thus she said :—
' Take comfort yet, and lift again thine head,
O foolish woman ! Dost thou think that fate
Has yet been stopped by any love or hate,
Or fear of death, or man's far-shouted fame ?
And still doubt not that I, who have to name
The wise Medea, in such ways as this
Have long been struggling for a life of bliss
I shall not gain ; and thus do all men do,
And win such wages as have happed to you.   100
    ' Rise up and gaze at what the fates have wrought,
And all the counsels they have brought to nought
On this same morn. Hearken the dash of oars
That never more ye thought would brush these shores ;
Behold the man stand on the high-raised prow
That this dead man so surely dead did know.
See how he raises in his conquering hand
The guarded marvel of the Colchian land,
This dead king deemed hid death and unknown woe.
See how his folk ashore the grapnels throw ;—   110
And see, and see ! beneath the risen sun,
How fair a day for this land is begun.

And let king Pelias rise if now he can,
And stop the coming of the half-shod man '

E'en as she spoke, the keel had touched the sand,
And catching up her raiment in her hand,
She ran with speed, and gained the temple close,
Made fragrant with that many-flowered white rose,
And o'er its daisied grass sped toward the beach ;
But when her feet the wrinkled sand did reach,   120
There, nigh the ship, alone did Jason stand,
Holding two spears within his ready hand ;
And right and left he peered forth warily,
As though he thought some looked-for thing to see.
But when he saw her hurrying him to meet,
With wild wind-tangled hair, and naked feet,
And outstretched hands, and scanty raiment black,
But for one moment did he start aback,
As if some guardian spirit of the land
Had come upon him ; but the next, his hand   130
Had caught her slim wrist, and he shouted out :
' Ashore, O heroes ! and no more have doubt
That all is well done we have wished were done ;
By this my love, by this the glorious one,
The saviour of my life, the Queen of Love,
To whom alone of all who are above,
Or on the earth, will I pour wine, or give
The life of anything that once did live.'

Then all men shouting, leapt forth on the sand,
And stood about them, shield and spear in hand,   140
Rejoicing that their mighty task was done ;
But as he saw the newly-risen sun
Shine on the town, upon their left that lay,
Then, smiling joyously, did Jason say :—
' O heroes, tell me, is the day not won ?
Look how the sun's rays now are stealing on,
And soon will touch that temple's marble feet
Where stood the king our parting keel to greet,

118 many-flowered white rose] many-flowered rose

But the great golden image of the God
Holds up, unlighted yet, his crystal rod,   150
And surely ere the noon shall gleam on it
Upon my father's throne his son shall sit,
Hedged round with spears of loyal men and true,
And all be done that we went forth to do.'

But, 'midst their shouting, spoke the queen again :—
' Jason, behold hereby this ancient fane—
Amidst its pillars let the heroes go
Until a marble stair they come unto,
And thereby mount into a pillared place,
At end whereof, upon an open space   160
Hung o'er the beach, that fire shall they see
That lighted you to finish gloriously
Your glorious journey ; and beside the fire
There shall they find the slayer of thy sire,
Who, soothly, shall not flee from them to-day,
Nor curse the men who carry him away.'

Then forth Menœtius and Nauphius stood,
Lynceus the keen, and Apheus of the wood,
To do the thing that she would have them do,
While unto Argo did Medea go,   170
And for the last time scaled the sea-beat side ;
There 'midst her silken curtains did she hide,
And taking forth the fairest weed she had,
In many a fragrant fold her body clad,
And on her feet bound golden sandals fair,
And set a golden garland on her hair.

But when again she reached the shell-strewn sand
She saw the shielded heroes wondering stand
About the new-slain body of the king,
Not knowing yet whose hands had wrought the thing.
For, scared amid their woe and misery,   181
By clash of arms, the wretched sisters three
Were lurking yet within the undercroft,
Amongst the close-set pillars, thinking oft
That now the whole round world should be undone.

But while they trembled, Æson's glorious son
Bade men make onward toward the market-place,

That there he might the wondering townsfolk face
For war or peace whichever it might be ;
But first upon a great oar carefully   190
They bound a spar crosswise, and hung thereon
That guarded marvel that their arms had won,
And as a banner bore it well aloft.
And fair Medea, upon cushions soft,
Laid upon spear-staves did they bear along,
Hedged round with glittering spears and bucklers strong,
And unarmed, fearless, mighty Jason led
Their joyous march, next whom, the man just dead,
The strong-armed heroes upon spear-shafts bore,
With dark blue sea-cloaks deftly covered o'er.   200
    So, following up the poor unkingly bier
Of him who erst, for love of gain and fear,
Had sent them forth to what he deemed their end,
They through the palace courts began to wend,
Not stayed of any, since the guards indeed
Still slept, made heavy by the drowsy weed
Eradne in their wine erewhile did steep.
And other folk, just risen from their sleep,
Looked from the windows 'mazed ; and like a dream
The queen, enthroned on golden cloths did seem,   210
And like a dream the high-raised, glittering Fleece,
And that new-slain long-hated pest of Greece.
And some indeed there were who saw full well
What wondrous tale there would be now to tell ;
Who the glad setting forth did not forget,
Unto whose eyes more fair, more glorious yet
The heroes showed, than when the sunny bay
First felt their keel upon a happy day.
Then, crying out for joy, beheld the Fleece,
And that fair Helper who had saved for Greece   220
The godlike heroes, and amidst of these
Seemed not the least of heavenly Goddesses.
    Withal they reached at last the brazen gate
Of Æson's house, outside of which did wait
Men armed and shouting, for that dawn a man
None knew, a fisher on the water wan,

                    219 Then] They

From house to house among the folk had gone,
Who said, that being in his own boat alone,
Casting his nets a little time before
The dawn, he heard the sound of many an oar,   230
And looking round, beheld a glittering prow
That he for Argo's armed beak did know ;
And as he gazed, her many-coloured side
Dashed past him like a dream with flood of tide,
As for the far-off ancient fane she made ;
And that thereon his anchor straight he weighed,
And made good haste the landing-place to gain.
' For certes,' said he, ' Pelias is slain,
And we are free once more.' So saying, he passed
From house to house, and reached the gates at last ;
Nor any saw him more on land or sea,   241
And, certes, none but clear-voiced Mercury
Spoke in that man by helpful Juno made,
No body, soothly, but a hollow shade.

  Now, therefore, when the gates were open wide,
Shouting, the folk drew back on either side,
All wild with joy ; but when they did behold
The high-raised Fleece of curling ruddy gold,
And the glad heroes' mighty heads beneath,
And throned Medea, with her golden wreath,   250
And folded hands, and chiefest thing of all,
The godlike man who went beside the pall,
Whereon the body of their tyrant lay,
Then did their voices fail them on that day,
And many a man of weeping there was fain.

  At last did Jason set his foot again
Upon the steps of that same ivory throne
Where once he fronted Pelias all alone,
And bare of friends : but now he turned about,
And, 'mid the thunder of the people's shout,   260
Scarce heard his fellows' spears : and by his side
There stood his gold-adorned Colchian bride,
With glad tears glistening in her sweet grey eyes :
And dead, at end of foiled treacheries,
There lay his foe, the slayer of his kin.

                228 his own boat] his boat

Then did he clasp the hand that lay within
His mighty and sword-hardened fingers brown,
And cried aloud above the shouting town :—

' Tell me, O people of my father's land,
Before whose ivory well-wrought throne I stand,   270
And whose fair-towered house mine eyes behold,
Glittering with brazen pillars, rich with gold ?

' A while ago we sailed across the sea,
To meet our deaths, if so the thing must be,
And there had died, had not the kind Gods been,
Who sent to us this lovely Colchian queen
To be our helper : many a land we saw
That knoweth neither tongue of man, or law
Of God or man : oft most things did we lack
That most men have, as still we struggled back   280
Unto the soft wind and the Grecian sea,
Until this morn our keel triumphantly
Furrowed the green waves of the well-known bay.
There to yon palace did I take my way,
As one who thought his father's face to see ;
Yet landing on the green shore warily,
(Since times may change, and friendship come to nought)
To this dead man straightway my feet were brought,
Whose face I knew, the face of Pelias.
' Then still more warily thence did we pass,   290
Till we met folk who told us everything,
Both of the slaying of the godlike king,
Æson, my father, and of other folk,
And how the whole land groaned beneath the yoke
Of this dead man, whom sure the Gods have slain
That all our labour might not be in vain,
Nor we, safe passing through the deadly land,
Lie slain in our own country at his hand.
So have the Gods wrought, therefore am I here,
No shield upon mine arm, no glittering spear   300
In my right hand, but by my unarmed side
This Colchian Queen, by many sorrows tried
Therefore, no fear of you is in my heart,
And if ye will, henceforth will I depart,

Nor take mine own ; or if it please this town
To slay me, let them lay my dead corpse down,
As on his tomb my father's image lies,
Like what he was before these miseries
Fell on his head. But in no wise will I
Take seat beneath this golden canopy,   310
Before ye tell me, people of this land,
Whose throne this is before the which I stand,
Whose towered house this is mine eyes behold,
Girt round with brazen pillars, bright with gold '

    Then, ere he ceased, the people's shouts broke in
Upon his speech : ' Most glorious of thy kin
Be thou our king—be thou our king alone,
That we may think the age of iron gone,
And Saturn come with every peaceful thing :—
Jason for king ! the Conqueror for king ! '   320
    Therewith the heroes clashed their spears and shields,
And as within the many-flowered fresh fields
This way and that the slim-stalked flowers do bend,
When sweeping gusts the soft west wind doth send
Among their hosts, so moved the people then,
When ceased the shouting of the armed men.
For each unto the other 'gan to speak,
And o'er the tall men's heads some dame would seek
To raise her child to look upon the king.
And as with smiles and laughter many a thing   330
They chattered through the great square joyously,
Each careless what his neighbour's words might be,
It sounded like some February mead,
Where thick the lustred starlings creep and feed,
And each his own song sings unto his mate,
Chiding the fickle spring so cold and late.
    But through the happy clamour of the folk,
At Jason's bidding, the great trumpet broke,
And great Echion's voice rang clear and strong,
As he cried silence ; then across the throng,   340
Did Jason cry : ' O people, thanked be ye,

322 many-flowered fresh fields] many-flowered fields
323 flowers do bend] flowers bend

That in such wise ye give yourselves to me.
And now, O friends, what more is there to say
But this ? Be glad, and feast this happy day,
Nor spend one coin of all your store for this ;
Nor shall the altars of the high Gods miss
Their due thankoffering : and She chief of all,
Who caused that this same happy time should fall,
Shall have a tithe of all that 'longs to me.
 ' And ye, O loved companions o'er the sea, 350
Come to my golden house, and let us feast,
Nor let time weary us this night at least ;
O ! be so glad that this our happy day
For all times past, all times to come may pay.'
 He ceased, and one more shout the people sent
Up to the heavens, as he descending went
With the fair Colchian through the joyous folk,
From whose well-ordered lane at times there broke
Some little child, thrust forward well to see
The godlike leader of the Minyæ : 360
Or here and there forth would some young man lean
To gaze upon the beauty of the queen
A little nearer, as they passed him by.

 Then, in such guise, they went triumphantly
To all the temples of that city fair,
And royal gifts they gave the great Gods there,
But chiefest from the Queen of Heaven's close
The clouds of incense in the air uprose,
And chiefly thither were the white lambs led,
And there the longest, Jason bowed the head 370
Well garlanded with lily flowers white.
But She, when all these things were done aright,
And Jason now had turned to go away,
In midmost of that cloudless sunny day
Bade Iris build her many-coloured bow,
That She her favour to the king might show.
 Then still more did the royal man rejoice,
And o'er the people, lifting up his voice,
Cried : ' See, Thessalians, who is on my side,

345 of all your store] of your store

Nor fear ye now but plenty will abide 380
In your fair land, and all folk speak of it,
From places whence the wavering swallows flit,
That they may live with us the sweet half year,
To earth where dwells the sluggish white-felled bear.'
    So spake he, glad past words ; and for the rest
Did Juno love him well since his great quest
Had brought home bitter death on Pelias,
And his love's words had brought the thing to pass,
That o'er that head was hanging, since the day
When from Sidero dead he turned away, 390
And as with Neleus down the steps he trod,
Thought things that fitted some undying God.

    Thence to his father's tomb did Jason go,
And found the old man's body laid alow,
Within a lone, unkingly grave, and bade
That straightway should a royal tomb be made
To lay him in, anigh the murmuring sea,
Where, celebrating their great victory,
They might do honour to his head recrowned,
And 'mid their shouts all mourning might be drowned,
Nor would they gladden Pelias' lonely shade 401
By weeping o'er the slaughter he had made.
    Therefrom unto his own house Jason came,
He had not entered since the night his name
Rang 'twixt the marble walls triumphantly,
And all folk set their hearts upon the sea.
So, now again, when shadows 'gan to fall
Still longer from the west, within that hall
Once more the heroes sat above their wine,
Once more they hearkened music nigh divine, 410
Once more the maidens' flower-scattering hands
Seemed better prizes than well-peopled lands.
    Glorious and royal, now the deed was done,
Seemed in that hall the face of every one
Who, 'twixt the thin plank and the bubbling sea,
Had pulled the smooth oar-handle past his knee.

384 earth] lands
401 Nor gladden the slain Pelias' lonely shade

Tuneful each voice seemed as the heroes told
The marvels that their eyes did erst behold,
Unto some merchant of the goodly town,
Or some rich man who on the thymy down   420
Fed store of sheep, and in whose lush green mead
The heavy uddered cows were wont to feed.

And she who all this world of joy had made,
And dared so many things all unafraid,
Now sat a Queen beside her crowned King
And as his love increased with everything
She did or said, forgot her happy state
In Æa of old times, ere mighty fate
Brought Argo's side from out the clashers twain,
Betwixt the rainbow and the briny rain.   430
Yet in the midst of her felicity
She trembled lest another day should see
Another fate, and other deeds for these,
Who hailed her not the least of Goddesses.
      Yet surely now, if never more again,
Had she and all these folk forgotten pain,
And idle words to them were Death and Fear ;
For in the gathering evening could they hear
The carols of the glad folk through the town,
The song of birds within the garden drown ;   440
And when the golden sun had gone away,
Still little darker was the night than day
Without the windows of the goodly hall.
      But many an hour after the night did fall,
Though outside, silence fell on man and beast,
There still they sat, nor wearied of the feast ;
Yea, ere they parted glimmering light had come
From the far mountains, nigh the Colchian's home,
And in the twilight birds began to wake.

      But the next morn, for slaughtered Æson's sake   450
The games began, with many a sacrifice,
And, these being all accomplished, gifts of price
The heroes took at Jason's open hands,

          444 after the night] after night

And, going homewards, unto many lands
They bore the story of their wandering.
    And now is Jason mighty lord and king,
And wedded to the fairest queen on earth,
And with no trouble now to break his mirth ;
And, loved by all, lives happy, free from blame,
Nor less has won the promised meed of fame.   460
So, having everything he once desired
Within the wild, ere yet his heart was fired
By Juno's word, he lives an envied man,
Holding these things that scarce another can,
Ease, love, and fame, and youth that knows no dread
Of any horrors lurking far ahead
Across the sunny, flowered fields of life :—
—Youth seeing no end unto the joyous strife.

    And thus in happy days, and rest, and peace,
Here ends the winning of the Golden Fleece.   470

BOOK XVII

Jason at Corinth—The wedding of Glauce—The death of Jason.

So ends the winning of the Golden Fleece,
So ends the tale of that sweet rest and peace
That unto Jason and his love befell ;
Another story now my tongue must tell,
And tremble in the telling. Would that I
Had but some portion of that mastery
That from the rose-hung lanes of woody Kent
Through these five hundred years such songs have sent
To us, who, meshed within this smoky net
Of unrejoicing labour, love them yet.   10
And thou, O Master !—Yea, my Master still,
Whatever feet have scaled Parnassus' hill,
Since like thy measures, clear, and sweet, and strong,
Thames' stream scarce fettered bore the bream along
Unto the bastioned bridge, his only chain.

464 Holding] Having

O Master, pardon me, if yet in vain
Thou art my Master, and I fail to bring
Before men's eyes the image of the thing
My heart is filled with : thou whose dreamy eyes
Beheld the flush to Cressid's cheeks arise,   20
When Troilus rode up the praising street,
As clearly as they saw thy townsmen meet
Those who in vineyards of Poictou withstood
The glittering horror of the steel-topped wood.

   Ten years have passed, since in the market-place
The hero stood with flushed and conquering face,
And life before him like one happy day ;
But many an hour thereof has passed away
In mingled trouble and felicity.
And now at Corinth, kissed by either sea,   30
He dwells, not governed now or governing,
Since there his kinsman Creon is a king.
   And with him still abides the Colchian,
But little changed, since o'er the waters wan
She gazed upon the mountains that she knew
Still lessening as the plunging Argo flew
Over the billows on the way to Greece.
But in these ten sweet years of rest and peace
Two fair man-children has she borne to him,
Who, joyous, fair of face, and strong of limb,   40
Full oft shall hear the glorious story told
Of Argo and the well-won Fleece of Gold,
By some old mariner ; and oft shall go
Where nigh the sea the wind-swept beech-trees grow,
And with a grey old woman tending them,
Shall make an Æa of some beech-tree's stem,
About whose roots there stands the water black.
Nor of the fleece shall they have any lack,
For in the bushes hangs much tangled wool
From wandering sheep who seek the shadow cool ;   50
And for the dragon shall there be thereby
A many-coloured snake, with glazed dull eye,
Slain by the shepherd ; so shall pass their days,

21 When] As

Whom folk look soon to gather wealth and praise.
 And 'midst these living things has Argo found
A home here also ; on the spot of ground
'Twixt Neptune's temple and the eastern sea,
She looks across the waves unceasingly ;
And as their ridges draw on toward the land,
The wind tells stories of the kingly band.   60
There, with the fixed and unused oars spread out
She lies, amidst the ghosts of song and shout,
And merry laughter, that were wont to fill
Her well-built hollow, slowly dying still,
Like all that glorious company of kings
Who in her did such well-remembered things.
 But as the day comes round when o'er the seas
She darted 'twixt the blue Symplegades,
And when again she rushed across the bar,
With King Æetes following her afar,   70
And when at length the heroes laid adown
The well-worn oars at old King Æson's town,—
When, year by year, these glorious days came round,
Bright with gay garments was that spot of ground,
And the grey rocks that o'ertop Cenchreæ
Sent echoes of sweet singing o'er the sea.
 For then the keel the maidens went about
Singing the songs of Orpheus, and the shout
Of rough-voiced sea-folk ended every song ;
And then from stem to stern they hung along   80
Garlands of flowers, and all the oars did twine
With garlands too, and cups of royal wine
Cast o'er her stem ; and at the stern a maid,
Clad like to Juno, on the tiller laid
Her slender fingers, while anigh the stem
Stood one with wings and many-coloured hem
About her raiment, like the messenger
Who bears the high Gods' dreadful words with her,
And through the sea of old that stem did lead.

 Lo, in such wise they honoured that great deed, 90
But Jason did they reverence as a God ;
And though his kinsman bore the ivory rod

And golden circlet, little could he do
Unless the great Thessalian willed it too.
　　Yet therefore Creon nowise bore him hate,
But reverencing the wise decrees of fate,
Still honoured him the more ; and therewith thought,
Would that this man by some means might be brought
To wed my daughter, since, when I am dead,
By none but him the people shall be led.　　　　100
And on this thought he brooded more and more,
And 'gan to hate the Colchian very sore,
And through the place, as lightly he might do,
He spread ill tales of false things and of true,
And unto Jason's self such words did say
As well he thought might turn his heart away
From faith and truth ; and as such words will come,
When wise men speak them, to a ready home,
So here they did ; though soothly for his part,
He knew it not, nor yet his restless heart.　　　110
　　But on a day it fell that as they sat
In Creon's porch, and talked of this or that,
The king said unto Jason : ' Brave thou art,
But hast thou never fear within thine heart
Of what the Gods may do for Pelias ? '
' Nay,' Jason said, ' let what will come to pass,
His day is past, and mine is flourishing,
But doubtless is an end to everything,
And soon or late each man shall have his day.'
　　Then said the king : ' Neither did thine hand slay
The man thyself, or bring his death about ;　　　121
Each man shall bear his own sin without doubt.
Yet do I bid thee watch and take good heed
Of what the Colchian's treacheries may breed.'
　　Then quickly Jason turned his head around
And said : ' What is there dwelling above ground
That loveth me as this one loveth me ?
O Creon ! I am honoured here as thee ;
All do my will as if a God I were ;
Scarce can the young men see me without fear,　　130
The elders without tears of vain regret.

　　　107 words] oft   122 Each man shall] Let each man

And, certes, had this worshipped head been set
Upon some spike of King Æetes' house,
But for her tender love and piteous,
For me she gave up country, kin, and name,
For me she risked tormenting and the flame,
The anger of the Gods and curse of man ;
For me she came across the waters wan
Through many woes, and for my sake did go
Alone, unarmed, to my most cruel foe,   140
Whom there she slew by his own daughters' hands,
Making me king of all my father's lands :
Note all these things, and tell me then to flee
From that which threateneth her who loveth me.'
    ' Yea,' said the king, ' to make and to unmake
Is her delight ; and certes for thy sake
She did all this thou sayest, yea, and yet more.
Seeing thee death-doomed on a foreign shore,
With hardy heart, but helpless ; a king's son,
But with thy thread of life well-nigh outrun ;   150
Therefore, I say, she did all this for thee,
And ever on the way to Thessaly
She taught thee all things needful since ye were
As void of helpful knowledge as of fear.
All this she did, and so was more than queen
Of thee and thine : but thou—thine age is green,
Nor wilt thou always dwell in this fair town,
Nor through the wild wood hunt the quarry down—
Bethink thee—of the world thou mayst be king,
Holding the life and death of everything,   160
Nor will she love thee more, upon that day
When all her part will be but to obey ;
Nor will it then be fitting unto thee
To have a rival in thy sovereignty
Laid in thy bed, and sitting at thy board.'
    Now somewhat Jason reddened at that word,
But said : ' O Creon, let the thing be so !
She shall be high the while that I am low,
And as the Gods in heaven rule over me,

147 and yet more] and more
153 Bade thee do this or that, since still ye were

Since they are greater, in such wise shall she,   170
Who as they gave me life, has given me life,
And glorious end to seeming hopeless strife.'
     Then Creon said : ' Yea, somewhat good it were
If thou couldst lead that life, and have no fear.'
Laughing he spoke ; but quickly changed his face,
And with knit brows he rose up from his place,
And with his hand on Jason's shoulder, said :—
' O careless man, too full of hardihead !
O thou ease-loving, little-thinking man,
Whate'er thou doest, dread the Colchian !   180
She will unmake thee yet, as she has made,
And in a bloody grave shalt thou be laid.'
     Then turning, to his palace went the king,
But Jason, left alone and pondering,
Felt in his heart a vague and gnawing fear,
Of unknown troubles slowly drawing near,
And, spite of words, the thing that Creon said
Touched in his heart that still increasing dread,
And he was moved by that grave elder's face,
For love was dying in the ten years' space.   190

     But Creon, sitting in his chamber, thought,
' Surely I deem my hero may be brought
To change his mate, for in his heart I see
He wearies of his great felicity,
Like fools, for whom fair heaven is not enough,
Who long to stumble over forests rough
With chance of death : yet no more will I say,
But let the bright sun bring about the day.'
     Now such an one for daughter Creon had
As maketh wise men fools, and young men mad,   200
Who yet in Corinth at this time was not,
But dwelt afar upon a woody spot
Anigh Cleonæ ; whither oft before
Had Jason gone for chasing of the boar
With Creon and his folk ; and on a day
With the old king again he took his way
To that dark wood, whereto, about the noon,

     190 the] that   192 deem] think   196 Who] And

They came, well harbingered by thrushes' tune,
And there straight fell to hunting of the boar ;
But, either through default of woodland lore,   210
Or bidden by the king, huntsmen and all
The king's stout servants from the chase did fall,
And Jason with him soon was left alone.
And both saw that the day would soon be done,
For 'midst the thick trees was it nigh twilight,
Then Jason said : ' Surely our bed to-night
Will be beneath these creaking boughs and black.'
　　' Nay,' said the king, ' surely we shall not lack
Soft golden beds such as old men desire,
Nor on the hearth the crackling of the fire,   220
For hereby is a little house of mine
Where dwells my daughter Glauce, near the shrine
Of round-armed Juno ; there, with two or three,
Matrons or maids, she guardeth reverently
The altar of the Goddess.'
　　　　　　　　　　　　With that word
Forward his jaded horse old Creon spurred,
And Jason followed him ; and when the sun
His burning course that day had well-nigh done,
The king and Jason came anigh the place
Where stood the house upon a swarded space   230
Amidst thick trees, that hedged it like a wall,
Whose shadows now o'er half the place did fall,
While, 'twixt their stems the low sun showed like fire,
And in the east the still white moon rose higher.
　　But midmost there a glittering roof of gold
Slim shafts of pale blue marble did uphold,
And under it, made by the art divine
Of some dead man, before a well-wrought shrine,
The Goddess stood, carved out of purest gold,
That her fair altar thence she might behold,   240
And round that temple was a little close
Shut by a gilded trellis of red rose
From off the forest green-sward ; and from thence
Carried by winds about the beech wood dense,

　　　214 With that both saw that nigh the day was done,
　　　237 made] wrought

The scent of lilies rose up in the air,
And store of pea-fowl was there roosting there,
Or moving lazily across the grass.
  But from the temple did the two kings pass
Unto a marble house that was thereby,
Not great indeed, but builded cunningly,   250
And set about with carven images,
Built in a close of slim young apple-trees ;
A marble fountain was there nigh the door,
And there the restless water trickled o'er
A smooth-hewn basin coloured like a shell,
And from the wet pink lip thereof it fell
By many a thin streak into a square pool,
From whence it ran again, the grass to cool,
In a small stream o'er sand, and earth, and flint,
Edged all about with fragrant blue-flowered mint,   260
Or hidden by the flat-leaved quivering sedge.
But from the pool's smooth-wrought and outmost edge
There went a marble step the fount to meet,
Well worn by many a water-drawer's feet.
  And thereon now they saw a damsel stand,
Holding the basin's lip with either hand,
While at her feet a brazen ewer stood ;
But when she heard them coming from the wood,
She turned about, and, seeing men near by,
Caught up the brazen vessel hastily,   270
And swiftly ran towards the marble house ;
But Creon, in his voice imperious,
Cried : ' Hither, Glauce, am I grown so old,
That without fear thou canst no more behold
Thy father, Creon ? Nay, come near, O child,
And bid us welcome to the forest wild.'
  Then straight she stopped, and setting down the urn,
Unto her father and his guest did turn,
While o'er his saddle-bow old Creon bent,
Rejoicing in her beauty as she went ;   280
And for one moment every scheme forgat,
For raising this thing and abasing that ;
As well he might, for as in poor array
She drew towards them at that end of day,

With raiment fluttering in the evening breeze,
She seemed like Her, the crown of Goddesses,
Who, o'er the dark sea, at the sunset came
To be in heaven a joy, on earth a flame.
Blushing, she came to Creon's saddle-bow,
And kissed him, who said, smiling : ' Fearest thou   290
Thy father, grown the oldest of old men ?
How wilt thou look upon this stranger then,
Who is no God, though such he seems to be,
But Jason, leader of the Minyæ ? '
Somewhat she started at the glorious name,
And o'er her face deeper the red flush came,
As she, with upraised face and shamefast eyes,
Said : ' Welcome, winner of the guarded prize !
Good hap it is indeed that thou art come
Unto my little-peopled woodland home.   300
Come then, my lords, to what awaits you here ;
Not Mæonean wine or dainty cheer
Your lips shall taste, but of fair simple flowers,
Plucked at the edges of the beechen bowers,
Your drink shall savour, and your meat shall be
Red-coated squirrels from the beechen tree.'
    Then fain to hide her eyes and blushing face,
She turned from them, and at a gentle pace
Unto the pillared porch she led the twain.
There they, alighting, the dark house did gain,   310
And there they ate and drank, making such cheer
As fasting men will do ; and still anear
Was Glauce to them, telling every maid
How such and such a thing should be arrayed ;
And ever the Thessalian's eager eyes
Did follow her, and to his heart did rise
Vague feelings of a new-found happiness.
    But now as the round moon was growing less,
And waxing brighter, and of fitting food
The kings had eaten as they thought it good,   320
Then Creon said : ' O daughter, rise and take
This full cup to the hero for my sake,

302 Not spiced Mæotic wine or dainty cheer
304 *This line was not in the first edition.*
321 daughter, rise and] daughter, straightly

And bid him drink thereof, and tell thee all
That unto him at Æa did befall,
And what fate did as still he journeyed home.'
    Then unto Jason did the maiden come,
Bearing the cup, and when he saw her thus,
The lapse of time seemed strange and piteous ;
For he bethought him of that other tide,
When certain-seeming death he did abide   330
In King Æetes' hall ; and when she drew
Anigh unto him, back the past years flew,
And he became that man entrapped again,
And newly felt, as then, that joyous pain,
And in his hand as then the cup he took,
With the warm fingers, and as then her look
Sent fire thoughout his veins ; yea, and as then
He had no heed of any Gods or men.
    Therewith her musical sweet voice he heard,
Speaking again the king her father's word :—   340
' O Jason, if it please thee, tell me all
That unto thee at Æa did befall,
And what thou sawedst as thou journeydst home,
And how it happed thee to thy land to come.'
    But ever as she spake she gazed at him,
And with new thoughts her simple eyes did swim,
Thinking her happy that this man had wed ;
And therewithal she turned from pale to red,
And red to pale. Then said he : ' Thou shalt know,
O fair king's daughter, all I have to show.'   350
And so the story of the Fleece began,
And how fair Argo crossed the water wan ;
While from his glittering eyes, deep sunk with eld,
The wily king those beauteous folk beheld,
As still from Jason's lips poured forth the tale,
And she sat listening, whiles with cheeks grown pale
And parted lips, and whiles with downcast eyes
And blushing for the thoughts that would arise
Uncalled for ; and thus passed that eve away
Till time of rest came. Then until the day,   360
In his fair silken bed did Jason dream

337 fire throughout] fire through

Of Argo struggling with the unknown stream,
And all the wonders of their long-past quest,
And well-known faces long time laid to rest.

But when the night was past, and the great sun
Another day for all things had begun,
The kings, arising, unto Corinth rode.
But ere they left the woodland fair abode,
Unto the Goddess did they sacrifice,
And on her altar in such woodland wise   370
As huntsmen use, their offerings did they lay.
With them was Glauce on that dawn of day,
Upon the left hand of the ancient king,
Unto the reverend Goddess ministring.
But when they turned once more unto the town,
The half-quenched censer did she lay adown,
And holding still the fresh-plucked flower-wreath,
Bade them farewell.
                    Then by thick wood and heath
They rode, and on their journey Jason said
Few words and wandering ; for still that maid   380
Did he behold before his waking eyes,
And with the oft-recurring memories
Of days and things a long time passed away
Her image mixed, and words that she did say.
But when upon the threshold of his house
He met Medea, who, with amorous
And humble words, spoke to him greetings kind,
He felt as he whose eyes the fire doth blind,
That presently about his limbs shall twine,
And in her face and calm grey eyes divine   390
He read his own destruction ; none the less
In his false heart fair Glauce's loveliness
Seemed that which he had loved his whole life long,
And little did he feel his old love's wrong.
Alas for truth ! each day, yea, hour by hour,
He longed once more to see the beechen bower,
And her who dwelt thereby.   Alas, alas !
Oft from his lips the hated words would pass :—
     ' O wavering traitor, still unsatisfied !

O false betrayer of the love so tried !   400
Fool ! to cast off the beauty that thou knowst,
Clear-seeing wisdom, better than a host
Against thy foes, and truth and constancy
Thou wilt not know again whate'er shall be ! '
  So oft he spoke words that were words indeed,
And had no sting, nor would his changed heart heed
The very bitterest of them all, as he
Thought of his woodland fair divinity,
And of her upturned face, so wondering
At this or that oft-told unheeded thing.   410
  Yet whiles, indeed, old memories had some power
Over his heart, in such an awful hour
As that, when darksome night is well-nigh done,
And earth is waiting silent for the sun ;
Then would he turn about his mate to see,
From lips half open, breathing peacefully,
And open, listless, the fair fingers laid,
That unto him had brought such mighty aid.
Then, groaning, from her would he turn away,
And wish he might not see another day,   420
For certainly his wretched soul he knew,
And of the cruel God his heart that drew.
But when the bright day had come round again,
With noise of men, came foolish thoughts and vain,
And, feeding fond desire, would he burn
Unto Cleonæ his swift steps to turn.
  Nor to these matters was the Colchian blind,
And though as yet his speech to her was kind,
Good heed she took of all his moody ways,
And how he loved her not as in past days ;   430
And how he shrunk from her, yet knew it not,
She noted, and the stammering words and hot,
Wherewith, as she grew kinder, still he strove
To hide from her the changing of his love.
  Long time she tried to shut her eyes to this,
Striving to save that fair abode of bliss ;
But so it might not be ; and day by day
She saw the happy time fade fast away ;
And as she fell from out that happiness,

Again she grew to be the sorceress,   440
Worker of fearful things, as once she was,
When what my tale has told she brought to pass.

  So, on a weary, hopeless day, she said :—
' Ah, poor Medea, art thou then betrayed
By that thou trustedst ? Art thou brought to nought
By that which erst, with wonders strangely wrought,
Thou madest live through happy days and long ?
Lo, now shall be avenged those poor maids' wrong,
Who, in that temple o'er the murmuring sea,
Ran maddening here and there ; and now shall be   450
That word accomplished that I uttered then,
Nor yet believed—that to all earthly men,
In spite of right and wrong, and love and hate,
One day shall come the turn of luckless fate.
Alas ! then I believed it not, when I
Saw Argo's painted prow triumphantly
Cleave the grey seas, and knew that I it was,
My very self, who brought those things to pass,
And lit those eyes unseen. How could I know
Unto what cruel folly men will grow ? '   460
  She wept therewith—and once more on that night
She stole abroad about the mirk midnight,
Once more upon a wood's edge, from her feet
She stripped her shoes and bared her shoulder sweet.
Once more that night over the lingering fire
She hung with sick heart famished of desire.
Once more she turned back when her work was done ;
Once more she fled the coming of the sun ;
Once more she reached her dusky, glimmering room ;
Once more she lighted up the dying gloom ;   470
Once more she lay adown, and in sad sleep
Her weary body and sick heart did steep.
Alas ! no more did tender Love come down
And smooth her troubled face of fear and frown ;
No more with hope half-opened lips did smile.
  Not long she slept, but in a little while,
Sighing, she rose, when now the sun was high,

466 of] with

And, going to her wallet wearily,
Took forth a phial thence, which she unstopped
And a small driblet therefrom slowly dropped   480
Upon a shred of linen, which straightway
In the sun's gleaming pathway did she lay ;
But when across it the first sunbeam came,
Therefrom there burst a colourless bright flame,
Which still burnt on when every shred was gone
Of that which seemed to feed the flame alone ;
Nor burnt it less for water, that she threw
Across it and across. Thereon she drew
A linen tunic from a brazen chest,
Wherein lay hid the fairest and the best   490
Of all her raiment ; this she held, and said :—
' Jason, thy love is fair by likelihead,
Pity it were to hide her over-much,
And when this garment her fair limbs shall touch,
So will it hide them as the waters green
Hid Citheræa, when she first was seen.'
  Soothly she spoke, because the web was fair
And thin, and delicate beyond compare,
And had been woven in no common loom,
For she herself within her fair-hung room   500
Had set the warp and watched the fine weft glide
Up from the roller, while from side to side,
Scarce seen, the shuttle flew from fingers thin
Of a dark Indian maid, whom gold did win
From some Phœnician, that loved nought but gold.
  But sighing now the raiment to behold,
She poured into a well-wrought bowl of brass
The thing that in the phial hidden was,
And therein, fold by fold, the linen laid,
Then for a little while her hands she stayed,   510
Till it had drunk the moisture thoroughly ;
Whereon she took it forth and laid it by,
Far from the sunlight, on her royal bed,
Saying : ' O thou who hast the hardihead,
Whoe'er thou art, to take from me mine own,
It had been better for thee that of stone

          516 It had been good for thee that of smooth stone

Thy limbs were wrought, nor made to suffer pain,
If this morn's deed has not been quite in vain.'
  So saying, did she mutter moodily,
Watching the spread-out linen slowly dry ;   520
At last she took it and within a bright
Fair silver casket hid it from the sight.
  This done, about the noble house she went,
And bitterly full oft her eyes she bent
On man and maid, and things grown old and dear,
'Midst hope of rest, no longer hoped for there.

  And, meantime, Jason, by the wily king
Still watched, had little joy in anything,
For while with fierce desire his heart still burned,
Yet now again for rest and peace he yearned,   530
Nor praise of other men yet counted nought,
And somewhat of the coming days he thought,
And helpless eld with many memories
Beset, and pictures of reproachful eyes ;
Yet thinking of the chain of days and nights
Stretched out all barren of once-hoped delights,
A sorry thing life seemed to him to be,
And one path only from that misery
Seemed open to him—where the fair girl stood,
Within the shadow of the beechen wood.   540
  But while he wavered thus 'twixt love and fear,
And something of the old time grown too dear
To cast off lightly, Creon noted all,
And surely now had hope that should befall
He long had wished for, and in such wise wrought
That all unto an ending soon be brought.
  Therefore it happed that on a July morn,
Jason at last, by many troubles torn,
Mounted his horse, and toward Cleonæ turned.
But as with pale face, and a heart that burned   550
To end all things in sweet love at the last,
He by the palace of King Creon passed ;
There Creon stood before the door, and said :—
' Where goest thou, O Jason ? By my head,
Wilt thou not sit at our high feast to-day ?

What do'st thou then, upon the stony way
That leads to Argolis ? '
                              O King,' said he,
' I am not meet for your solemnity,
Because the Gods to-day have made me sad ;
Nor knew I yet what feast here should be had,   560
But thought to-day to see my arrows fly
Within the green glades of the woods hereby.'
    ' Nay,' said the king ; ' full surely many a day
Of summer will there be to play this play
But on this day to Citheræa's house
Folk go, both maids and young men amorous ;
Yea, elders like to me will hold this feast,
Who in their foolish hearts can mourn at least
For days and things that never come again.
Yet, for myself, I shall not feast in vain,   570
For on this day my daughter comes to me,
That nigh Cleonæ erewhile thou didst see,
And she too goes with flower-bearing hands
To kiss the foot that on the tortoise stands.'
    So saying, did his ancient wily eyes
Behold the blood to Jason's brow arise,
And inwardly he laughed ; but Jason said :—
' Yea, then, O King, to chase my drearihead,
This were a fair sight for mine eyes to see,
And since thou willest, I will go with thee.'   580
    Then 'lighting from his horse, beside the king
He stood, and talked of this or that light thing,
And saw meanwhile full many a broad-wheeled wain,
Filled with fair flowers plucked from the unshorn plain,
Go toward the temple of the Cyprian queen,
And youths and maidens, wreathed about with green,
Pass singing carols through the listening street.
    At last the king said : ' Come, and let us meet
This joyous band within the very fane.'
So forth they went, and soon the place did gain,   590
Where the fair temple of the Goddess rose
From 'midst a grassy apple-planted close.
But each side of the door a maid there stood,

Clad in thin silken raiment red as blood,
Who had by her a gilded basket light,
Filled full of flowers woven for delight,
Wherefrom unto the passing kings they gave
Wreaths bound with gold, that somewhat they might
    have
To offer to the dread divinity,
Whose image, wrought of silver cunningly,   600
Stood 'neath a canopy of gleaming gold
Midmost the place, where damsels fair did hold
Baskets of flowers, or swung rich censers high ;
Then to the precious shrine they drew anigh
And forth stood Creon, and the fragrant wreath
Laid on the altar, and beneath his breath
Some prayer he muttered ; and next Jason laid
His gift by Creon's, but of much afraid,
And hoping much, he made not any prayer
Unto the Goddess ; then amid the fair   610
Slim pillars did he stand beside the king,
Confused as in a dream, and wondering
How all would end. But as they waited thus,
Within that fragrant place and amorous,
Languid grew Jason with the roses' scent
And with the incense-cloud that ever went
Unto the half-seen golden roof above,
Amongst whose glimmering the grey-winged dove
Hung crooning o'er his wrongs ; moreover there
The temple-damsels passed them, shy and fair,   620
With white limbs shining through their thin attire,
And amorous eyes, the hearts of men to fire,
Beneath their heavy crowns of roses red ;
And veiled sweet voices through the place did shed
Strange fitful music, telling more than words,
Confused by twitter of the restless birds
Within the temple-eaves, and by the doves,
Who 'mid the pillars murmured of their loves.
    But when the pleasure of that temple fair
Had sunk into his soul, upon the air   630

        603 swung rich censers] swung censers
        615 roses' scent] flowers' scent

Was borne the sound of flutes from folk outside,
And soon the greatest doors were opened wide,
And all the rout of worshippers poured in,
Clad in fair raiment, summer-like and thin,
And holding wreaths, part twined of fragrant flowers—
The children of the soft, sweet April showers—
And part of blossoms wrought in ruddy gold.
Now back the incense from the altar rolled
At their incoming, driven by the wind,
And round the pillars of the place it twined,   640
Enwrapping Jason, so that faint and dim
The fair show of the maidens was to him,
As each upon the altar laid adown
The blossoms mingled with the golden crown,
And prayed her prayer, then passed behind the shrine.
    At last from 'midst that cloud did Venus shine
Before the eyes of the Thessalian,
Who, with fixed eyes, and lips grown thin and wan,
Stared at the image, little though he saw,
But at her feet a sweet face, grave with awe,   650
Just bending over toward the silver feet,
Which Glauce with a timid kiss did greet,
And this being done, drew backward murmuring
Her prayer to Venus : ' Goddess, a small thing
Before this altar do I ask of thee,
That I my hero and my love may see,
That I '—but therewithal her face she raised,
And met his hungry eyes that on her gazed,
And stopped all trembling, letting fall adown
The hand that held the gold-enwoven crown.   660
    Yet little anger Venus had therefore,
But rather smiled to see her learn her lore
Within her house upon her festal day.
    But now upon the altar did she lay
Her offering, and yet she finished not
Her prayer begun, though in her poor heart, hot
With thoughts of love, full many a prayer she prayed.
    And now was all that pageant well arrayed
To pass about the temple, and her place

644 blossoms] flowers

Did Glauce take with flushed and eager face ;   670
But on her finger did she loose a ring,
Which that same day the wise Corinthian king
Had given her, therewith she went along,
Murmuring faint words amidst her fellows' song.

   Then past the kings the long procession swept,
And somewhat from the pillars Jason stepped,
Seeking a sign from that desired face ;
And when the damsels at a gentle pace
Went by him, and for fear of him and awe
Shrunk back, and with their slender hands did draw
Closer about them the thin fragrant weed ;   681
Still nought of all their beauty did he heed,
But as the amorous army passed him by
Into sweet Glauce's eyes appealingly
He gazed, who, trembling like some snow-trapped dove,
From her soft eyes sent forth one look of love,
Then dropped the lids, as, blind with love and shame,
Unto the place where stood the kings she came.
And there her hand that down beside her hung
She raised a little, and her faltering tongue   690
Just framed the words : ' O love, for thee, for thee ! '
And with that word she trembled piteously,
In terror at the sound of her own voice.
And much did wily Creon then rejoice,
Looking askance, and feigning to see nought,
When he beheld those hands together brought.

   But Jason, when those fingers touched his own,
Forgat all joys that he had ever known ;
And when her hand left his hand with the ring,
Still in the palm, like some lost, stricken thing   700
He stood and stared, as from his eyes she passed.
And from that hour all fear away was cast,
All memory of the past time, all regret
For days that did those changed days beget,
And therewithal adown the wind he flung
The love whereon his yearning heart once hung.

678 when] as   683 *This line was not in the first edition.*
684 Into sweet Glauce's] But into Glauce's   685 He] Still

Ah! let me turn the page, nor chronicle
In many words the death of faith, or tell
Of meetings by the newly-risen moon,
Of passionate silence 'midst the brown birds' tune,   710
Of wild tears wept within the noontide shade,
Of wild vows spoken, that of old were made,
For other ears, when, amidst other flowers,
He wandered through the love-begetting hours.
Suffice it, that unhappy was each day
Which without speech from Glauce passed away,
And troublous dreams would visit him at night,
When day had passed all barren of her sight.
And at the last, that Creon, the old king,
Being prayed with gifts, and joyful of the thing,   720
Had given a day when these twain should be wed.

Meanwhile, the once-loved sharer of his bed
Knew all at last, and fierce tormenting fire
Consumed her as the dreadful day drew nigher,
And much from other lips than his she heard,
Till, on a day, this dreadful, blighting word,
Her eyes beheld within a fair scroll writ,
And 'twixt her closed teeth still she muttered it :—
  ' Depart in peace ! and take great heaps of gold,
For nevermore thy body will I fold   730
Within these arms. Let Gods wed Goddesses
And sea-folk wed the women of the seas,
And men wed women ; but thee, who can wed
And dwell with thee without consuming dread,
O wise kin of the dreadful sorceress !
And yet, perchance thy beauty still may bless
Some man to whom the world seems small and poor,
And who already stands beside his door,
Armed for the conquest of all earthly things.
  ' Lo, such an one, the vanquisher of kings,   740
And equal to the Gods should be thy mate.
But me, who for a peaceful end but wait,
Desiring nought but love—canst thou love me ?
Or can I give my whole heart up to thee ?
  ' I hear thee talk of old days thou didst know—

Are they not gone ?—wilt thou not let them go,
Nor to their shadows still cling desperately,
Longing for things that never more can be ?
  ' What! wilt thou blame me still that the times change?
Once through the oak-wood happy did I range,   750
And thought no ill ; but then came over me
Madness, I know not why, and o'er the sea
I needs must go in strife to win me fame,
And certes won it, and my envied name
Was borne with shouts about the towns of Greece.
  ' All that has vanished now, and my old peace,
Through lapse of changing years, has come to me.
Once more I seem the woodland paths to see,
Tunes of old songs are ringing in mine ears,
Heard long ago in that place free from fears,   760
Where no one wept above his fellow dead,
And looked at death himself with little dread.
The times are changed, with them is changed my heart,
Nor in my life canst thou have any part,
Nor can I live in joy and peace with thee,
Nor yet, for all thy words, canst thou love me.
  ' Yet, is the world so narrow for us twain
That all our life henceforth must be but vain ?
Nay, for departing shalt thou be a queen
Of some great world, fairer than I have seen,   770
And wheresoe'er thou goest shalt thou fare
As one for whom the Gods have utmost care.'

    Yea, she knew all, yet when these words she read,
She felt as though upon her bowed-down head
Had fallen a misery not known before,
And all seemed light that erst her crushed heart bore,
For she was wrapped in uttermost despair,
And motionless within the chamber fair
She stood, as one struck dead and past all thought.
    But as she stood, a sound to her was brought   780
Of children's voices, and she 'gan to wail
With tearless eyes, and, from writhed lips and pale,
Faint words of woe she muttered, meaningless,
But such as such lips utter none the less.

Then all at once thoughts of some dreadful thing
Back to her mind some memory seemed to bring,
As she beheld the casket gleaming fair,
Wherein was laid that she was wont to wear,
That in the philtre lay that other morn,
And therewithal unto her heart was borne   790
The image of two lovers, side by side.
    Then with a groan the fingers that did hide
Her tortured face slowly she drew away,
And going up to where her tablets lay,
Fit for the white hands of the Goddesses,
Therein she wrote such piteous words as these.

    ' Would God that Argo's brazen-banded mast
'Twixt the blue clashing rocks had never passed
Unto the Colchian land ! Or would that I
Had had such happy fortune as to die   800
Then, when I saw thee standing by the Fleece,
Safe on the long-desired shore of Greece !
Alas, O Jason ! for thy cruel praise !
Alas, for all the kindness of past days !
That to thy heart seems but a story told
Which happed to other folk in times of old.
But unto me, indeed, its memory
Was bliss in happy hours, and now shall be
Such misery as never tongue can tell.
    ' Jason, I heed thy cruel message well,   810
Nor will I stay to vex thee, nor will stay
Until thy slaves thrust me thy love away.
Be happy ! think that I have never been—
Forget these eyes, that none the less have seen
Thy hands take life at my hands, and thy heart
O'erflow in tears, when needs was we should part
But for a little ; though, upon the day
When I for evermore must go away,
I think, indeed, thou wilt not weep for this ;
Yea, if thou weepest then, some honied kiss   820
From other lips shall make thy grey eyes wet,
Betwixt the words that bid thee to forget
Thou ever hast loved aught but her alone.

' Yet of all times mayst thou remember one,
The second time that ever thou and I
Had met alone together—mournfully
The soft wind murmured on that happy night,
The round moon, growing low, was large and bright,
As on my father's marble house it gleamed,
While from the fane a baneful light outstreamed,   830
Lighting the horror of that prodigy,
The only fence betwixt whose wrath and thee
Was this poor body. Ah ! thou knowest then
How thou beheldst the shadows of thy men
Steal silently towards Argo's painted head.
Thou knowest yet the whispered words I said
Upon that night—thou never canst forget
That happy night of all nights. Ah ! and yet
Why make I these long words, that thou the more
Mayst hate me, who already hat'st me sore,   840
Since 'midst thy pleasure I am grown a pain.
' Be happy ! for thou shalt not hear again
My voice, and with one word this scroll is done—
Jason, I love thee, yea, love thee alone—
God help me, therefore !—and would God that I
Such as thou sayst I am, were verily,
Then what a sea of troubles shouldst thou feel
Rise up against thy life, how shouldst thou steel
Thy heart to bear all, failing at the last,
Then wouldst thou raise thine head, o'erwhelmed,
       downcast,   850
And round about once more shouldst look for me,
Who led thee o'er strange land and unknown sea.
' And not in vain, O dearest ! not in vain !
Would I not come and weep at all thy pain,
That I myself had wrought ? would I not raise
Thy burdened head with hopes of happy days ?
Would I not draw thee forth from all thy woe ?
And fearless by thy side would I not go,
As once I went, through many unknown lands
When I had saved thee from my father's hands ?   860
' All would I do, that I have done erewhile,
To have thy love once more, and feel thy smile,

As freed from snow about the first spring days
The meadows feel the young sun's fickle rays.
  ' But I am weak, and past all, nor will I
Pray any more for kindly memory ;
Yet shalt thou have one last gift more from me,
To give thy new love, since men say that she
Is fairer than all things man can behold.
  ' Within this casket lies in many a fold   870
Raiment that my forgotten limbs did press,
When thou wert wont to praise their loveliness.
Fear not to take it from the sorceress' hands,
Though certainly with balms from many lands
Is it made fragrant, wondrous with a charm
To guard the wearer's body from all harm.
  ' Upon the morn that she shall make thee glad,
With this fair tunic let her limbs be clad,
But see that no sun falls upon its folds
Until her hand the king, her father, holds,   880
To greet thine eyes : then, when in godlike light
She shines, with all her beauty grown so bright,
That eyes of men can scarcely gaze thereon—
Then, when thy new desire at last is won—
Then, wilt thou not a little think of me,
Who saved thy life for this felicity ? '

  She ceased, and moaning to herself she said :—
' Ah ! when will all be ended ?   If the dead
Have unto them some little memory left
Of things that while they lived Fate from them reft,
Ere life itself was reft from them at last,   891
Yet would to God these days at least were past,
And all be done that here must needs be done !
  ' Ah ! shall I, living underneath the sun,
I wonder, wish for anything again,
Or ever know what pleasure means, and pain ?—
—And for these deeds I do ; and thou the first,
O woman, whose young beauty has so cursed
My hapless life, at least I save thee this—
The slow descent to misery from bliss,   900
With bitter torment growing day by day,

And faint hope lessening till it fades away
Into dull waiting for the certain blow.
But thou, who nought of coming fate dost know,
One overwhelming fear, one agony,
And in a little minute shalt thou be
Where thou wouldst be in threescore years at most,
And surely but a poor gift thou hast lost.
The new-made slave, the toiler on the sea,
The once rich fallen into poverty, 910
In one hour knows more grief than thou canst know ;
And many an one there is who fain would go
And try their fortune in the unknown life
If they could win some ending to this strife,
Unlooked-for, sudden, as thine end shall be.
Kindly I deal with thee, mine enemy ;
Since swift forgetfulness to thee I send.
But thou shalt die—his eyes shall see thine end—
Ah ! if thy death alone could end it all !

　' But ye—shall I behold you when leaves fall, 920
In some sad evening of the autumn-tide ?
Or shall I have you sitting by my side
Amidst the feast, so that folk stare and say,
" Sure the grey wolf has seen the queen to-day."
What ! when I kneel in temples of the Gods,
Must I bethink me of the upturned sods,
And hear a voice say : " Mother, wilt thou come
And see us resting in our new-made home,
Since thou wert used to make us lie full soft,
Smoothing our pillows many a time and oft ? 930
O mother, now no dainty food we need,
Whereof thou once wert wont to have such heed.
O mother, now we need no gown of gold,
Nor in the winter time do we grow cold ;
Thy hands would bathe us when we were thine own,
Now doth the rain wash every shining bone.
No pedagogue we need, for surely heaven
Lies spread above us, with the planets seven,
To teach us all its lore."

　　932 Whereof of old thou usedst to have such heed
MORRIS
　　　P p

                              Ah ! day by day
Would I have hearkened all the folk would say.   940
Ah ! in the sweet beginning of your days
Would I have garnered every word of praise.
" What fearless backers of the untamed steed,"
" What matchless spears, what loyal friends at need,"
" What noble hearts, how bountiful and free,"
" How like their father on the troublous sea ! "
    ' O sons, with what sweet counsels and what tears
Would I have hearkened to the hopes and fears
Of your first loves : what rapture had it been
Your dear returning footsteps to have seen   950
Amidst the happy warriors of the land ;
But now—but now—this is a little hand
Too often kissed since love did first begin
To win such curses as it yet shall win,
When after all bad deeds there comes a worse ;
Praise to the Gods ! ye know not how to curse.
    ' But when in some dim land we meet again
Will ye remember all the loss and pain ?
Will ye the form of children keep for aye
With thoughts of men ? and " Mother," will ye say,
" Why didst thou slay us ere we came to know   961
That men die ? hadst thou waited until now,
An easy thing it had been then to die,
For in the thought of immortality
Do children play about the flowery meads,
And win their heaven with a crown of weeds."
    ' O children ! that I would have died to save,
How fair a life of pleasure might ye have,
But for your mother :—nay, for thee, for thee,
For thee who might'st have lived so happily ;   970
For thee, O traitor ! who didst bring them here
Into this cruel world, this lovely bier
Of youth and love, and joy and happiness,
That unforeseeing happy fools still bless.'
    Amid these wild words had the evening come
Of the last day in that once happy home ;
So, rising, did she take the casket fair,

          970 *This line was not in the first edition.*

And gave it to a faithful slave to bear,
With all those wailing words that she had writ
To Jason, her love once ; then did she sit   980
Within that chamber, with her heavy head
Laid on her arms, and scarce more than the dead
She moved, for many hours, until at last
A stupor over her some kind God cast,
So that she slept, and had forgetfulness
A little while from fury and distress.

But Jason, when he read that bitter word
Was sore ashamed, and in his ears he heard
Words that men durst not speak before his face ;
Therewith, for very shame, that silver case   990
And what it held he sent unto his bride,
And therewithal this word : ' Whatso betide,
Let not the sun shine on it till the hour
When thou hast left for aye thy maiden bower,
And with the king thou standest in the hall,
Then unto thee shall all good things befall.'
So to his rest he went, but, sooth to say,
He slept but little till the dawn of day,
So troubled was his mind with many a thing,
And in his ears long-spoken words did ring.   1000
' Good speed, O traitor ! who shall think to wed
Soft limbs and white, and find thy royal bed
Dripping with blood and burning up with fire.'
So there, 'twixt fear and shame and strong desire,
Sleepless he lay until the day began—
The conqueror, the king, the envied man.

But on the chamber where sweet Glauce lay
Fair broke the dawning of that dreadful day,
And fairer from her bed did she arise,
And looking down with shamefast timid eyes,   1010
Beheld the bosom that no man had seen,
And round limbs worthy of the Sea-born Queen.
With that she murmured words of joy and love,
No louder than the grey, pink-footed dove,
When at the dawn he first begins his tale,

Not knowing if he means a song or wail.
   Then soon her maidens came, and every rite
That was the due of that slim body white,
They wrought with careful hands ; and last they took
Medea's gift, and all the folds outshook,   1020
And in a cool room looking toward the north,
They clad the queen therewith, nor brought her forth
Till over all a gold cloak they had laid.
Then to King Creon did they bring the maid,
Rejoicing in the greatness of her love,
Which well she thought no lapse of time could move,
And on the daïs of the royal hall
They waited till the hour should befall
When Jason and his friends would bear her thence
With gentle rape and tender violence,   1030
As then the manner was, and the old king
Sat there beside her, glad at every thing.
   Meanwhile the people thronged in every way,
Clad in gay weed, rejoicing for that day,
Since that their lords had bidden them rejoice,
And in the streets was many a jocund voice,
That carolled to the honour of the twain
Who on that day such blissful life should gain.
   But Jason set out from his pillared house,
Clad in rich raiment, fair and amorous,   1040
Forgetful of the troubles of the night,
Nor thinking more of that impending blight,
Nor those ill words the harpies spoke of old,
As with his fellows, glittering with gold,
Towards Creon's palace did he take his way,
To meet the bride that he should wed that day.
   But in the hall the pillars one by one
Had barred the pathway of the travelling sun,
As toward the west he turned, and now at last
Upon the daïs were his hot rays cast,   1050
As they within heard the glad minstrelsy
Of Jason to his loved one drawing nigh.
   Then Creon took fair Glauce by the hand,
And round about her did her damsels stand,
Making a ring 'gainst that sweet violence,

That soon should bear their lovely mistress thence.
While Glauce, trembling with her shamefast joy,
With the gold mantle's clasp began to toy,
Eager to cast that covering off, and feel
The hero's mighty arms about her steal.   1060

Meanwhile, her lover through the court had passed,
And at the open door he stood at last,
Amidst his friends, and looking thence, he saw
The white arms of the damsels round her draw
A wall soon to be broken ; but her face
Over their flower-crowned heads made glad the place :
Giddy with joy one moment did he gaze
And saw his love her slender fingers raise
Unto the mantle's clasp—the next the hall
Was filled with darting flames from wall to wall,   1070
And bitter screams rang out, as here and there,
Scorched, and with outspread arms, the damsels fair
Rushed through the hall ; but swiftly Jason ran,
Grown in one moment like an old worn man,
Up to the daïs, whence one bitter cry
He heard, of one in utmost agony,
Calling upon his once so helpful name ;
But when unto the fiery place he came,
Nought saw he but the flickering tongues of fire
That up the wall were climbing high and higher ;   1080
And on the floor a heap of ashes white,
The remnant of his once beloved delight,
For whom his ancient love he cast away,
And of her sire who brought about that day.
Then he began to know what he had done,
And madly through the palace did he run,
Calling on Glauce, mingling with her name
The name of her that brought him unto fame,
Colchian Medea, who, for her reward,
Had lonely life made terrible and hard,   1090
By love cast back, within her heart to grow
To madness and the vengeance wrought out now ;
But as about the burning place he ran,
Full many a maid he met and pale-faced man,

Wild with their terror, knowing not what end
That which their eyes had seen might yet portend :
But these shrunk backward from his brandished sword,
And open shouting mouth, and frenzied word,
As still from chamber unto chamber fair
He rushed, scarce knowing what he sought for there,
Nor where he went, till his unresting feet   1101
Had borne him out at last into the street,
Where armed and unarmed people stood to gaze
On Creon's palace that began to blaze
From every window out into the air,
With strange light making pale that noontide fair.

   But they, bewildered sore, and timorous,
Gazed helplessly upon the burning house,
And dreaded yet some hidden enemy,
Thinking indeed a dreadful God to see,   1110
Bearing a fresh destruction in his hand.

   But now, when Jason with his glittering brand
Broke in upon them from the growing fire,
With wild pale face, and half-burnt rich attire,
They fell back shuddering as his face they knew,
Changed though it was, and soon a murmur grew :—
' Death to the sorceress, the Colchian ! '
But he, unheeding still, from 'midst them ran,
Until unto his own fair house he came,
Where gazed his folk upon the far-off flame,   1120
And muttered low for fear and woefulness.

   Then he knew not his own, but none the less,
Into the court he passed, and his bright sword
Cast down and said : ' What feeble, timid lord
Hides here when all the world is on a blaze,
And laughing, from their heaven the high Gods gaze
At foolish men shut in the burning place ? '
With that he turned about his haggard face,
And stared upon his own fair-sculptured frieze,
Carved into likeness of the tumbling seas,   1130
And Argo, and the heroes he had led,
And fair Medea. Then he cried, and said :—
' Lo, how the Gods are mocking me with this,
And show me pictures of my vanished bliss,

As though on earth I were, and not in hell ;
And images of things I know full well
Have set about me. Can I die again,
And in some lower hell forget the pain
My life is passed in now ? '

      And with that word
He cast his eyes upon his glittering sword,   1140
And caught it up and set it to his breast,
And in one moment had he been at rest
From all his troubles, when a woman old,
His nurse in past times, did the deed behold,
And ran and caught the hero's mighty hand,
And hanging round about him did she stand,
And cried : ' Ah, Jason ! ah, my lord, let be !
For who can give another life to thee ?
And though to-day the very sun looks black,
And wholesome air the whole world seems to lack,   1151
Yet shalt thou yet have wealth of happy days,
And well fulfilled desires, and all men's praise ;
Unless the Gods have quite forgotten thee.
O Jason ! O my child ! come now with me,
That I may give thee sweet forgetfulness
A little while of sorrow and distress.'

 Then with the crone did Jason go along,
And let her thin hand hold his fingers strong,
As though a child he were in that old day,
Ere in the centaur's woodland cave he lay.   1160
But through the house unto a distant room,
Dark-hung, she brought him, where, amidst the gloom,
Speechless he lay, when she had made him drink
Some potion pressed from herbs plucked by the brink
Of scarce-known lakes of Pontus ; then she said,
As she beheld at last his weary head
Sink on the pillow : ' Jason, rest thee now,
And may some kind God smooth thy wrinkled brow.
Behold to-morrow comes, and thou art young,
Nor on one string are all life's jewels strung ;   1170
Thou shalt be great, and many a land shalt save,
And of thy coming life more joy shalt have
Than thou hast thought of yet.'

               He heard her words,
But as the far-off murmur of the birds
The townsman hears ere yet the morn is late,
While streets are void and shut is every gate ;
But still they soothed him, and he fell asleep,
While at his feet good watch the crone did keep.

    But what a waking unto him shall be !
And what a load of shameful misery   1180
His life shall bear ! His old love cast away,
His new love dead upon that fearful day,
Childless, dishonoured, must his days go by.
For in another chamber did there lie
Two little helpless bodies side by side,
Smiling as though in sweet sleep they had died,
And feared no ill. And she who thus had slain
Those fruits of love, the folk saw not again,
Nor knew where she was gone ; yet she died not,
But fleeing, somehow, from that fatal spot,   1190
She came to Athens, and there long did dwell,
Whose after life I list not here to tell.

    But as for Jason ;—Creon now being slain,
And Corinth kingless, every man was fain,
Remembering Jason's wisdom and sharp sword,
To have the hero for their king and lord.
So on his weary brows they set the crown,
And he began to rule that noble town.
And 'midst all things, somewhat his misery
Was dulled unto him, as the days went by,   1200
And he began again to cast his eyes
On lovely things, and hope began to rise
Once more within his heart.
                   But on a day
From out the goodly town he took his way,
To where, beneath the cliffs of Cenchreæ,
Lay Argo, looking o'er the ridgy sea.
Being fain once more to ponder o'er past days,
Ere he should set his face to winning praise
Among the shouts of men and clash of steel.
    But when he reached the well-remembered keel,

The sun was far upon his downward way,   1211
At afternoon of a bright summer day.
Hot was it, and still o'er the long rank grass,
Beneath the hull, a widening shade did pass ;
And further off, the sunny daisied sward,
The raised oars with their creeping shadows barred ;
And grey shade from the hills of Cenchreæ
Began to move on toward the heaving sea.
　　So Jason, lying in the shadow dark
Cast by the stem, the warble of the lark,   1220
The chirrup of the cricket, well could hear ;
And now and then the sound would come anear
Of some hind shouting o'er his laden wain.
But looking o'er the blue and heaving plain,
Sailless it was, and beaten by no oar,
And on the yellow edges of the shore
The ripple fell in murmur soft and low,
As with wide-sweeping wings the gulls did go
About the breakers crying plaintively.
　　But Jason, looking out across the sea,   1230
Beheld the signs of wind a-drawing nigh,
Gathering about the clear cold eastern sky,
And many an evening then he thought upon
Ere yet the quays of Æa they had won,
And longings that had long been gathering
Stirred in his heart, and now he felt the sting
Of life within him, and at last he said :—
' Why should I move about as move the dead,
And take no heed of what all men desire ?
Once more I feel within my heart the fire   1240
That drave me forth unto the white-walled town,
Leaving the sunny slopes, and thick-leaved crown
Of grey old Pelion, that alone I knew,
Great deeds and wild, and desperate things to do.
　　' Ah ! the strange life of happiness and woe
That I have led, since my young feet did go
From that grey, peaceful, much-beloved abode.
But now, indeed, will I cast off the load
Of memory of vain hopes that came to nought,
Of rapturous joys with biting sorrows bought.   1250

The past is past, though I cannot forget
Those days, with long life laid before me yet.
    ' Ah, but one moment, ere I turn the page,
And leave regret to white hairs and to age.
    ' Once did I win a noble victory,
I won a kingdom, and I cast it by
For rest and peace, and rest and peace are gone.
I had a fair love, that loved me alone,
And made me that I am in all men's eyes ;
And like my hard-earned kingdom, my fair prize,   1260
I cast my tender heart, my Love away ;
Yet failed I not to love, until a day,
A day I nigh forget, took all from me
That once I had.—And she is gone, yea, she
Whose innocent sweet eyes and tender hands
Made me a mocking unto distant lands :
Alas, poor child ! yet is that as a dream,
And still my life a happy life I deem,
But ah ! so short, so short ! for I am left
Of love, of honour, and of joy bereft—   1270
And yet not dead—ah, if I could but see
But once again her who delivered me
From death and many troubles, then no more
Would I turn backward from the shadowy shore,
And all my life would seem but perfect gain.
    ' Alas ! what hope is this ? is it in vain
I long to see her ? Lo, am I not young ?
In many a song my past deeds have been sung,
And these my hands that guided Argo through
The blue Symplegades, still deeds may do.   1280
For now the world has swerved from truth and right,
Cumbered with monsters, empty of delight,
And, 'midst all this, what honour I may win,
That she may know of and rejoice therein,
And come to seek me, and upon my throne
May find me sitting, worshipped, and alone.
Ah ! if it should be, how should I rejoice
To hear once more that once beloved voice

1264-7 *In place of these the first edition had the single line:*
    That once I had—yet is that as a dream,

Rise through the burden of dull words, well-known ;
How should I clasp again my love, mine own,   1290
And set the crown upon her golden head,
And with the eyes of lovers newly wed,
How should we gaze each upon each again.
    ' O hope not vain ! O surely not quite vain !
For, with the next returning light will I
Cast off my moody sorrow utterly,
And once more live my life as in times past,
And 'mid the chance of war the die will cast.
    ' And surely, whatso great deeds have been done,
Since with my fellows the Gold Fleece I won,   1300
Still, here, some wild bull clears the frightened fields ;
There, a great lion cleaves the sevenfold shields
There, dwells some giant robber of the land ;
There, whirls some woman-slayer's red right hand.
Yea, what is this they speak of even now,
That Theseus, having brought his conquering prow
From lying Crete, unto the fairwalled town,
Now gathers folk, since there are coming down
The shielded women of the Asian plain,
Myriads past counting, in the hope to gain   1310
The mastery of this lovely land of Greece ?
So be it, surely shall I snatch fair peace
From out the hand of war, and calm delight
From the tumultuous horror of the fight.'

    So saying, gazing still across the sea
Heavy with days and nights of misery,
His eyes waxed dim, and calmer still he grew,
Still pondering over times and things he knew,
While now the sun had sunk behind the hill,
And from a white-thorn nigh a thrush did fill   1320
The balmy air with echoing minstrelsy,
And cool the night-wind blew across the sea,
And round about the soft-winged bats did sweep.

    So 'midst all this at last he fell asleep,
Nor did his eyes behold another day,
For Argo, slowly rotting all away,

Had dropped a timber here, and there an oar,
All through that year, but people of the shore
Set all again in order as it fell.
But now the stempost, that had carried well,   1330
The second rafter in King Pelias' hall,
Began at last to quiver towards its fall,
And whether loosed by some divinity,
Or that the rising wind from off the sea
Blew full upon it, surely I know not—
But, when the day dawned, still on the same spot,
Beneath the ruined stem did Jason lie
Crushed, and all dead of him that here can die.

What more ?—Some shepherd of the lone grey slope,
Drawn to the sandy sea-beach by the hope   1340
Of trapping quick-eared rabbits, found him there,
And running back, called from the vineyards fair,
Vine-dressers and their mates who through the town
Ere then had borne their well-filled baskets brown,
These, looking on his dead face, straightway knew
This was the king that all men kneeled unto,
Who dwelt between the seas ; therefore they made
A bier of white-thorn boughs, and thereon laid
The dead man, straightening every drawn-up limb ;
And, casting flowers and green leaves over him,   1350
They bore him unto Corinth, where the folk,
When they knew all, into loud wailing broke,
Calling him mighty hero, crown of kings.
But him ere long to where the sea-wind sings
O'er the grey hill-side did they bear again.
And there, where he had hoped that hope in vain,
They laid him in a marble tomb carved fair
With histories of his mighty deeds ; and there
Such games as once he loved yet being alive,
They held for ten days, and withal did give   1360
Gifts to the Gods with many a sacrifice,
But chiefest, among all the things of price,
Argo they offered to the Deity
Who shakes the hard earth with the rolling sea.

And now is all that ancient story told
Of him who won the guarded Fleece of Gold.

MISCELLANEOUS POEMS

1856–70

WINTER WEATHER [1]

WE rode together
In the winter weather
  To the broad mead under the hill;
Though the skies did shiver
With the cold, the river
  Ran, and was never still.

No cloud did darken
The night; we did hearken
  The hound's bark far away.
It was solemn midnight   10
In that dread, dread night,
  In the years that have pass'd for aye.

Two rode beside me,
My banner did hide me,
  As it droop'd adown from my lance;
With its deep blue trapping,
The mail over-lapping,
  My gallant horse did prance.

So ever together
In the sparkling weather   20
  Moved my banner and lance;
And its laurel trapping,
The steel over-lapping,
  The stars saw quiver and dance.

We met together
In the winter weather
  By the town-walls under the hill;
His mail-rings came clinking,
They broke on my thinking,
  For the night was hush'd and still.   30

Two rode beside him,
His banner did hide him,
  As it droop'd down strait from his lance;
With its blood-red trapping,
The mail over-lapping,
  His mighty horse did prance.

[1] Reprinted from *The Oxford and Cambridge Magazine,* January 1856.

And ever together
In the solemn weather
 Moved his banner and lance ;
And the holly trapping,
The steel overlapping,
 Did shimmer and shiver, and dance.

Back reined the squires
Till they saw the spires
 Over the city wall ;
Ten fathoms between us,
No dames could have seen us,
 Tilt from the city wall.

There we sat upright
Till the full midnight
 Should be told from the city chimes :
Sharp from the towers
Leapt forth the showers
 Of the many clanging rhymes.

'Twas the midnight hour,
Deep from the tower
 Boom'd the following bell ;
Down go our lances,
Shout for the lances !
 The last toll was his knell.

There he lay, dying ;
He had, for his lying,
 A spear in his traitorous mouth ;
A false tale made he
Of my true, true lady ;
 But the spear went through his mouth.

In the winter weather
We rode back together
 From the broad mead under the hill ;
And the cock sung his warning
As it grew toward morning,
 But the far-off hound was still.

Black grew his tower
As we rode down lower,
   Black from the barren hill ;
And our horses strode
Up the winding road
   To the gateway dim and still.

At the gate of his tower,
In the quiet hour,   80
   We laid his body there ;
But his helmet broken,
We took as a token ;
   Shout for my lady fair !

We rode back together
In the winter weather
   From the broad mead under the hill ;
No cloud did darken
The night ; we did hearken
   How the hound bay'd from the hill.   90

THE GOD OF THE POOR [1]

THERE was a lord that hight Maltête,
Among great lords he was right great,
On poor folk trod he like the dirt,
None but God might do him hurt.
          Deus est Deus pauperum.

With a grace of prayers sung loud and late
Many a widow's house he ate,
Many a poor knight at his hands
Lost his house and narrow lands.
          Deus est Deus pauperum.   10

He burnt the harvests many a time,
He made fair houses heaps of lime ;
Whatso man loved wife or maid
Of Evil-head was sore afraid.
          Deus est Deus pauperum.

[1] Reprinted from *The Fortnightly Review*, August 1868.

He slew good men and spared the bad ;
Too long a day the foul dog had,
As all dogs will have their day ;
But God is as strong as man, I say.
              Deus est Deus pauperum.   20

For a valiant knight, men called Boncœur,
Had hope he should not long endure,
And gathered to him much good folk,
Hardy hearts to break the yoke.
              Deus est Deus pauperum.

But Boncœur deemed it would be vain
To strive his guarded house to gain ;
Therefore, within a little while,
He set himself to work by guile.
              Deus est Deus pauperum.   30

He knew that Maltête loved right well
Red gold and heavy ; if from hell
The devil had cried, ' Take this gold cup,'
Down had he gone to fetch it up.
              Deus est Deus pauperum.

Twenty poor men's lives were nought
To him, beside a ring well wrought.
The pommel of his hunting-knife
Was worth ten times a poor man's life.
              Deus est Deus pauperum.   40

A squire new-come from over sea
Boncœur called to him privily,
And when he knew his lord's intent,
Clad like a churl therefrom he went.
              Deus est Deus pauperum.

But when he came where dwelt Maltête,
With few words did he pass the gate,
For Maltête built him walls anew,
And, wageless, folk from field he drew.
              Deus est Deus pauperum.   50

Now passed the squire through this and that,
Till he came to where Sir Maltête sat,
And over red wine wagged his beard,
Then spoke the squire as one afeard.
Deus est Deus pauperum.

' Lord, give me grace, for privily
I have a little word for thee.'
' Speak out,' said Maltête, ' have no fear,
For how can thy life to thee be dear ? '
Deus est Deus pauperum. 60

' Such a one I know,' he said,
' Who hideth store of money red.'
Maltête grinned at him cruelly.
' Thou florin-maker, come anigh.'
Deus est Deus pauperum.

' E'en such as thou once preached of gold,
And showed me lies in books full old.
Nought gat I but evil brass,
Therefore came he to the worser pass.
Deus est Deus pauperum. 70

' Hast thou will to see his skin ?
I keep my heaviest marks therein,
For since nought else of wealth had he,
I deemed full well he owed it me.'
Deus est Deus pauperum.

Nought know I of philosophy,'
The other said, ' nor do I lie.
Before the moon begins to shine,
May all this heap of gold be thine.
Deus est Deus pauperum. 80

' Ten leagues hence a man there is
Who seemeth to know little bliss,
And yet full many a pound of gold
A dry well nigh his house doth hold.
Deus est Deus pauperum.

'John-a-Wood is he called, fair lord,
Nor know I whence he hath this hoard.'
Then Maltête said, ' As God made me,
A wizard over-bold is he !
Deus est Deus pauperum.   90

' It were a good deed, as I am a knight,
To burn him in a fire bright ;
This John-a-Wood shall surely die,
And his gold in my strong chest shall lie.
Deus est Deus pauperum.

' This very night I make mine avow,
The truth of this mine eyes shall know.
Then spoke an old knight in the hall,
' Who knoweth what things may befall ?
Deus est Deus pauperum.   100

' I rede thee go with a great rout,
For thy foes ride right thick about.'
' Thou and the devil may keep my foes,
Thou redest me this gold to lose.
Deus est Deus pauperum.

' I shall go but with some four or five,
So shall I take my thief alive.
For if a great rout he shall see,
Will he not hide his wealth from me ? '
Deus est Deus pauperum.   110

The old knight muttered under his breath,
' Then mayhap ye shall ride to death.'
But Maltête turned him quickly round,
' Bind me this grey-beard under ground !
Deus est Deus pauperum.

' Because ye are old, ye think to jape.
Take heed, ye shall not long escape.
When I come back safe, old carle, perdie,
Thine head shall brush the linden-tree.'
Deus est Deus pauperum.   120

Therewith he rode with his five men,
And Boncœur's spy, for good leagues ten,
Until they left the beaten way,
And dusk it grew at end of day.

Deus est Deus pauperum.

There, in a clearing of the wood,
Was John's house, neither fair nor good.
In a ragged plot anigh,
Thin coleworts grew but wretchedly.

Deus est Deus pauperum. 130

John-a-Wood in his doorway sat,
Turning over this and that,
And chiefly how he best might thrive,
For he had will enough to live.

Deus est Deus pauperum.

Green coleworts from a wooden bowl
He ate ; but careful was his soul,
For if he saw another day,
Thenceforth was he in Boncœur's pay.

Deus est Deus pauperum. 140

So when he saw how Maltête came,
He said, ' Beginneth now the game ! '
And in the doorway did he stand
Trembling, with hand joined fast to hand.

Deus est Deus pauperum.

When Maltête did this carle behold
Somewhat he doubted of his gold,
But cried out, ' Where is now thy store
Thou hast through books of wicked lore ? '

Deus est Deus pauperum. 150

Then said the poor man, right humbly,
' Fair lord, this was not made by me,
I found it in mine own dry well,
And had a mind thy grace to tell.

Deus est Deus pauperum.

' Therefrom, my lord, a cup I took
This day ; that thou thereon might look,
And know me to be leal and true,'
And from his coat the cup he drew.
                    Deus est Deus pauperum.   160

Then Maltête took it in his hand,
Nor knew he aught that it used to stand
On Boncœur's cupboard many a day.
' Go on,' he said, ' and show the way.
                    Deus est Deus pauperum.

' Give me thy gold, and thou shalt live,
Yea, in my house thou well may'st thrive.'
John turned about, and 'gan to go
Unto the wood with footsteps slow.
                    Deus est Deus pauperum.   170

But as they passed by John's woodstack,
Growled Maltête, ' Nothing now doth lack
Wherewith to light a merry fire,
And give my wizard all his hire.'
                    Deus est Deus pauperum.

The western sky was red as blood,
Darker grew the oaken-wood ;
' Thief and carle, where are ye gone ?
Why are we in the wood alone ?
                    Deus est Deus pauperum.   180

' What is the sound of this mighty horn ?
—Ah, God ! that ever I was born !
The basnets flash from tree to tree ;
Show me, thou Christ, the way to flee ! '
                    Deus est Deus pauperum.

Boncœur it was, with fifty men,
Maltête was but one to ten,
And his own folk prayed for grace,
With empty hands in that lone place.
                    Deus est Deus pauperum.   190

'Grace shall ye have,' Boncœur said,
'All of you but Evil-head.'
Lowly could that great lord be.
Who could pray so well as he ?
          Deus est Deus pauperum.

Then could Maltête howl and cry,
Little will he had to die.
Soft was his speech, now it was late,
But who had will to save Maltête ?
          Deus est Deus pauperum.   200

They brought him to the house again,
And toward the road he looked in vain.
Lonely and bare was the great highway,
'Neath the gathering moonlight grey.
          Deus est Deus pauperum.

They took off his gilt basnet,
That he should die there was no let ;
They took off his coat of steel,
A damned man he well might feel.
          Deus est Deus pauperum.   210

'Will ye all be rich as kings,
Lacking nought of all good things ? '
'Nothing do we lack this eve ;
When thou art dead, how can we grieve ? '
          Deus est Deus pauperum.

'Let me drink water ere I die,
None henceforth comes my lips anigh.'
They brought it him in that bowl of wood.
He said ' This is but poor men's blood ! '
          Deus est Deus pauperum.   220

They brought it him in the cup of gold.
He said ' The women I have sold
Have wept it full of salt for me ;
I shall die gaping thirstily.'
          Deus est Deus pauperum.

On the threshold of that poor homestead
They smote off his Evil-head ;
They set it high on a great spear,
And rode away with merry cheer.
Deus est Deus pauperum. 230

At the dawn, in lordly state,
They rode to Maltête's castle-gate.
' Whoso willeth laud to win,
Make haste to let your masters in ! '
Deus est Deus pauperum.

Forthwith opened they the gate,
No man was sorry for Maltête.
Boncœur conquered all his lands,
A good knight was he of his hands.
Deus est Deus pauperum. 240

Good men he loved, and hated bad ;
Joyful days and sweet he had ;
Good deeds did he plenteously ;
Beneath him folk lived frank and free.
Deus est Deus pauperum.

He lived long, with merry days ;
None said aught of him but praise.
God on him have full mercy ;
A good knight merciful was he.
Deus est Deus pauperum. 250

The great lord, called Maltête, is dead ;
Grass grows above his feet and head,
And a holly-bush grows up between
His rib-bones, gotten white and clean.
Deus est Deus pauperum.

A carle's sheep-dog certainly
Is a mightier thing than he.
Till London-Bridge shall cross the Nen,
Take we heed of such-like men.
Deus est Deus pauperum. 260

THE TWO SIDES OF THE RIVER [1]

The Youths.

O WINTER, O white winter, wert thou gone
No more within the wilds were I alone,
Leaping with bent bow over stock and stone ;

No more alone my love the lamp should burn,
Watching the weary spindle twist and turn,
Or o'er the web hold back her tears and yearn.

O winter, O white winter, wert thou gone !

The Maidens.

Sweet thoughts fly swiftlier than the drifting snow,
And with the twisting thread sweet longings grow,
And o'er the web sweet pictures come and go ;　　10

For no white winter are we long alone.

The Youths.

O stream, so changed, what hast thou done to me,
That I thy glittering ford no more can see
Wreathing with white her fair feet lovingly ?

See in the rain she stands ; and, looking down
With frightened eyes upon thy whirlpools brown,
Drops to her feet again her girded gown.

O hurrying, turbid stream, what hast thou done ?

The Maidens.

The clouds lift, telling of a fairer day,
When through the thin stream I shall take my way,　20
Girt round with gold, and garlanded with may.

What rushing stream can keep us long alone ?

The Youths.

O burning Sun ! O master of unrest !
Why must we, toiling, cast away the best,
Now when the bird sleeps by his empty nest ?

[1] Reprinted from *The Fortnightly Review*, October 1868.

See, with my garland lying at her feet,
In lonely labour stands mine own, my sweet,
Above the quern, half-filled with half-ground wheat.

O red task-master, that thy flames were done !

The Maidens.

O love, to-night across the half-shorn plain,　　30
Shall I not go to meet the yellow wain,
A look of love at end of toil to gain ?

What flaming sun can keep us long alone ?

The Youths.

To-morrow, said I, is grape-gathering o'er ;
To-morrow and our loves are twinned no more.
To-morrow came, to bring us woe and war.

What have I done, that I should stand with these,
Hearkening the dread shouts borne upon the breeze,
While she, far off, sits weeping 'neath her trees ?

Alas ! O kings, what is it ye have done ?　　40

The Maidens.

Come love, delay not, come and slay my dread ;
Already is the banquet-table spread,
In the cool chamber flower-strewn is my bed.

Come, love ; what king can keep us long alone ?

The Youths.

O city, city, open thou thy gate ;
See with life snatched from out the hand of fate,
Still on this glittering triumph must I wait.

Are not her hands stretched out to me ? her eyes,
Are they not weary as each new hope dies,
And lone before her still the long road lies ?　　50

O golden city, fain would I be gone !

The Maidens.

Ah ! thou art happy amid shouts and songs,
And all that unto conquering men belongs ;
Night hath for me no fear, and day no wrongs.

What brazen city-gates can keep us lone ?

The Youths.

O long, long road, how bare thou art, and grey :
Hill after hill thou climbest, and the day
Is ended now, O moonlit endless way !

And she is standing where the rushes grow,
And still with white hand shades her anxious brow,   60
Though 'neath the world the sun has fallen now.

O dreary road, when will thy leagues be done ?

The Maidens.

O tremblest thou, grey road, or do my feet
Tremble with joy thy flinty face to meet
Because my love's eyes soon mine eyes shall greet ?

No heart thou hast to keep us long alone.

The Youths.

O wilt thou ne'er depart, thou heavy night ?
When will thy slaying bring on the morning bright,
That leads my weary feet to my delight ?

Why lingerest thou, filling with wandering fears   70
My lone love's tired heart ; her eyes with tears,
For thoughts like sorrow for the vanished years ?

Weaver of ill thoughts, when wilt thou begone ?

The Maidens.

Love, to the East are thine eyes turned, as mine,
In patient watching for the night's decline ?
And hast thou noted this grey widening line ?

Can any darkness keep us long alone ?

The Youths.

O day ! O day ! is this a little thing
That thou so long unto thy life must cling
Because I gave thee such a welcoming ?   80

I called thee king of all felicity,
I praised thee that thou broughtest joy so nigh—
Thine hours are turned to years ; thou wilt not die.

O day so longed for, would that thou wert gone !

The Maidens.

The light fails, love ; the long day soon shall be
Nought but a pensive, happy memory,
Blessed for the tales it told to thee and me.

How hard it was, O love, to be alone.

ON THE EDGE OF THE WILDERNESS [1]

Puellæ.

WHENCE comest thou, and whither goest thou ?
Abide, abide ! longer the shadows grow ;
What hopest thou the dark to thee will show ?

Abide, abide ! for we are happy here.

Amans.

Why should I name the land across the sea
Wherein I first took hold on misery ?
Why should I name the land that flees from me ?

Let me depart since ye are happy here.

Puellæ.

What wilt thou do within the desert place
Whereto thou turnest now thy careful face ?   10
Stay but a while to tell us of thy case.

Abide, abide ! for we are happy here.

Amans.

What, nigh the journey's end shall I abide,
When in the waste mine own love wanders wide,
When from all men for me she still doth hide ?

Let me depart, since ye are happy here.

Puellæ.

Nay, nay ; but rather she forgetteth thee,
To sit upon the shore of some warm sea,
Or in green gardens where sweet fountains be.

Abide, abide ! for we are happy here.   20

[1] Reprinted from *The Fortnightly Review,* April 1869.

Amans.

Will ye then keep me from the wilderness,
Where I at least, alone with my distress,
The quiet land of changing dreams may bless ?

Let me depart, since ye are happy here.

Puellæ.

Forget the false forgetter, and be wise,
And 'mid these clinging hands and loving eyes,
Dream not in vain thou knowest paradise.

Abide, abide ! for we are happy here.

Amans.

Ah ! with your sweet eyes shorten not the day,
Nor let your gentle hands my journey stay !   30
Perchance love is not wholly cast away.

Let me depart, since ye are happy here.

Puellæ.

Pluck love away, as thou wouldst pluck a thorn
From out thy flesh ; for why shouldst thou be born
To bear a life so wasted and forlorn ?

Abide, abide ! for we are happy here.

Amans.

Yea, why then was I born, since hope is pain,
And life a lingering death, and faith but vain,
And love the loss of all I seemed to gain ?

Let me depart, since ye are happy here.   40

Puellæ.

Dost thou believe that this shall ever be,
That in our land no face thou e'er shalt see,
No voice thou e'er shalt hear to gladden thee ?

Abide, abide ! for we are happy here.

Amans.

No longer do I know of good or bad,
I have forgotten that I once was glad
I do but chase a dream that I have had.

Let me depart, since ye are happy here.

Puellæ.

Stay ! take one image for thy dreamful night ;
Come look at her, who in the world's despite   50
Weeps for delaying love and lost delight.

Abide, abide ! for we are happy here.

Amans.

Mock me not till to-morrow. Mock the dead—
They will not heed it, or turn round the head,
To note who faithless are, and who are wed.

Let me depart, since ye are happy here.

Puellæ.

We mock thee not. Hast thou not heard of those
Whose faithful love the loved heart holds so close,
That death must wait till one word lets it loose.

Abide, abide ! for we are happy here.   60

Amans.

I hear you not : the wind from off the waste
Sighs like a song that bids me make good haste
The wave of sweet forgetfulness to taste.

Let me depart, since ye are happy here.

Puellæ.

Come back ! like such a singer is the wind,
As to a sad tune sings fair words and kind,
That he with happy tears all eyes may blind.

Abide, abide ! for we are happy here.

Amans.

Did I not hear her sweet voice cry from far,
That o'er the lonely waste fair fields there are,   70
Fair days that know not any change or care ?

Let me depart, since ye are happy here.

Puellæ.

Oh no, not far thou heardest her, but nigh—
Nigh, 'twixt the waste's edge and the darkling sky.
Turn back again, too soon it is to die.

Abide ! a little while be happy here.

Amans.

How with the lapse of lone years could I strive,
And can I die now that thou biddest live ?
What joy this space 'twixt birth and death can give.

Can we depart, who are so happy here ?   80

HAPLESS LOVE[1]

Hic.

WHY do you sadly go alone,
O fair friend ? Are your pigeons flown,
Or has the thunder killed your bees,
Or he-goats barked your apple-trees ?
Or has the red-eared bull gone mad,
Or the mead turned from good to bad ?
Or did you find the merchant lied
About the gay cloth scarlet-dyed ?
And did he sell you brass for gold,
Or is there murrain in the fold ?   10

Ille.

Nay, no such thing has come to me.
In bird and beast and field and tree,
And all the things that make my store,
Am I as rich as e'er before ;

[1] Reprinted from *Good Words*, April 1869.

And no beguilers have I known
But Love and Death ; and Love is gone.
Therefore am I far more than sad,
And no more know good things from bad.

Hic.

Woe worth the while ! Yet coming days
May bring another, good to praise. 20

Ille.

Nay, never will I love again,
For loving is but joyful pain
If all be at its very best ;
A rose-hung bower of all unrest ;
But when at last things go awry,
What tongue can tell its misery ?
And soon or late shall this befall—
The gods send death upon us all.

Hic.

Nay, then, but tell me how she died,
And how it did to thee betide 30
To love her ; for the wise men say
To talk of grief drives grief away.

Ille.

Alas, O friend, it happed to me
To see her passing daintily
Before my homestead day by day.
Would she had gone some other way !
For one day, as she rested there
Beneath the long-leaved chestnuts fair,
In very midst of mid-day heat,
I cast myself before her feet, 40
And prayed for pity and for love.
How could I dream that words could move
A woman ? Soft she looked at me ;
' Thou sayest that I a queen should be,'
She answered with a gathering smile ;
' Well, I will wait a little while,
Perchance the gods thy will have heard.'

And even with that latest word,
The clash of arms we heard anigh;
And from the wood rode presently   50
A fair knight well apparelled.
And even as she turned her head,
He shortened rein, and cried aloud—
' O beautiful, among the crowd
Of queens thou art the queen of all ! '

But when she let her eyelids fall,
And blushed for pleasure, and for shame,
Then quickly to her feet he came,
And said, ' Thou shalt be queen indeed ;
For many a man this day shall bleed   60
Because of me, and leave me king
Ere noontide fall to evening.'

Then on his horse he set the maid
Before him, and no word she said
Clear unto me, but murmuring
Beneath her breath some gentle thing,
She clung unto him lovingly ;
Nor took they any heed of me.

Through shade and sunlight on they rode,
But 'neath the green boughs I abode,   70
Nor noted aught that might betide.
The sun waned, and the shade spread wide ;
The birds came twittering over head ;
But there I lay as one long dead.

But ere the sunset, came a rout
Of men-at-arms with song and shout,
And bands of lusty archers tall,
And spearmen marching like a wall,
Their banners hanging heavily,
That no man might their blazon see ;   80
And ere their last noise died away,
I heard the clamour of the fray

That swelled, and died, and rose again ;
Yet still I brooded o'er my pain
Until the red sun nigh was set,
And then methought I e'en might get
The rest I sought, nor wake forlorn
Midst fellow men the morrow morn ;
So forth I went unto the field,
One man without a sword or shield.   90

But none was there to give me rest,
Tried was it who was worst and best,
And slain men lay on every side ;
For flight and chase were turned aside,
And all men got on toward the sea ;
But as I went right heavily
I saw how close beside the way
Over a knight a woman lay
Lamenting, and I knew in sooth
My love, and drew a-near for ruth.   100

There lay the knight who would be king
Dead slain before the evening,
And ever my love cried out and said,
' O sweet, in one hour art thou dead
And I am but a maiden still !
The gods this day have had their will
Of thee and me ; whom all these years
They kept apart ; that now with tears
And blood and bitter misery
Our parting and our death might be.'   110

Then did she rise and look around,
And took his drawn sword from the ground
And on its bitter point she fell—
No more, no more, O friend, to tell !
No more about my life, O friend !
One course it shall have to the end.

O Love, come from the shadowy shore,
And by my homestead as before,
Go by with sunlight on thy feet !
Come back, if but to mock me, sweet !   120

Hic.

O fool ! what love of thine was this,
Who never gave thee any kiss,
Nor would have wept if thou hadst died ?
Go now, behold the world is wide.
Soon shalt thou find some dainty maid
To sit with in thy chestnut shade,
To rear fair children up for thee,
As those few days pass silently,
Uncounted, that may yet remain
'Twixt thee and that last certain pain.   130

Ille.

Art thou a God ? Nay, if thou wert,
Wouldst thou belike know of my hurt,
And what might sting and what might heal ?
The world goes by 'twixt woe and weal
And heeds me not ; I sit apart
Amid old memories. To my heart
My love and sorrow must I press ;
It knoweth its own bitterness.

PREFATORY SONNET TO
'THE STORY OF GRETTIR THE STRONG'
(1869)

A LIFE scarce worth the living, a poor fame
Scarce worth the winning, in a wretched land,
Where fear and pain go upon either hand,
As toward the end men fare without an aim
Unto the dull grey dark from whence they came :
Let them alone, the unshadowed sheer rocks stand
Over the twilight graves of that poor band,
Who count so little in the great world's game !

Nay, with the dead I deal not ; this man lives,
And that which carried him through good and ill,
Stern against fate while his voice echoed still
From rock to rock, now he lies silent, strives
With wasting time, and through its long lapse gives
Another friend to me, life's void to fill.

R r 2

A PROLOGUE IN VERSE

(to the Volsunga Saga, 1870)

O HEARKEN, ye who speak the English Tongue,
  How in a waste land ages long ago,
The very heart of the North bloomed into song
  After long brooding o'er this tale of woe !
  Hearken, and marvel how it might be so,
That such a sweetness so well crowned could be
Betwixt the ice-hills and the cold grey sea.

Or rather marvel not, that those should cling
  Unto the thoughts of great lives passed away,
Whom God has stripped so bare of everything,   10
  Save the one longing to wear through their day,
  In fearless wise ; the hope the Gods to stay,
When at that last tide gathered wrong and hate
Shall meet blind yearning on the Fields of Fate.

Yea, in the first grey dawning of our race,
  This ruth-crowned tangle to sad hearts was dear.
Then rose a seeming sun, the lift gave place
  Unto a seeming heaven, far off, but clear ;
  But that passed too, and afternoon is here ;
Nor was the morn so fruitful or so long   20
But we may hearken when ghosts moan of wrong.

For as amid the clatter of the town
  When eve comes on with unabated noise,
The soaring wind will sometimes drop adown
  And bear unto our chamber the sweet voice
  Of bells that 'mid the swallows do rejoice,
Half-heard, to make us sad, so we awhile
With echoed grief life's dull pain may beguile.

Naught vague, naught base our tale, that seems to say,—
  ' Be wide-eyed, kind ; curse not the hand that smites ;
Curse not the kindness of a past good day,   31
  Or hope of love ; cast by all earth's delights,
  For very love : through weary days and nights,
Abide thou, striving, howsoe'er in vain,
The inmost love of one more heart to gain ! '

So draw ye round and hearken, English Folk,
    Unto the best tale pity ever wrought !
Of how from dark to dark bright Sigurd broke,
    Of Brynhild's glorious soul with love distraught,
    Of Gudrun's weary wandering unto naught,   40
Of utter love defeated utterly,
Of Grief too strong to give Love time to die !

RHYME SLAYETH SHAME

(*Atlantic Monthly*, February 1870)

IF as I come unto her she might hear,
If words might reach her when from her I go,
Then speech a little of my heart might show,
Because indeed nor joy nor grief nor fear
Silence my love ; but her grey eyes and clear,
Truer than truth, pierce through my weal and woe ;
The world fades with its words, and naught I know
But that my changed life to My Life is near.

Go, then, poor rhymes, who know my heart indeed,
And sing to her the words I cannot say,—
That Love has slain Time, and knows no to-day
And no to-morrow ; tell her of my need,
And how I follow where her footsteps lead,
Until the veil of speech death draws away.

†

MAY GROWN A-COLD

(*Atlantic Monthly,* May 1870)

O CERTAINLY, no month this is but May !
Sweet earth and sky, sweet birds of happy song,
Do make thee happy now, and thou art strong,
And many a tear thy love shall wipe away
And make the dark night merrier than the day,
Straighten the crooked paths and right the wrong,
And tangle bliss so that it tarry long.
Go cry aloud the hope the Heavens do say !

Nay, what is this ? and wherefore lingerest thou ?
Why sayest thou the sky is hard as stone ?
Why sayest thou the thrushes sob and moan ?
Why sayest thou the east tears bloom and bough ?
Why seem the sons of man so hopeless now ?
Thy love is gone, poor wretch, thou art alone !

DESCRIPTIVE AND CRITICAL
ARTICLES

1856

DESCRIPTIVE AND CRITICAL ARTICLES

THE CHURCHES OF NORTH FRANCE

No. 1.—*Shadows of Amiens.*

(*Oxford and Cambridge Magazine*, Feb. 1856)

Not long ago I saw for the first time some of the churches of North France ; still more recently I saw them for the second time ; and, remembering the love I have for them and the longing that was in me to see them, during the time that came between the first and second visit, I thought I should like to tell people of some of those things I felt when I was there ;—there among those mighty tombs of the long-dead ages.

And I thought that even if I could say nothing else about these grand churches, I could at least tell men how much I loved them ; so that, though they might laugh at me for my foolish and confused words, they might yet be moved to see what there was that made me speak my love, though I could give no reason for it.

For I will say here that I think those same churches of North France the grandest, the most beautiful, the kindest and most loving of all the buildings that the earth has ever borne ; and, thinking of their past-away builders, can I see through them, very faintly, dimly, some little of the mediaeval times, else dead, and gone from me for ever,—voiceless for ever.

And those same builders, still surely living, still real men, and capable of receiving love, I love no less than the great men, poets and painters and such like, who are on earth now, no less than my breathing friends whom I can see looking kindly on me now. Ah ! do I not love them with just cause, who certainly loved me, thinking of me sometimes between the strokes of their chisels ; and for this love of all men that they had, and moreover for the great love of God, which they certainly had too ; for this, and for this work of theirs, the upraising of the great cathedral front with its beating heart of the thoughts of men, wrought into the leaves and flowers of the fair earth ; wrought into the faces of good men and true, fighters against the wrong, of angels who upheld them, of God who rules all things ; wrought through the lapse of years, and years, and years, by the dint of chisel, and stroke of hammer, into stories of life and death, the second life, the second death, stories of God's dealing in love and wrath with the nations of the earth, stories of the faith and love of man that dies not : for their love, and the deeds through which it worked, I think they will not lose their reward.

So I will say what I can of their works, and I have to speak of Amiens first, and how it seemed to me in the hot August weather.

I know how wonderful it would look, if you were to mount one of the steeples of the town, or were even to mount up to the roof of one of the houses westward of the cathedral ; for it rises up from the ground, grey from the paving of the street, the cavernous porches of the west front opening wide, and marvellous with the shadows of the carving you can only guess at ; and above stand the kings, and above that you would see the twined mystery of the great flamboyant rose window with its thousand openings, and the shadows of the flower-work carved round it, then the grey towers and gable, grey against the blue of the August sky, and behind them all, rising high into the quivering air, the tall spire over the crossing.

But from the hot Place Royale here with its stunted pollard acacias, and statue of some one, I know not whom, but some citizen of Amiens I suppose, you can see nothing but the graceful spire ; it is of wood covered over with lead, and was built quite at the end of the flamboyant times. Once it was gilt all over, and used to shine out there, getting duller and duller, as the bad years grew worse and worse ; but the gold is all gone now ; when it finally disappeared I know not, but perhaps it was in 1771, when the chapter got them the inside of their cathedral white-washed from vaulting to pavement.

The spire has two octagonal stages above the roof, formed of trefoiled arches, and slim buttresses capped by leaded figures ; from these stages the sloping spire springs with crocketed ribs at the angles, the lead being arranged in a quaint herring-bone pattern ; at the base of the spire too is a crown of open-work and figures, making a third stage ; finally, near the top of the spire the crockets swell, till you come to the rose that holds the great spire-cross of metal-work, such metal-work as the French alone knew how to make ; it is all beautiful, though so late.

From one of the streets leading out of the Place Royale you can see the cathedral, and as you come nearer you see that it is clear enough of houses or such like things ; the great apse rises over you, with its belt of eastern chapels ; first the long slim windows of these chapels, which are each of them little apses, the Lady Chapel projecting a good way beyond the rest, and then, running under the cornice of the chapels and outer aisles all round the church, a cornice of great noble leaves ; then the

parapets in changing flamboyant patterns, then the conical roofs
of the chapels hiding the exterior tracery of the triforium, then
the great clerestory windows, very long, of four lights, and stilted,
the tracery beginning a long way below the springing of their
arches ; and the buttresses are so thick, and their arms spread
so here, that each of the clerestory windows looks down its own
space between them, as if between walls : above the windows
rise their canopies running through the parapet, and above all
the great mountainous roof, and all below it, and around the
windows and walls of the choir and apse, stand the mighty army
of the buttresses, holding up the weight of the stone roof within
with their strong arms for ever.

We go round under their shadows, past the sacristies, past the
southern transept, only glancing just now at the sculpture there,
past the chapels of the nave, and enter the church by the small
door hard by the west front, with that figure of huge St. Christo-
pher quite close over our heads ; thereby we enter the church, as
I said, and are in its western bay. I think I felt inclined to shout
when I first entered Amiens cathedral; it is so free and vast and
noble, I did not feel in the least awe-struck, or humbled by its
size and grandeur. I have not often felt thus when looking on
architecture, but have felt, at all events, at first, intense exultation at the beauty of it ; that, and a certain kind of satisfaction
in looking on the geometrical tracery of the windows, on the
sweeping of the huge arches, were, I think, my first feelings in
Amiens Cathedral.

We go down the nave, glancing the while at the traceried
windows of the chapels, which are later than the windows above
them ; we come to the transepts, and from either side the
stained glass, in their huge windows, burns out on us ; and, then,
first we begin to appreciate somewhat the scale of the church,
by looking up, along the ropes hanging from the vaulting to the
pavement, for the tolling of the bells in the spire.

There is a hideous renaissance screen, of solid stone or marble,
between choir and nave, with more hideous iron gates to it,
through which, however, we, walking up the choir steps, can look
and see the gorgeous carving of the canopied stalls ; and then,
alas ! ' the concretion of flattened sacks, rising forty feet above
the altar ; ' but, above that, the belt of the apse windows, rich
with sweet mellowed stained glass, under the dome-like roof.

The stalls in the choir are very rich, as people know, carved in
wood, in the early sixteenth century, with high twisted canopies,
and histories, from the Old Testament mostly, wrought about
them.   The history of Joseph I remember best among these.
Some of the scenes in it I thought very delightful ; the story told
in such a gloriously quaint, straightforward manner.   Pharaoh's

dream, how splendid that was ! the king lying asleep on his elbow, and the kine coming up to him in two companies. I think the lean kine was about the best bit of wood-carving I have seen yet. There they were, a writhing heap, crushing and crowding one another, drooping heads and starting eyes, and strange angular bodies ; altogether the most wonderful symbol of famine ever conceived. I never fairly understood Pharaoh's dream till I saw the stalls at Amiens.

There is nothing else to see in the choir ; all the rest of the fittings being as bad as possible. So we will go out again, and walk round the choir-aisles. The screen round the choir is solid, the upper part of it carved (in the flamboyant times), with the history of St. John the Baptist, on the north side ; with that of St. Firmin on the south. I remember very little of the sculptures relative to St. John, but I know that I did not like them much. Those about St. Firmin, who evangelized Picardy, I remember much better, and some of them especially I thought very beautiful ; they are painted too, and at any rate one cannot help looking at them.

I do not remember, in the least, the order in which they come, but some of them are fixed well enough in my memory ; and, principally, a bishop, (St. Firmin,) preaching, rising out of a pulpit from the midst of the crowd, in his jewelled cope and mitre, and with a beautiful sweet face. Then another, the baptizing of the king and his lords, was very quaint and lifelike. I remember, too, something about the finding of St. Firmin's relics, and the translation of the same relics when found ; the many bishops, with their earnest faces, in the first, and the priests, bearing the reliquaries, in the second ; with their long vestments girded at the waist and falling over their feet, painted too, in light colours, with golden flowers on them. I wish I remembered these carvings better, I liked them so much. Just about this place, in the lower part of the screen, I remember the tomb of a priest, very gorgeous, with gold and colours ; he lay in a deep niche, under a broad segmental arch, which is painted with angels ; and, outside this niche, angels were drawing back painted curtains, I am sorry to say. But the priest lay there in cope and alb, and the gentle colour lay over him, as his calm face gazed ever at the angels painted in his resting-place. I have dim recollection of seeing, when I was at Amiens before, not this last time, a tomb, which I liked much, a bishop, I think it was, lying under a small round arch, but I forget the figure now. This was in a chapel on the other side of the choir. It is very hard to describe the interior of a great church like this, especially since the whitewash (applied, as I said, on this scale in 1771) lies on everything so ; before that time, some book says, the church was painted from end to end with patterns of flowers and stars, and histories : think—I might have been able to say something about it then, with that solemn glow of colour all about me, as I walked there from sunrise to sunset ; and yet, perhaps, it would have filled my heart too full for speaking, all that beauty ; I know not.

Up into the triforium, and other galleries, sometimes in the church, sometimes in narrow passages of close-fitting stone, sometimes out in the open air ; up into the forest of beams between the slates and the real stone roof : one can look down through a hole in the vaulting and see the people walking and praying on the pavement below, looking very small from that height, and strangely foreshortened.   A strange sense of oppression came over me at that time, when, as we were in one of the galleries of the west front, we looked into the church, and found the vaulting but a foot or two (or it seemed so) above our heads ; also, while I was in the galleries, now out of the church, now in it, the canons had begun to sing complines, and the sound of their singing floated dimly up the winding staircases and half-shut doors.

The sun was setting when we were in the roof, and a beam of it, striking through the small window up in the gable, fell in blood-red spots on the beams of the great dim roof. We came out from the roof on to the parapet in the blaze of the sun, and then going to the crossing, mounted as high as we could into the spire, and stood there a while looking down on the beautiful country, with its many water-meadows, and feathering trees.

And here let me say something about the way in which I have taken this description upon me ; for I did not write it at Amiens ; moreover, if I had described it from the bare reminiscences of the church, I should have been able to say little enough about the most interesting part of all, the sculptures, namely ; ˙ so, though remembering well enough the general effect of the whole, and, very distinctly, statues and faces, nay, leaves and flower-knots, here and there ; yet, the external sculpture I am describing as well as I can from such photographs as I have ; and these, as everybody knows, though very distinct and faithful, when they show anything at all, yet, in some places, where the shadows are deep, show simply nothing. They tell me, too, nothing whatever of the colour of the building ; in fact, their brown and yellow is as unlike as possible to the grey of Amiens. So, for the facts of form, I have to look at my photographs ; for facts of colour I have to try and remember the day or two I spent at Amiens, and the reference to the former has considerably dulled my memory of the latter. I have something else to say, too ; it will seem considerably ridiculous, no doubt, to many people who are well acquainted with the iconography of the French churches, when I talk about the stories of some of the carvings ; both from my want of knowledge as to their meaning, and also from my telling people things which everybody may be supposed to know ; for which I pray forgiveness, and so go on to speak of the carvings about the south transept door.

It is divided in the midst by a pillar, whereon stands the Virgin, holding our Lord. She is crowned, and has a smile upon her face now for ever ; and in the canopy above her head are three angels, bearing up the aureole there ; and about these angels, and the aureole and head of the Virgin, there is still some gold and vermilion left. The Holy Child, held in His mother's left arm, is draped from his throat to his feet, and between His hands He holds the orb of the world. About on a level with the Virgin, along the sides of the doorway, are four figures on each side, the innermost one on either side being an angel holding a censer ; the others are ecclesiastics, and (some book says) benefactors to the church. They have solemn faces, stern, with firm close-set lips, and eyes deep-set under their brows, almost frowning, and all but one or two are beardless, though evidently not young ; the square door valves are carved with deep-twined leaf-mouldings, and the capitals of the door-shafts are carved with varying knots of leaves and flowers. Above the Virgin, up in the tympanum of the doorway, are carved the Twelve Apostles, divided into two bands of six, by the canopy over the Virgin's head. They are standing in groups of two, but I do not know for certain which they are, except, I think, two, St. James and St. John ; the two first in the eastern division. James has the pilgrim's hat and staff, and John is the only beardless one among them ; his face is rather sad, and exceedingly lovely, as, indeed, are all those faces, being somewhat alike ; and all in some degree like the type of face received as the likeness of Christ himself. They have all long hair falling in rippled bands on each side of their faces, on to their shoulders. Their drapery, too, is lovely ; they are very beautiful and solemn. Above their heads run a cornice of trefoiled arches, one arch over the head of each apostle ; from out of the deep shade of the trefoils flashes a grand leaf cornice, one leaf again to each apostle ; and so we come to the next compartment, which contains three scenes from the life of St. Honoré, an early French bishop. The first scene is, I think, the election of a bishop, the monks or priests talking the matter over in chapter first, then going to tell the bishop-elect. Gloriously-draped figures the monks are, with genial faces full of good wisdom, drawn into quaint expressions by the joy of argument. This one old, and has seen much of the world ; he is trying, I think, to get his objections answered by the young man there, who is talking to him so earnestly; he is listening, with a half-smile on his face, as if he had made up his mind, after all. These other two, one very energetic indeed, with his head and shoulders swung back a little, and his right arm forward, and the other listening to him, and but half-convinced yet. Then the two next, turning to go with him who is bearing to the new-chosen bishop the book of the Gospels and pastoral staff; they look satisfied and happy. Then comes he with the pastoral staff and Gospels; then, finally, the man who is announcing the news to the bishop himself, the most beautiful figure in the whole scene, perhaps, in the whole doorway; he is stooping down, lovingly, to the man they have chosen, with his left hand laid on his arm, and his long robe falls to his feet from his shoulder all along his left side, moulded a little to the shape of his body, but falling heavily and with scarce a fold in it, to the ground : the chosen one sitting there, with his book held between his two hands, looks up to him with his brave face, and he will be bishop, and rule well, I think. So, by the next scene he is bishop, I suppose, and is sitting there ordering the building of a church ; for he is sitting under a trefoiled canopy, with his mitre on his head, his right hand on a reading-desk by his side. His book is lying open, his head turned toward what is going forwards. It is a splendid head and face. In the photograph I have of this subject, the mitre, short and simple, is in full light but for a little touch of shade on one side ; the face is shaded, but the crown of short crisp curls hanging over it, about half in light, half in shade. Beyond the trefoil canopy comes a wood of quaint conventional trees, full of stone, with a man working at it with a long pick : I cannot see his face, as it is altogether in shade, the light falling on his head however. He is dressed in a long robe, quite down to his feet, not a very convenient dress, one would think, for working in. I like the trees here very much ; they are meant for hawthorns and oaks. There are a very few leaves on each tree, but at the top they are all twisted about, and are thicker, as if the wind were blowing them. The little capitals of the canopy, under which the bishop is sitting, are very delightful, and are common enough in larger work of this time (thirteenth century) in France. Four bunches of leaves spring from long stiff stalks, and support the square abacus, one under each corner. The next scene, in the division above, is some miracle or other, which took place at mass, it seems. The bishop is saying mass before an altar ; behind him are four assistants ; and, as the bishop stands there with his hand raised, a hand coming from some-where by the altar, holds down towards him the consecrated wafer. The thing is gloriously carved, whatever it is. The assistant immediately behind the bishop, holding in his hands a candlestick, somewhat slantwise towards the altar, is, especially in the drapery, one of the most beautiful in the upper part of this tympanum ; his head is a little bent, and the line made from the back of it over the heavy hair, down along the heavy-swinging robe, is very beautiful.

The next scene is the shrine of some Saint. This same bishop, I suppose, dead now, after all his building and ruling, and hard fighting possibly, with the powers that be ; often to be fought with righteously in those times. Over the shrine sits the effigy of the bishop, with his hand raised to bless. On the western side are two worshippers ; on the eastern, a blind and a deaf man are being healed, or waiting to be healed, by the touch of the dead bishop's robe. The deaf man is leaning forward, and the servant of the shrine holds to his ear the bishop's robe. The deaf man has a very deaf face, not very anxious though; not even showing very much hope, but faithful only.   The blind one is coming up behind him with a crutch in his right hand, and led by a dog ; the face was either in its first estate, very ugly and crabbed, or by the action of the weather or some such thing, has been changed so.

So the bishop being dead and miracles being wrought at his tomb, in the division above comes the translation of his remains ; a long procession taking up the whole of the division, which is shorter than the others, however, being higher up towards the top of the arch. An acolyte bearing a cross heads the procession, then two choristers ; then priests bearing relics and books ; long vestments they have, and stoles crossed underneath their girdles ; then comes the reliquary borne by one at each end, the two finest figures in this division, the first especially ; his head raised and his body leaning forward to the weight of the reliquary, as people nearly always do walk when they carry burdens and are going slowly ; which this procession certainly is doing, for some of the figures are even turning round. Three men are kneeling or bending down beneath the shrine as it passes ; cripples they are, all three have beautiful faces, the one who is apparently the worst cripple of the three (his legs and feet are horribly twisted) has especially a wonderfully delicate face, timid and shrinking, though faithful : behind the shrine come the people, walking slowly together with reverent faces ; a woman with a little child holding her hand are the last figures in this history of St. Honoré : they both have their faces turned full south, the woman has not a beautiful face, but a happy good-natured genial one.

The cornice below this division is of plain round-headed trefoils very wide, and the spandril of each arch is pierced with a small round trefoil, very sharply cut, looking, in fact, as if it were cut with a punch : this cornice, simple though it is, I think very

beautiful, and in my photograph the broad trefoils of it throw
sharp black shadows on the stone behind the worshipping figures,
and square-cut altars.

In the triangular space at the top of the arch is a representation
of our Lord on the cross ; St. Mary and St. John standing on
either side of him, and, kneeling on one knee under the sloping
sides of the arch, two angels, one on each side. I very much wish
I could say something more about this piece of carving than I can
do, because it seems to me that the French thirteenth century
sculptors failed less in their representations of the crucifixion
than almost any set of artists ; though it was certainly an easier
thing to do in stone than on canvas, especially in such a case
as this where the representation is so highly abstract ; nevertheless, I wish I could say something more about it ; failing which,
I will say something about my photograph of it.

I cannot see the Virgin's face at all, it is in the shade so much ;
St. John's I cannot see very well ; I do not think it is a remark-
able face, though there is sweet expression in it ; our Lord's face
is very grand and solemn, as fine as I remember seeing it anywhere in sculpture. The shadow of the body hanging on the
cross there, falls strangely and weirdly on the stone behind—
both the kneeling angels (who, by the way, are holding censers,)
are beautiful. Did I say above that one of the faces of the twelve
Apostles was the most beautiful in the tympanum ? if I did,
I retract that saying, certainly, looking on the westernmost of
these two angels. I keep using the word beautiful so often that
I·feel half inclined to apologize for it ; but I cannot help it,
though it is often quite inadequate to express the loveliness of
some of the figures carved here ; and so it happens surely with
the face of this angel. The face is not of a man, I should think ;
it is rather like a very fair woman's face ; but fairer than any
woman's face I ever saw or thought of : it is in profile and easy
to be seen in the photograph, though somewhat in the shade.
I am utterly at a loss how to describe it, or to give any idea of the
exquisite lines of the cheek and the rippled hair sweeping back
from it, just faintly touched by the light from the south-east.
I cannot say more about it. So I have gone through the carvings
in the lower part of this doorway, and those of the tympanum.
Now, besides these, all the arching-over of the door is filled with
figures under canopies, about which I can say little, partly from
want of adequate photographs, partly from ignorance of their
import.

But the first of the cavettos wherein these figures are, is at any
rate filled with figures of angels, some swinging censers, some
bearing crowns, and other things which I cannot distinguish.
Most of the niches in the next cavetto seem to hold subjects ; but

the square camera of the photographer clips some, many others are in shadow, in fact the niches throw heavy shadows over the faces of nearly all ; and without the photograph I remember nothing but much fretted grey stone above the line of the capitals of the doorway shafts ; grey stone with something carved in it, and the swallows flying in and out of it. Yet now there are three niches I can say something about at all events. A stately figure with a king's crown on his head, and hair falling in three waves over his shoulders, a very kingly face looking straight onward ; a great jewelled collar falling heavily to his elbows : his right hand holding a heavy sceptre formed of many budding flowers, and his left just touching in front the folds of his raiment that falls heavily, very heavily to the ground over his feet. Saul, King of Israel.—A bending figure with covered head, pouring, with his right hand, oil on the head of a youth, not a child plainly, but dwarfed to a young child's stature before the bending of the solemn figure with the covered head. Samuel anointing David.—A king again, with face hidden in deep shade, holding a naked sword in his right hand, and a living infant in the other ; and two women before him, one with a mocking smile on her face, the other with her head turned up in passionate entreaty, grown women they are plainly, but dwarfed to the stature of young girls before the hidden face of the King. The judgement of Solomon.—An old man with drawn sword in right hand, with left hand on a fair youth dwarfed, though no child, to the stature of a child ; the old man's head is turned somewhat towards the presence of an angel behind him, who points downward to something unseen. Abraham's sacrifice of Isaac.—Noah too, working diligently that the ark may be finished before the flood comes.—Adam tilling the ground, and clothed in the skins of beasts.—There is Jacob's stolen blessing, that was yet in some sort to be a blessing though it was stolen.—There is old Jacob whose pilgrimage is just finished now, after all his doings and sufferings, all those deceits inflicted upon him, that made him remember, perforce, the lie he said and acted long ago,—old Jacob blessing the sons of Joseph. And many more which I remember not, know not, mingled too with other things which I dimly see have to do with the daily occupations of the men who lived in the dim, far-off thirteenth century.

I remember as I came out by the north door of the west front, how tremendous the porches seemed to me, which impression of greatness and solemnity, the photographs, square-cut and brown-coloured, do not keep at all ; still however I can recall whenever I please the wonder I felt before that great triple porch ; I remember best in this way the porch into which I first entered, namely the northernmost, probably because I saw most of it, coming in and out often by it, yet perhaps the fact that I have seen no photograph of this doorway somewhat assists this impression.

Yet I do not remember even of this anything more than the fact that the tympanum represented the life and death of some early French bishop; it seemed very interesting. I remember, too, that in the door-jambs were standing figures of bishops in two long rows, their mitred heads bowed forward solemnly, and I remember nothing further.

Concerning the southernmost porch of the west front.—The doorway of this porch also has on the centre pillar of it a statue of the Virgin standing, holding the Divine Child in her arms. Both the faces of the Virgin Mother and of her Son are very beautiful; I like them much better than those in the south transept already spoken of; indeed I think them the grandest of all the faces of the Madonna and Child that I have seen carved by the French architects. I have seen many, the faces of which I do not like, though the drapery is always beautiful; their faces I do not like at all events, as faces of the Virgin and Child, though as faces of other people even if not beautiful they would be interesting. The Child is, as in the transept, draped down to the feet; draped too, how exquisitely I know not how to say. His right arm and hand is stretched out across His mother's breast, His left hangs down so that His wrist as His hand is a little curved upwards, rests upon His knee; His mother holds Him slightly with her left arm, with her right she holds a fold of her robe on which His feet rest. His figure is not by any means that of an infant, for it is slim and slender, too slender for even a young boy, yet too soft, too much rounded for a youth, and the head also is too large; I suppose some people would object to this way of carving One who is supposed to be an infant; yet I have no doubt that the old sculptors were right in doing so, and to my help in this matter comes the remembrance of Ruskin's answer to what Lord Lindsay says concerning the inability of Giotto and his school to paint young children: [1] for he says that it might very well happen that Giotto could paint children, but yet did not choose to in this instance, (the Presentation of the Virgin,) for the sake of the much greater dignity to be obtained by using the more fully developed figure and face; and surely, whatever could be said about Giotto's paintings, no one who was at all acquainted with Early French sculpture could doubt that the carvers of this figure here, *could* have carved an infant if they had thought fit so to do, men who again and again grasped

[1] In the explanatory remarks accompanying the engravings from Giotto's frescoes in the Arena Chapel, published by the Arundel Society. I regret not being able to give the reference to the passage, not having the work by me.

eagerly common everyday things when in any way they would tell their story. To return to the statues themselves. The face of the young Christ is of the same character as His figure, such a face as Elizabeth Browning tells of, the face of One ' who never sinned or smiled ' ; at least if the sculptor fell below his ideal somewhat, yet for all that, through that face which he failed in a little, we can see when we look, that his ideal was such an one. The Virgin's face is calm and very sweet, full of rest,—indeed the two figures are very full of rest ; everything about them expresses it from the broad forehead of the Virgin, to the resting of the feet of the Child (who is almost self-balanced) in the fold of the robe that she holds gently, to the falling of the quiet lines of her robe over her feet, to the resting of its folds between them.

The square heads of the door-valves, and a flat moulding above them which runs up also into the first division of the tympanum, is covered with faintly cut diaper-work of four-leaved flowers.

Along the jambs of the doorway on the north side stand six kings, all bearded men but one, who is young apparently ; I do not know who these are, but think they must be French kings ; one, the farthest toward the outside of the porch, has taken his crown off, and holds it in his hand : the figures on the other side of the door-jambs are invisible in the photograph except one, the nearest to the door, young, sad, and earnest to look at— I know not who he is. Five figures outside the porch, and on the angles of the door-jambs, are I suppose prophets, perhaps those who have prophesied of the birth of our Lord, as this door is apportioned to the Virgin.

The first division of the tympanum has six sitting figures in it ; on each side of the canopy over the Virgin's head, Moses and Aaron ; Moses with the tables of the law, and Aaron with great blossomed staff : with them again, two on either side, sit the four greater prophets, their heads veiled, and a scroll lying along between them, over their knees ; old they look, very old, old and passionate and fierce, sitting there for so long.

The next division has in it the death and burial of the Virgin— the twelve Apostles clustering round the deathbed of the Virgin. I wish my photograph were on a larger scale, for this indeed seems to me one of the most beautiful pieces of carving about this church, those earnest faces expressing so many things mingled with their regret that she will be no more with them ; and she, the Virgin-Mother, in whom all those prophecies were fulfilled, lying so quiet there, with her hands crossed downwards, dead at last. Ah ! and where will she go now ? whose face will she see always ? Oh ! that we might be there too ! Oh ! those faces so full of all tender regret, which even They must feel for Her ; full of all yearning, and longing that they too might finish the long fight, that they might be with the happy dead : there is a wonder on their faces too, when they see what the mighty power of Death is. The foremost is bending down, with his left hand laid upon her breast, and he is gazing there so long, so very long ; one looking there too, over his shoulder, rests his hand on him ; there is one at the head, one at the foot of the bed ; and he at the head is turning round his head, that he may see her face, while he holds in his hands the long vestment on which her head rests.

In my photograph the shadow is so thick that I cannot see much of the burial of the Virgin, can see scarce anything of the faces, only just the forms, of the Virgin lying quiet and still there, of the bending angels, and their great wings that shadow everything there.

So also of the third and last division filling the top of the arch. I only know that it represents the Virgin sitting glorified with Christ, crowned by angels, and with angels all about her.

The first row in the vaulting of the porch has angels in it, holding censers and candlesticks ; the next has in it the kings who sprung from Jesse, with a flowing bough twisted all among them ; the third and last is hidden by a projecting moulding.

All the three porches of the west front have a fringe of cusps ending in flowers, hanging to their outermost arch, and above this a band of flower-work, consisting of a rose and three rose-leaves alternating with each other.

Concerning the central porch of the west front.—The pillar which divides the valves of the central porch carries a statue of Our Lord ; his right hand raised to bless, his left hand holding the Book ; along the jambs of the porch are the Apostles, but not the Apostles alone, I should think ; those that are in the side that I can see have their distinctive emblems with them, some of them at least. Their faces vary very much here, as also their figures and dress ; the one I like best among them is one who I think is meant for St. James the Less, with a long club in his hands : but they are all grand faces, stern and indignant, for they have come to judgement.

For there above in the tympanum, in the midst over the head of Christ, stand three angels, and the midmost of them bears scales in his hands, wherein are the souls being weighed against the accusations of the Accuser, and on either side of him stands another angel, blowing a long trumpet, held downwards, and their long, long raiment, tight across the breast, falls down over their feet, heavy, vast, ungirt ; and at the corners of this same division stand two other angels, and they also are blowing long trumpets held downwards, so that their blast goes round the world and through it ; and the dead are rising between the robes of the angels with their hands many of them lifted to heaven ; and above them and below them are deep bands of wrought flowers ; and in the vaulting of the porch are eight bands of niches with many, many figures carved therein ; and in the first row in the lowest niche Abraham stands with the saved souls in the folds of his raiment.   In the next row and in the rest of the niches are angels with their hands folded in prayer ; and in the next row angels again, bearing the souls over, of which they had charge in life ; and this is, I think, the most gloriously carved of all those in the vaulting.   Then martyrs come bearing their palm-boughs ; then priests with the chalice, each of them ; and others there are which I know not of.   But above the resurrection from the dead, in the tympanum, is the reward of the good, and the punishment of the bad.   Peter standing there at the gate, and the long line of the blessed entering one by one ; each one crowned as he enters by an angel waiting there ; and above their heads a cornice takes the shape of many angels stooping down to them to crown them.   But on the inferno side the devil drives before him the wicked, all naked, presses them on toward hell-mouth, that gapes for them, and above their heads the devil-cornice hangs and weighs on them.   And above these the Judge showing the wounds that were made for the salvation of the world : and St. Mary and St. John kneeling on either side of Him, they who stood so once at the Crucifixion ; two angels carrying cross and spear and nails ; two others kneeling, and, above, other angels, with their wings spread, and singing.   Something like this is carved in the central porch at Amiens.

Once more forgive me, I pray, for the poor way in which I have done even that which I have attempted to do ; and forgive me also for that which I have left undone.

And now, farewell to the church that I love, to the carved temple-mountain that rises so high above the water-meadows of the Somme, above the grey roofs of the good town.   Farewell to the sweep of the arches, up from the bronze bishops lying at the west end, up to the belt of solemn windows, where, through the painted glass, the light comes solemnly.   Farewell to the cavernous porches of the west front, so grey under the fading August sun, grey with the wind-storms, grey with the rain-storms, grey with the beat of many days' sun, from sunrise to sunset ; showing white sometimes, too, when the sun strikes it strongly ; snowy-white, sometimes, when the moon is on it, and the shadows grow-ing blacker ; but grey now, fretted into deeper grey, fretted into black by the mitres of the bishops, by the solemn covered heads of the prophets, by the company of the risen, and the long robes of the judgement-angels, by hell-mouth and its flames gaping there, and the devils that feed it ; by the saved souls and the crowning angels; by the presence of the Judge, and by the roses growing above them all for ever.

Farewell to the spire, gilt all over with gold once, and shining out there, very gloriously; dull and grey now, alas; but still it catches, through its interlacement of arches, the intensest blue of the blue summer sky; and, sometimes at night you may see the stars shining through it.

It is fair still, though the gold is gone, the spire that seems to rock, when across it, in the wild February nights, the clouds go westward.

'DEATH THE AVENGER' AND 'DEATH THE FRIEND'

(*Oxford and Cambridge Magazine*, August 1856)

THE names of two wonderful wood engravings by Alfred Rethel, a German, and one to be remembered in the aftertime.

Now Death the Avenger commemorates the first appearance of the Cholera, in 1831, which happened in Paris at a masked ball.

It is there, in that room, the Cholera, and Death; a strangely chosen room, one thinks, in its architecture, for a ball-room; liker to a tomb than that; it might have served well in those old times for the followers of John and Paul to meet in—to feel new life come upon them; new thoughts, new love, new longings, new hope.

Thick walls and heavy roof, and deep splayed windows it has, but withal gorgeous patterned hangings from gallery and pillar and dais; gorgeous, but ugly; the patterns crawl like evil poisonous spiders, like the blotches of damp on foul walls.

And in this ball-room only one dances now—Death—arrayed in hood and the long robes of a pilgrim, girt about the middle with a rope; one leg showing from the long drapery is thrown forward in mockery of dancing; and the dancers? there are two of them lying there, a man and a woman, both dead and stiff—the man's mask has fallen down, covers all his face except the eyes and forehead—and very strangely contrasted are the calm, self-satisfied, inane features of the mask with the wrinkled forehead and brows contracted in pain of the face that was alive once; the woman's mask, fastened to her hat, has fallen back, and her open mouth shows free from it; her arms are hidden by her dress, a long flower-garland trails round about her. And the rest of the maskers are rushing in mad race out of the room, the last wearing a fantastic dress with a fool's hump on the back of it, his arms muffled in his mumming-dress.

Others are there who rush out also, the musicians; huddled all together, their instruments blocking up the way, no man looking at his neighbour to see how he fares, or caring for him: for the grinning skeleton, Death, standing there with his head thrown on one side, has two bones in his hands, which he uses as fiddle and fiddle-bow, playing so wonderfully that, as you look at the drawing, you almost seem to hear the wild terrible skirling of some mad reel.

Most terrible figure of all, in the background sits The Cholera, waiting; in her right hand a triple scourge armed at the end with goads; such firm grip of that scourge; and her left hand clasps her right arm just below the wrist, fearful strong arms and hands —she is wrapped in long raiment that trails on the ground, and has flames all about it—her face is black, her mouth stern, indignant, with lips drawn up tight together; fixed eyes, glaring straight forward, and lidless, no drooping eyelids to her, beneath any rebuke, any defiance; is it not strange, that with all this the face is not a cruel one? Such a sense the thing seems to have that it too is God's creature, called up in his quarrel; strange that there should be even pity in it.

This is ' Death the Avenger '.—Then ' Death the Friend '.

In an old tower just below the belfry, in the place where they ring the bells: there is Death again in his pilgrim's dress, tolling for one who is just dead, the Sacristan of that Church; this Death is draped tenderly down to the feet; there is no maddening horror about him, awe only; he is not grinning as in the other picture, but gazes downward, thoughtfully, almost sadly, thinking of the old man's life that has been. And he, with his hands laid together and his eyes closed, is leaning back in his chair: many a time these latter years has he leant back so; then needs must that he rise stiffly and wearily to go about his duties; but now he need never rise again; his lips, parted a little now, need never again be drawn together close, at sight of weary injustice and wrong; he will soon understand why all these things were. The dragons on the spire eaves lean forward open-mouthed, disappointed because he has got quit of all that now; near the head of him against the wall is a figure of Christ on the Cross, a Bible is open by the side of him; near the stairs is a horn hanging, a huntsman's horn, and through the window, on the sill of which a bird is singing, you can see the fair sunset-country stretching away for leagues and leagues (for we are high up here, just under the spire).

They say he was a hunter in the old time, this man; that he heard the north wind sing about his ears, as he dashed over the open spaces; that the young beech-leaves in the early summer quivered at the blasts of his horn; that many a time he rode into that village you can see down there, wherein he was born, where his father and his father's father lived, weary with riding ; that some one used to look out for him when he rode in, in the evenings. But that too is all gone by—only in memories perhaps—yet he had other hopes then perhaps than this, a mere old sacristan dying lonely in the old belfry.

What matter ? for the setting sun is bright over all that country, and the bird sings still in the window sill—not afraid of death.

This is ' Death the Friend '.

MEN AND WOMEN

By Robert Browning [1]

(Oxford and Cambridge Magazine, March 1856)

I am not going to attempt a regular classification of Robert Browning's ' Men and Women ' ; yet the poems do fall naturally into some order, or rather some of them go pretty much together ; and, as I have no great space, I will go through those that do so fall together, saying little or nothing about the others.

The three that strike me first are ' The Epistle of Karshish ', ' Cleon ', and ' Bishop Blougram's Apology '. They have all three to do with belief and doubt, with the thoughts and fancies, and strange longings that circle round these ; they are dramatic too, not expressing, except quite incidentally, the poet's own thoughts. ' Cleon ', and the ' Epistle of Karshish ', are especially dramatic, and are very considerably alike : they both tell of the desires and doubts of men out of Christianity, and in the days when Christianity was the true faith of a very few unknown men, not a mere decent form to all the nations.

Karshish is an Arab physician, a man of science ; Cleon is poet, painter, sculptor. The Arab is the more genial of the two, less selfish, somewhat deeper too, I think ; Cleon, with his intense appreciation of beauty, even with his long life spent in producing that beauty, is yet intensely selfish ; he despises utterly the common herd ; he would bring about, if he could, a most dreary aristocracy of intellect, where the commoners would be bound hand and foot, mere slaves to the great men, and their great lordly minds, not loyal freemen, honouring the heroes ; he plumes himself, too, on being no less great than his fathers, greater even than they, saying :

> Marvel not,
> We of these latter days, with greater mind

[1] *Men and Women*, by Robert Browning; 2 vols. : Chapman & Hall, 1855.

> Than our forerunners, since more composite,
> Look not so great (beside their simple way),
> To a judge who only sees one way at once,
> One mind-point, and no other at a time ;
> Compares the small part of a man of us
> With some whole man of the heroic age,
> Great in his way—not ours, nor meant for ours,
> And ours is greater, had we skill to know.

Saying wrongly, too, as I am sure, for it was little more than mere restless vanity that made him try to master so many things, instead of giving up his mind to one, as the grand elders did.

Yes, he is selfish—so selfish that he can see little joy in those powers of creation which he possessed ; the king had said, in his letter, that though he, a mere king, would die utterly, yet it would not be so with Cleon, for his pictures, poems, statues, would live after him, he would live through them. Cleon says the king stumbles at mere words ; that the reality is otherwise :

> What ? dost thou verily trip upon a word,
> Confound the accurate view of what joy is,
> (Caught somewhat clearer by my eyes than thine,)
> With feeling joy ? confound the knowing how
> And showing how to live (my faculty)
> With actually living ? Otherwise,
> Where is the artist's vantage o'er the king ?
> I know the joy of kingship : well—thou art king !

He says too, that this same appreciation of beauty, of enjoyment, all the knowledge that he has, all his desires, so much finer than those of other men, only make the fear of death bitterer than it otherwise would be :

> Every day my sense of joy
> Grows more acute, my soul (intensified
> In power and insight) more enlarged, more keen,
> While every day my hairs fall more and more,
> My hand shakes, and the heavy years increase,
> The horror quickening still from year to year,
> The consummation coming past escape,
> When I shall know most, and yet least enjoy.

Till at last, in his agony, fierce words are wrung from the calm proud man ; he cannot help it—he cries out,

> It is so horrible,
> I dare at times imagine to my need
> Some future state reveal'd to us by Zeus,
> Unlimited in capability
> For joy, as this is in desire for joy,
> To seek which, the joy-hunger forces us,
> That, stung by straitness of our life, made strait

> On purpose to make sweet the life at large,
> Freed by the throbbing impulse we call death,
> We burst then as the worm into the fly,
> Who while a worm still, wants his wings. But no!
> Zeus has not yet reveal'd it; and, alas!
> He must have done so, were it possible!

And from this agony he comes down again to a kind of careless despair, and ends by saying just a little, contemptuously enough, of Paulus and his new doctrines; the cursed pride of knowledge lowering him so, that he even seems to be jealous that the king has sent presents and enquiries to Paulus also, a barbarian, one circumcised; so that about the doctrines of Paulus, he says:

> And (as I gathered from a by-stander)
> His doctrines could be held by no sane man.

Poor Cleon! he was not wont to accept things on hearsay; yet now so has his pride lowered him; and we must leave him and his longings for Karshish the Arab.

Karshish is, as I said, a better man than Cleon; a simpler man, one with great knowledge, always thirsting after more, and brave in his pursuit of it; yet on the whole, I think, kindly, and not puffed up with that knowledge. He writes from Jerusalem to his old master, to tell him how he has seen Lazarus; yet he is half fearful that he will seem ridiculous, unphilosophical, and does not like to acknowledge at first, even to himself, till he grows warmer from the longings that stir within him, what impression has been made on him; and he breaks off now and then to talk about his knowledge; yet he comes back to this always at last, for he cannot help it; and so he writes; very beautifully does he tell of the perfect faith of Lazarus, of his love of God and man, nay, of beasts, nay, of the very flowers; of his resignation and obedience to God through everything; of his strange clear second-sight; yearningly does he dwell on all this, excusing himself from ridicule now and then, by saying, 'yet the man was mad.' He knows how little all knowledge is, how it can never be perfected through all the generations; but he longs to love perfectly; his God is different from Lazarus's God; his idea of Him is so different, that he mentions with shuddering horror that which Lazarus had told him; 'that he, Lazarus, who stood there in the flesh, had seen God in the flesh too;' in horror; yet if it only could be true, that story told by the madman!

> The very God! think, Abib, dost thou think?
> So, the All-great, were the All-Loving too;
> So, through the thunder comes a human voice,
> Saying, 'O heart I made, a heart beats here!
> Face, my hands fashion'd, see it in myself.

> Thou hast no power nor may'st conceive of mine,
> But love I gave thee, with myself to love,
> And thou must love me who have died for thee!'
> The madman saith he said so : it is strange.

You see, too, he does not say, as Cleon did to his dream of
Heaven, ' it is not possible ; ' he only says, ' it is strange.'

It is all gloriously told ; here is something beside our present
question which I quote for its beauty ; Karshish's first meeting
with Lazarus :

> I met him thus—
> I cross'd a ridge of short sharp broken hills,
> Like an old lion's cheek-tooth—out there came
> A moon made like a face, with certain spots
> Multiform, manifold, and menacing :
> Then a wind rose behind me. So we met
> In this old sleepy town at unaware,
> The man and I.

Concerning ' Bishop Blougram's Apology ' I can say little
here, it embraces so many things ; the Bishop's interlocutor,
' Gigadibs, the literary man,' comes in only as an objector, or
little else ; he is a man without fixed faith ; the bishop is one
who is trying to ' believe that he believes ', and is succeeding,
I think, pretty well : for my part I dislike him thoroughly, yet
he says many true things, as Browning says in the Epilogue :
' he said true things, but called them by wrong names.'

He agrees too with Cleon concerning the unpleasantness of the
possession of the creative power. It is of no use to *him*, he says ;
he is more selfish even than Cleon, and not nearly so interesting :
he is tolerably well content with the present state of things as
regards himself, has no such very deep longings, and is not so
much troubled with doubts probably as even he says he is.
Browning says of him, ' For Blougram, he believed, say half
he spoke.'

I will go on to the next band that seem to go together, those
about art, namely ; they are Andrea del Sarto, Fra Lippo Lippi,
Old Pictures at Florence, A Toccata of Galuppi, and Master
Hugues of Saxe-Gotha.

Andrea del Sarto, and Fra Lippo Lippi are a good deal alike,
only the first has more about the man, the second about the art
he lives in. What a joy it is to have these men brought up before
us, made alive again, though they have passed away from the
earth so long ago ; made alive, seeming indeed not as they might
very likely have seemed to us, the lesser men, had we lived in
their times ; but rescued from the judgement of the world,
' which charts us all in its broad blacks or whites '—and shown
to us as they really were.

Think of Andrea del Sarto sitting there in Florence, looking over to Fiesole, trying to forget all the shame, all the weariness, to forget the pain of them at least, to live for one half-hour in the present ; yet so, that the past and the future may mingle with it very quietly, like the long weeds that the stream sways with it. And Lucrezia is sitting by him, Lucrezia, who he knows is not worthy of his love—no, not even of *his* love, the breaker of troth, the runaway ; and yet he goes on loving her nevertheless, she has wound her toils about him so. Oh ! true story, told so often, in so many ways. And it shall all go into a picture for the wearied man resting there :

> The whole seems to fall into a shape,
> As if I saw alike my work and self,
> And all that I was bound to be and do,
> A twilight-piece.

And how calmly he can talk of himself and his art, his great success that was rather a bitter failure to him now :

> I do what many dream of all their lives,
> —Dream ? strive to do, and agonize to do,
> And fail in doing. I could count twenty such
> On twice your fingers, and not leave this town,
> Who strive—you don't know how the others strive
> To paint a little thing like that you smear'd,
> Carelessly passing with your robes afloat,
> Yet do much less, so much less, some one says,
> (I know his name, no matter) so much less !
> Well, less is more, Lucrezia ! I am judged,
> There burns a truer light of God in them,
> In their vex'd, beating, stuff'd and stopp'd-up brain,
> Heart, or whate'er else, than goes on to prompt
> This low-pulsed forthright craftsman's hand of mine.
> Their works drop groundward, but themselves, I know,
> Reach many a time a heaven that's shut to me,
> Enter and take their place there sure enough,
> Though they come back and cannot tell the world.

Calmly he speaks of the wrong she had been to him, of what she might have been ; calmly of his life in France, and of his sin even when he fled from thence a very thief : and she, in spite of all, is rather in a hurry to get away, is rather bored by his talk, howsoever loving, for her ' cousin ' waits for her below : and so you can almost see the flutter of her dress through the doorway, almost hear her feet down the stairs, and the greeting of the bad woman without a heart with that ' cousin '. Almost ? nay, quite.

Then for Fra Lippo Lippi. He, found in questionable haunts by the police, first awes them somewhat by mention of his

patron's name, Cosimo de Medici ; then, being a man with
wrongs and one who must speak to somebody, he tells the officer
the very simple story of his life, and his grievance :

> Rub all out ! well, well, there 's my life, in short,
> And so the thing has gone on ever since—
> I'm grown a man no doubt, I've broken bounds.
>
> And yet the old schooling sticks—the old grave eyes
> Are peeping o'er my shoulder as I work,
> The heads shake still. ' It 's Art's decline, my son !
> You're not of the true painters, great and old :
> Brother Angelico 's the man, you'll find :
> Brother Lorenzo stands his single peer—
> Fag on at flesh, you'll never make the third.'
>
> I'm not the third then : bless us, they must know !
> Don't you think they're the likeliest to know !
> They, with their Latin ? so I swallow my rage,
> Clench my teeth, suck my lips in tight, and paint
> To please them.

This too is an often-told tale, to be told many times again
I fear before the world is done with. To this same officer he
vindicates himself : everything almost is worth painting, surely
it is best (whatever may be good) to paint everything as well as
possible :

> You be judge !
> You speak no Latin more than I, belike—
> However, you 're my man, you 've seen the world—
> The beauty and the wonder and the power,
> The shapes of things, their colours, lights and shades,
> Changes, surprises,—and God made it all !
>
> What 's it all about ?
> To be pass'd o'er, despised ? or dwelt upon,
> Wonder'd at ? oh, this last of course, you say ;
> But why not do as well as say,—paint these
> Just as they are, careless of what comes of it ?
> God's works—paint any one, and count it crime
> To let a truth slip. Don't object, ' His works
> Are here already—nature is complete :
> Suppose you reproduce her—(which you can't)
> There 's no advantage ! you must beat her, then ! '
> For, don't you mark ? we 're made so that we love
> First, when we see them painted, things we have pass'd
> Perhaps a hundred times, nor cared to see ;
> And so they are better, painted—better to us,
> Which is the same thing. Art was given for that—
> God uses us to help each other so,
> Lending our minds out.

It is very grand, this intense love of art ; and I suppose that those who cannot paint, and who therefore cannot feel quite the same herein, have nevertheless sometimes had a sick longing for the power to do so, without being able to give any reason for it, such a longing as I think is felt for nothing else under the sun,— at least for no other power.

And so we leave Fra Lippo Lippi, not certainly feeling alto- gether disgusted with the man, in spite of his sins ; you see, he had not a very good education, and yet is not so selfish as one might have expected him to be either.

No less great than these two is ' Old Pictures at Florence ' ; beautiful in the beginning, that gazing on Florence from the garden, in spring-tide ; beautiful and very true, that indignant vindication of the early mediaeval painters ; that comparison of their imperfect painting, with the perfect sculpture of the Greeks, perfect, but not so good as the other ; for the other was higher in its aim, higher in the thoughts that it called up in men's minds ; higher too, that in its humility it gave more sympathy to poor struggling, falling men. Here is a stanza or two of that vindication :—

> Wherever a fresco peels and drops,
>   Wherever an outline weakens and wanes
> Till the latest life in the painting stops,
>   Stands one whom each fainter pulse-tick pains !
> One, wishful each scrap should clutch its brick,
>   Each tinge not wholly escape the plaster,
> A lion who dies of an ass's kick,
>   The wrong'd great soul of an ancient master. .
>
> For oh, this world and the wrong it does !
>   They are safe in heaven with their backs to it,
> The Michaels and Rafaels, you hum and buzz
>   Round the works of, you of the little wit !
> Do their eyes contract to the earth's old scope,
>   Now that they see God face to face,
> And have all attain'd to be poets, I hope ?
>   'Tis their holiday now, in any case.
>
> Much they reck of your praise and you !
>   But the wronged great souls—can they be quit
> Of a world where all their work is to do ?

These are the three that have most to do with artists and paint- ing. Then come two concerning music, ' A Toccata of Galuppi,' and ' Master Hugues of Saxe-Gotha '.

There is not so much to say about the first of these, it seems to have been written principally for the music ; yet I think Galuppi's music itself could not have beaten it, played though it was between the sea and the palaces, it rings so gloriously throughout ; not one line in it falls from beginning to end, from the first :

Oh, Galuppi Baldassaro, this is very sad to find !
I could hardly misconceive you ; it would prove me deaf and blind ;
But although I give you credit, 'tis with such a heavy mind !

to the last :

' Dust and ashes ! ' so you creak it, and I want the heart to scold.
Dear dead women, with such hair, too—what 's become of all the gold
Used to hang and brush their bosoms ? I feel chilly and grown old.

Worthy to go with this for music is ' Master Hugues ' ; exquisite in melody, it is beautiful also in its pictures, true in its meaning. As to its melody, there is to me something perfectly wonderful in the piling up of the words from verse to verse. The thing fascinates me, though I cannot tell where the wonder is ;—but it *is* there ; the first stanza is almost as good as any for this music :

Hist, but a word, fair and soft !
    Forth and be judged, Master Hugues !
Answer the question I've put you so oft—
    What do you mean by your mountainous fugues ?
See, we're alone in the loft.

Then these others go together in my mind ; ' Before ' and ' After ', ' Childe Roland to the dark tower came ', ' The Patriot ', ' A light Woman ', and perhaps some others ; but these will do. They are all more concerned with action than thought, and are wholly dramatical.

Here is the first stanza from ' The Patriot ' :—

It was roses, roses, all the way,
    With myrtle mixed in my path like mad.
The house-roofs seem'd to heave and sway,
    The church-spires flamed, such flags they had,
A year ago on this very day !

The poem is very short, yet very attractive, somehow ; the man's life is shown wonderfully, though the poem is so short ; how he knew before, when he liberated these people, that they would not be faithful to him for long, yet, nevertheless, went on hoping against hope ! He is not vain, for he knows he could not have done other than he did ; yet he knows he has done well, and so comforts himself, thinking of the next world :—

Thus I enter'd Brescia, and thus I go !
    In such triumphs people have dropp'd down dead.
' Thou paid by the world—what dost thou owe
    Me ? ' God might have question'd : but now instead,
'Tis God shall requite ! I am safer so.

Yet, to the reader, it is very sad to read this ' old story ' ; and I think also it was bitter to him, in spite of all.

Telling lies for truth's sake, acting unfaithfully for faith's sake, are what is treated of in the ' Light Woman ' ; it is told, slight sketch though it is, in a masterly way ; perhaps we shall hear something more about it soon, judging from the last two lines :

> And, Robert Browning, you writer of plays,
> Here 's a subject made to your hand !

' Before ' and ' After ', are rather parts of the same poem, than separate poems. ' Before,' written in a splendid fighting measure, is spoken by a by-stander, just before a duel : listen, here !

> Why, you would not bid men, sunk in such a slough,
> Strike no arm out further, stick and stink as now,
> Leaving right and wrong to settle the embroilment,
> Heaven with snaky hell, in torture and entoilment ?

> Which of them 's the culprit, how must he conceive
> God 's the queen he caps to, laughing in his sleeve !
> 'Tis but decent to profess oneself beneath her—
> Still, one must not be too much in earnest either.

> Better sin the whole sin, sure that God observes,
> Then go live his life out ! life will try his nerves,
> When the sky which noticed all, makes no disclosure,
> And the earth keeps up her terrible composure.

> Let him pace at pleasure, past the walls of rose,
> Pluck their fruits when grape-trees graze him as he goes ;
> For he 'gins to guess the purpose of the garden,
> With the sly mute thing beside there for a warden.

> What 's the leopard-dog-thing, constant to his side,
> A leer and lie in every eye on its obsequious hide ?
> When will come an end of all the mock obeisance,
> And the price appear that pays for this misfeasance ?

Yes, truly so ! the one poisoning sin in a man's life, never to leave him in the midst of his dearly-bought pleasures ; he has gone wrong once, and the chance of his turning back is desperate indeed ; all his life is a lie now, with that terrible unrepented sin lying on him. Did ever any of you read Hawthorne's ' Scarlet Letter ' ? Then for his adversary :—

> So much for the culprit ? Who 's the martyr'd man ?
> Let him bear one stroke more, for be sure he can.
> Him that strove thus evils lump with good to leaven,
> Let him give his blood at last and get his heaven.

Yet with neither wronger nor wronged has it come to this yet ;

death may equalize it somewhat : so in ' After ', this has indeed
happened. I quote it entire without comment :

> Take the cloak from his face, and at first
>   Let the corpse do its worst—
> How he lies in the rights of a man !
>   Death has done all death can.
> And absorb'd in the new life he leads,
>   He recks not, he heeds
> Nor his wrong nor my vengeance—both strike
>   On his senses alike,
> And are lost in the solemn and strange
>   Surprise of the change.
> Ha ! what avails death to erase
>   His offence, my disgrace ?
> I would we were boys as of old
>   In the field, by the fold ;—
> His outrage, God's patience, man's scorn,
>   Were so easily borne.
> I stand here now,—he lies in his place—
>   Cover the face.

I think these two among the most perfect short poems that
Robert Browning has written, as perfect in their way as ' Evelyn
Hope ' among the love-poems. ' Childe Roland,'—how grand
that is ! some reviewer thinks it an ' allegory ', and rates the
poet for not having told us what happened to Childe Roland
inside the ' round, squat turret '.

Well, it may in some sort be an allegory, for in a certain sense
everything is so, or almost everything that is done on this earth.
But that is not its first meaning ; neither, as some people think,
was it written for the sake of the fearful pictures merely, or even
principally ; they, grand as they are, the grandest things of the
kind that I have ever read, are yet only a means to an end ; for
the poet's real design was to show us a brave man doing his duty,
making his way on to his point through all dreadful things.
What do all these horrors matter to him ? he must go on, they
cannot stop him ; he will be slain certainly, who knows by what
unheard-of death ; yet he can leave all this in God's hands, and
go forward, for it will all come right at the end. And has not
Robert Browning shown us this well ? Do you not feel as you
read, a strange sympathy for the lonely knight ? so very, very
lonely ; not allowed even the fellowship of kindly memories :

> I shut my eyes and turn'd them on my heart,
>   As a man calls for wine before he fights,
> I ask'd one draught of earlier, happier sights
> Ere fitly I could hope to play my part.
> Think first, fight afterwards—the soldier's art :
>   One taste of the old times sets all to rights !

Not it ! I fancied Cuthbert's reddening face
  Beneath its garniture of curly gold,
  Dear fellow, till I almost felt him fold
An arm in mine to fix me to the place
That way he used. Alas ! one night's disgrace !
  Out went my heart's new fire and left it cold.

Better this present than a past like that—
  Back therefore to my darkening path again.

Yet, for all this utter loneliness, for all these horrors, so subtly has the consummate poet wrought, through the stately flow of the magnificent rhythm, that we do not feel desponding, but rather triumphant, at the glorious end ; an end so glorious, that the former life, whatever it was, was well worth living with that to crown it ; and it was well too for the poet to leave us there, so that we see not the mere struggle of physical courage, or the mere groans and tears of suffering humanity under those things which are to be borne indeed, but hardly ever very calmly, hardly ever very resignedly ; but now ' Childe Roland ' passes straight from our eyes to the place where the true and brave live for ever ; and as far as we go, his life flows out triumphantly with that blast he blew.

And was it not well to leave us with that snatch of old song ringing through our ears like the very horn-blast that echoed all about the windings of that dismal valley of death ?

  I saw them and I knew them all ; and yet
  Dauntless the stag-horn to my lips I set,
  And blew : ' *Childe Roland to the dark tower came* '.

In my own heart I think I love this poem the best of all in these volumes.

And yet I scarcely know ; for this and all the others seem to me but a supplement to the love-poems, even as it is in all art, in all life ; love I mean of some sort ; and that life or art where this is not the case, is but a wretched mistake after all.

And in these love-poems of Robert Browning there is one thing that struck me particularly ; that is their intense, unmixed love ; love for the sake of love, and if that is not obtained, disappointment comes, falling-off, misery. I suppose the same kind of thing is to be found in all very earnest love-poetry, but I think more in him than in almost anybody else.

' Any wife to any husband,' ' The last ride together,'—read them, and I think you will see what I mean. I cannot say it clearly, it cannot be said so but in verse ; love for love's sake, the only true love, I must say.—Pray Christ some of us attain to it before we die !

Yet after all I am afraid I shall be able to say less about these love-poems than the others.

'Evelyn Hope' is quite perfect in its way; Tennyson himself has written nothing more beautiful; it is easy to be understood; very simple, everybody *must* like it: so full of faith and quiet manly tenderness, hopeful and brave; a very jewel set in the gold of the poet's crown. I must quote a little:

> I claim you still, for my own love's sake,
>   Delay'd it may be for more lives yet
> Through worlds I shall traverse, not a few:
>   Much is to learn and much to forget
> Ere the time be come for taking you.

> But the time will come,—at last it will,
>   When, Evelyn Hope, what meant, I shall say,
> In the lower earth, in the years long still,
>   That body and soul so pure and gay?
> Why your hair was amber, I shall divine,
>   And your mouth of your own geranium's red—
> And what you would do with me, in fine,
>   In the new life come in the old one's stead.

> I have lived, I shall say, so much since then,
>   Given up myself so many times,
> Gain'd me the gains of various men,
>   Ransack'd the ages, spoil'd the climes;
> Yet one thing, one in my soul's full scope,
>   Either I miss'd or itself miss'd me—
> And I want and find you, Evelyn Hope!
>   What is the issue? let us see!

> I loved you, Evelyn, all the while;
>   My heart seem'd full as it could hold—
> There was place and to spare for the frank young smile,
>   And the red young mouth, and the hair's young gold:
> So, hush! I will give you this leaf to keep;
>   See, I shut it inside the sweet cold hand.
> There, that is our secret! go to sleep;
>   You will wake, and remember, and understand.

Do you not see them there, in the darkened room,—the wise, learned, world-worn man hanging over the fair, dead girl, who 'perhaps had scarcely heard his name'? Coming close to 'Evelyn Hope' is 'A Woman's Last Word', and almost as beautiful as that:

> Be a god and hold me
>   With a charm—
> Be a man, and fold me
>   With thine arm!

> Teach me, only teach, Love!
>   As I ought
> I will speak thy speech, Love,
>   Think thy thought.

Meet, if thou require it,
  Both demands,
Laying flesh and spirit
  In thy hands !

That shall be to-morrow
  Not to-night :
I must bury sorrow
  Out of sight.

Must a little weep, Love !
  Foolish me !
And so fall asleep, Love,
  Loved by thee.

Is it not perfect in thought as in music ? and does it not illustrate what I said just now about the intense passion of these poems ?

So does this next one that I come to, ' By the Fireside.' It is the history of a life of love, that life which first began by the chapel there in Italy ; all things to this man, past, present, and to come, are centred in that one fact :

I am named and known by that hour's feat,
  There took my station and degree.
So grew my own small life complete
  As nature obtain'd her best of me—
One born to love you, sweet !

It reminds me a good deal of Tennyson in parts, of ' Maud ' especially ; but I suppose that is the effect of its melody ; it is all told in such sweet, half-mournful music, as though in com- passion to those who have not obtained this love, who will not obtain it while they live on earth, though they may in heaven.

Such love too is in it for the beautiful country where the new life came to him :

Oh ! woman-country, woo'd, not wed ;
  Loved all the more by earth's male-lands,
Laid to their hearts instead.

Such pictures of the fair autumn-tide :

Oh ! the sense of the yellow mountain-flowers,
  And the thorny balls, each three in one,
The chestnuts throw on our path in showers,
  For the drop of the woodland fruit 's begun,
These early November hours.

I like it one of the best of all.

' The Statue and the Bust ' is a story, a sad story too. Unlaw- ful love that was never acted, but thought only, thought through life ; yet were the lovers none the less sinners, therefore ; rather

the more, in that they were cowards ; for in thought they
indulged their love freely, and no fear of God, no hate of wrong
or love of right restrained them, but only a certain cowardly
irresolution. So Robert Browning thinks :

> So ! while these wait the trump of doom !
> How do their spirits pass, I wonder,
> Nights and days in the narrow room ?
>
> Still, I suppose, they sit and ponder
> What a gift life was, ages ago,
> Six steps out of the chapel yonder.
>
> Surely they see not God, I know,
> Nor all that chivalry of His,
> The soldier-saints, who, row on row,
>
> Burn upward each to his point of bliss—
> Since the end of life being manifest,
> He had cut his way through the world to this.

I cannot tell the story, you must read it ; it is one of the best
in the two volumes : the rhythm so wonderfully suited to the
story, it draws you along through the days and years that the
lovers passed in delay, so quietly, swiftly, smoothly.

Here is another, ' The last ride together ; ' one disappointed
in his best hopes of love, looking on the whole world struggling so,
with calm hopeless eyes ; so calm, though not altogether miserable. There is no need for him to struggle now he thinks ; he has
failed ; that is enough, failed as all others fail : he is not worse
off than his fellows. Meanwhile she is riding with him ; the
present is somewhat blissful ; moreover he says :

> Who knows what 's fit for us ? Had fate
> Proposed bliss here should sublimate
> My being ; had I signed the bond—
> Still one must lead some life beyond,
> Have a bliss to die with, dim-descried.
> This foot once planted on the goal,
> This glory-garland round my soul,
> Could I descry such ? Try and test !
> I sink back shuddering from the quest—
> Earth being so good, would heaven seem best ?
> Now, Heaven, and she are beyond this ride.

Then over him comes a strange feeling—he does not know—
it is all so blissful, so calm : ' She has not spoke so long,'—
suppose it be that it was Heaven now at this moment.

> What if we still ride on, we two,
> With life for ever old, yet new,
> Changed not in kind but in degree,
> The instant made eternity—
> And Heaven just prove that I and she
> Ride, ride together, for ever ride ?

' In a Balcony ' is a strange poem, hard to make out at first ; and for my part, I am not at all sure that I apprehend it rightly.

It seems to me, that Constance and Norbert, being cowardly, did at first intend merely to deceive the queen, then, that Constance, moved by the poor woman's joy at her supposed lover, and by her unexpected declaration of affection for herself, really intended to sacrifice her love to the queen ; but that Norbert's sick fear, his wild passionate terror, overcomes her, and their love is declared, with who knows what fate in store for them ; but it is all intricate and difficult—like human action..

' Women and roses' I must mention, seeing that some reviewer thinks it impossible to solve the riddle of it. I will try, not thinking it so very difficult either. Some man thinking, dreaming of women, they fall into three bands—those that have been, those that are, those that will be ; but with neither of these bands can he feel entire sympathy. He cannot enter into the heart of them ; their very vividness of face and form draws his heart away from their souls, and so they seem to him cold and unloving.

It certainly does not sound very well as I have put it ; in fact it does not often help poems much to *solve* them, because there are in poems so many exquisitely small and delicate turns of thought running through their music, and along with it, that cannot be done into prose, any more than the infinite variety of form, and shadow, and colour in a great picture can be rendered by a coloured woodcut.

Which (in the case of the poem) is caused, I suppose, by its being concentrated thought.

I quote some of this poem (' Women and roses ') :—

> I dream of a red-rose tree,
> And which of its roses three
> Is the dearest rose to me ?
> Round and round, like a dance of snow
> In a dazzling drift, as its guardians, go
> Floating the women, faded for ages,
> Sculptured in stone, on the poet's pages.
> Then follow the women, fresh and gay,
> Living and loving, and loved to-day.
> Last, in the rear, flee the multitude of maidens,
> Beauties unborn : and all, to one cadence,
> They circle the rose on my rose-tree.

Very worthily are the love-poems crowned by the final dedication to E. B. B. I quote the last four lines :

> Oh their Rafael of the dear Madonnas,
> Oh, their Dante of the dread Inferno,
> Wrote one song—and in my brain I sing it ;
> Drew one angel—borne, see, on my bosom !

Pardon me, reader, that I have said little about many of the best poems; that I have said nothing at all about several; nothing about the ecstasy of prayer and love in ' Saul '; nothing about the sacrifice of life, and its enjoyments, to knowledge in the ' Grammarian's Funeral '; nothing about the passionate ' Lover's Quarrel ', about ' Mesmerism ', ' Any wife to any husband ', and many others. My consolation is, that we shall have a good deal more to say of Robert Browning in this Magazine, and then we can make amends.

Yet a few words, and I have done. For, as I wrote this, many times angry indignant words came to my lips, which stopped my writing till I could be quieter. For I suppose, reader, that you see whereabouts among the poets I place Robert Browning; high among the poets of all time, and I scarce know whether first, or second, in our own : and it is a bitter thing to me to see the way in which he has been received by almost everybody; many having formed a certain theory of their own about him, from reading, I suppose, some of the least finished poems among the ' Dramatic Lyrics ', make all facts bend to this theory, after the fashion of theory-mongers : they think him, or say they think him, a careless man, writing down anyhow anything that comes into his head. Oh truly ! ' The statue and the bust ' shows this ! or the soft solemn flow of that poem, ' By the Fireside ' ! ' Paracelsus ' !—that, with its wonderful rhythm, its tender sadness, its noble thoughts, must have been very easy to write, surely !

Then they say, too, that Browning is so obscure as not to be understood by any one. Now, I know well enough what they mean by ' obscure ', and I know also that they use the word wrongly ; meaning difficult to understand fully at first reading, or, say at second reading, even : yet, taken so, in what a cloud of obscurity would ' Hamlet ' be ! Do they think this to be the case ? they daren't *say* so at all events, though I suspect some of them of thinking so.

Now, I don't say that Robert Browning is not sometimes really obscure. He would be a perfect poet (of some calibre or other) if he were not ; but I assert, fearlessly, that this obscurity is seldom so prominent as to make his poems hard to understand on this ground : while, as to that which they call obscurity, it results from depth of thought, and greatness of subject, on the poet's part, and on his readers' part, from their shallower brains and more bounded knowledge ; nay, often I fear from mere wanton ignorance and idleness.

So I believe that, though this obscurity, so called, would indeed be very objectionable, if, as some seem to think, poetry is merely a department of ' light literature ' ; yet, if it is rather one of the very grandest of all God's gifts to men, we must not

think it hard if we have sometimes to exercise thought over
a great poem, nay, even sometimes the utmost straining of all
our thoughts, an agony almost equal to that of the poet who
created the poem.

However, this accusation against Browning of carelessness,
and consequent roughness in rhythm, and obscurity in language
and thought, has come to be pretty generally believed ; and
people, as a rule, do not read him ; this evil spreading so, that
many, almost unconsciously, are kept from reading him, who, if
they did read, would sympathize with him thoroughly.

But it was always so ; it was so with Tennyson when he first
published his poems ; it was so last year with Maud ; it is so
with Ruskin ; they petted him indeed at first ; his wonderful
eloquence having some effect even upon the critics ; but, as his
circle grew larger and larger, embracing more and more truth,
they more and more fell off from him ; his firm faith in right
they call arrogance and conceit now ; his eager fighting with
falsehood and wrong they call unfairness. I wonder what they
will say to his new volume.

The story of the Pre-Raphaelites—we all know that, only
here, thank Heaven ! the public has chosen to judge for itself
somewhat, though to this day their noblest pictures are the least
popular.

Yes, I wonder what the critics would have said to 'Hamlet
Prince of Denmark', if it had been first published by Messrs.
Chapman & Hall in the year 1855.

POEMS BY DANTE GABRIEL ROSSETTI [1]

(*The Academy;* May 14, 1870)

TEN years ago with the publication of his beautiful and
scholarly volume of translations from the early Italian poets,
Mr. Rossetti announced the preparation of a volume of original
poems. This book, so eagerly looked for by those who knew
the author by his great works in painting, has now been given
to the public ; nor is it easy to exaggerate the value and im-
portance of that gift, for the book is complete and satisfactory
from end to end ; and in spite of the intimate connexion between
one art and another, it is certainly to be wondered at, that
a master in the supremely difficult art of painting should have
qualities which enable him to deal with the other supremely
difficult one of poetry : and to do this not only with the utmost

[1] London : Ellis, 1870.

depth of feeling and thought, but also with the most complete
and unfaltering mastery over its material; that he should find
in its limitations and special conditions, not stumbling-blocks or
fetters, but just so many pleasures, so much whetting of invention
and imagination. In no poems is the spontaneous and habitual
interpenetration of matter and manner, which is the essence of
poetry, more complete than in these. An original and subtile
beauty of execution expresses the deep mysticism of thought,
which in some form and degree is not wanting certainly to any
poets of the modern school, but which in Mr. Rossetti's work is
both great in degree and passionate in kind; nor in him has it
any tendency to lose itself amid allegory or abstractions; indeed,
instead of turning human life into symbols of things vague and
not understood, it rather gives to the very symbols the personal
life and variety of mankind. No poem in this book is without
the circle of this realizing mysticism, which deals wonderingly
with all real things that can have poetic life given them by
passion, and refuses to have to do with any invisible things that
in the wide scope of its imagination cannot be made perfectly
distinct and poetically real. Of all turns of mind this must be
the fittest to give the concentration and intensity necessary for
lyrical works, and the corresponding patience and untiring energy
to carry them out: nothing but this could have given us the
magnificent collection of sonnets at the end of this volume,
which, though there are some among upwards of eighty that are
not free from obscurity, the besetting vice of sonnets, are nevertheless unexampled in the English language since Shakespeare's
for depth of thought, and skill and felicity of execution. A
mediocre sonnet is more hateful to gods and men than any other
versified mediocrity, a crabbed one is harder to read than any
other form of crabbed verse; and complete success is not
common even when the thought is not over deep; but to express
some deep piece of thought or feeling completely and with beauty
in the narrow limits of fourteen lines, and in such a way that
no line should be useless or barren of some reflex of the main
idea; to leave the due impression of the whole thought on the
mind by the weight and beauty of the ending; and to do all
this without losing simplicity, without affectation of any kind,
and with exquisite choiceness of diction and rhyme, is as surely
a very great achievement, and among the things most worth
doing, as it is exceedingly rare to find done. But few of these
sonnets fall short of this highest standard; and they seem
withal the most natural and purest expression of the peculiar
mysticism spoken of above. Two poems are to be named here,
as having in them much of the feeling of the strongest of the
sonnets, with a sweetness and simplicity of their own, ' A Little

While', and 'The Sea Limits'; the completeness with which the thought is grasped, amid its delicate flux and reflux from stanza to stanza, is very characteristic of Mr. Rossetti's best work. 'Love's Nocturn' classes itself with these and the sonnets also. It is a very beautiful and finished piece of work, and full of subtle melody, but sometimes obscure with more than the obscurity of the dreamy subject, and sometimes with a certain sense of over labour in it. Both these faults may be predicated also of a poem of the same class, 'The Stream's Secret,' which nevertheless is wonderfully finished, and has very high musical qualities, and a certain stateliness of movement about it which coming among its real and deep feeling makes it very telling and impressive.

Among pieces where the mystical feeling is by necessity of subject most simple and most on the surface, 'The Blessed Damozel' should be noticed, a poem in which wild longing, and the shame of life, and despair of separation, and the worship of love, are wrought into a palpable dream, in which the heaven that exists as if for the sake of the beloved is as real as the earthly things about the lover, while these are scarcely less strange or less pervaded with a sense of his passion, than the things his imagination has made. The poem is as profoundly sweet and touching and natural as any in the book, that is to say, as any in the whole range of modern poetry. At first sight the leap from this poem to the 'Jenny' may seem very great, but there is in fact no break in the unity of the mind that imagined both these poems; rather one is the necessary complement to the other. The subject is difficult for a modern poet to deal with, but necessary for a man to think of; it is thought of here with the utmost depths of feeling, pity, and insight, with no mawkishness on the one hand, no coarseness on the other: and carried out with perfect simplicity and beauty. It is so strong, unforced, and full of nature, that I think it the poem of the whole book that would be most missed if it were away. With all this, its very simplicity and directness make it hard to say much about it: but it may be noticed, as leading to the consideration of one side of Mr. Rossetti's powers, how perfectly the *dramatic* quality of the soliloquiser is kept: his pity, his protest against the hardness of nature and chance never make him didactic, or more or less than a man of the world, any more than his 'Shame of his own shame' makes him brutal, though in the inevitable flux and reflux of feeling and habit and pleasure he is always seeming on the verge of touching one or other of these extremes. How admirably, too, the conclusion is managed with that dramatic breaking of day, and the effect that it gives to the chilling of enthusiasm and remorse, which it half produces and is half typical of ; coming after the grand passage about lust that brings to a climax the musings over so much beauty and so many good things apparently thrown away causelessly.

The dramatic quality of Mr. Rossetti's work has just been mentioned, which brings one to saying that, though it seemed necessary to dwell so strongly on the mystical and intensely lyrical side of his poems, they bear with them signs of the highest dramatic power, whatever its future application may be. This is shown not merely in the vivid picturing of external scenes —as that of the return of the humbled exiles to Florence in the noble poem of ' Dante at Verona '—but more conclusively still in the steady purpose running through all those poems in which character or action, however lyrical, is dealt with ; in ripeness of plan, and in the congruity of detail with which they are wrought out ; all this, of course, in addition to their imaginative qualities. This is well seen in ' Sister Helen ', which is, in fact, a ballad (the form of poem of all others in which, when it is complete, the lyrical and dramatic sides of art are most closely connected), and in which the wild and picturesque surroundings, and the growing force of the tremendous burden, work up surely and most impressively to the expected but still startling end, the effect of which, as almost always in Mr. Rossetti's poems, is not injured by a word too much. As widely different as it may be in character of execution to this, there is the same dramatic force amidst the magnificent verses of ' Eden Bower ', where the strangest and remotest of subjects is wonderfully realized by the strength and truth of its passion, though the actors in it add supernatural characteristics to the human qualities that make it a fit subject for poetry. The ' Last Confession ', whose subject connects itself somewhat with these two last, is the poem in the book whose form is the least characteristic of Mr. Rossetti's work, the most like what is expected of a poet with strong dramatic tendencies ; it is, however, most complete and satisfactory, and the character of the man is admirably imagined and developed, so as both to make the catastrophe likely, and to prevent it from becoming unpoetical, and just merely shocking : a character, elevated and tender and sensitive, but brooding, and made narrow both naturally and by the force of the continual tragedy of oppression surrounding his life ; wrought upon by the neces-sary but unreasonable sense of wrong that his unreturned love brings him, till despair and madness, but never hate, comes from it. Well befitting such a character, but also indicating the inevitable mystical tendency of the author, as small as the indication may be, is the omen of the broken toy of Love that sheds the first blood, and that other typical incident of the altars of the two Madonnas. In speaking of a book where the poems are so singularly equal in merit as this, it has been scarcely possible to do more than name the most important, and several even must remain unnamed ; but it is something of a satisfaction to finish with mentioning the 'Song of the Bower', so full of passion and melody, and more like a song to be sung than any modern piece I know. To conclude, I think these lyrics, with all their other merits, the most *complete* of their time ; no difficulty is avoided in them—no subject is treated vaguely, languidly, or heartlessly: as there is no commonplace or second-hand thought left in them to be atoned for by beauty of execution, so no thought is allowed to overshadow that beauty of art which compels a real poet to speak in verse and not in prose. Nor do I know what lyrics of any time are to be called *great* if we are to deny that title to these.

WILLIAM MORRIS.

INDEX OF FIRST LINES OF POEMS